Ottawa
1962

Thermodynamics

and

Statistical

Thermodynamics

JOHN GELDART ASTON

Professor of Organic Chemistry
and Director of the Low Temperature Laboratory

JAMES JOHN FRITZ

Associate Professor of Chemistry

The Pennsylvania State University

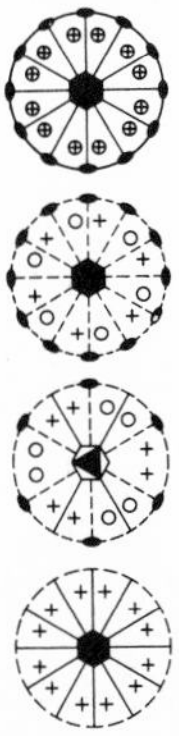

Thermodynamics and Statistical Thermodynamics

New York · John Wiley & Sons, Inc.

London · Chapman & Hall, Ltd.

Library of Congress Catalog Card Number: 59–5883

Printed in the United States of America

Dedicated
to the memory of
Frank Clifford Whitmore

Preface

This book contains the material which we present, or refer to, during a one-year graduate course (three hours a week each semester) in Thermodynamics and Statistical Thermodynamics. We believe that the same material could be presented in a similar course to senior undergraduate honor students.

It has been our experience that lack of understanding of the First Law is often responsible for difficulty in using the Second Law. If the concept of thermodynamic temperature is properly understood, the full meaning of the Second Law is as easy to grasp intuitively as that of the first, if not easier. The order of presentation of subject matter of the first fifteen chapters has been governed entirely by these considerations. For this reason there is deliberate reiteration.

We have found, likewise, that the development of statistical thermodynamics using the distribution laws and energy levels to calculate the energy of a system *first* with many numerical examples has considerable advantage over a more general introduction. It is only after making such a start and deducing other thermodynamic properties from the energy (often clumsily perhaps) that the beginner can grasp the beauty of the general apology for thermodynamics that is summarized in our final chapter. The development of the latter half of the book, sometimes repetitiously, follows these considerations.

The first fifteen chapters are covered during the first semester, and the remainder of the book during the second semester. During the first semester the students always construct an entropy diagram; to lighten the work they do so in groups with two or three students in each. Very little time is spent on the general treatments of Gibbs or on the variables other than pressure, volume, temperature, and composition. In the second semester the students individually make calculations of thermodynamic properties using the accurate rotational-vibrational partition functions for diatomic gases and the approximate rotational and vibrational partition functions for complex molecules with internal rotation. For this purpose a rather complete chapter (Chapter 16) on energy levels is included along with an appendix giving selection rules and group theory tables.

There are about 260 numerical problems and about 130 problems involving derivations of the formulae stated but not fully derived in the text or of formulae which are an extension of those derived in the text. The Appendix contains outlines of mathematical methods as well as tables of functions and of data to supplement the material in the text.

Chemists should find the book sufficiently self-contained to be useful as a reference book and as a means of acquiring facility in advanced methods. With the exception of the treatment of crystals, the statistical thermodynamic treatment is limited to systems without interactions (i.e., to perfect gases). Systems with interactions are dealt with in more advanced books. For the same reason quantum mechanically degenerate gases are not discussed.

In the table below are suggestions concerning the most suitable material for a one-year graduate course and two senior one-semester courses, respectively dealing with thermodynamics and statistical thermodynamics. In each case it is assumed that the semester consists of approximately forty-five class hours.

The first four chapters of the book have proved very useful in our courses, for we have found that the historical approach is almost essential to a thorough understanding of the two laws of thermodynamics and to the proper understanding of thermodynamic temperatures.

There are two chapters dealing with the methods of Gibbs. One of these deals with his thermodynamic generalizations, the second deals with the application of statistical mechanics for the sole purpose of understanding the principles of thermodynamics. While these are not used directly in our class work, they are considered essential supplementary reading for the student and highly desirable for the general reader.

The last chapter gives a sufficiently general treatment of statistical thermodynamics to form an introduction to advanced study.

Suggested Chapters for Typical Courses

Type of Course	Chapters Covered Thoroughly	Chapters Covered Partially	Chapters Omitted
One-year graduate course	1 through 11; 16 through 20	12 through 15; 21	22, 23
One-semester senior course in thermodynamics	1 through 3; 6, 7, 12	4, 8, 10, 11, 13, 14	15
One-semester senior course in statistical thermodynamics	17, 18	19, 20	16, and 21 through 23

J. G. A.
J. J. F.

State College, Pennsylvania
March, 1959

Acknowledgments

We wish to thank Dr. M. R. Fenske, from whom one of us inherited the course in thermodynamics, for much advice; also, some of the early students, particularly Dr. E. Willihnganz, Dr. G. H. Messerly, and Professor M. L. Eidinoff. Professor Eidinoff wrote the first draft of Chapter 2 over ten years ago, and made many suggestions in the planning of the book. Professors A. W. Hutchinson and D. H. Rank, who formed part of a seminar in the early days of the development of methods of calculation of thermodynamic properties from spectroscopic and molecular data, have indirectly contributed much to this book.

We are particularly indebted to Dr. D. M. Nace and Dr. W. A. Pavelich, who helped with the writing of Chapter 10 (Imperfect Gases; Fugacity and Entropy Diagrams); also to Dr. W. A. Steele, who helped with the writing of Chapter 15 (Systems Involving Other Variables). We wish to thank the Chemistry Department of this University for a great deal of help and consideration which materially aided in the preparation of the manuscript. We wish also to thank our past students who have contributed data which we have used in problems or have otherwise contributed to the development of this text. They are M. L. Eidinoff, E. Willihnganz, G. H. Messerly, C. W. Siller, S. C. Schumann,

W. S. Forster, R. M. Kennedy, P. M. Doty, H. L. Fink, M. Sagenkahn, G. J. Szasz, S. Isserow, G. W. Moessen, H. E. Zuhr, C. W. Ziemer, E. L. Pace, S. V. R. Mastrangelo, E. J. Rock, R. J. Tykodi, T. P. Zolki, Kuo Hao Hu, F. L. Gittler, P. E. Wills, H. Segall, H. L. Pinch, J. Greyson, D. M. Nace, R. N. Selby, and C. R. Fuget. Finally, we wish to acknowledge the great help given by students of recent years in detecting errors in the main part of this book which, in a multilithed version, has been used as distributed notes in the graduate course in Thermodynamics and Statistical Thermodynamics at this University. Notable among these have been Thomas E. Taylor, Charles Knobler, and Carolyn Berk Knobler.

We wish also to thank Gwen Ray, who checked all references and tables against the original literature as well as prepared most of the index and otherwise helped with the proof.

J. G. A.
J. J. F.

Contents

The Scope of Thermodynamics, Chemical Thermodynamics, and Statistical Thermodynamics

CHAPTER 1

1.1 Thermodynamics

In its early development, thermodynamics was the branch of physics which dealt with the interconversion of the different forms of energy but now its scope has become much wider.

The two laws of thermodynamics are:

Law I. *Energy cannot be created or destroyed.*

Law II. *It is impossible to convert heat into work at constant temperature.*

These have come to be recognized, by every layman, if not in a formal manner, at least implicitly in much the same way as the law of conservation of matter. The first practical demonstration of the utilization of atomic energy[1] probably showed the intelligent layman that the more accurate equivalents of law I and the law of conservation of matter are:

(Ia) *Matter and energy are equivalent.*

(Ib) *The quantity of energy in the universe can only be changed by a corresponding change in the quantity of matter.*

The use of these laws in the study of heat engines for power and refrigeration is a major concern of thermodynamics.

[1] Henry DeWolf Smyth, *Atomic Energy*, Princeton University Press, Princeton, N. J., 1945, p. 98; see also New York *Times*, Aug. 7, 1945, p. 1, columns 4–8.

1.2 Chemical Thermodynamics

The role of thermodynamics in the designing of heat engines is widely known and apparent from a superficial inspection of the first and second laws. The manner in which it can place certain limitations on the physical and chemical conditions which may exist in a system and on the changes which may occur is not so apparent.

For example, it is not possible for sulfur vapor, liquid, rhombic, and monoclinic sulfur to exist together at equilibrium; if this were possible, the phenomenon could be made a basis for converting heat into work at constant temperature. At 280°C and at 1 atm NO_2 is 13% dissociated into NO and oxygen at equilibrium. If oxygen is added to this system, a certain fraction of it must combine with NO. This fraction can be calculated from thermodynamics. If it were possible to add oxygen at equilibrium without this fraction combining, this process could be used to invent a perpetual motion machine.

Thus from thermodynamics it is possible to calculate the maximum fraction of a mixture of nitrogen and hydrogen that can be converted into ammonia at any temperature and pressure; the maximum yield for any other chemical reaction can be calculated if the necessary data are available. The separation of components from a solution as solids, as gases, or in any other equilibrium fashion can be treated by thermodynamics. Thus we may predict the solubility of one compound in another.

When an electrolytic cell discharges against an opposing electromotive force under equilibrium conditions, electrical work is done. By thermodynamics we can calculate this work or, knowing its value, can predict the conditions of equilibrium in the chemical reaction of the cell.

By thermodynamics we are able to calculate only what may happen in a chemical reaction and to state what can never (or hardly ever) happen. We cannot predict whether a process will occur in a finite time, since thermodynamics deals only with equilibrium; many processes are so slow that equilibrium is never reached. From a practical point of view, it is extremely useful to know the conditions which favor appreciable amounts of reaction products at equilibrium. Such knowledge can save futile efforts to find a catalyst for a reaction which cannot possibly occur under the conditions employed. The application of the laws of thermodynamics to such problems is one of the principal tasks of chemical thermodynamics.

1.3 Statistical Thermodynamics

Count Rumford, among others, recognized the fact that heating a body increases the kinetic energy of the molecules within it. At present we have a fair understanding of the situation. With a complete knowledge of the energies that atoms or molecules may assume, we can calculate all the thermodynamic properties of actual systems involving such atoms and molecules, including the final state of a chemical reaction at equilibrium.

The study of the distribution of atoms and molecules among their energy levels and the consequent adjustments of the system with changes of pressure, volume, and temperature, including the ability to withdraw heat and do work, is called *statistical thermodynamics.*

1.4 Relation of Energy Levels and Spectroscopy to Thermodynamics

We now take for granted that atoms and molecules can acquire energy only in steps; that is, they can exist only in a discrete series of energy states. Other values of the energy are not allowed. In many instances there are closed mathematical expressions for these energies in terms of the masses of the atoms, the geometry of the molecules, and force laws which determine their motion.

These expressions will be discussed in a later chapter to justify their acceptance on faith. In the same chapter it will be shown how many of these energy levels may be obtained directly from lines observed in the absorption or emission spectra (for example, how the rotational and vibrational energy levels of hydrogen chloride may be obtained from its infrared spectrum).

In some cases energy levels or molecular structure may be deduced by working backwards from the thermodynamic properties. Thus statistical thermodynamics, spectroscopy, and the mechanics of atoms and molecules are all interdependent.

1.5 Scope and Nature of This Book

Our object has been to cover those important parts of thermodynamics and statistical thermodynamics which allow exact calculation and are now quite fully understood. It is intended that the following presentation, while primarily designed to constitute a textbook, should be understood and read with pleasure by the properly prepared reader without taking a formal course. It is suggested that such readers, as well as students using this book as a text, read the preface at this point. This preface not only explains in detail the reasons for our order of presentation, but also emphasizes the milestones along the way. For this reason frequent reference to the preface is advised, particularly where there is doubt about the relationship of one section of the book to another.

Physical Units, Accepted Constants, and Empirical Temperatures

CHAPTER 2

2.1 Fundamental Units

The basic units of measurement are those of length, mass, and time. The fundamental unit of *length* (l) is the *meter* (m); by convention, the meter represents the distance (at 0°C) between two ruled lines on a standard platinum-iridium bar maintained at the International Bureau of Weights and Measures at Sèvres, France. Similarly, the fundamental unit of *mass*, the kilogram (kg), is the mass of a standard block of platinum deposited at Sèvres. Copies of these standards have been deposited with the National Bureau of Standards in Washington, D.C.

The *centimeter* (cm) and *millimeter* (mm) correspond to one hundredth and one thousandth of a meter, respectively. Of the corresponding units of area (A), the square centimeter (1 cm^2) is the most commonly used. The *gram* (g) is one thousandth of a kilogram. The centimeter and gram are commonly considered standard units.

The *liter* (l) has been commonly accepted by chemists as the basic unit of volume (V). The liter is defined as the volume of one kilogram of pure water at the temperature corresponding to its maximum density under a pressure of one atmosphere. The *milliter* (ml) is one thousandth of a liter. From careful density measurements it has been established that 1 liter is equal to 1000.027 cubic centimeters (cm^3).

The fundamental unit of *time* (t), the *second* (sec), is defined as 1/86,400 of a *mean solar day*. (A mean solar day is the average, over a year, of the day as defined by the apparent transit of the sun through a vertical plane.)

The units of other physical quantities are derived in terms of those of length, mass, and time. The so-called cgs system is obtained when this is done in terms of the centimeter, gram, and second. Various derived quantities are considered in the following sections.

2.2 Force and Pressure

The numerical calculation of *force* (F) is based on Newton's second law of motion, which relates the force acting on a freely moving body to its rate of change of momentum. The *dyne* is the cgs unit of force, and it corresponds to the force which imparts to a freely moving mass of one gram an acceleration of one centimeter per second per second. The standard gravitational acceleration (g) is defined as 980.665 cm/sec^2. A *gram force* is the force required to give a mass of one gram the standard gravitational acceleration, and is thus equal to 980.665 dynes.

Pressure (P) is an important variable in the definition of the state of a chemical system. It is defined as the force acting on a unit area. The cgs unit of pressure is the *dyne per square centimeter*. Commonly, pressure is expressed and measured in terms of an equivalent height (h) of a fluid column of density ρ:

$$P = \frac{\mathrm{F}}{\mathrm{A}} = \rho g\mathrm{h}. \tag{2.2–1}$$

The *normal* or *standard atmosphere* (atm) has been adopted as a practical unit of pressure. This unit is defined as the pressure exerted by a mercury column having a height of 760 mm and a density of 13.5951 g/cm^3. The latter is the density of mercury at 0°C, sea level, and 45° latitude (g = 980.665). The standard atmosphere is equal to 1,013,250 dynes/cm^2. Laboratory pressure data are frequently given in *millimeters of mercury* (mm Hg). An International millimeter of mercury is defined as 1/760 of a standard atmosphere. Pressures ranging up to 1000 atmospheres are employed in industrial chemical practice.

Problem 2.2-1. Calculate the height of mercury, in millimeters, corresponding to 1 atm in San Francisco, California, at 22°C. (*Note.* Values of g for representative localities are given in the *International Critical Tables.*[1]) If the scale is of silver and calibrated to read correctly at 0°C, what will be the height, in millimeters, observed on the scale at 22°C?

Problem 2.2-2. A weight of 15 g is placed on a circular slab of steel of weight 1 kg. By acting as a piston, this device prevents gas from escaping from a cylinder. If the

[1] *International Critical Tables*, McGraw-Hill, New York, 1927.

slab and the cross section of the cylinder both have a diameter of 10 cm, calculate the difference between the pressure of the gas and that of the surrounding atmosphere for (a) Denver, Colorado; (b) San Francisco, California.

2.3 Work

When a body moves under the influence of a force, work (w) is done. In thermodynamic calculations, work is usually considered in terms of the displacement of a system against forces external to it. Thus, if a system is displaced a small amount $\mathrm{d}l$ in the same direction as, but opposed to, that of an external force F, the work performed, w, is given by the expression

$$w = \mathrm{F}\,\mathrm{d}l. \tag{2.3–1}$$

Over a specified path from A to B the work done by the system is

$$w = \int_{\mathrm{A}}^{\mathrm{B}} \mathrm{F}\,\mathrm{d}l, \tag{2.3–2}$$

which is obtained by taking the line integral corresponding to equation (2.3–1). Defined in this manner, work done by a system against external forces has a *positive sign.* In a general mechanical consideration, where X, Y, Z represent the rectangular components of the external forces and $\mathrm{d}x$, $\mathrm{d}y$, and $\mathrm{d}z$ the corresponding displacements of the system,

$$w = X\,\mathrm{d}x + Y\,\mathrm{d}y + Z\,\mathrm{d}z. \tag{2.3–3}$$

The work w done by the system is the line integral of w and is dependent on the path of integration.

Of special interest in thermodynamics is the work done by an expanding fluid. Using the definition of pressure P in Section 2.2 and the increment of volume $\mathrm{d}V = \mathrm{A}\,\mathrm{d}l$,

$$\mathrm{d}w = P\mathrm{A}\,\mathrm{d}l = P\,\mathrm{d}V. \tag{2.3–4}$$

From (2.3–4), the work done by the system against the external pressure P is given by

$$w = \int_{V_1}^{V_2} P\,\mathrm{d}V. \tag{2.3–5}$$

In the case of constant external pressure,

$$w = P\int_{V_1}^{V_2} \mathrm{d}V = P\,\Delta V. \tag{2.3–6}$$

Equations (2.3–4) and (2.3–5) permit a simple geometrical interpretation as illustrated in Fig. 2.3–1. The points A and B correspond to the initial and final states of the system. The points A and A′ define an infinitesimal expansion dV. The work done by the system in the latter expansion, w, is equal to $P\,dV$, where P is the average pressure in this small interval. In Fig. 2.3–1a this corresponds to the shaded area of the strip under

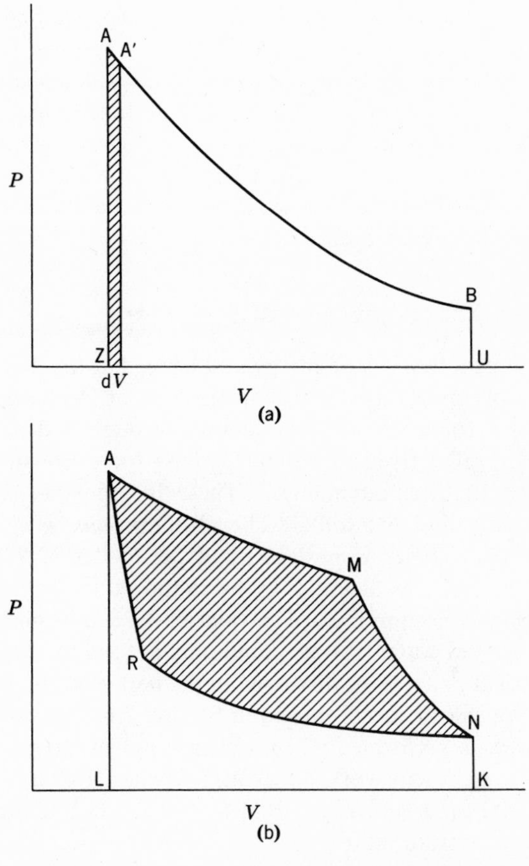

Fig. 2.3–1. Geometrical illustration of expansion work.

AA′. In the expansion from A to B, the work done by the system is the definite integral

$$\int_{V_A}^{V_B} P\,dV$$

and is therefore represented in the figure as the area under the curve AB, area ABUZ. The work done by the system in going from B to A along the same path is equal in magnitude but opposite in sign to the value mentioned above, indicating that in this case work is done on the system by the external forces. For the cycle shown in Fig. 2.3–1b, the path of the system is represented by AMNRA. In the expansion from A to N, the work done by the system is positive and is equal to the area under the curve AMN, area KLAMN. In the change from N to A along the path NRA, the work done by the system is negative and is equal to the area of the curve under NRA, area KLARN. The net work done by the system over the cycle is therefore equal to the difference between the two areas mentioned above, in other words, the shaded area, AMNRA. According to our convention, this represents positive work. The net work for the cyclical process ARNMA has the same magnitude but is of opposite sign, indicating that net work is done on the system by the external forces during each cycle.

2.4 Units for Expressing Quantity of Work

Work represents a transfer of energy and hence has the units of energy. The cgs unit of energy (or work) is the *erg* or *dyne-centimeter*. It corresponds to a force of one dyne acting through a distance of one centimeter. Several derived and defined units for expressing work are commonly used in thermodynamics. These include the *joule*, *calorie*, *kilocalorie*, *cc atm*, and *liter atm*. The absolute *joule* is defined to be equal to 10^7 ergs. The *cc atmosphere* and the *liter atmosphere* may be calculated in terms of ergs or joules by using the value of the atmosphere in cgs units given in Section 2.2. The calorie, defined originally in terms of the specific heat of water, is now commonly defined in terms of the cgs system of electrical units, to be discussed in the next section. The various definitions of the calorie are discussed in Section 2.6.

Electrical work is performed when a charge moves against a potential difference. The electrical work w performed when a charge $d\mathcal{Q}$ moves across a potential difference $\mathcal{E}$ is equal to $\mathcal{E}\, d\mathcal{Q}$. In common chemical applications $\mathcal{E}$ is constant and

$$\text{electrical work} = \mathcal{E} \times \mathcal{Q}. \tag{2.4–1}$$

The units commonly used with equation (2.4–1) are defined in the following section.

2.5 Electrical Units

The electrical units used in thermodynamics are based on the fundamental or absolute cgs electromagnetic units, abbreviated cgsm. Of these, the fundamental units are those of current and resistance, with the others derived therefrom. Unit current is defined in terms of the force exerted on a unit magnetic pole placed at the center of a circular loop of wire carrying the current. Unit resistance is defined by comparison with inductance, which can be calculated from the geometry of the circuit. For a sinusoidal alternating current of one cycle per second, 2π cgsm units of resistance produce the same impedance as one unit of self-inductance.

The "practical" units of current, resistance, etc., are defined in terms of the fundamental units by appropriate conversion factors, some of which are given in Table 2.5–1.

Table 2.5–1
Comparison of Fundamental and Practical Units

1 ampere (amp)	= 10^{-1}	cgsm unit of current
1 ohm	= 10^{9}	cgsm units of resistance
1 volt	= 10^{8}	cgsm units of electromotive force
1 henry	= 10^{9}	cgsm units of inductance
1 coulomb	= 1	ampere-second
1 joule	= 1	volt-ampere second or 1 volt coulomb = 10^{7} erg

In the past, it was found convenient to express electrical measurements in terms of laboratory standards selected by international agreement. These so-called "International" (practical) units were defined in 1908 so as to be equivalent to the absolute (practical) units such as those defined in Table 2.5–1. The *international volt* is defined to be 1/1.0183 of the electromotive force furnished by the Weston normal cell at 20°C. The *international ampere* is defined as the uniform current that will deposit 0.00111800 g of silver per second in a properly designed coulometer. The *international ohm* is the resistance at 0°C of a mercury column of uniform cross section, whose mass is 14.4521 g and whose length is 106.300 cm.

The international units do not agree with the absolute units within the limits of present-day experimental precision. Descriptions of early measurements of absolute units and comparisons with the international units are given by Glazebrook.[2] The result of more recent comparisons are described by Curtis.[3] The most recent correlations between absolute units and the international standards as maintained by the U.S. National Bureau of Standards[4] are given in Table 2.5–2. On January 1, 1948, by international agreement, the absolute ohm and the absolute ampere

[2] R. Glazebrook, *Dictionary of Applied Physics*, Vol. II, Macmillan, London, 1922.

[3] H. L. Curtis, *J. Research Natl. Bur. Standards*, **33**, 235 (1944).

[4] F. D. Rossini, F. T. Gucker, H. L. Johnston, L. Pauling, and G. W. Vinal, *J. Am. Chem. Soc.*, **74**, 2699 (1952).

became the primary standards in terms of which calibrations are to be expressed.

Table 2.5–2
Relationships between Absolute and International Standards

	Absolute	International (NBS)
Ohm	1	0.999505 ± 0.000015
Ampere	1	1.000165 ± 0.000025
Volt	1	0.999670 ± 0.000029
Joule	1	0.999835 ± 0.000052

2.6 The Calorie (cal)

The *calorie* (or *gram-calorie*) was originally defined as the heat required to raise the temperature of one gram of water by one centigrade degree. Careful measurements soon showed that the specific heat of water varied with the temperature; as a result, at least three different calorie units were defined and used:

1. The *15° calorie:* the quantity of heat required to raise 1 g of water from 14.5° to 15.5°C.
2. The *20° calorie:* the heat required to raise 1 g of water from 19.5° to 20.5°C.
3. The *mean calorie:* 1/100 the heat required to raise 1 g of water from 0° to 100°C.

Since modern calorimetric practice now employs absolute units for electrical energy input, a *defined calorie* has become widely accepted by thermochemical workers.[5,6] The defined calorie is equal to 4.1840 joules. (absolute). Unless directly specified otherwise, in this book the word *calorie* shall mean the defined calorie, and *ampere*, *ohm*, *volt*, and *joule* shall each refer to the *absolute* unit.

Problem 2.6-1. When a long spring is compressed by a force F, the change Δl in its length is connected with the applied force by the equation

$$F = 10^7 \, \Delta l + 10^3 \, (\Delta l)^2,$$

for l in centimeters and F in dynes.

(a) Calculate the work in ergs, joules, and defined calories which must be done to compress this spring 1 cm.

(b) Calculate how many grams weight it would take to compress this spring 0.5 mm in Denver, Colorado.

[5] F. R. Bichowsky and F. D. Rossini, *Thermochemistry of Chemical Substances*, Reinhold, New York, 1936.

[6] F. D. Rossini, *J. Research Natl. Bur. Standards*, **22**, 407 (1939).

2.7 Charge per Chemical Equivalent

The electrical charge per oxidation-reduction equivalent weight of an element or compound is called the *Faraday* ($\mathscr{F}$). Its value is 96,493.1 coulombs, or 23,062.4 calories per volt-equivalent.

2.8 Temperature

In order to account for heat disposal in thermodynamic calculations, it is necessary to specify the *temperature*. The units of temperature are not derivable in *any manner* from those described above. As far as energy conservation is concerned, the definition and measurement of temperature may be quite arbitrary, as in the empirical methods described below. However, it will be shown in later chapters that the *second law of thermodynamics supplies a scale of temperature which is fundamental, independent of any material used as a thermometric substance, and capable of dealing with all limitations placed by nature on the interconversion of various forms of energy*. It will also be shown that the methods of statistical mechanics supply an interpretation of temperature in terms of the averaged behavior of a large number of molecular particles.

Qualitatively, the meaning of temperature in terms of "hotness" and "coldness" of a body is a familiar one. In order to obtain a number which can be associated with this idea, we resort to the use of a *thermometer*. This is obviously a device that has associated with it a temperature-dependent *physical property* capable of reasonable precise measurement. The device may be a liquid column in a glass capillary, a bulb containing a gas at constant volume, a bulb containing a gas at constant pressure, a wire of measurable resistance, or a thermocouple. The physical properties associated with these "thermometers" are, respectively, *length*, *pressure*, *volume*, *electrical resistance*, and *electromotive force*. Readings of these properties when the thermometer is in contact with a body A are taken to be an *index* of the temperature of A. Actually such instruments are really indicators of heat transfer and hence their name, thermo (heat) meters (measurers).

Thus several simple yet fundamental observations are readily made by using any of these thermometers. When two bodies A and B are placed in contact with each other for a sufficient time, it is observed that they reach the same temperature. They are then said to be in thermal equilibrium with each other. If A and B are each in thermal equilibrium with another body, C, they are found to be in thermal equilibrium with each other. If "hot" and "cold" are defined in a relative manner based on the magnitude of the length of a liquid column thermometer, it is easily verified that, when a "hot" body is placed in contact with a "cold" body, the former becomes colder and the latter becomes warmer. The final "equilibrium" temperature is found to lie somewhere between the initial temperatures of the two bodies.

2.9 Arbitrary Temperature Scales

In order to set up a quantitative scale, it is first necessary to decide on an easily reproducible *standard temperature interval* defined by two fixed points. Usually the lower point chosen is the melting point of ice under atmospheric pressure (the *ice point*), and the upper is the boiling point of

Table 2.9–1
Comparison of Empirical Temperature Scales within the Same Fundamental Interval†

Constant Volume Hydrogen Thermometer	Constant Volume Air Thermometer	Platinum Resistance Thermometer	Thermocouple (Pt, Pt–Rh)	Mercury Thermometer
t_v	t_v	t_{Pt}	t_{th}	t_{Hg}
0	0	0	0	0
20	20.008	20.240	20.150	20.091
40	40.001	40.360	40.297	40.111
60	59.990	60.360	60.293	60.086
80	79.897	80.240	80.147	80.041
100	100.	100.	100.	100.

† By permission from *Heat and Thermodynamics*, 3rd ed., by M. W. Zemansky. Copyright, 1951, by McGraw-Hill Book Co.

pure water under a pressure of 1 atm (the *steam point*). This interval is then designated as corresponding to a definite number of degrees. On the centigrade scale, the standard interval corresponds to 100°; on the Fahrenheit scale, to 180°. The standard interval is divided into a number of equal subintervals or degrees by use of a thermometer. Let G_i and G_s represent the readings of a thermometric device at the lower and upper ends of the interval. Let us arbitrarily take the ice point as 0° and the steam point as 100°. If the thermometer gives a reading G_t when in contact with a substance at an unknown temperature t, the unknown centigrade temperature is defined as

$$t = 100 \frac{G_t - G_i}{G_s - G_i}. \tag{2.9–1}$$

Thus, in the case of a mercury-in-glass thermometer for which the length L is measured,

$$t = 100\,\frac{L_t - L_i}{L_s - L_i}\,. \tag{2.9–2}$$

The scales thus defined will be identical only if every one of the properties varies linearly with any other as the temperature changes. Since this is only approximately true for any of the properties under consideration, it is immediately evident that *the temperature scale will not be the same for the different thermometer types within and outside the fixed interval.* This is illustrated in Table 2.9–1, which contains the readings given by a variety of thermometers at six temperatures.

2.10 The Gas Thermometer

Although relatively cumbersome to use for ordinary laboratory measurements, the gas thermometer is a primary standard for the establishment of the so-called Centigrade Gas Thermometer Scale. By extrapolation of the observed temperatures to zero measuring pressure, the scale can be made independent of the particular gas used; it leads naturally to the Absolute Temperature Scale. It will be shown by means of the second law of thermodynamics (Chapter 6) that the absolute scale thus defined measures *thermodynamic temperatures which, in contrast to the temperatures just discussed, are quite fundamental.*

A typical constant volume gas thermometer is shown schematically in Fig. 2.10–1. The gas is contained principally in the bulb (A) except for the small "dead space" volume in the capillary (B). The bulb is filled with gas at the ice point until a chosen pressure (say 1000 mm Hg) is obtained. The volume of the system is kept constant by use of a leveling device to adjust the mercury level L_2 to coincide with the pointer before the pressure is measured. The pressure is measured with the bulb (A) at the steam point and thereafter at desired unknown temperatures. The readings are corrected for the small dead space volume and for the expansion of glass and mercury.

The constant pressure gas thermometer is constructed and used in a similar manner. In this thermometer, volumes are measured at constant pressure. Temperatures measured on the constant volume and constant pressure gas thermometers are denoted by t_v and t_p, respectively, and are equal to

$$t_v = 100\,\frac{P_t - P_i}{P_s - P_i} \tag{2.10–1}$$

and

$$t_p = 100\,\frac{V_t - V_i}{V_s - V_i}\,. \tag{2.10–2}$$

Typical results obtained when several different gases were used, each with ice point pressures of 1000 mm Hg, are given in Table 2.10–1. It is observed from the table that for a filling pressure of 1000 mm the various gases give different results; for the same gas, the two methods fail to agree exactly. However, if the filling pressures are made to approach

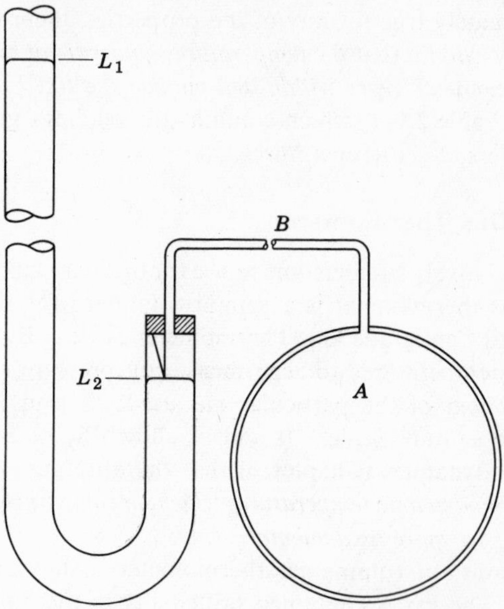

Fig. 2.10–1. Constant volume gas thermometer.

In general, the gas is contained in bulb A, which is surrounded by the system whose temperature is to be measured. A length of capillary B joins the bulb A to the mercury column. The gas volume is kept exactly constant by manipulation of the mercury column so that the mercury in the right-hand arm is always at L_2. The pressure of the gas is equal to the pressure on the surface of L_1 plus the difference in levels $L_2 - L_1$. The pressure readings must be corrected for the effects of the small "dead space" volume in which the temperature differs from that of the bulb A, the expansion of the bulb, and the expansion of the mercury.

zero, *all gases* in both constant pressure and constant volume thermometers indicate the *same* temperature since each substance approaches perfect gas behavior. This fact, together with the arbitrary statement that the interval between the ice point and the steam point represents 100°, suffices to fix the Centigrade Perfect Gas Scale.

The approximate temperatures t_v and t_p are obtained directly from experimental observations by use of equations (2.10–1) and (2.10–2), for

Table 2.10-1

Temperatures Obtained with Gas Thermometers Using Various Gases†

(Pressure of gas when bulb is surrounded by ice = 1000 mm.)

	Temperature approx. 50°C		Temperature approx. 200°C	
Gas	t_v	t_p	t_v	t_p
Hydrogen	50.003	50.004	199.976	199.976
Helium	50.001	50.000	199.994	199.999
Neon	50.001	50.002	199.997	199.990
Nitrogen	50.010	50.032	199.978	199.877
Air	50.013	50.033	199.976	199.874
Argon	50.014	50.034	199.971	199.863
Oxygen	50.016	50.035	199.929	199.839

† By permission from *Heat and Thermodynamics*, 3rd ed., by M. W. Zemansky. Copyright, 1951, by McGraw-Hill Book Co.

each of several filling pressures. The centigrade perfect gas scale temperature may then be obtained by extrapolating the readings to zero pressure.

One can also define the centigrade temperature in terms of the PV product of an ideal gas, $(PV)_t^{P=0}$; thus

$$t°\mathrm{C} = 100\,\frac{(PV)_t^{P=0} - (PV)_i^{P=0}}{(PV)_s^{P=0} - (PV)_i^{P=0}}. \tag{2.10–3}$$

It is obvious that at some negative temperature $(PV)^{P=0}$ must become zero. The value of t at this temperature is obtained by placing $(PV)_t^{P=0}$ equal to zero in equation (2.10–3). The value thus found is $-273.150 \pm 0.010°$. An absolute scale may be defined by taking the temperature thus found as the new zero. The absolute temperature is then defined by

$$T = 100\,\frac{(PV)_T^{P=0}}{(PV)_s^{P=0} - (PV)_i^{P=0}}. \tag{2.10–4}$$

Thus the absolute temperature corresponding to 0°C is 273.150°. The scale defined by equation (2.10–4) is known as the Centigrade Absolute Perfect Gas Scale.

The temperature can also be defined by an equation

$$T = \frac{(PV)_T^{P=0}}{(PV)_{\mathrm{triple}}^{P=0}}\,T_{\mathrm{triple}}, \tag{2.10–5}$$

where an arbitrary value is given to the absolute temperature of the triple point of water, T_{triple}, at which the PV product is $(PV)_{\mathrm{triple}}^{P=0}$. A proposal to define absolute temperature such that $T_{\text{triple}} = 273.1600 \cdots 000$ has been accepted by an international commission.[7] The triple point of water is 0.01° above its freezing point. It is not certain that, in this scale, there will be exactly 100° between the ice point and the steam point. The difference will be considerably less than 0.005°, however.

Conversion factors for the units discussed in this chapter, values of the fundamental constants, and useful related quantities are tabulated in Appendix 1.

[7] *Procès-verbaux com. int. Poids et Més.* (1954).

Historical Background of the First and Second Laws of Thermodynamics

CHAPTER 3

3.1 Introduction

It cannot be too strongly emphasized that thermodynamics is a science, whose laws have been developed as the result of the success or failure of experiments. The laws thus developed have given rise to a formal mathematical framework which is useful in correlation and prediction of experimental results. Now the equations of thermodynamics can be developed from the basic laws and necessary definitions in a manner analogous to Euclid's geometry.

Historically, few concepts of thermodynamics were developed by mathematical reasoning. For this reason the development of the first and second laws of thermodynamics will be discussed in this chapter in historical context. It is hoped that from this development the reader will gain an appreciation of the physical significance of the concepts involved. A formal development of the laws of thermodynamics is reserved for later chapters.

3.2 Mechanical Energy and Heat

Whenever mechanical work is performed some observable change occurs. For instance, a weight may be lifted or bodies set in motion. In the first case, we say a gain in *potential energy* has resulted; in the second, a gain in *kinetic energy.* Both potential energy and kinetic energy are forms of mechanical energy. If nothing else has happened, loss by friction, for example, the total gain in potential and kinetic energy is equal to the work done; this is a consequence of Newton's laws of motion. The conservation of mechanical energy in the absence of friction was recognized in the latter half of the seventeenth century.[1]

When a definite weight of a substance has its temperature (as measured by some sort of thermometer) raised by some fixed amount, it is obvious that something extra must have been added. This "extra" is, of course, heat; for a while it was thought to be a material substance and was called "caloric." Hence the word thermometer (derivation given in Section 2.8.). Joseph Black[2] found that the final temperature obtained when equal weights of a hot liquid and a cold one were mixed was not the arithmetic mean of the low and high temperatures. He thus was the first to conceive the notion of *sensible* heat and consequently of *heat capacity.* At the same time Black noted that heat was taken up when a solid melted without a change in temperature; he thus also developed the idea of heats of fusion and vaporization, which he termed *latent* heats.

3.3 Heat and Its Mechanical Equivalent

In 1798 Count Rumford noted the large quantities of heat evolved when a cannon was bored, and he wondered about its origin. He was thus led to devise an experiment in which a blunt rod replaced the borer; he found that, qualitatively, *heat* was generated in proportion to the *mechanical energy* expended. His paper, entitled "An Inquiry Concerning the Source of Heat Which is Excited by Friction,"[3] expresses clearly the ideas existing about heat at that time. It also shows how mental inquiry together with experiment led to clarification of these ideas. For these reasons, parts of his paper are quoted here.

> Being engaged lately in superintending the boring of cannon, in the workshops of the military arsenal at Munich, I was struck with the very considerable degree of heat which a brass gun acquires, in a short time in being bored; and with the still more intense heat (much greater than that of boiling water, as I found by experiment), of the metallic chips separated from it by the borer . . . The hollow cylinder having been previously cleaned out, and the inside of its bore wiped with

[1] Newton, *Principia*, 1687, trans. by Molte, 1803; Leibnitz, *Acta Eruditorium*, 1686; see William Francis Magie, *Source Book in Physics*, McGraw-Hill, New York, 1935 (hereafter referred to as *S. B. P.*), pp. 30 ff.

[2] Joseph Black, *Lectures on the Elements of Chemistry*, 1803; see *S. B. P.* pp. 134 ff.

[3] Benjamin Count of Rumford, *Phil. Trans.*, **88**, 80–102 (1798); see *S. B. P.*, pp. 151 ff.

a clean towel till it was quite dry, the square iron bar, with the blunt steel borer fixed to the end of it, was put in its place; the mouth of the bore of the cylinder being closed at the same time, by means of the circular piston, through the center of which the iron bar passed. This being done, the box was put in its place, and the joinings of the iron rod, and of the neck of the cylinder, with the two ends of the box, having been made water-tight, by means of collars of oiled leather, the box was filled with cold water, (viz. at the temperature of 60°) and the machine was put in motion.

The result of this beautiful experiment was very striking, and the pleasure it afforded me amply repaid me for all the trouble I had had, in contriving and arranging the complicated machinery used in making it.

The cylinder, revolving at the rate of about 32 times in a minute, had been in motion but a short time, when I perceived, by putting my hand into the water, and touching the outside of the cylinder, that heat was generated; and it was not long before the water which surrounded the cylinder began to be sensibly warm . . .

At two hours and twenty minutes it was at 200; and at 2 hours 30 minutes it ACTUALLY BOILED ! . . .

. . . And, in reasoning on this subject, we must not forget to consider that most remarkable of circumstance, that the source of the heat generated by friction, in these experiments, appeared evidently to be *inexhaustible*.

It is hardly necessary to add, that any thing which any *insulated* body, or system of bodies, can continue to furnish *without limitation*, cannot possibly be a *material substance*; and it appears to me to be extremely difficult, if not quite impossible, to form any distinct ideal of any thing, capable of being excited, and in the manner the heat was excited and communicated in these experiments, except it be MOTION . . .

This paper ended the notion that heat was a material substance. Rumford's investigations led to the more thorough ones of Joule, who made careful determinations of the *mechanical equivalent of heat*.[4]

To give a definition of heat, other than in terms of its mechanical equivalent, is not a simple matter. Precisely this problem bothered Rumford and Joule, who both came to the conclusion that heat was motion. To define a mechanical equivalent of heat, Joule required some quantitative measure of heat. His unit was the quantity of heat required to raise a standard mass of water through a fixed temperature increment, as measured by a thermometer. (Again note derivation of the word.) The thermometers of his time consisted of expansion instruments, and temperature was defined arbitrarily, as in Chapter 2, without much consideration of its meaning.

The experiments of Joule consisted of direct measurements of the number of heat units, as determined by the temperature rise, which were

[4] James Prescott Joule, *Phil. Trans.*, **140**, 61 (1850); see also *S. B. P.*, pp. 203 ff.

produced when a liquid was stirred mechanically with a measured amount of mechanical energy (measured force causing measured displacement).

During this period when the relation between mechanical work and electrical energy was being studied thoroughly, Joule[5] himself showed the identity of electrical energy and heat, and later made accurate measurements of the mechanical equivalent of heat electrically.[6] Relationships between the various forms of energy are illustrated in the problems below.

Problem 3.3-1. A metal ball weighing 50 lb is dropped from a height of 100 ft into a large tank of water. Calculate (in calories) the amount of heat given to the water by the impact. Assume that the entire system was initially at the same temperature, and neglect the heat generated by friction with the air during fall.

Problem 3.3-2. A projectile weighing 100 g is fired vertically, leaving the ground at a speed of 10,000 cm sec^{-1}. Noting that its total energy must remain constant except for loss due to friction, calculate the height at which it stops: (a) neglecting frictional losses; (b) assuming that during its ascent 50 cal of heat is dissipated to the atmosphere.

Problem 3.3-3. An electrolytic cell situated in a thermostat has a voltage of 1.0 v. When it is discharged through a frictionless motor which has windings of negligible resistance, the cell absorbs 3000 cal of heat when a faraday of electricity flows. No work is done against any other external system.

(a) Calculate the net energy loss of the cell, in calories.

(b) Calculate the electrical work done and the net heat given to the thermostat when the cell discharges at 0.001 amp until 1 faraday has flowed through a resistance of 100 ohms placed in the thermostat in series with the motor. This resistance is very much larger than the cell resistance.

(c) Calculate the net heat given to the thermostat per faraday if the cell is shorted by a resistance, placed in the thermostat, much smaller than the internal resistance of the cell. (*Note.* This corresponds to the heat given off if the reaction occurs spontaneously in the absence of electrical connections.)

The energy loss of the cell must be the same in each process described above.

3.4 Other Forms of Energy

The heat observed when work is dissipated (does not produce an increase in mechanical energy) is not always equal to the amount calculated from the mechanical equivalent of heat. For example, when an iron arc operates under water in a transparent quartz vessel, the rate of temperature increase in the water is not that which would be calculated as the equivalent of the voltage times the current passing. Some of the energy of the arc is emitted in the form of *radiation*. If this system is placed in an enclosure with blackened walls, the temperature of the walls will increase; the gain of energy by the walls is equal to that not accounted

[5] James Prescott Joule, *Phil. Mag.*, **19**, 260 (1841).

[6] James Prescott Joule, *Report of the British Association for the Advancement of Science*, Dundee, 1867.

for by the temperature rise in the water. This increase in the energy of the walls is due to absorption of radiation from the iron arc; that is, it is due to light of frequencies ranging from the infrared to the ultraviolet. The process by which the water gained heat was largely *convection* and *conduction* from the hot iron electrodes. The walls of the enclosure gained heat by *radiation.* These effects are by no means purely academic; for example, they must be eliminated in an apparatus for determination of the boiling point of sulfur in the calibration of thermometers. Burning of wood or paper by use of a magnifying glass is an extreme example.

It will not be until Chapter 18, when statistical thermodynamics is discussed, that the reader will understand how far-seeing Count Rumford was. It is hoped, however, that this discussion of radiation will convince the reader that at this stage it is difficult, if not impossible, to hold any notion of heat apart from the temperature rise it produces.

3.5 General Definition of Heat and Work

In the last two sections we have talked about mechanical energy and its quantitative conversion to other forms of energy, such as electrical energy, heat, and radiant energy. It has been implied that heat energy can be transmitted in the form of radiant energy. We could discuss other forms of energy and class them as fundamentally mechanical or fundamentally thermal (heat) energy. In such a classification there would be an anticipation of the second law of thermodynamics. However, it seems best at once to distinguish two kinds of energy as follows:

> When a body loses or gains energy by radiation, conduction, or convection, it is said to gain or lose heat; if it gives up or gains energy by other means, it is said to do work or have work done on it.

The full significance of the experiments of Rumford and Joule can now be seen. If all radiation is excluded from a system along with all contact which would allow energy to be gained by conduction or convection, the system is said to be *thermally isolated.* If now a quantity of work $(-w)$ is done on the system, the increase of energy of the isolated system is given by

$$\Delta E = -w. \tag{3.5–1}$$

This is the most easily grasped statement of the first law of thermodynamics. The increase of energy will be observed as an increase in temperature or change in physical state of the system. If the former,

$$\Delta E = C\,\Delta t, \tag{3.5–2}$$

where C is the heat capacity of the system defined, for the particular process, by the ratio of thermal energy acquired to the temperature rise; that is,

$$C = \frac{\Delta E}{\Delta t}. \tag{3.5–3}$$

Thus only through the work which is done, with other disturbances excluded, do we understand the temperature rise.

3.6 First Law of Thermodynamics

The experiments of Rumford, Mayer, and Joule have established the law: *Energy can neither be created nor destroyed.* This is the first law of thermodynamics. It is not sufficient that a loss of energy in one place be compensated by an equivalent gain at another. The passage of energy must be continuous, so that in any volume element in space the energy entering must equal that leaving plus the net gain.

One of the corollaries of the theory of relativity states that matter and energy are interconvertible and that a mass m is equivalent to a quantity of energy

$$E = \mathrm{m}c^2 \tag{3.6–1}$$

where c is the velocity of light. If m and c are expressed in cgs units, the energy is given in ergs. An accurate statement of the first law takes this principle into account. As the conversion of matter into energy will not be considered further in this book, the above statement of the first law, expressed by equation (3.5–1) for a thermally isolated system, is adequate for our purpose.

Problem 3.6-1. In the nuclear reaction by which a gram atom each of ordinary hydrogen and deuterium react to produce the radioactive isotope tritium, there is a net loss of mass of 6 mg. Calculate, in calories, the energy liberated.

Problem 3.6-2. The combustion of a mole of normal octane liberates 1.3×10^6 cal of heat. Calculate the mass of material which must be lost in this reaction.

3.7 Second Law of Thermodynamics

Not long after the equivalence of heat and work as forms of energy had been established, questions were asked concerning the transformation of heat into mechanical energy. It was evident that mechanical energy could be transformed quantitatively into heat; the question whether the reverse process could occur became the subject of discussion.

Strangely enough, the speculations concerning the conditions governing the *development* of mechanical energy from heat were first made when heat was thought to be a substance. This substance was supposed to produce the motive power *without being consumed*, just as water flowing down hill can turn a water wheel to produce work. Carnot[7] considered that the temperature difference determined the maximum amount of mechanical energy which could be obtained from a fixed quantity of heat when heat flowed from a higher to a lower temperature. The work was produced by a cycle involving some substance, but Carnot did not think of any of the heat, which was thereby transferred from the hot to the cold reservoir, as being used up in the process. He did, however, prove that the minimum mechanical energy required to restore the heat to its original temperature must equal the maximum obtained initially. He did this by showing that otherwise work would be produced without any other change. This was the first clear idea of the importance of the reversible process and the impossibility of obtaining work at constant temperature. These ideas are unimpaired by the fact that Carnot failed to understand the first law of thermodynamics.

It is not difficult to correct Carnot's ideas. It is merely necessary to add that the heat flowing to the colder reservoir is less than that leaving the hot reservoir by the mechanical equivalent of the work done. Thus, if h is the heat leaving the hot reservoir (source) and c is the heat entering the cold reservoir (sink), the work done, w, in a completely reversible cycle is the difference between the two. The fraction of the heat converted into work is

$$\frac{w}{h} = \frac{h - c}{h} \tag{3.7–1}$$

and is a function of t_h and t_c, where t_h and t_c are the temperatures of the hot and cold reservoirs as read on one of the arbitrary thermometers discussed in Chapter 2.

Lord Kelvin used this principle to define his thermodynamic scale of temperature:

$$\frac{w}{h} = \frac{h - c}{h} = \frac{T_h - T_c}{T_h}. \tag{3.7–2}$$

He showed that T_h and T_c thus defined were simply the values of the absolute temperature of the hot and cold reservoirs on a perfect gas scale as defined in Chapter 2.[8]

Equation (3.7–2) may be generalized to apply to a refrigeration process as well, in the form

$$\frac{w}{h_2} = \frac{T_2 - T_1}{T_2}, \tag{3.7–3}$$

[7] Sadi Carnot, *Reflexions sur la Puissance Motrice du Feu*, 1824; translated in *S. B. P.*, p. 221.

[8] William Thomson (Lord Kelvin), *Phil. Mag.*, [4] **4,** 8 (1852).

where T_2 is the temperature of the reservoir from which heat is removed, T_1 the temperature of the other reservoir, and h_2 the heat removed. The work w is then negative, since work must be done *on* the system. For a "heat pump," equation (3.7–2) applies as written, with w and h both negative, since work is done *on* the system and heat given *to* the hot reservoir.

The problems below can now be solved; if the reader prefers, they may be solved (with less pleasure) after the detailed formality has been outlined in Chapter 6. The above identification is treated there in detail, along with the formal treatment of the second law.

Problem 3.7-1. The steam in an engine operates between temperature limits of 150° and 30°C, corresponding to the hot and cold reservoirs described above. Calculate the maximum amount of mechanical energy which this engine can produce by the expenditure of 1000 cal of heat.

Problem 3.7-2. By use of equation (3.7–3), calculate the minimum amount of work which must be done to remove 1000 cal of heat (a) at 15°C, and (b) at −50°C, by a refrigeration machine giving up its heat at 25°C.

Problem 3.7-3. (a) By use of equation (3.7–2), calculate the minimum amount of work required to supply 1000 Btu to the room (1 Btu = 252 cal) by means of a system giving up heat at 25°C and taking it on at −10°C. (b) Assume that the work in part (a) is supplied by an electric motor whose power efficiency is 90%, using power whose cost is 1.0 cent per kilowatt hour (1 kwhr = 9×10^5 cal). Calculate the cost of producing 1000 Btu of heat under the conditions described. Compare this with the cost of producing the same amount of heat by burning liquefied petroleum gas which costs 2.5 cents per pound and whose combustion produces 20,000 Btu/lb. (*Note.* The cost of installation of such a "heat pump" tends to be high, and, as with other heat engines, the practical efficiency is likely to be much less than that calculated above.)

Equations of State

CHAPTER 4

4.1 Introduction

In order to specify the *state* of a system, it is necessary to give the values of a set of variables, such as pressure (P), volume (V), temperature (T) (for the present arbitrarily defined), and the number of moles (n) of each material present. These quantities are known as *variables of state*, and their values as *data of state*. An *equation of state* defines a particular state of matter by giving a relationship between the otherwise unrelated variables P, V, T, and n. This takes the form $f(P,V,T,n) = 0$. Since the volume, other things being equal, is directly proportional to the number of moles, it is convenient to express the equation of state in terms of the *molar volume* $\tilde{V}$ as $f(P,\tilde{V},T) = 0$.[1]

Equations of state permit the calculation not only of the quantities involved but also of their derivatives. They are used for the calculation of thermodynamic quantities. This chapter will consider equations of state for gases only. The details of the form of equations of state are apt to be uninspiring unless related to molecular models. However, it is necessary to discuss the equations at this point because they provide the only way in which certain of the thermodynamic properties can be related. Accurate equations of state for all the components in a gaseous reaction are essential if the conditions for equilibrium are to be calculated accurately.

[1] Throughout this book, the value of a property for an arbitrary number of moles will be indicated by an *italic* capital letter (e.g., V), and that for a mole of material by an italic capital letter with tilde above (e.g., $\tilde{V}$).

4.2 Perfect Gas Law

The simplest equation of state for a gas is the perfect gas law,

$$P\tilde{V} = RT,$$

which was originally deduced from the experiments of Boyle and Charles. It can also be derived from the kinetic theory for a system of hard elastic particles of negligible volume with no interactions between them. Although this equation is at best an approximation to the behavior of any real gas, it is important as a partial expression of the limiting behavior of any gas at very low pressures (or high molar volumes). This fact may be expressed mathematically by the statement that for all gases the condition

$$\frac{P\tilde{V}}{RT} \to 1 \quad \text{as} \quad P \to 0$$

must be obeyed by any satisfactory equation of state.

For this equation to have its full meaning, the temperature must be defined as in Section 3.7. In the following paragraphs in which specific equations of state are discussed, it is taken for granted that the temperature

Table 4.3–I
Compressibility of Carbon Monoxide†

Pressure (atm)	$P\tilde{V}/RT$ −70°C	−25°C	25°C	100°C	200°C
1	0.9981	0.9992	0.9998	1.0002	1.0004
25	0.9447	0.9834	0.9951	1.0062	1.0143
50	0.8917	0.9646	0.9919	1.0124	1.0247
75	0.8497	0.9497	0.9920	1.0204	1.0358
100	0.8261	0.9481	0.9949	1.0288	1.0471
125	0.8209	0.9488	1.0027	1.0403	1.0592
150	0.8319	0.9531	1.0151	1.0526	1.0732
200	0.8910	0.9925	1.0453	1.0824	1.1016
300	1.0691	1.1098	1.1370	1.1558	1.1647
400	1.2678	1.2546	1.2477	1.2411	1.2337
500	1.4675	1.4117	1.3681	1.3343	1.3057
600	1.6645	1.5713	1.4942	1.4308	1.3805
800	2.0476	1.8872	1.7412	1.6275	1.5363
1000	2.4179	2.1933	2.0015	1.8243	1.6887

† Calculated from the data of E. P. Bartlett, H. C. Hetherington, H. M. Kvalnes, and T. H. Tremeane, *J. Am. Chem. Soc.*, **52**, 1374 (1930).

is thermodynamically defined by equation (3.7–2). Otherwise, as will be clear from the discussion of the arbitrary temperature scales (Chapter 2, Section 2.8), these equations merely define a temperature scale.

4.3 Behavior of Real Gases

The deviations of a real gas from the perfect gas law are readily displayed by a plot of the ratio $P\tilde{V}/RT$ against P for a particular temperature. Figure 4.3–1 shows the behavior of several typical gases near room

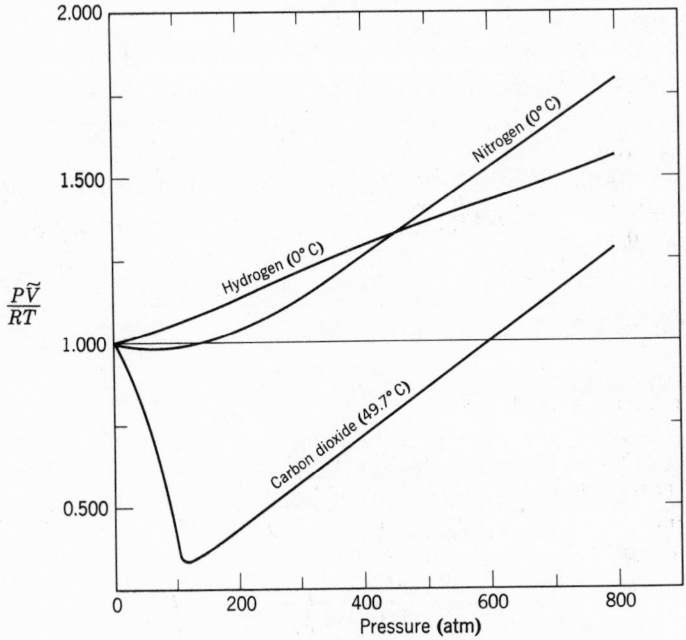

Fig. 4.3–1. Behavior of gases near room temperature.

temperature. The ratio $P\tilde{V}/RT$ is usually called the *compressibility factor*, and is given the symbol Z. Table 4.3–1 gives the compressibility factor of carbon monoxide between −70° and 200°C, for pressures up to 1000 atm.

Problem 4.3-1. Plot the compressibility data of Table 4.3–1 against pressure at −70°C, 25°C, and 200°C. Note the resemblance of the curves to those of Fig. 4.3–1 and the approach to perfect gas behavior with increase in temperature. Explain.

Data of state are reported in the literature in a variety of ways. Those principally used are (a) tables of compressibility factors, as in Table 4.3–1, and (b) tables of the pressure-volume product in Amagat units[2] (PV_a) as a function either of pressure or of Amagat density (ρ_a, frequently also given as d_a). The Amagat volume and density are defined by the equations

$$V_a = \frac{V}{V_0}, \qquad \rho_a = \frac{1}{V_a}, \tag{4.3–1}$$

where V_0 is the volume of the material at 0°C, 1 atm. As an example, the molar volume of carbon monoxide at 1 atm, 0°C, is 22,405 cm.[3] (It should be noted that $\tilde{V}_0$ varies from gas to gas and is never exactly equal to RT_0 for any real gas.) From Table 4.3–1, the molar volume of CO at 25°C, 500 atm, is calculated to be 66.95 cm³. The Amagat volume, V_a, is thus 0.002988; the Amagat density, ρ_a, is 334.7; and PV_a is 1.4940.

At sufficiently low temperatures the application of pressure will cause the gas to liquefy. The temperature above which the gas will no longer become liquid is known as the *critical temperature* (T_c); the pressure required for liquefaction at this temperature is called the *critical pressure* (P_c), and the volume under these conditions the *critical volume* (V_c). At the critical point so defined, the derivatives $(\partial P/\partial V)_T$ and $(\partial^2 P/\partial V^2)_T$ are both zero; that is, this is an inflection point in a plot of P against V at the temperature T_c.

4.4 Virial Equations

It is evident that the compressibility factor ($P\tilde{V}/RT$) can be represented, at a particular temperature, by a power series in pressure or reciprocal volume. Such an equation is called a *virial equation*. The original virial equation of Kamerlingh Onnes[3] was

$$\frac{P\tilde{V}}{RT} = A + \frac{B}{\tilde{V}} + \frac{C}{\tilde{V}^2} + \frac{D}{\tilde{V}^4} + \frac{E}{\tilde{V}^6} + \frac{F}{\tilde{V}^8} + \cdots \tag{4.4–1}$$

The constants A, B, C, etc., are called the first, second, third, etc., *virial coefficients*[4] and are functions of temperature only. If actual molal volumes are used, the constant A is unity. Other "virial equations" give the compressibility factor ($P\tilde{V}/RT$) or the pressure-volume product in Amagat units (PV_a) as a function either of pressure or of Amagat density. If Amagat units are used, the constant A takes on a value characteristic

[2] These units are named in honor of the pioneering work of E. H. Amagat; see, for example, E. H. Amagat, *Ann. chim. et phys.*, [5] **19**, 345 (1884).

[3] H. Kamerlingh Onnes, *Comm. Phys. Lab. Univ. of Leiden, No.* **71** (1901).

[4] The power series in equation (4.4–1) is in the form given originally by Onnes. At present, terms in V^{-3}, V^{-5}, etc., are often included, and the symbols used for the coefficients occasionally vary.

of each temperature. Tables of virial coefficients of several gases are given in Appendix 2.

The virial equation is advantageous because it is completely general and can be made to fit any data of state. Moreover, it is possible to calculate all the virial coefficients from a knowledge of the potential energies of interaction of gas molecules. The virial equation is sometimes difficult to use, because its constants depend on temperature; their values can seldom be extrapolated beyond the temperature range for which data are available.

An equation utilizing only the first and second virial coefficients is sufficient to represent most data at moderate pressures; this may be expressed

$$\frac{P\tilde{V}}{RT} = 1 + \frac{B}{\tilde{V}}. \tag{4.4–2}$$

Other equations similar to (4.4–2) may be written. Three such equations are

$$\frac{P\tilde{V}}{RT} = 1 + B'P, \tag{4.4–3}$$

$$P\tilde{V}(1 - \beta P) = RT, \tag{4.4–4}$$

and

$$P(\tilde{V} - \mathrm{b}) = RT, \tag{4.4–5}$$

in which the constants $B' \approx \beta \approx B/RT$ and $\mathrm{b} \approx B$ are functions of the temperature. The approximate equations (4.4–2), (4.4–3), (4.4–4), and (4.4–5) are sufficiently accurate for many purposes, and choice between them is primarily a matter of convenience.

The following problems will give the reader an idea of the order of magnitude and temperature coefficient of the virial coefficients. The results of Problem 4.4–2 are used later to calculate several thermodynamic properties.

Problem 4.4-1. (a) Using the data of Table 4.3–1, obtain the constant B' of equation (4.4–3) for carbon monoxide at −70°C, 25°C, and 100°C. (*Hint.* Plot the data against pressure up to 100 atm at each temperature, and draw tangents to the curves at zero pressure; the slopes of these lines are the values of B'.)

(b) Plot B' against temperature.

(c) Estimate for each temperature the range of pressures within which equation (4.4–3) will represent the data within 1%.

Problem 4.4-2. (a) Using the data of Table 4.3–1, obtain approximate equations of the form $P\tilde{V}/RT = 1 + B'P + C'P^2$ for carbon monoxide at −70°C and 100°C. This may be done as follows at each temperature: Calculate approximate values of the compressibility at 100 and 200 atm from equation (4.4–3), using the values of B' obtained in the previous problem. For each pressure, obtain the term $C'P^2$ by comparison with the data, and from it a value of C'. Then average the values of C' for each temperature.

(b) Use the equations obtained in part (a) to calculate values of the compressibility at each of the pressures listed in Table 4.3–1, up to 300 atm, and compare with the actual values. Note that the quadratic equation fits much better at the higher temperature.

Problem 4.4-3. The results of Michels, Wijker, and Wijker[5] on P-V-T relationships for argon from 1 to 2900 atm are expressed in terms of the equation

$$PV_a = A + B\rho_a + C\rho_a^2 + Z\rho_a^3 + D\rho_a^4 + I\rho_a^5 + E\rho_a^6,$$

where $V_a = \tilde{V}/\tilde{V}_0 = 1/\rho_a$ and $\tilde{V}_0$ is the molar volume at 0°C, 1 atm. The constants for this equation at 0°C are given below.

(a) Convert this equation to one at 0°C in terms of $\tilde{V}$ only, taking $\tilde{V}_0 = 22.40$ liters.

(b) Use the new equation to calculate the pressure under which the gas has molar volumes at 0°C of 0.040, 0.100, and 1.000 liter.

(c) Determine the range of pressure within which a linear equation in $1/\tilde{V}$ could be used with less than 0.1% error.

(At 0°C, $A = 1.001$, $B = 9.44 \times 10^{-4}$, $C = 2.10 \times 10^{-6}$, $Z = 2.36 \times 10^{-9}$, $D = 6.77 \times 10^{-12}$, $Y = 1.69 \times 10^{-15}$, $E = -5.47 \times 10^{-18}$.)

4.5 The van der Waals and Berthelot Equations

The equation of van der Waals,[6]

$$\left(P + \frac{\mathrm{a}}{\tilde{V}^2}\right)(\tilde{V} - \mathrm{b}) = RT, \qquad (4.5\text{–}1)$$

has been widely used for estimation of gas volumes.

Problem 4.5-1. Calculate the pressure exerted by 1 mole of methane in a volume of 0.200 liter at 0°C: (a) from the perfect gas law; (b) from the van der Waals equation, using the constants of Appendix 2. Compare with the actual pressure of 89.75 atm.

The constants of the van der Waals equation may be obtained directly from experimental data of state, but are more commonly evaluated from critical constants. The procedure is as follows:

Equation (4.5–1) is used to obtain expressions for $(\partial P/\partial V)_T$ and $(\partial^2 P/\partial V^2)_T$, both of which are zero at the critical point. Substitution of the critical pressure (P_c), volume (V_c), and temperature (T_c) into (4.5–1) and into the equations for the two derivatives gives three equations relating the constants a and b and the critical constants. Solution of these equations gives three relationships: $T_c = 8\mathrm{a}/27\mathrm{b}R$; $\tilde{V}_c = 3\mathrm{b}$; $P_c = \mathrm{a}/27\mathrm{b}^2$, any two of which suffice for determination of a and b. If the equations involving T_c and P_c are used to evaluate a and b, the third equation determines $\tilde{V}_c$. For some gases the value of $\tilde{V}_c$ thus obtained agrees fairly well with the experimental value; for others, the agreement is poor, indicating clearly that the equation does not represent the data of

[5] A. Michels, Hub. Wijker, and H. K. Wijker, *Physica*, **15**, 627 (1949).

[6] J. D. van der Waals, Thesis, University of Leiden, 1873.

state at all well. A table of critical and van der Waals constants is given in Appendix 2.

Problem 4.5-2. Perform the calculation indicated above to verify the relationships given for T_c, P_c, and V_c in terms of the van der Waals constants a and b. From these relationships obtain expressions for a and b in terms of T_c and P_c.

Problem 4.5-3. Calculate the van der Waals constants a and b for carbon dioxide from the critical data in Appendix 2.

The main advantages of the van der Waals equation are its simplicity and the fact that its constants may be obtained from a very limited amount of data. (The critical constants can even be estimated if not known.) It gives a reasonable approximation to the data under many conditions, but is never very satisfactory, and is seldom used in the computation of thermodynamic quantities.

At low pressures, the van der Waals equation may be expanded into a simplified virial equation such as equation (4.4–2) or (4.4–3). The second virial coefficient B is then equal to $(\mathrm{b} - \mathrm{a}/RT)$, with $B' \approx B/RT$.

Problem 4.5-4. Show that at low pressures the van der Waals equation may be reduced to the approximate form $P\tilde{V} = 1 + B/\tilde{V}$, with $B = (\mathrm{b} - \mathrm{a}/RT)$.

Problem 4.5-5. The second virial coefficient (B) of 1-butene, from the data of Roper[7] is -1.94 liter mole^{-1} at 202.3°K and -0.89 liter mole^{-1} at 266.5°K. It is nearly linear in $1/T$.

(a) Use these data to estimate the van der Waals constants a and b for 1-butene.

(b) Calculate the percentage by which 1-butene vapor differs from ideal gas behavior at the normal boiling point (266.9°K) and 1 atm.

Berthelot[8] observed that the van der Waals equation could be made to fit available data better if the constant a were made a function of temperature, and proposed the equation

$$\left(P + \frac{\mathrm{a}'}{T\tilde{V}^2}\right)(\tilde{V} - \mathrm{b}) = RT. \tag{4.5–2}$$

The constant b is the same as in the van der Waals equation. If the constants are evaluated from critical data, $\mathrm{a}' = \mathrm{a}T_c$. This equation is rarely used in its original form, but is quite frequently employed in the reduced form known as the *modified Berthelot equation*:

$$\frac{P\tilde{V}}{RT} = 1 + \frac{9PT_c}{128P_cT}\left(1 - \frac{6T_c^{\,2}}{T^2}\right). \tag{4.5–3}$$

This was obtained from the original equation as follows: The values of a and b were obtained in terms of P_c and T_c, as described for the van der Waals equation,

[7] E. E. Roper, *J. Phys. Chem.*, **44**, 835 (1940).

[8] D. Berthelot, *J. Phys.*, [3] **8**, 263 (1899).

and substituted into equation (4.5–2). The resulting equation was expanded as a series in P and T and simplified to the final form. The numerical constants were then adjusted slightly to provide a better fit with typical data at low pressures.

The modified Berthelot equation has proved useful in treatment of the thermodynamic properties of gases at moderate pressures. It may be obtained from equation (4.4–2) by using the value[9] of B as

$$B = \frac{9P\tilde{V}T_c}{128P_cT}\left(1 - \frac{6T_c^2}{T^2}\right), \tag{4.5–4a}$$

or from (4.4–3) by setting

$$B' = \frac{9T_c}{128P_cT}\left(1 - \frac{6T_c^2}{T^2}\right). \tag{4.5–4b}$$

Problem 4.5-5 From the modified Berthelot equation obtain for oxygen, at 0°C, the constant in the equation $P\tilde{V}/RT = 1 + B'P$. For oxygen, $P_c = 49.7$ atm, $T_c = 164.5$°K. The experimental value of B' is -9.4×10^{-4} atm.

4.6 Other Equations of State

Several other equations of state have been used in treatment of thermodynamic data; each of these represents a modification of the van der Waals equation. The equation of Dieterici[10] is

$$P(\tilde{V} - \mathrm{b}) = RTe^{-\mathrm{a}/RT\tilde{V}} \tag{4.6–1}$$

This equation may be obtained from the van der Waals equation if the additive correction to the P is replaced by an exponential factor. It reduces to the van der Waals equation at large molar volumes.

Problem 4.6-1. Show by expanding the exponential and replacing $\tilde{V}$ by $\tilde{V} - \mathrm{b}$ in the appropriate places that, at low pressure, equation (4.6–1) leads to the van der Waals equation (not to the Berthelot equation) with a and b identical with those of the van der Waals equation.

Keyes[11] proposed a 4-constant equation,

$$P = \frac{RT}{\tilde{V} - Be^{-\alpha/\tilde{V}}} - \frac{\mathrm{a}}{(\tilde{V} - l)^2}. \tag{4.6–2}$$

[9] Note that at low pressures $P\tilde{V} \approx RT$.
[10] C. Dieterici, *Ann. phys.*, [4] **5,** 51 (1901).
[11] F. G. Keyes, *Proc. Natl. Acad. Sci. U.S.*, **3,** 323 (1927).

Beattie and Bridgeman[12] used a 5-constant equation, originally written

$$P = \frac{RT(1-\epsilon)}{\tilde{V}^2}(\tilde{V}+B) - \frac{A}{\tilde{V}^2}, \qquad (4.6\text{–}3)$$

with $A = A_0(1 - \mathrm{a}/\tilde{V})$, $B = B_0(1 - \mathrm{b}/\tilde{V})$, $\epsilon = \mathrm{c}/\tilde{V}T^3$. This may also be written in the virial form as

$$\frac{P\tilde{V}}{RT} = 1 + \frac{\beta}{RT}\left(\frac{1}{\tilde{V}}\right) + \frac{\gamma}{RT}\left(\frac{1}{\tilde{V}^2}\right) + \frac{\delta}{RT}\left(\frac{1}{\tilde{V}^3}\right), \qquad (4.6\text{–}4)$$

with $\beta = RTB_0 - A_0 - R\mathrm{c}/T^2$, $\gamma = -RTB_0\mathrm{b} + A_0\mathrm{a} - RT_0\mathrm{c}/T^2$, $\delta = RB_0\mathrm{bc}/T^2$. The resulting equation (4.6–4) is a 4-constant form of the virial equation, with the temperature dependence of each virial coefficient given explicitly. In this fact lies the most evident virtue of the equation. Tables of constants for the Beattie–Bridgeman equation are given in Appendix 2.

Benedict, Webb, and Rubin[13] have used an 8-constant modification of the Beattie–Bridgeman equation:

$$P = RT\mathrm{d_m} + \left(B_0RT - A_0 - \frac{C_0}{T^2}\right)\mathrm{d_m} + (\mathrm{b}RT - \mathrm{a})\mathrm{d_m}^3 + \mathrm{a}\alpha\mathrm{d_m}^6$$
$$+ \frac{\mathrm{cd_m}^3(1 + \gamma\mathrm{d_m}^3)}{T^2}\mathrm{e}^{-\gamma\mathrm{d_m}^2} \qquad (4.6\text{–}5)$$

where $\mathrm{d_m} = 1/\tilde{V}$; the constants A_0, B_0, C_0, a, b, etc., must be determined empirically.

4.7 Evaluation of Equations of State

It is not possible to make a general comparison of equations of state, since the accuracy of any one equation will depend on the gas considered, the method by which constants were obtained, and the range of pressure and temperature examined. A relatively good equation of state, such as the Beattie–Bridgeman equation, is capable of predicting P-V-T relationships of a number of simple gases within about 0.1% at pressures up to 100 atm.

Many thermodynamic quantities depend not only on P, V, and T, but also on derivatives of these quantities; thus they may be very sensitive to small defects in an equation of state. For example, the rate of change of

[12] J. A. Beattie and O. C. Bridgeman, *J. Am. Chem. Soc.*, **49**, 1665 (1927).
[13] M. Benedict, G. B. Webb, and L. C. Rubin, *J. Chem. Phys.*, **8**, 334 (1940).

heat capacity with pressure $(\partial C_P/\partial P)_T$ depends on the second derivative with respect to temperature of the difference between the actual volume and that of the ideal gas at the same pressure and temperature. In the case of *n*-heptane[14] at room temperature, the Beattie–Bridgeman equation is in error by over 50% in the value of this derivative below 1 atm. This sort of limitation means that very often only a virial equation is suitable for accurate thermodynamic calculations. Conversely, it will be seen later that thermodynamic measurements may be used to define suitable equations of state.

Table 4.7–1 compares experimental values of $P\tilde{V}/RT$ for nitrogen at 0°C and at pressures to 400 atm with those calculated from the modified Berthelot equation, the van der Waals equation, and the Beattie–Bridgeman equation. The constants of the first two equations were obtained from the critical temperature and pressure of nitrogen; the constants of the Beattie–Bridgeman equation were evaluated empirically. It will be seen that the Beattie–Bridgeman equation represents the data within about 3% over the entire range, and within 0.25% to 200 atm. The van der Waals equation is almost as good at the highest pressures, but fails badly to represent the curvature at intermediate pressures, and is in error by 6% at 100 atm. The modified Berthelot equation, since it is linear in pressure, fails utterly above 200 atm. It is considerably better than the van der Waals equation at low pressures, owing to the adjustments referred to previously.

Table 4.7–1
Comparison of Equations of State for Nitrogen at 0°C

Pressure (atm)	$P\tilde{V}/RT$			
	Observed†	Modified Berthelot Equation	van der Waals Equation	Beattie–Bridgeman Equation‡
1	1.000	1.000	1.000	1.000
50	0.985	0.987	0.957	0.983
100	0.985	0.973	0.927	0.986
200	1.0365	0.947	0.998	1.0341
300	1.1335	0.919	1.131	1.1227
400	1.2557	0.892	1.300	1.2163

† E. P. Bartlett, *J. Am. Chem. Soc.*, **50**, 1284 (1928).
‡ Constants used are from K. C. Beattie and O. C. Bridgeman, *Z. Physik*, **62**, 95 (1930).

[14] G. Waddington, S. S. Todd, and H. M. Huffman, *J. Am. Chem. Soc.*, **69**, 22 (1947).

4.8 Law of Corresponding States

Van der Waals,[6] in his examination of data of state for gases, observed that the molar volumes of all gases were similar at corresponding values of the reduced temperature (T/T_c) and pressure (P/P_c). This correspondence in P-V-T behavior is implicit in the van der Waals equation, and becomes explicit if the constants a and b are expressed in terms of T_c, P_c, and $\tilde{V}_c$.

Problem 4.8-1. Show that a gas which obeys the van der Waals equation completely must satisfy the equation

$$\left(P_R + \frac{3}{V_R^2}\right)(3V_R - 1) = 8T_R \tag{4.8–1}$$

where $P_R = P/P_c$, $V_R = \tilde{V}/\tilde{V}_c$, and $T_R = T/T_c$.

Hint. Replace the constants a and b in (4.5–1) by their values in terms of $\tilde{V}_c$ and $\tilde{P}_c$ given in Section 4.5, divide by $P_c\tilde{V}_c$, and use the relationship $P_c\tilde{V}_c/T_c = 3R/8$ to simplify the result. Note that equation (4.8–1) contains no term characteristic of the individual gas.

The similarity in gas behavior at corresponding values of reduced temperature and pressure is quite general, regardless of the extent to which the individual gases follow any particular equation of state. According to the *law of corresponding states, the reduced volumes* (and other reduced properties) will have the same values for *all gases at corresponding values of reduced temperature and pressure.*

This correspondence in gas behavior has been widely used by engineers in the estimation not only of P-V-T data but also of properties related thereto, such as the effect of gas imperfections on enthalpy, entropy, and heat capacity. Hougen and Watson[15] have given charts of the compressibility factor plotted against reduced temperature and pressure. These charts were obtained by averaging experimental data for a number of common gases; they give the compressibility factors of most gases within a few per cent.

4.9 Theoretical Equations of State

If the potential energy of interaction between molecules is known, it is possible to calculate virial coefficients by means of statistical mechanics. The virial coefficients thus obtained are intimately related to the nature of intermolecular collisions.[16] The first virial coefficient (A) neglects all

[15] O. A. Hougen and K. M. Watson, *Chemical Process Principles*, Part II, *Thermodynamics*, Wiley, New York, 1947, Fig. 103, p. 489.

[16] The term "collision" in this sense is not restricted to "direct hits" of one molecule by another. In the language of the theory a collision is recorded whenever one molecule causes a change in the motion of another.

molecular collisions, the second (B) accounts for only binary collisions, the third for ternary collisions, and so on. The relations between intermolecular forces and the virial coefficients are complicated integral equations.

In practice, calculations of virial coefficients beyond the third are very difficult. However, many calculations have been made of second virial coefficients, and a few of third virial coefficients. The results are expressed as tables[17] of virial coefficients which are functions of temperature and of the parameters of the potential energy expression assumed. If these parameters are known, virial coefficients can readily be calculated; conversely, measured virial coefficients can be used to deduce information about intermolecular forces.

It can be shown[18] that, if the interaction law is of a fairly simple type, the theoretical approach leads to the law of corresponding states.

4.10 Equations of State of Gas Mixtures

The P-V-T relationships of a given gas mixture may readily be described in terms of the molar volume, $\tilde{V}$, defined by the equation

$$\tilde{V} = \frac{V}{n_1 + n_2 + \cdots}, \qquad (4.10\text{–}1)$$

where V is the total volume of a given mixture; n_1, n_2, etc., are the numbers of moles of each component present. For a given composition, the dependence of compressibility on pressure or molar volume may be given as before. The data for this composition may be expressed in terms of any of the equations of state previously considered; the constants used will depend on the composition of the mixture, whether or not this is explicitly stated.

Whereas the P-V-T relationships of many pure gases have been thoroughly investigated, very few measurements have been made on gas mixtures. In many cases the only method for obtaining the properties of a gas mixture is to estimate them from those of the pure components. This procedure is facilitated by the sort of theoretical considerations mentioned in Section 4.9, and it has proved reasonably successful for mixtures whose properties are known.

If a virial equation is to be used, the virial coefficients B and C may frequently be estimated directly from the composition and the corresponding

[17] J. O. Hirschfelder, C. F. Curtiss, and R. B. Bird, *Molecular Theory of Gases and Liquids*, Wiley, New York, 1954, Appendixes I, II, VI.

[18] K. S. Pitzer, *J. Chem. Phys.*, **7**, 583 (1939); E. A. Guggenheim, *J. Chem. Phys.*, **13**, 253 (1945).

virial coefficients for the pure gases.[17] If another type of equation is to be used, its constants may be related to those of the virial equation as was done in Sections 4.4 to 4.6. Theoretical considerations are used to relate the constants for a given mixture to those of the pure gases. The results obtained for the van der Waals equation are given below.

The van der Waals equation for a binary gas mixture may be written

$$\left(P + \frac{a_m}{\tilde{V}^2}\right)(\tilde{V} - b_m) = RT, \tag{4.10–2}$$

where $\tilde{V}$ is defined by equation (4.10–1); a_m and b_m are constants for a given mixture, given by [19]

$$a_m = \tilde{N}_1^2 a_{11} + 2\tilde{N}_1\tilde{N}_2 a_{12} + \tilde{N}_2^2 a_{22} \qquad (4.10\text{–}3)^{**}$$

and

$$b_m = \tilde{N}_1^2 b_{11} + 2\tilde{N}_1\tilde{N}_2 b_{12} + \tilde{N}_2^2 b_{22}. \qquad (4.10\text{–}4)^{**}$$

In these equations $\tilde{N}_1$ and $\tilde{N}_2$ are the mole fractions of the components, and a_{11}, b_{11}, a_{22}, b_{22} are the van der Waals constants for the pure components 1 and 2. The constants a_{12} and b_{12} are given by

$$a_{12} = (a_{11}a_{22})^{1/2}; \qquad b_{12} = \left(\frac{b_{11}^{1/3} + b_{22}^{1/3}}{2}\right)^3. \qquad (4.10\text{–}5)^{**}$$

The same procedure may be employed to estimate a_m and b_m for use with the original Berthelot equation (4.5–2) and the Dieterici equation (4.6–1). Similar methods of estimation may be developed for use with other equations of state.

Problem 4.10-1. The van der Waals constants for methane and ethane are: for methane, a = 2.25 atm liter^2; b = 0.0428 l; for ethane, a = 5.39 atm liter^2; b = 0.0638 liter. Show that the corresponding constants for a mixture containing 60 mole per cent methane, 40 mole per cent ethane are a_m = 3.48 atm liter^2; b_m = 0.0510 l.

Problem 4.10-2. Using the results of Problem 4.10–1, calculate the pressure exerted in a volume of 0.500 liter at 50°C by a mole of (a) pure methane, (b) a mixture containing 60 mole per cent methane, 40 mole per cent ethane, and (c) pure ethane. Compare with the observed values of 49.8, 46.1, and 38.2 atm, respectively.

[19] Throughout the remainder of this book, asterisks will be used to mark approximate equations. A single asterisk (*) will denote an approximation dependent on assumption of the perfect gas law. Equations based on other assumptions will be labeled with a double asterisk (**).

The First Law of Thermodynamics and Its Formal Applications

CHAPTER 5

5.1 First Law of Thermodynamics

The formal treatment of thermodynamics requires, first, precise and general statements, in terms of measurable quantities, of the experimental laws on which it is based. In the application of these laws, it is convenient to introduce defined functions, which are often not directly measurable. The interrelationships between the set of measurable quantities and defined functions make up the mathematical framework of thermodynamics. In this chapter we proceed with a formal examination of the first law of thermodynamics. The law itself is stated in this section. In subsequent sections, its consequences are considered in logical order and the defined quantities introduced when the occasion arises. The second law of thermodynamics is considered in a similar fashion in Chapter 6. Detailed applications of the principles elucidated in these chapters are taken up later.

The equivalence between change in energy ΔE and work w, which was given in equation (3.5–1), may be stated generally as follows:

Law I. *If a thermally insulated system (hereafter called adiabatic) can be taken from a state I to a state II by alternative paths, the work done by the system has the same value for every such (adiabatic) path and is equal to the decrease in energy of the system.* That is,

$$\Delta E = -w \text{ (adiabatic).} \tag{5.1–1}$$

The quantity w is taken as positive for work done *by the system.* If the system is completely isolated, so that it does no work on its surroundings, there is no change in energy. That is,

$$\Delta E = 0 \text{ (isolated system).} \tag{5.1–2}$$

If our universe is considered as an isolated system, equation (5.1–2) states the law of conservation of energy and equation (5.1–1) states the equivalence of work and energy.

If the restriction of thermal insulation is removed, so that energy may enter in the form of heat, the heat q withdrawn from the surroundings will be

$$q = \Delta E + w$$

or (5.1–3)

$$q = \Delta E - (-w).$$

Equation (5.1–3) merely states that, if a system gains more energy than the work performed on it, $-w$, the extra energy must have been gained by the withdrawal of a quantity of heat q from the surroundings. It is clear from Chapter 3 that this is the only way in which heat is uniquely defined. Thus the equation

$$\Delta E = q - w \tag{5.1–4}$$

gives the increase in energy of a system which takes in energy as a quantity of heat q (withdrawn from the surroundings) and supplies mechanical energy in amount w (done against forces which are part of the surroundings). *All the heat withdrawn by a system from the surroundings during such a process is not destined to remain in the body; only the part of it ΔE is retained.*[1]

The energy retained by a system must depend only on the initial and final states of the system (i.e., only the initial and final values of P, V, T, etc.). If this were not so, it would be possible to construct a process in which the system liberated energy without itself suffering any change. As a simple example, suppose that a system liberates an amount of energy, $-\Delta E$, in going from a state A to another state B. If the energy required to return the system to state A were less than ΔE, a cyclic process in which the system went from A to B and back to A would make available the difference. The production of the "extra" energy is contrary to the

[1] It has been the authors' experience that the confusion between q and ΔE which is so frequently encountered will never arise if heat is considered as coming from or going to the *surroundings*. The quantity characteristic of the system itself is its internal energy; this energy resides in the *system*. There is never confusion about the part of the energy which is called *work*, since the mechanical systems on which it is done are usually simple and visible and clearly *not part of the system* under consideration.

experiments on which the first law is based. By exactly the same argument it may be shown that the energy change must be the same for all processes connecting the same initial and final states. Consequently, the energy of a system must be uniquely determined by specification of the *state* of the system. It is therefore spoken of as a *property* of the system, in the same sense that pressure, volume, etc., are properties of the system.

The measurable quantities work w and heat q, which describe the effect of a *process* on the *surroundings*, are not uniquely determined by the change in state of the *system*. Thus, although the total transfer of energy during a process is determined by the change of state of the system (or vice versa), the distribution of this transfer between work and heat is not so regulated. (It will be seen in Chapter 6 that the second law puts certain limitations on this distribution, but still does not specify either the heat or the work uniquely.) The heat and work for a process thus depend on the path which the process takes, not solely on its initial and terminal points.

The meaning of the term *work* and its sign are discussed in Section 2.3. This section should be reread in its entirety before continuing with the next one.

5.2 Latent Heat, Heat of Phase Changes, and Heats of Reaction at Constant Pressure. The Enthalpy

Consider the vaporization of a liquid or any other phase change which occurs under a constant pressure by pushing back a frictionless piston on which a force acts which exactly balances the pressure of this system. Such a process requires exactly the same amount of work to reverse it and is therefore called reversible (see Section 6.2).[1a] The work done by the system is given by equation (2.3–6) as

$$w = P\,\Delta V, \tag{2.3–6}$$

where P is the constant *external* pressure and ΔV is the increase in volume of the system.

Since the piston moves so as to permit an increase in volume, work is done against the forces retarding the motion of the piston. We concern ourselves here with the amount of work done by the system and not with the manner in which energy is stored or the forces which cause the motion. By *convention*, work done *by the system* is regarded as positive, and this is the physical entity of which we think. If the system were made to contract, the external forces would be in the opposite direction, and work would be

[1a] This restricted definition of reversibility anticipates a more general one (see Section 6.2). It is required here for purposes of definition.

done on the system. In this case energy would be stored by the system; according to the sign convention, the work done would be negative.

This is purely a matter of convention, for in actual practice the work is made manifest only by changes in the external apparatus, just as heat is made manifest only by temperature changes of heat reservoirs. The energy change alone is characteristic of the system, but ironically its value can be deduced only by subtraction of one of the physical entities from the other.

The heat of a reaction at constant pressure or of a phase change is related to the energy change and the work done by equation (5.1–3). This is

$$q = \Delta E + P\,\Delta V. \tag{5.2–1}$$

Let E_A and V_A be the energy and volume of the system before the process, while E_B and V_B are the corresponding quantities when the process is complete. Then

$$q = E_B - E_A + P(V_B - V_A). \tag{5.2–2}$$

We now consider the situation where the process is reversible, that is, where the constant external pressure is essentially equal to the pressure exerted *by the system.* In this case the pressure, as well as the volume and energy, becomes a *property* of the system. Taking P_A for the pressure in the initial state and P_B for that in the final state (for the sake of generality, since in this case P_A and P_B are equal), we may write

$$q = (E_B + P_BV_B) - (E_A + P_AV_A) = \Delta(E + PV) = H_B - H_A = \Delta H, \tag{5.2–3}$$

where H_A and H_B have been written for $(E_A + P_AV_A)$ and $(E_B + P_BV_B)$, respectively. The quantity H is defined in general by the equation

$$H = E + PV. \tag{5.2–4}$$

This quantity is obviously a *property* of the system, since the quantities which compose it are all properties of the system.

It is convenient to give H or $(E + PV)$ a name. It is called the *enthalpy*. This is the first of a set of arbitrarily defined thermodynamic quantities which make up a system of variables designed for ease of computation. Unfortunately, the quantity is often called the "heat content." The lack of fortune in such a name is due to the fact that the enthalpy is an arbitrarily defined function. Changes in enthalpy become measurable in a single determination only for processes, either *physical* or *chemical*, at constant pressure, in which case $\Delta H = q$. There is no physical meaning to the function itself except that it is the sum of the energy and the PV product of the system.

In general, the heat withdrawn from the surroundings by a system undergoing a chemical reaction or phase change is equal to the energy change plus the work contribution for all its parts. If substances are formed in the process, they make a positive contribution; if used up, a negative one. If the various parts of the system are at constant but different pressures, P_i,

$$q = \Delta E + \sum P_i V_i, \tag{5.2–5}$$

where V_i is positive for substances which are produced and negative for substances used up. From the definition of H it is then clear that, *in general, where all the pressures are held constant*

$$q = \Delta H, \tag{5.2–6}$$

where

$$H = E + \sum P_j V_j; \tag{5.2–7}$$

this sum $\sum P_j V_j$ is taken over all the pressures of the system. This result is evidently due to the fact that all the P_i in (5.2–5) are constant.

Problem 5.2-1. For CO_2: (a) What is the change in enthalpy when 1 mole of solid carbon dioxide changes to the vapor in equilibrium with it at 1 atm and 195°K (the sublimation point)?

(b) Calculate this same change when 1 mole of solid carbon dioxide at the same temperature vaporizes into a vacuum to produce a final pressure of 0.01 atm.

(c) Calculate the heat withdrawn from the surroundings, the energy change, and the work done in (a) and (b).

The density of solid carbon dioxide at 195°K is 1.56 g cm^{-3}. The heat of sublimation of solid carbon dioxide at 195°K is 6070 cal mole^{-1}. At 195°K the energy of a mole of gaseous carbon dioxide is 9 cal less at 1 atm than at 0.01 atm. Use the van der Waals equation for carbon dioxide, with the constants given in Appendix 2. (Note the results of Problem 4.5–4.)

Problem 5.2-2. (a) Calculate the change in enthalpy when a mole of gaseous carbon dioxide at 25°C expands against a piston always balancing the pressure of the gas from 1 atm to 0.01 atm. The energy increase in this process is 5.9 cal.

(b) Calculate the work done and the heat withdrawn from the surroundings.

(c) Compare the result in (a) with the heat calculated in (b), and show that the change in enthalpy is smaller than the heat withdrawn from the surroundings by an amount equal to the absolute value of $\int_{0.01}^{1} V\,dP$.

Use the van der Waals equation with the constants given in Appendix 2.

Problem 5.2-3. Calculate the work done on and the heat withdrawn from the surroundings if the gas in Problem 5.2-2 is allowed to expand from 1 atm into an evacuated vessel of such size that the final pressure is 0.01 atm. What are ΔE and ΔH for this process? Explain.

It is convenient at this point to give a general expression for the heat withdrawn from the surroundings where expansion work is done, and to compare it with the change in enthalpy. For the differential process,

$$\mathrm{d}E = q - P\,\mathrm{d}V, \tag{5.2–8}$$

so that

$$q = \mathrm{d}E + P\,\mathrm{d}V, \tag{5.2–9}$$

where the pressure is that of the *surroundings*. From the definition of the enthalpy (equation 5.2–4), the corresponding change in H is

$$\mathrm{d}H = \mathrm{d}(E + P\,\mathrm{d}V) = \mathrm{d}E + P\,\mathrm{d}V + V\,\mathrm{d}P, \tag{5.2–10}$$

where the pressure is that of the *system*. If the pressure of the system is equal to that of the surroundings, and both are constant, as in the previous cases, the enthalpy change and the heat are identical, since the last term in equation (5.2–10) is zero. If the pressure of the system is equal to that of the surroundings but not constant,

$$q = \mathrm{d}H - V\,\mathrm{d}P. \tag{5.2–11}$$

5.3 Heat Capacity

The amount of heat which must be withdrawn from the surroundings to raise the temperature of a given system by any definite amount is determined by the *heat capacity* of the system. The heat capacity C is defined as the limit, for very small temperature changes, of the ratio of the heat withdrawn from the surroundings to the temperature increase. In mathematical terms the definition is

$$C = \lim_{\delta T \to 0} \frac{q}{\delta T}. \tag{5.3–1}$$

The heat capacity of a system will depend on the conditions imposed during the heating process. Three possible conditions are of particular importance. These are:

(a) The system is kept at constant volume; in this case $w = 0$, and $q = \mathrm{d}E$. The heat capacity is called the *heat capacity at constant volume*; it is denoted by C_V. From (5.3–1) it is defined by

$$C_V = \left(\frac{\partial E}{\partial T}\right)_V, \tag{5.3–2}$$

and it gives the dependence of energy on temperature at constant volume.

(b) The system is maintained at constant pressure. In this case, according to equation (5.2–9),

$$q = \mathrm{d}E + P\,\mathrm{d}V = \mathrm{d}(E + PV) = \mathrm{d}H. \tag{5.3–3}$$

The corresponding heat capacity C_P is known as the *heat capacity at constant pressure*; it is given by

$$C_P = \left(\frac{\partial H}{\partial T}\right)_P, \tag{5.3–4}$$

and it represents the rate of change of enthalpy with temperature at constant pressure.

(c) A condensed phase is maintained in equilibrium with its vapor, so that the pressure of the system is kept at the value required for equilibrium as the temperature is changed. The heat capacity is then known as the *saturated* heat capacity; it is given the symbol C_{sat}.

$$C_{\text{sat}} = \lim_{\delta T \to 0} \left(\frac{q}{\delta T}\right)_{\text{sat}} \tag{5.3–5}$$

or

$$C_{\text{sat}} = \left(\frac{\partial E}{\partial T}\right)_{\text{sat}} + P_{\text{sat}}\left(\frac{\partial V}{\partial T}\right)_{\text{sat}}. \tag{5.3–6}$$

The subscript "sat" denotes functions for a condensed phase in equilibrium with its vapor, i.e., "saturated." The vapor can be treated similarly.

The amount of heat required to change a system from one temperature to another under specified conditions is obtained by integration of the appropriate heat capacity with respect to temperature over the desired range.

The several heat capacities are readily related; the relationship between C_{sat} and C_P is an important example. According to equation (5.2–11),

$$q = \mathrm{d}H - V\,\mathrm{d}P, \tag{5.3–7}$$

since the applied pressure is that of the system. (Note that $\mathrm{d}H = \mathrm{d}E + P\,\mathrm{d}V + V\,\mathrm{d}P$, where the pressure required is that of the system and not necessarily the external pressure.) The saturated heat capacity, C_{sat}, is thus (*for saturated condensed phase or equilibrium vapor*)

$$C_{\text{sat}} = \lim_{\delta T \to 0} \left(\frac{q}{\delta T}\right)_{\text{sat}} = \left(\frac{\partial H}{\partial T}\right)_{\text{sat}} - V\left(\frac{\partial P}{\partial T}\right)_{\text{sat}}. \tag{5.3–8}$$

From the general equation of partial derivatives (see Appendix 5),

$$\mathrm{d}H = \left(\frac{\partial H}{\partial T}\right)_P \mathrm{d}T + \left(\frac{\partial H}{\partial P}\right)_T \mathrm{d}P,$$

so that

$$\left(\frac{\partial H}{\partial T}\right)_{\text{sat}} = \left(\frac{\partial H}{\partial T}\right)_P + \left(\frac{\partial H}{\partial P}\right)_T \left(\frac{\partial P}{\partial T}\right)_{\text{sat}}. \tag{5.3–9}$$

Substitution for $(\partial H/\partial T)_{\text{sat}}$ in (5.3–8) gives

$$C_{\text{sat}} = \left(\frac{\partial H}{\partial T}\right)_P + \left[\left(\frac{\partial H}{\partial P}\right)_T - V\right]\left(\frac{\partial P}{\partial T}\right)_{\text{sat}}. \qquad (5.3\text{–}10)$$

In the same way it may be shown that

$$C_P - C_V = \left[V - \left(\frac{\partial H}{\partial P}\right)_T\right]\left(\frac{\partial P}{\partial T}\right)_V. \qquad (5.3\text{–}11)$$

The second law of thermodynamics provides methods of expressing derivatives such as $(\partial H/\partial P)_T$ in terms of P, V, and T. Upon substitution of the appropriate relationships, equations (5.3–10) and (5.3–11) may be put into forms containing only these variables.

Problem 5.3-1. (a) Derive equation (5.3–11) in a manner similar to that used for (5.3–10).

(b), (c) Derive the equations

$$C_P - C_V = \left[P + \left(\frac{\partial E}{\partial V}\right)_T\right]\left(\frac{\partial V}{\partial T}\right)_P \qquad (5.3\text{–}12)$$

and

$$C_{\text{sat}} - C_V = \left[P + \left(\frac{\partial E}{\partial V}\right)_T\right]\left(\frac{\partial V}{\partial T}\right)_{\text{sat}}. \qquad (5.3\text{–}13)$$

The changes of energy and enthalpy with temperature, under suitable conditions, are obtained by integration of equations (5.3–2) and (5.3–4). Thus, for a change between T_{A} and T_{B} at constant volume,

$$\Delta E = E_{\text{B}} - E_{\text{A}} = \int_{T_{\text{A}}}^{T_{\text{B}}} C_V \, dT, \qquad (5.3\text{–}14)$$

and at constant pressure

$$\Delta H = H_{\text{B}} - H_{\text{A}} = \int_{T_{\text{A}}}^{T_{\text{B}}} C_P \, dT. \qquad (5.3\text{–}15)$$

Problem 5.3-2. The table below lists values of $\tilde{C}_V$ for silver from 35° to 100°K. By graphical integration of the data obtain $\tilde{E}_{100} - \tilde{E}_{35}$. The units of $\tilde{C}_V$ are cal mole^{-1} deg^{-1}.

T	$\tilde{C}_V$	T	$\tilde{C}_V$
35.0	1.59	51.4	2.81
39.1	1.92	53.8	2.97
42.9	2.22	77.0	4.07
45.5	2.43	100.0	4.72

Problem 5.3-3. The enthalpy of solid B_2O_3, at 1 atm, as given by Kerr, Hersh, and Johnston,[2] is tabulated below between 100° and 250°K. The function listed is

[2] E. C. Kerr, H. N. Hersh, and H. L. Johnston, *J. Am. Chem. Soc.*, **72**, 4738 (1950).

$(\tilde{H} - \tilde{H}_0)$ in cal mole^{-1}, where $\tilde{H}_0$ is the unknown but constant enthalpy at 0°K. Evaluate $\tilde{C}_P$ at 125°, 175°, and 225°K.

T	$\tilde{H} - \tilde{H}_0$	T	$\tilde{H} - \tilde{H}_0$
100	181.56	200	967.34
125	325.26	225	1244.5
150	505.65	250	1549.9
175	720.38		

Problem 5.3-4. Show that for a perfect gas $\tilde{C}_P = \tilde{C}_V + R$.

5.4 Isothermal Expansion of a Fluid

Consider an expansion process against a piston exerting a force which exactly balances the pressure of the gas, which does no work other than by expansion. According to equations (5.2–9) and (5.2–11),

$$q = \mathrm{d}E + P\,\mathrm{d}V \tag{5.2–9}$$

or

$$q = \mathrm{d}H - V\,\mathrm{d}P. \tag{5.2–11}$$

The heat withdrawn from the surroundings, in isothermal expansion of a fluid (liquid or gas) from state A to state B, is

$$q = E_{\mathrm{B}} - E_{\mathrm{A}} + \int_{V_{\mathrm{A}}}^{V_{\mathrm{B}}} P\,\mathrm{d}V \tag{5.4–1}$$

$$= H_{\mathrm{B}} - H_{\mathrm{A}} - \int_{P_{\mathrm{A}}}^{P_V} V\,\mathrm{d}P. \tag{5.4–2}$$

The meaning of this result is illustrated by Problem 5.2–2, particularly part c.

5.5 Adiabatic Expansion of a Fluid

A process in which no heat is withdrawn from the surroundings is called an adiabatic process ($q = 0$). For such a process

$$\mathrm{d}E = -w, \tag{5.5–1}$$

and any work done by the system is accompanied by a corresponding loss of energy. When work is done on such a system, the energy of the system is increased by a like amount. As a result there is a temperature increase. If the process is one of expansion against a piston which always exactly balances the pressure of the system, according to equation (5.2–8)

$$dE = -w = -P\,dV. \tag{5.5–2}$$

The work of adiabatic expansion can be calculated once the equation of state of the substance is known.

5.6 Energy Change on Expansion of Gases. Free Expansion

When a gas is expanded from one pressure to another without doing any work on the surroundings, the process is called *free expansion.* Experiments of this sort were first performed by Gay-Lussac[3] and later, with greater precision, by Joule.[4]

Suppose, as in Joule's first experiments, that two identical calorimeters, each separately insulated, are connected by a valve; one of the calorimeters (A) is filled with a gas at a pressure P', while the other is evacuated. When the valve is opened, the gas in calorimeter A, as it continues to expand, does work on the gas already expanded into calorimeter B. As a result of the work done, when the gas expands the energy of A is decreased, so that its temperature falls by an amount ΔT_A; at the same time the temperature of B increases by an amount ΔT_B because of the work done on the gas in it.[5]

Besides experiments of this kind, Joule also carried out experiments with both containers and the valve in a single calorimeter and found that there was no observable temperature change in the calorimeter after equilibrium had been reached. For such a process

$$q = \Delta E - w = E'' - E' + w, \tag{5.6–1}$$

where E' and E'' are the energies in the initial and final states. If the calorimeter is insulated, q is zero. Moreover the net work w is zero, since the work done *by* the gas in one container is the work done *on* the gas in the other;[6] thus $E'' - E' = 0$, or $E'' = E'$. The over-all result is mathematically the same as if the volume of a single system increased without change in energy continuously from an initial pressure P' to a final pressure P''.

[3] Gay-Lussac, *Mémoirs de la Société d'Arcueil I* (1807); translated in *Free Expansion of Gases*, by J. S. Ames, Harper, New York, 1898.

[4] J. P. Joule, *Phil. Mag.*, [3] **26,** 369 (1845).

[5] Some readers will be gratified that they held out against apparently opposite statements. Any reader who is still confused will do well to consult the original paper of Joule.[4]

[6] It is this result that has led to the loose statement that for an adiabatic expansion into an evacuated container no work is done. This statement is emphatically untrue unless the adjective *net* precedes the word *work*.

The energy is considered as a function of the pressure and temperature alone, so that, for an infinitesimal pressure change for the entire system,

$$\mathrm{d}E = \left(\frac{\partial E}{\partial P}\right)_T \mathrm{d}P + \left(\frac{\partial E}{\partial T}\right)_P \mathrm{d}T = 0 \tag{5.6–2}$$

or

$$\mathrm{d}T = -\frac{(\partial E/\partial P)_T}{(\partial E/\partial T)_P}\,\mathrm{d}P.$$

The over-all change in temperature is obtained by integration between the initial pressure P' and the final pressure P''. It is

$$T'' - T' = \int_{P'}^{P''} \frac{(\partial E/\partial P)_T}{C_P - P(\partial V/\partial T)_P}\,\mathrm{d}P, \tag{5.6–3}$$

in which $(\partial E/\partial T)_P$ has been replaced by

$$\left(\frac{\partial E}{\partial T}\right)_P = \left(\frac{\partial E}{\partial T}\right)_V + \left(\frac{\partial E}{\partial V}\right)_T \left(\frac{\partial V}{\partial T}\right)_P, \tag{5.6–4}$$

followed by use of equation (5.3–12). (See Appendix 5 for this transformation in general terms.)

C_P is the heat capacity at constant pressure of the entire system. The term $(\partial V/\partial T)_P$ applies to the gas, since the contribution of the calorimeter to this term is very small. If the heat capacity of the gas is small compared to that of the calorimeter, this last term can be neglected and C_P taken as the heat capacity of the calorimeter. If $(\partial E/\partial P)_T$ is zero, T'', the final temperature, is equal to T', the initial temperature. In the case of real gases, $(\partial E/\partial P)_T$ is not zero but, if the experiment is performed in a calorimeter of appreciable heat capacity, C_P is so large that the value of the integral is too small to detect by experiment. Thus at first it was thought (incorrectly) that $(\partial E/\partial P)_T$ was zero for gases in general. A perfect gas is defined so that this derivative is zero.

Problem 5.6-1. It was found by Joule and Thomson[7] that for air at 15°C

$$\frac{1}{PV}\left(\frac{\partial E}{\partial P}\right)_T = 0.0024 \text{ (approximately) atm}^{-1}.$$

Joule[8] expanded 0.13 lb of air at 21 atm and 15°C from one vessel into another vessel of equivalent size in the same calorimeter. The calorimeter and vessels contained 16.5 lb of water, 28 lb of copper, and 7 lb of iron.

[7] J. P. Joule and W. Thomson, *Phil. Trans.*, **144**, 65 (1852).
[8] J. P. Joule, *Phil. Mag.*, **26** (Ser. 3), 369 (1845).

(a) Show that a fall of temperature of only 0.003°C occurred. Take the heat capacities per gram of water, copper, and iron as 1, 0.109, and 0.101 cal/°C and C_P of air as 0.24 cal g^{-1} deg^{-1}. Assume that $(\partial E/\partial P)_T$ is constant and that $PV = nRT$ (approximately).

(b) Show that the temperature rise would be about 3°C if the heat capacities of the vessel and calorimeter were reduced to zero.

5.7 The Joule-Thomson Effect

The effect of pressure on the energy may be observed less directly but with greater sensitivity by a somewhat different experimental procedure. In the famous porous plug experiment devised by Joule and Thomson,[9] gas at a constant pressure P_A was allowed to flow through a plug of cotton wool, from which it emerged at a constant pressure P_B. The whole apparatus was insulated. The work done on the gas in pushing a fixed amount of it through the plug is $P_A V_A$, where V_A is the volume at the pressure P_A and energy E_A; the work done by the gas as it leaves the plug is $P_B V_B$, where V_B is the volume at the pressure P_B and energy E_B. Thus the total work done by the gas is $P_B V_B - P_A V_A$, and the energy change is $E_B - E_A$. The process is adiabatic so that

$$q = \Delta E + w = 0$$

or

$$E_B - E_A + P_B V_B - P_A V_A = 0 \tag{5.7–1}$$

and

$$H_B - H_A = \Delta H = 0. \tag{5.7–2}$$

This result could have been derived directly from equations (5.2–6) and (5.2–7) where it states that, generally, ΔH is equal to the heat withdrawn from the surroundings for any change in which the parts of a system are at *different* but *constant* pressures. It states that the Joule-Thomson experiment is a process at constant enthalpy.

For the differential process in which P and T are the variables,

$$dH = \left(\frac{\partial H}{\partial P}\right)_T dP + \left(\frac{\partial H}{\partial T}\right)_P dT; \tag{5.7–3}$$

thus, since (5.7–3) refers to a process at constant enthalpy, $dH = 0$, and

$$\left(\frac{\partial T}{\partial P}\right)_H = -\frac{(\partial H/\partial P)_T}{(\partial H/\partial T)_P} = -\frac{(\partial H/\partial P)_T}{C_P}. \tag{5.7–4}$$

[9] J. P. Joule and W. Thomson, *Phil. Trans.*, **143,** 357 (1853); **144,** 321 (1854); **150,** 325 (1860); **152,** 579 (1862).

The quantity $(\partial T/\partial P)_H$ is called the Joule-Thomson coefficient and denoted by μ. Thus

$$\left(\frac{\partial H}{\partial P}\right)_T = -\mu C_P. \tag{5.7–5}$$

Equation (5.7–5) can be used to calculate the change of enthalpy with pressure for a system (usually a gas) from data on the Joule-Thomson coefficient. In order to obtain the change of energy with pressure it is necessary also to have data of state for the substance.

Problem 5.7-1. When nitrogen gas at 200 atm and 10°C is allowed to expand freely and adiabatically through a valve to 1 atm, the temperature of the exit gas is −16°C. The heat capacity of nitrogen at 1 atm is 5.9 cal mole^{-1} deg^{-1}. Calculate the difference in enthalpy at 10°C between nitrogen at 200 atm and nitrogen at 1 atm.

Problem 5.7-2. In a Hampson-type liquefier, precooled gas at high pressure partially liquefies upon Joule-Thomson expansion through a valve. A suitable heat exchanger warms the unliquefied portion of the gas to the temperature of the incoming high pressure gas by cooling the latter. Each of the two gas streams in the heat exchanger is maintained at essentially constant pressure during the process. The liquefier is insulated to prevent heat flow from its surroundings.

(a) Show that for such a process the enthalpy of the products (liquid and low pressure exit gas) must equal the enthalpy of the entering high pressure gas.

(b) Show that the fraction liquefied may be calculated from the equation (neglecting heat leak)

$$x = \frac{\tilde{H}_{\text{exit}} - \tilde{H}_{\text{inlet}}}{\tilde{H}_{\text{exit}} - \tilde{H}_{\text{liq}}},$$

where $\tilde{H}_{\text{inlet}}$ is the molal enthalpy of the high pressure gas entering, $\tilde{H}_{\text{exit}}$ that of the low pressure gas leaving, and $\tilde{H}_{\text{liq}}$ that of the liquid produced.

Problem 5.7-3. (a) Calculate the percentage liquefaction (neglecting heat leak) of a Hampson-type hydrogen liquefier in which hydrogen at 100 atm is precooled by liquid nitrogen to 77°K, then put through the heat exchangers and expansion valve described in Problem 5.7–2. The necessary enthalpy data are listed below.

(b) Repeat the calculation for a liquefier in which the hydrogen is precooled to 65°K by nitrogen boiling under reduced pressure.

Enthalpies (with respect to liquid at 1 atm, 20°K)

H_2 (100 atm, 77°K),	$\tilde{H} = 420$ cal mole^{-1};
H_2 (100 atm, 65°K),	$\tilde{H} = 294$ cal mole^{-1};
H_2 (1 atm, 77°K),	$\tilde{H} = 502$ cal mole^{-1};
H_2 (1 atm, 65°K),	$\tilde{H} = 418$ cal mole^{-1}.

Problem 5.7-4. Calculate the percentage liquefaction of a helium liquefier in which the gas at 30 atm is precooled by liquid hydrogen to (a) 20°K, (b) 14°K, and (c) by another stage of helium refrigeration to 10°K. The enthalpy data for helium are

at 20°K:	$\tilde{H}$ (30 atm) = 96.0 cal mole^{-1},	$\tilde{H}$ (1 atm) = 107.5 cal mole^{-1};
at 14°K:	$\tilde{H}$ (30 atm) = 58.4 cal mole^{-1},	$\tilde{H}$ (1 atm) = 75.0 cal mole^{-1};
at 10°K:	$\tilde{H}$ (30 atm) = 33.6 cal mole^{-1},	$\tilde{H}$ (1 atm) = 54.0 cal mole^{-1};

all with reference to liquid at 1 atm, 4.2°K.

Problem 5.7-5. Show that the differentiation of equation (5.7–5) with respect to temperature at constant pressure yields the results

$$\left(\frac{\partial C_P}{\partial P}\right)_T = -\mu\left(\frac{\partial C_P}{\partial T}\right)_P - C_P\left(\frac{\partial \mu}{\partial T}\right)_P, \tag{5.7–6}$$

and

$$\left(\frac{\partial \ln \mu}{\partial T}\right)_P = -\left(\frac{\partial \ln C_P}{\partial T}\right)_P - \frac{1}{\mu}\left(\frac{\partial \ln C_P}{\partial P}\right)_T. \tag{5.7–7}$$

Problem 5.7-6. From the data of Roebuck,[10] the Joule-Thomson coefficient for air at 100 atm is 0.128°C/atm at 50°C and 0.107°C/atm at 75°C, and the molar heat capacities at these two temperatures are 7.91 and 7.79 respectively. Assuming that both of these properties are changing linearly with temperature, estimate the rate of change of the heat capacity with pressure at 50°C. The observed value is 7.3×10^{-3} cal mole^{-1} deg^{-1} atm^{-1}.

Problem 5.7-7. The heat capacity of air at 223°K is given below as a function of pressure. At 140 atm, the heat capacity is decreasing by 0.4% per degree. The Joule-Thomson coefficient is 0.1815 at 223°K and 140 atm. Estimate its value at 248°K and 140 atm. The observed value is 0.164.[11]

P_{atm}	C_P (cal g^{-1})	P_{atm}	C_P (cal g^{-1})
1	0.2394	100	0.3264
20	0.2556	140	0.3561
60	0.2883	180	0.3747

Problem 5.7-8. Using approximate thermodynamic equations, explain why a porous plug rather than a simple valve was used for the Joule-Thomson experiment.[9,12]

5.8 Application. Perfect Gases

The criteria for a perfect gas are[13]

$$PV = nRT \tag{5.8–1*}$$

and

$$\left(\frac{\partial E}{\partial V}\right)_T = 0 \quad \text{or} \quad \left(\frac{\partial E}{\partial P}\right)_T = 0. \tag{5.8–2*}$$

Problem 5.8-1. Prove that for a perfect gas

$$\left(\frac{\partial H}{\partial P}\right)_T = 0. \tag{5.8–3*}$$

[10] J. R. Roebuck, *Proc. Am. Acad. Arts Sci.*, **60**, 535 (1925).

[11] All data in this problem are from J. R. Roebuck, *Proc. Am. Acad. Arts Sci.*, **64**, 287 (1930).

[12] H. L. Johnston, *J. Am. Chem. Soc.*, **68**, 2362 (1946).

[13] An asterisk after the equation number denotes an equation which applies only to a perfect gas. (See footnote 19 in Section 4.10.)

For a perfect gas thus defined some simple equations can be derived from the results of previous sections. The work done and the heat absorbed in the isothermal expansion of a perfect gas against a piston which balances the pressure are, from equation (5.4–1),

$$w = q = nRT \int_{V_A}^{V_B} \frac{dV}{V}$$

$$= nRT \ln \frac{V_B}{V_A} \qquad (5.8\text{–}4)^*$$

$$= nRT \ln \frac{P_A}{P_B} \cdot \qquad (5.8\text{–}5)^*$$

Problem 5.8-2. Calculate the work done when 1 mole of helium at 100°C expands from 200 atm to 1 atm isothermally and reversibly. (Here the perfect gas law is a reasonable assumption.)

Equation (5.5–1), for the work of adiabatic reversible expansion of a fluid, also assumes a simple form for a perfect gas. In the general equation

$$dE = \left(\frac{\partial E}{\partial T}\right)_V dT + \left(\frac{\partial E}{\partial V}\right)_T dV, \qquad (5.8\text{–}6)$$

the last term is zero; thus from equation (5.3–2)

$$dE = C_V\, dT. \qquad (5.8\text{–}7)^*$$

Substituting (5.8–7)* in (5.5–2) and using molal quantities,

$$\tilde{C}_V\, dT = -P\, d\tilde{V}. \qquad (5.8\text{–}8)^*$$

After substituting for P its value in terms of T and $\tilde{V}$ from the perfect gas law, this equation may be put in the form

$$\frac{\tilde{C}_V}{T} dT = -\frac{R}{\tilde{V}} d\tilde{V}. \qquad (5.8\text{–}9)^*$$

Upon integration, assuming $\tilde{C}_V$ to be constant,

$$\tilde{C}_V \ln T = -R \ln \tilde{V} + \text{constant}, \qquad (5.8\text{–}10)^*$$

or

$$\ln T^{\tilde{C}_V} \tilde{V}^R = \text{constant}, \qquad (5.8\text{–}11)^*$$

or

$$T\tilde{V}^{R/\tilde{C}_V} = \text{constant}, \qquad (5.8\text{–}12)^*$$

where the constants in equations (5.8–10)* and (5.8–12)* are different.

Noting that, for a perfect gas, application of equation (5.3–12) gives

$$\tilde{C}_P - \tilde{C}_V = R, \qquad (5.8\text{–}13)^*$$

and substituting γ for $\tilde{C}_P/\tilde{C}_V$, equation (5.8–12)* becomes

$$T\tilde{V}^{\gamma-1} = \text{constant}. \qquad (5.8\text{–}14)^*$$

Problem 5.8-3. Prove that for the adiabatic expansion of a perfect gas

(a) $$P\tilde{V}^{\tilde{C}_P/\tilde{C}_V} = \text{constant}, \qquad (5.8\text{–}15)^*$$

(b) $$T = \text{constant } P^{R/\tilde{C}_P}. \qquad (5.8\text{–}16)^*$$

The work done *by* adiabatic expansion of 1 mole of a perfect gas from P_1 to P_2 is

$$w = -(\tilde{E}_2 - \tilde{E}_1) = -\int_{T_1}^{T_2} \tilde{C}_V \, dT, \qquad (5.8\text{–}17)^*$$

where T_1 and T_2 are the initial and final temperatures. Again assuming $\tilde{C}_V$ constant, this becomes

$$w = -(\tilde{E}_2 - \tilde{E}_1) = -\tilde{C}_V(T_2 - T_1). \qquad (5.8\text{–}18)^*$$

Taking the relationship between initial and final temperature from equation (5.8–16),*

$$\begin{aligned} w &= \tilde{C}_V T_1 \left(1 - \frac{T_2}{T_1}\right) \\ &= \tilde{C}_V T_1 \left[1 - \left(\frac{P_2}{P_1}\right)^{(\gamma-1)/\gamma}\right] \\ &= \frac{\tilde{C}_V}{R} P_1 V_1 \left[1 - \left(\frac{P_2}{P_1}\right)^{(\gamma-1)/\gamma}\right]. \end{aligned} \qquad (5.8\text{–}19)^*$$

This is the negative of the work *required* for a process in which gas is compressed adiabatically from a pressure P_1 to a higher pressure P_2.

If a compressor is used for this purpose, an amount of work equal to $P_2\tilde{V}_2$ is required to push the gas out of the cylinder after compression. An amount $P_1\tilde{V}_1$ is done by the gas as it is drawn into the cylinder prior to compression. The net work done *on* the gas by these two steps is thus

$$P_2\tilde{V}_2 - P_1\tilde{V}_1 = R(T_2 - T_1)$$

per mole in addition to the work required to compress the gas.

Problem 5.8-4. Prove that the work required by an adiabatic compressor when it takes in 1 mole of a perfect gas at P_1 and delivers it at P_2 is

$$w = -\frac{\gamma}{\gamma - 1} P_1 V_1 \left[1 - \left(\frac{P_2}{P_1}\right)^{(\gamma-1)/\gamma}\right] \qquad (5.8\text{–}20)^*$$

Problem 5.8-5. A 200-cm^3 copper bomb contains helium gas at 20 atm pressure and a temperature of 10°K to which it has been cooled by solid hydrogen evaporating under reduced pressure. The container is connected to the atmosphere through a thin German silver tube closed by a valve at room temperature. It is heat-insulated by evacuating the envelope (which is surrounded by solid hydrogen) to 10^{-5} mm Hg, and finally the valve is opened. Against what is the work done?

Calculate the fraction of helium left in the bomb, as gas, at the critical temperature (6°K). Assume that the bomb has negligible heat capacity and consider that, roughly, C_V of gaseous helium may be taken equal to 3/2 R and the gas treated as perfect. (This is the basis of a method for liquefying helium.)[14]

Problem 5.8-6. Calculate the work, in kilowatt hours, required to compress 10 lb of ammonia from 1 atm at 300°K to 5 atm adiabatically: (a) using a piston with one stroke starting and ending with the gas in the cylinder; (b) using a single-stage compressor starting with the gas in a holder and ending with it in an external cylinder. Assume that ammonia behaves as a perfect gas with a heat capacity of 9 cal $mole^{-1}$ deg^{-1} at constant pressure.

Problem 5.8-7. Assuming perfect gas behavior throughout, calculate the final temperature reached when helium gas is expanded adiabatically and reversibly, at 300°K, from 20 atm to 1 atm in a thermally insulated container. Assume negligible heat capacity for both machine and container. Why is the air gun impractical as a weapon?

5.9 Extensive and Intensive Properties

Up to the present we have used the quantities P, T, V, E, H, C_V, and C_P. It is clear that the pressure and temperature of a system do not involve amounts of substance in their definition. It is equally clear that, if we double the size of our system, the quantities V, E, H, C_V, and C_P are doubled. Quantities like P and T, which do not involve the size of the system, are called *intensive.* Those which involve the size of the system are called *extensive.*

For *extensive* properties it is useful to consider the value of the property per mole of the system (molal properties). These we shall denote by italic capital letters with tilde above. Thus $\tilde{V}$, $\tilde{E}$, $\tilde{H}$, $\tilde{C}_V$, and $\tilde{C}_P$ denote the molal volume, molal energy, molal enthalpy (heat content), molal heat capacity at constant volume, and molal heat capacity at constant pressure, respectively. The molal quantities are intensive from their very definition. The extensive quantities applying to an arbitrary number of moles, n, will be denoted by *italic capitals*: V, E, H, etc.

With these molal quantities it is simple to symbolize change suffered by extensive properties in chemical reactions. Consider the chemical reaction

$$\mathrm{a}\tilde{A} + \mathrm{b}\tilde{B} = \mathrm{l}\tilde{L} + \mathrm{m}\tilde{M}. \tag{5.9–1}$$

The capital letters in this equation stand for the gram molecular weight

[14] F. Simon and J. E. Ahlberg, *Z. Physik*, **81,** 816 (1933).

of the compounds in question, and thus (5.9–1) is a statement of the conservation of matter. Suppose that the capital letters represent the molal volume or some other extensive property; we can then write

$$a\tilde{A} + b\tilde{B} = l\tilde{L} + m\tilde{M} + x. \tag{5.9–2}$$

In this equation x measures the amount by which the value of the extensive property has decreased after the reaction represented by (5.9–1) has occurred. For example, if $\tilde{A}$, $\tilde{B}$, $\tilde{L}$, and $\tilde{M}$ in (5.9–2) represent the molal volumes of the substances in (5.9–1), then the x is the contraction caused by the reaction.

5.10 Heats of Reaction at Constant Volume and at Constant Pressure

The heat withdrawn from the surroundings when a chemical reaction occurs at constant volume (i.e., does no work) is now evidently equal to the change in energy, ΔE. According to Section 5.9, in equation (5.9–2),

$$a\tilde{A} + b\tilde{B} = l\tilde{L} + m\tilde{M} + x, \tag{5.9–2}$$

$\tilde{A}$, $\tilde{B}$, $\tilde{L}$, and $\tilde{M}$ represent the molal energies of the substances A, B, L, and M, and x is equal to $-\Delta E$; that is, x is the heat given out in the course of the chemical reaction at constant volume. The energy change ΔE is thus given by

$$\Delta E = l\tilde{E}_L + m\tilde{E}_M - a\tilde{E}_A - b\tilde{E}_B = q_V, \tag{5.10–1}$$

where $\tilde{E}_L$, etc., are the molal energies of the substances involved and q_V is the heat of reaction at constant volume. ΔE can also be calculated from the heat of reaction at constant pressure in the manner discussed below.

The energy of an individual substance cannot be assigned an absolute value. To do so would require complete knowledge of the distribution of energy into mechanical motion, molecular motion, electronic and nuclear energies, etc. For example, the 13,000 kcal of energy liberated when a mole of octane is burned, or the 1.3×10^8 kcal produced when a gram atom of hydrogen fuses with a gram atom of deuterium, obviously resided in the reactants, although its exact location would be nearly impossible to specify. However, the change of energy accompanying a chemical or physical process is a measure of the relative energies of the substances involved, and this is sufficient for our purposes. If molal energies are expressed with respect to suitable reference states, all necessary changes in energy can be obtained. (One way of doing this is described in connection with enthalpy below.)

Problem 5.10-1. When a mole of nitrogen combines completely with 3 moles of hydrogen at 298°K and 1 atm, 22,080 cal of heat is liberated and 1185 cal of work is done *on* the system by the atmosphere.

(a) Calculate the energy change for this reaction.

(b) Show that, if all substances are considered to be perfect gases, the result of part (a) is also the heat of the reaction at constant volume.

(c) Show that, if the products are not perfect gases,

$$q_V = \Delta E_{\mathrm{a}} + \int_1^{P_f} \frac{\partial E_p}{\partial P}\, dP,$$

where ΔE_{a} is the energy change in part (a), E_p is the energy of the products, and P_f is the final pressure to maintain constant volume.

The heat withdrawn from the surroundings when a chemical reaction occurs under a constant pressure (exerted by a frictionless piston or, more usually, the atmosphere) is equal to the change in enthalpy, just as for any other process at constant pressure (see Section 5.2). Thus, when an equation like (5.9–2) is written, in which $\tilde{A}$, $\tilde{B}$, etc., stand for the molal enthalpies of the substances involved, x is equal to $-\Delta H$ and is the heat given out when the reaction occurs at constant pressure. It is this equality between the decrease in enthalpy and the heat liberated when a chemical reaction occurs at constant pressure which has given rise to the name "heat content" for the function denoted by H. This nomenclature is misleading, since it is only for this particular type of process that the decrease in enthalpy appears as heat.

The enthalpy change for the process considered can thus be given as

$$\Delta H = \mathrm{l}\tilde{H}_{\mathrm{l}} + \mathrm{m}\tilde{H}_{\mathrm{M}} - \mathrm{a}\tilde{H}_{\mathrm{A}} - \mathrm{b}\tilde{H}_{\mathrm{B}}, \tag{5.10–2}$$

where $\tilde{H}_{\mathrm{l}}$, etc., are the molal enthalpies. Although ΔH is a well-defined and measurable quantity, the molal enthalpies cannot be assigned absolute values for the same reason that the energies could not be so assigned. (Note that $\tilde{H} = \tilde{E} + P\tilde{V}$.) Frequently the enthalpies of specified compounds are listed relative to the enthalpies of the elements of which they are composed, each in its normal state at 1 atm, and the temperature specified. Such a "standard enthalpy" (heat of formation) is, of course, the enthalpy change of the reaction in which the compound is produced from its elements, and is the negative of the heat given out when this reaction occurs at constant pressure. Heats of formation may be used with equation (5.10–2) to get enthalpy changes for other reactions, since the absolute enthalpies of all elements cancel out except for those directly involved in the reaction.

The relation between heats of reaction at constant volume and those at constant pressure is clear. The heat of a reaction (defined as the heat withdrawn from the surroundings) at constant pressure is greater than that for the corresponding reaction at constant volume by the work it does, and by the decrease in energy which occurs when the products are taken from the initial pressure to the final pressure attained at constant volume. (See Problem 5.10–1.)

Heats of combustion are most frequently measured by using a bomb calorimeter. Thus the heat of combustion at constant volume is obtained. The calculations necessary to obtain heats of combustion at constant pressure are by no means simple, as will be evident from Problem 5.10–1 (remembering that there is always an excess of oxygen). The subject is discussed fully by Washburn.[15]

If all gases present are assumed to be perfect, the second correction disappears; similarly, if the volumes of the liquids and solids present are neglected, the work term is simply $RT\,\Delta n(\mathrm{g})$, where $\Delta n(\mathrm{g})$ represents the change in number of moles of gas during the reaction. Thus, approximately,

$$\Delta H \approx \Delta E + RT\,\Delta n(\mathrm{g}). \qquad (5.10\text{–}3)^*$$

Problem 5.10-2. The heats of formation ("standard enthalpies") at 298°K of a number of compounds are given in Table 5.2–1. Calculate the heat given to the surroundings when each of the reactions below occurs with each substance at a constant pressure.

(a) $C_2H_4(g) + H_2O(g) = C_2H_5OH(g)$.
(b) $C_2H_4(g) + H_2(g) = C_2H_6(g)$.
(c) $C_2H_4(g) + 3O_2(g) = 2CO_2(g) + 2H_2O(g)$.

Table 5.2–1

Heats of Formation of Various Simple Substances

Substance	Heat of Formation at 25°C	Substance	Heat of Formation at 25°C
$H_2(g)$	0	$C_2H_6(g)$	−23,400
$O_2(g)$	0	$C_2H_5OH(g)$	−55,800
$CO_2(g)$	−94,400	$H_2O(g)$	−57,800
$C_2H_4(g)$	+9,560		

5.11 Change of Heat of Reaction with Temperature

From equations (5 3–4) and (5.3–2), the change of the heats of reaction at constant pressure and volume with temperature are given by

$$\left(\frac{\partial \Delta H}{\partial T}\right)_P = \Delta \tilde{C}_P \qquad (5.11\text{–}1)$$

and

$$\left(\frac{\partial \Delta E}{\partial T}\right)_V = \Delta \tilde{C}_V. \qquad (5.11\text{–}2)$$

[15] E. W. Washburn, *J. Research Natl. Bur Standards*, **10**, 525 (1933).

$\Delta\tilde{C}_P$ and $\Delta\tilde{C}_V$ are the values of $-x$ in equation (5.9–2). $\tilde{A}$, $\tilde{B}$, $\tilde{C}$, and $\tilde{D}$ refer in one case to molal heat capacities at constant pressure and in the other to molal heat capacities at constant volume.

Problem 5.11-1. Prove equations (5.11–1) and (5.11–2).

Problem 5.11-2. (a) Show that the assumption that a heat of reaction is independent of temperature implies that the heat capacity of the mixture is not changed by the reaction.

(b) Show that, if the total heat capacity of the products is greater than that of the reactants, the heat given off by the reaction must decrease with increasing temperature.

Formal Treatment of the Second Law of Thermodynamics

CHAPTER 6

6.1 The Second Law of Thermodynamics

This law states that any process whose *only* result is the conversion of heat to work at constant temperature is an impossibility. *It is an experimental law*, and from it simple results follow. An alternative statement is that no cyclic process can convert heat into work without leaving changes in the surroundings; it is shown below that the essential change is a flow of heat from a higher to a lower temperature.

6.2 Maximum and Minimum Work

Let us consider the process by which a system changes from a state A to another state B at constant temperature. The greatest (maximum) work can be derived from this process if all friction is eliminated, if no electrical energy is converted to thermal energy, and if all unneccessary heat transfer is eliminated. In the complete reversal of this process, the least (minimum) work will be required if all friction is eliminated, etc. The maximum and minimum work are numerically equal, for, if less work were required for the reverse process than had been obtained in the forward process, work would accumulate in each cycle. This work could only be gained at the expense of heat unless the first law were violated.

Problem 6.2-1. Small drops of liquid spontaneously coalesce into larger drops. Using the second law and qualitative reasoning only, prove with the aid of an appropriate cycle that the vapor pressure of small drops must be larger than that of large drops.

Problem 6.2-2. In a manner similar to that used in Problem 6.2–1, prove that the vapor pressure of a liquid must increase with applied (external) pressure.

In Section 3.7 it was pointed out that Carnot was the first to recognize that no more work could be obtained from any process than was required to reverse it. When a process is conducted so that the maximum work is performed or the minimum work is required, it is said to be *reversible*. This is a more inclusive definition of reversibility than the preliminary definition given in Section 5.1.

6.3 Qualitative Definition of Temperature

For the present, temperature can only be defined logically so that heat flows from a body with a higher temperature to one with a lower temperature. The temperature will be considered a variable of state, with all the qualitative properties discussed in Section 2.8. The quantitative aspects of the empirical temperature scales cannot possibly be used, since there can be no simple connection between the work obtained using two heat reservoirs and the readings (volume, pressure, resistance, etc.) of some arbitrary material immersed in the reservoirs. This cannot be emphasized too strongly, since many students, in an attempt to relate this efficiency to such arbitrary measures of temperature, have involved themselves in an impossible situation with regard to understanding the beautiful logic on which thermodynamics is based, a logic possible only because it defines its own temperature scale. The procedure followed in thermodynamics will soon be found to be analogous in every respect to that used by Newton in defining force.

6.4 Efficiency of a Heat Engine and the Thermodynamic Temperature Scale

In any cycle of changes by which heat, at a temperature θ_1, is converted into work, it follows from the second law that some additional heat must flow from the reservoir at the temperature θ_1 to a lower temperature θ_2. Otherwise heat would be converted into work at constant temperature, in violation of the second law. The efficiency of a heat engine is defined as the fraction of the heat drawn from the reservoir at the temperature θ_1 which is converted into work. The efficiency will be a maximum when all processes are reversible. Let the positive quantity of heat, $-q_1$, be drawn from the reservoir at the temperature θ_1, and the positive quantity of heat, q_2, be given to a reservoir at a lower temperature θ_2 in a *reversible cycle of changes*. The changes must form a cycle; otherwise there will be other results as well as the conversion of heat into work and flow of heat to the lower temperature. (Thus, in a non-cyclic process, an ideal gas expands from a pressure P_1 to a pressure P_2 at a constant temperature, converting heat, from a reservoir, quantitatively into work. However, the gas has suffered a decrease in its pressure and thereby a diminution in its capacity to do further work.)

The work done by the engine in the cycle is

$$w = -q_1 - q_2. \tag{6.4–1}$$

The efficiency is

$$e = \frac{w}{-q_1} = \frac{-q_1 - q_2}{-q_1}. \tag{6.4–2}$$

The ratio between the temperatures θ_1 and θ_2 can now be defined quantitatively in terms of the measured efficiency of a reversible cycle by the arbitrary equation

$$\frac{w}{-q_1} = \frac{-q_1 - q_2}{-q_1} = \frac{\theta_1 - \theta_2}{\theta_1}, \tag{6.4–3}$$

so that

$$\frac{q_1}{\theta_1} + \frac{q_2}{\theta_2} = 0. \tag{6.4–4}$$

Definition: *The thermodynamic temperature of a reservoir is proportional to the heat it receives in a reversible cycle of changes in which some standard amount of heat is withdrawn from a reservoir at some fixed temperature.*

The thermodynamic temperature scale was first defined in this way by Kelvin.

6.5 Entropy and the Second Law

The quantity q/θ is called the entropy change of the reservoir. For small changes this will be denoted by dS.

So far the quantity q/θ applies only to heat reservoirs. Actually the name entropy was first given to such a quantity by Clausius with a general significance which will appear later in this chapter. For purposes of continuity the name is taken conveniently but somewhat prematurely at this juncture.

Alternative Definition of Temperature: *In a reversible cycle of changes (whose only result is to convert heat into work and for heat to flow to a lower temperature) the total entropy change is zero.*

If the process whose efficiency is given by equation (6.4–2) is carried out with any irreversibility (as in practice), less work than the maximum will be obtained and relatively more heat given to the cold reservoir. Thus, if the same quantity of heat, $-q_1$, is drawn from the hot reservoir, the heat, q_2, given to the cold reservoir will be greater than it was in the reversible process. In this case,

$$\frac{q_1}{\theta_1} + \frac{q_2}{\theta_2} \text{ (irreversible)} > 0. \qquad (6.5\text{–}1)$$

(*Note.* When a gas expands into a vacuum, the process is highly irreversible. There are no thermal effects. However, this is *not a cycle of changes.*)

Alternative Statement of the Second Law of Thermodynamics: *With the temperature defined so that in any reversible cycle of changes the total entropy change for the isolated system is zero, in an actual cycle the total entropy change is greater than zero.*

Thus, in equation (6.5–2), the equality defines temperature, the inequality states the second law.

$$\oint \mathrm{d}S \geqq 0 \qquad \text{(Law II).} \qquad (6.5\text{–}2)$$

The implications of these results are discussed more fully in Section 6.7.

6.6 The Efficiency of a Heat Engine in Terms of the Perfect Gas Scale of Temperature. Carnot's Cycle

The efficiency of a reversible cycle such as discussed above can be calculated in terms of the perfect gas absolute centigrade temperature scale (see Section 2.10), thus relating this scale to the thermodynamic temperature scale of Kelvin. The cycle which was first considered by Carnot contains the following steps:

(a) Isothermal expansion from P_1 to P_2 at a temperature T', withdrawing $-q'$ calories from the hot reservoir at T'. Let the work done be w_a.

(b) Adiabatic expansion of the gas from P_2 to P_3, with the temperature falling to T''. Let ΔE_b and w_b be the energy change and the work done, respectively.

(c) Isothermal compression to P_4, giving q'' calories to the reservoir at T''. Let the work done be w_c.

(d) Adiabatic compression back to P_1, thus bringing the temperature to T' again. Let the energy change and work done be ΔE_d and w_d.

For convenience the amount of gas is taken as 1 mole.

The efficiency (originally calculated incorrectly by Carnot) is correctly obtained as follows. In (a), since the gas is perfect, it follows from equation (5.8–5)* that

$$w_a = -q' = RT' \ln \frac{P_1}{P_2}. \qquad (6.6\text{–}1)^*$$

In (b), since the process is the adiabatic expansion of a perfect gas, use of equation (5.8–18)* gives

$$w_b = -\Delta E_b = -\tilde{C}_V(T'' - T'). \qquad (6.6\text{–}2)^*$$

(For convenience the heat capacity is assumed to be constant.) In (c), following the procedure used in (a),

$$w_c = -q'' = RT'' \ln \frac{P_3}{P_4}. \qquad (6.6\text{–}3)^*$$

For (d), by the procedure used in (b),

$$w_d = -E_d = -\tilde{C}_V(T' - T''). \qquad (6.6\text{–}4)^*$$

Finally, w, the total work done in the cycle, is obtained by summing the work given by (6.6–1)*, (6.6–2)*, (6.6–3)*, and (6.6–4)*:

$$w = -q' - q'' = RT' \ln \frac{P_1}{P_2} + RT'' \ln \frac{P_3}{P_4}. \qquad (6.6\text{–}5)^*$$

The pressures P_2 and P_3 are the initial and final pressures of a reversible adiabatic expansion between T' and T'', and P_1 and P_4 are similarly related; thus, by equation (5.8–16)*,

$$\frac{T''}{T'} = \left(\frac{P_3}{P_2}\right)^{R/\tilde{C}_P} = \left(\frac{P_4}{P_1}\right)^{R/\tilde{C}_P}, \qquad (6.6\text{–}6)^*$$

so that

$$\frac{P_1}{P_2} = \frac{P_4}{P_3}, \qquad (6.6\text{–}7)^*$$

and

$$w = RT'\left(\ln \frac{P_1}{P_2}\right) - RT''\left(\ln \frac{P_1}{P_2}\right). \qquad (6.6\text{–}8)^*$$

The efficiency of the cycle is

$$\frac{w}{-q'} = \frac{R(T' - T'') \ln (P_1/P_2)}{RT' \ln (P_1/P_2)} = \frac{T' - T''}{T'}. \qquad (6.6\text{–}9)^*$$

The last equation becomes identical with (6.4–3) if θ_1 and θ_2 are identified with T' and T'', respectively. As the temperatures T' and T'' were perfect gas scale temperatures, it is thus seen that the thermodynamic temperatures are either identical with those of the perfect gas temperature scale or directly proportional to them. Accordingly this scale will be denoted hereafter by degrees Kelvin, it being understood that on it 0°C equals 273.15° Kelvin. This is in keeping with Kelvin's original suggestion that the size of the degree be determined by defining one fixed point only.[1]

[1] See W. F. Giauque, *Nature*, **143**, 623 (1939).

6.7 The Entropy Change in Any Process and Its Calculation

In the processes described above, heat was converted into work by a cycle of changes in which the substances involved ended in exactly the same state as that in which they began. A reversible cycle was discussed in the preceding section. An irreversible cycle will now be considered. (To be specific a particular process is considered, but the same argument holds for any irreversible cycle.) Let a substance be used to convert heat into work by a process in which the substance is first expanded isothermally, at one temperature, then cooled at constant volume to a lower temperature, compressed isothermally to the original volume, and finally heated at constant volume to the original temperature. It is assumed that part of the work of the expansion and compression is dissipated as friction, and that finite temperature differences are used in heating and cooling steps. The entropy changes in heat reservoirs accompanying the process are shown in Fig. 6.7–1, which gives also the details of the particular process.

In Fig. 6.7–1a the value of

$$\int \mathrm{d}S_r\,; \quad \text{i.e.,} \left(\Sigma\,\frac{q_r}{T}\right),$$

for the heat reservoirs is plotted against the energy E_s of the substance. This curve represents the projection on the S–E plane of a curve in an S–E–V diagram; the third coordinate (not shown) is the volume of the substance. The work done in a cycle in which the substance(s) goes (go) from state A to state B and back again is

$$w = -\sum q_r = -\oint T\,\mathrm{d}S_r. \tag{6.7–1}$$

It should be noted that on the return path the substance passes through volumes different from those from A to B (i.e., it passes through different states). By the first law, when the substances are back in state A they have returned to the same energy, but by (6.5–1) the path is *not closed*, for $\oint \mathrm{d}S$ is positive for an actual irreversible process. Only if the processes are all reversible is $\oint \mathrm{d}S$ zero for the cycle and the path closed.[2]

Problem 6.7-1. (a) Calculate the work done and the heat withdrawn from the surroundings for each step of the irreversible process described by Fig. 6.7–1a, using the data given in the legend.

(b) Calculate the value of q_r/T for each step and the total change in the entropy of the reservoir ($\Sigma q_r/T$) for the over-all process.

[2] The reader may omit the material immediately following and continue with the paragraph which contains equation 6.7–4, if he desires.

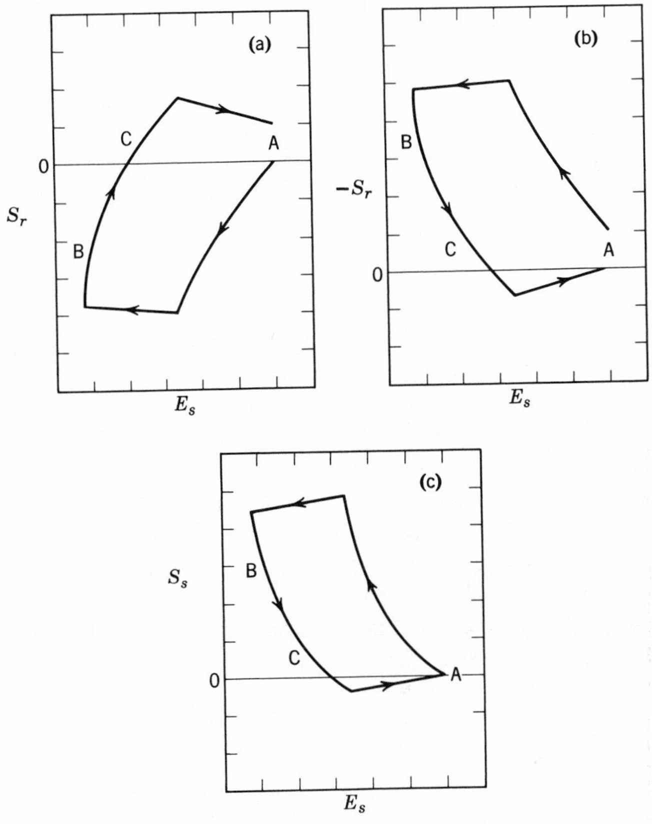

Fig. 6.7–1. Entropy change in a cyclic process.

This figure describes a cyclic process in which a mole of a gas following the van der Waals equation (a = 5 atm liter^{-2}; b = 100 cm^3 mole^{-1}, $\tilde{C}_V$ = 5.0 cal mole^{-1} deg^{-1}) is treated as follows: step 1, isothermal expansion from 1 liter to 10 liters at 300°K; step 2, constant volume cooling at 10 liters to 280°K; step 3, isothermal compression to 1 liter at 280°K; step 4, constant volume heating at 1 liter to 300°K.

In the irreversible process described by (a) and (b), 20% of the work done in steps (1) and (3) is dissipated as frictional heat; in addition, the cooling in step 2 is done by a bath at 250°K, and the heating in step 4 is done by a bath at 300°K.

In the reversible process (c) there is no friction; the cooling and heating steps are carried out using a series of baths each infinitesimally colder or hotter than the gas.

It should be noted that the total entropy change, in the cycle, for the reservoirs is positive if any segment of the process is irreversible. Thus the curves in (a) and (b) would be open if only some small section BC of the path were irreversible, with all the rest reversible. The location of the zeros in the ordinate is not important, since the total entropy change is always summed between two points such as A and B.

(c) Calculate the net work done in the over-all process. (For convenience the van der Waals equation may be put in the virial form as described in Section 4.5.)

Problem 6.7-2. Repeat the calculations of Problem 6.7-1 for a process in which the gas goes through the same changes of state as before, but with no friction and with the reservoirs always maintained at the temperature of the gas. (Note that, for steps 2 and 4, $\Sigma q_r/T$ must be obtained by integration between 280° and 300°K.) Observe that $(\Sigma q_r/T)$ is now zero for the over-all process.

In Fig. 6.7–1b the negative of $\oint \mathrm{d}S_r$ is plotted against E_s of the substance for the same process as before. The quantity plotted is now $\Sigma q/T$, in which q is given by

$$q = \Delta E + w, \tag{6.7–2}$$

where ΔE is the energy change in the substance, and w is the same work done as before.

Let us now suppose that the substance undergoes exactly the same changes (i.e., the substance passes through the same energies and volumes) as before but that the process is reversible and therefore the path is closed. (The entropy changes in the reservoirs are, of course, different.) Let us denote $-\mathrm{d}S_r$ for the reversible process by $\mathrm{d}S_s$. The resulting diagram is shown in Fig. 6.7–1c. Now add the values of the ordinates for Figs. 6.7–1a and 6.7–1c at each value of E. At any value of E this addition means that q/T has been taken for a cycle in which the substance is returned to its initial state. Since Fig. 6.7–1a represents an irreversible process, the result must always be positive; thus, in going from A to B,

$$\int_{\mathrm{A}}^{\mathrm{B}} \mathrm{d}S_s + \int_{\mathrm{A}}^{\mathrm{B}} \mathrm{d}S_r \geqq 0. \tag{6.7–3}$$

For any value of E,

$$\oint \mathrm{d}S_s \text{ must be equal to the maximum value of } -\oint \mathrm{d}S_r,$$

namely, that of the process by which the substance has undergone the specified changes of state reversibly. The maximum value is uniquely determined by E and V and is thus a property of the substance.

Problem 6.7-3. Using the results of Problems 6.7-1 and 6.7-2, obtain the quantity $(\Delta S_r + \Delta S_s)$ for each step of the irreversible process described by Fig. 6.7–1a, and for the over-all process. Observe that each step of the irreversible process contributes a positive quantity to the sum regardless of the respective signs of ΔS_r and ΔS_s.

The quantity $-\int \mathrm{d}S_r$ for the reversible process, which we have denoted by $\int \mathrm{d}S_s$, is called *the entropy change in the substance*. The substance and its heat revervoirs constitute a thermally isolated system. With the entropy change of the substance so defined, we can say that the sum of all entropy changes for reservoirs and compounds in an isolated system is zero for a reversible process in which the substance goes from any point A to another point B. For an irreversible process, this sum is positive.

The quantity $-\int_{A}^{B} dS_r$ *for a reversible process is called* the entropy change, ΔS, of the substance in going from A to B; thus

$$\Delta S = S_B - S_A = -\int_{A}^{B} dS_r \quad \text{(reversible)}. \tag{6.7–4}$$

Entropy is thus a property of the substance, and values S_A and S_B, respectively, can be given to it in states A and B. It is the second of the arbitrarily defined thermodynamic quantities, and perhaps the most important in systematic computation.

Clausius[3] was the first to see the need for a thermodynamic function of this nature, and he gave it the name entropy (formed by addition of the prefix "en" to the Greek word meaning change).

Some readers will find the following argument, which is essentially that of Clausius, somewhat easier to follow. In a reversible process which is not a cycle, a quantity of heat q_s is absorbed from the reservoirs by the machine (of negligible heat capacity) and working substances; that is, the reservoir absorbs $q_r = -q_s$ and the working substance (*together with the necessary machinery for reversibility*, hereafter understood) absorbs q_s. The temperatures of both must be the same or an irreversible process would result. The total entropy change of the system is the sum of the entropy changes (q/T) for the substance and reservoir, for an infinitesimal change,

$$dS_r + dS_s = 0, \tag{6.7–5}$$

where the subscripts r and s refer to reservoir and substances respectively; or

$$\frac{q_r}{T} + \frac{q_s}{T} = 0. \tag{6.7–6}$$

In any reversible process, the total entropy change is zero when all reservoirs of the isolated system are included.

Let us now consider a substance which is subjected to an irreversible process (such as the free expansion of a gas or the freezing of a supercooled liquid). The process is not itself a cycle. A cycle is completed by bringing the substance back to its original state reversibly. We may then view the situation in two ways.

(1) The entire cycle is not reversible because the first step is not reversible.

[3] Clausius, *Pogg. Ann.*, **125**, 400 (1865).

For the entire cycle the thermal changes lie in the heat reservoirs only, and by equation (6.5–1), for an irreversible cycle,

$$\Sigma \frac{q_i}{T_i} = \frac{q_1}{T_1} + \frac{q_2}{T_2} + \frac{q_3}{T_3} + \cdots > 0 \qquad (6.7\text{–}7)$$

with all heat reservoirs counted. This positive total entropy change measures the "irreversibility" of the irreversible process.

(2) All steps except the first in the cycle are reversible. By our definition of entropy the combined entropy change of substance and reservoirs in each of these reversible steps is zero. The entropy increase calculated by (1) must have occurred in the first step. This will be the entropy change of the reservoirs plus the entropy change of the substance. *The entropy change in a reservoir is the heat it absorbs divided by the temperature, as the heat is the same whether it is gained reversibly or not, the only process being the transfer of heat. The entropy change of the substance is the heat absorbed in the reversible process by the substance and the machine divided by the temperature.* Thus the total entropy in any irreversible (actual) process is positive when all entropy changes for the system and reservoirs are added up; that is,

$$dS_s + dS_r \geqq 0 \qquad \text{(Law II)}, \qquad (6.7\text{–}8)$$

where dS_s is the entropy change in the system as defined, and dS_r is the entropy change in the reservoirs. The equality refers to the reversible process, and the inequality to the actual process.

The problems below are especially designed to clarify the foregoing reasoning. The procedure which should be followed is shown first for two simple examples.

Example 1. Calculate the entropy change, when 1 mole of water in a bath of kerosene at 0°C changes to ice, (a) for the water, (b) for the bath, (c) for the entire isolated system.

The molal heat of fusion of ice is 1421 cal, so that 1421 cal is given to the bath. The entropy change in the water in (a) can be obtained at once since the process is reversible. It is $-1421/273.16$ or -5.21.

The entropy change in the bath is equal and opposite to this, namely, $+5.21$. Thus the entropy change for the isolated system is $(-5.21 + 5.21)$ or zero.

Example 2. Calculate the entropy change, when 1 mole of supercooled water in a bath of kerosene at -5°C changes to ice, (a) for the water, (b) for the bath, (c) for the entire isolated system.

To calculate the entropy change in the bath in (b), the heat of fusion of ice at -5°C must be first calculated using equation (5.11–1):

$$q = \Delta H = 1421 + \int_{273}^{268} (18 - 9)\, dT = 1421 - (5 \times 9) = 1376 \text{ cal.}$$

The entropy change in the bath is thus 1376/268 or 5.14 cal deg^{-1} mole^{-1}. To calculate the entropy change in the water in (a) we must consider a process by which supercooled water at $-5°C$ changes reversibly to ice at $-5°C$. The calculation is made by using the reversible process: First heat the water reversibly to zero; second, reversibly freeze the water; third, cool the ice reversibly to $-5°$. In each step the reservoir from which the heat is drawn must be at a temperature only infinitesimally higher than that of the water itself. To carry out a heating reversibly, the process must be done stepwise, using a series of baths, each at the same temperature as the substance. The heat absorbed in each step is $C_P\, dT$, and the corresponding entropy change in each step is $C_P\, dT/T$. If C_P is constant, the entropy change for a finite change from T_A to T_B is therefore found by integration to be $C_P \ln (T_B/T_A)$. The entropy change in the water is

$$\text{Step I:} \qquad \Delta S = 18 \times 2.303 \log \frac{273}{268} = 0.336.$$

$$\text{Step II:} \qquad \Delta S = -5.21.$$

$$\text{Step III:} \qquad \Delta S = 9 \times 2.303 \log \frac{268}{273} = -0.168.$$

The total entropy change is obtained by summing over the three steps; it is

$$\Delta S = 0.336 - 5.21 - 0.168 = -5.04.$$

Thus the entropy change in the water required in (a) is just -5.04 cal mole^{-1} deg^{-1}, which can only be calculated by reference to a reversible process. The total entropy change for the entire isolated system in (c) is

$$(a) + (b) = +0.10.$$

Thus in solving the problems below the first step in the procedure is always to devise a reversible process for carrying out the change.

Problem 6.7-4. Calculate the entropy change in the gas which occurs when 1 mole of a perfect gas expands from P_1 to P_2 at a constant temperature T.

$$\textit{Ans.} \quad \Delta S = R \ln \frac{P_1}{P_2}. \tag{6.7–9)*}$$

Problem 6.7-5. n_1 moles of hydrogen are mixed with n_2 moles of helium at temperature T and constant total pressure P. Calculate the entropy change in the gases, assuming the gases to be perfect. (*Hint.* Devise a reversible process for separating the gases.)

$$\textit{Ans.} \quad \Delta S = -(n_1 R \ln \tilde{N}_1) - (n_2 R \ln \tilde{N}_2) \qquad (6.7\text{–}10)^*$$

where

$$\tilde{N}_1 = \frac{n_1}{n_1 + n_2}; \qquad \tilde{N}_2 = \frac{n_2}{n_1 + n_2}. \qquad (6.7\text{–}11)$$

Problem 6.7-6. n_1 moles of toluene are mixed with n_2 moles of benzene. Calculate the entropy change in the substances, assuming that the solution is perfect (i.e., that the partial pressure of each substance is proportional to its mole fraction in the liquid). (*Hint.* Vaporize the liquids. Expand each to its proper partial pressure for reversible condensation through a membrane into the solution.)

$$\textit{Ans.} \quad \Delta S = -(n_1 R \ln \tilde{N}_1) - (n_2 R \ln \tilde{N}_2), \qquad (6.7\text{–}12)^{**}$$

where $\tilde{N}_1$ and $\tilde{N}_2$ are defined by equation (6.7–11).

Problem 6.7-7. Calculate the entropy change which occurs in the helium when 1 mole of helium ($\tilde{C}_P = 5/2R$) is heated from a temperature T_1 to a temperature T_2 at constant pressure.

$$\text{Ans.} \quad \Delta S = \frac{5}{2} R \ln \frac{T_2}{T_1} . \qquad (6.7\text{–}13)$$

Problem 6.7-8. Calculate the entropy change when liquid water, superheated to 120°C at 1 atm, changes to steam at 120°C (a) for the surroundings (heat reservoir); (b) for the water; (c) for the isolated system. The molal heat of vaporization of water is 9700 cal at 100°C. The heat capacity of the liquid may be taken at 18 cal/mole, and that of the gas at $8.6 + 0.003T$, where T is in degrees Kelvin.

Problem 6.7-9. A perfect gas is contained in a 100-cm³ bomb at 200 atm and 25°C. This bomb is connected to another completely evacuated 100-cm³ bomb by a valve. The whole system is in a thermostat at 25°. The valve is opened and the entire system allowed to come to temperature equilibrium.

(a) Calculate the entropy change in the thermostat.

(b) Calculate the entropy change in the isolated system.

Problem 6.7-10. The construction and operation of a Hampson-type liquefier was described in Problem 5.7-2. In the use of such a liquefier for oxygen, the gas is compressed isothermally from 1 atm to 200 atm at 298°K before admission to the thermally insulated liquefier. In the liquefier, 11% of the material is liquefied and is withdrawn as liquid at 90°K, 1 atm; the remainder is given off at 1 atm at 298°K and is returned to the compressor. Per mole of oxygen liquefied, calculate the theoretical entropy change (a) in the oxygen, (b) in the surroundings, and (c) in the entire isolated system. Neglect the effect of gas imperfections, which in this case affect the entropy changes only very slightly. For oxygen, take $\tilde{C}_P = 6.7$ cal mole^{-1} deg^{-1}; $\Delta\tilde{H}_{\text{vap}} =$ 1630 cal mole^{-1}.

Problem 6.7-11. Devise a method for liquefying oxygen reversibly, and tell what the entropy change in the isolated system would be. Explain.

Problem 6.7-12. A certain chemical reaction, when carried out at constant temperature (25°C) and pressure, liberates 10,000 cal. When carried out reversibly in an electric cell, it absorbs 2000 cal.

(a) Calculate the entropy change in the chemical reaction.

(b) The entropy change in the surroundings when the reaction occurs spontaneously (does no electrical work).

(c) The entropy change in the isolated system when the process is carried out spontaneously (i.e., does no electrical work).

(d) Relate the value in (c) to the maximum electrical work for the process.

Problem 6.7-13. A mole of water is cooled from 100°C to 25°C by immersion in a large bath (or baths) of water (a) at 25°C; (b) at 0°C; (c) in a series of baths at 75°, 50°, and 25°, allowing equilibrium to be reached in each bath. Calculate the entropy change, in the bath (or baths), in the mole of water, and in the isolated system in each case. (*Hint.* Use $\tilde{C}_P\, dT/T$ for the entropy change in the reversible cooling.)

6.8 Entropy as a Function of Temperature and Volume

Consider an infinitesimal reversible process in which a system changes its volume, so that work is done only against a pressure P, equal to that of the system, at the expense of an energy decrease $-dE$ and/or of heat withdrawn from the surroundings $T\,\mathrm{d}S$. The work done, $P\,\mathrm{d}V$, is given by

$$P\,\mathrm{d}V = -\mathrm{d}E + T\,\mathrm{d}S, \tag{6.8–1}$$

which is true for any process, as considered in the problem below.

Problem 6.8-1. By considering each term separately, show that equation (6.8–1) also applies to an irreversible process, providing P is the pressure of the system and T the temperature of the system.

If there is no volume change and therefore no work done,

$$\mathrm{d}E = T\,\mathrm{d}S. \tag{6.8–2}$$

Division by $\mathrm{d}T$ and passage to the limit at constant volume yields the derivative

$$\left(\frac{\partial S}{\partial T}\right)_V = \frac{1}{T}\left(\frac{\partial E}{\partial T}\right)_V. \tag{6.8–3}$$

Using equation (5.3–2), this becomes

$$\left(\frac{\partial S}{\partial T}\right)_V = \frac{C_V}{T}. \tag{6.8–4}$$

By *differentiation* of (6.8–3) with respect to volume at constant temperature,

$$\frac{\partial^2 S}{\partial T\,\partial V} = \frac{(\partial C_V/\partial V)_T}{T} = \frac{1}{T}\frac{\partial^2 E}{\partial T\,\partial V}. \tag{6.8–5}$$

A rate of change of entropy may now be obtained from equation (6.8–1) through *division* by $\mathrm{d}V$. Passage to the limit *at constant* T yields

$$P = -\left(\frac{\partial E}{\partial V}\right)_T + T\left(\frac{\partial S}{\partial V}\right)_T. \tag{6.8–6}$$

This equation can now be differentiated with respect to T at constant volume, giving

$$\left(\frac{\partial P}{\partial T}\right)_V = -\left[\frac{\partial(\partial E/\partial V)_T}{\partial T}\right]_V + \left(\frac{\partial S}{\partial V}\right)_T + T\left[\frac{\partial(\partial S/\partial V_T)}{\partial T}\right]_V. \tag{6.8–7}$$

Noting that the order of partial differential is immaterial, the first and last terms on the right side cancel (see equation 6.8–5). Thus

$$\left(\frac{\partial P}{\partial T}\right)_V = \left(\frac{\partial S}{\partial V}\right)_T. \tag{6.8–8}$$

6.9 Entropy as a Function of Temperature and Pressure

From equation (5.2–4),

$$dH = dE + P\,dV + V\,dP. \tag{6.9–1}$$

Upon substitution for dE from (6.9–1), equation (6.8–1) can be rewritten

$$-V\,dP = -dH + T\,dS. \tag{6.9–2}$$

From this equation it is obvious that for a process at constant pressure

$$dH = T\,dS, \tag{6.9–3}$$

and

$$\left(\frac{\partial H}{\partial T}\right)_P = T\left(\frac{\partial S}{\partial T}\right)_P; \tag{6.9–4}$$

whence, using equation (5.3–4),

$$\left(\frac{\partial S}{\partial T}\right)_P = \frac{C_P}{T}. \tag{6.9–5}$$

By differentiation of (6.9–4) with respect to P at constant T,

$$\frac{\partial^2 S}{\partial T\,\partial P} = \frac{(\partial C_P/\partial P)_T}{T} = \frac{\partial^2 H/\partial T\,\partial P}{T}. \tag{6.9–6}$$

By the procedure used in the previous section,

$$V = \left(\frac{\partial H}{\partial P}\right)_T - T\left(\frac{\partial S}{\partial P}\right)_T \tag{6.9–7}$$

and

$$\left(\frac{\partial V}{\partial T}\right)_P = -\left(\frac{\partial S}{\partial P}\right)_T. \tag{6.9–8}$$

Problem 6.9-1. Derive equations (6.9–7) and (6.9–8). Start with equation (6.9–2) divide by dP, and pass to the limit at constant T. Finally, differentiate with respect to T and use equation (6.9–6).

6.10 Thermodynamic Equations of State

By substitution of (6.8–8) into (6.8–6) one obtains

$$P = T\left(\frac{\partial P}{\partial T}\right)_V - \left(\frac{\partial E}{\partial V}\right)_T, \tag{6.10–1}$$

and by substitution of (6.9–8) into (6.9–7),

$$V = T\left(\frac{\partial V}{\partial T}\right)_P + \left(\frac{\partial H}{\partial P}\right)_T. \tag{6.10–2}$$

These two equations are called *thermodynamic equations of state*. Their great utility in obtaining thermodynamic quantities from the ordinary data of state will be made evident from the problems below.

Problem 6.10-1. (a) Assuming that nitrogen obeys van der Waals' equation with the constants given in Appendix 2, obtain an expression for $(\partial E/\partial V)_T$.

(b) From the result of (a) calculate the difference between the heat content at molal volumes of 25 liters and 0.100 liter, both at 0°C.

(c) Assuming that a mole of nitrogen expands at a valve from a pressure corresponding to a volume of 0.100 liter at 0°C to a pressure corresponding to a volume of 25 liters at 0°C and returns over coils carrying the entering gas so that it leaves an insulated liquefier at 0°C without further pressure drop, calculate the fraction liquefied. The heat of vaporization of nitrogen is 1400 cal at the boiling point under 1 atm pressure (77°K), and the average heat capacity of nitrogen near 1 atm is 7.0 cal deg^{-1} mole^{-1}. (*Hint.* ΔH for the liquefier process is zero.)

Problem 6.10-2. Calculate $(\partial H/\partial P)_T$ for hydrogen at 25°C and 5 atm, assuming that the gas obeys a modified Berthelot equation with the critical constants given in Appendix 2.

6.11 Thermodynamic Temperature Scale

Suppose that T had been defined only by equation (6.4–4),

$$\frac{q_1}{\theta_1} + \frac{q_2}{\theta_2} = 0, \tag{6.4–4}$$

by substitution of T for θ in that equation without identification with the perfect gas scale as was done in Section 6.6.

For a perfect gas $(\partial E/\partial V)_T$ and $(\partial H/\partial P)_T$ are zero, as defined in Section 5.8. The application of equations (6.10–1) and (6.10–2) to a perfect gas therefore yields the equations

$$P = T\left(\frac{\partial P}{\partial T}\right)_V \tag{6.11–1)*$$

and

$$V = T\left(\frac{\partial V}{\partial T}\right)_P. \tag{6.11–2)*$$

The first of these equations yields on integration at constant volume

$$\int \frac{dP}{P} = \int \frac{dT}{T} + \text{constant} \tag{6.11–3)*$$

or

$$\ln P = \ln \alpha' T, \tag{6.11–4)*$$

where the constant in equation (6.11–3)* has been replaced by ln α'. Thus, for a perfect gas at constant volume,

$$P = \alpha' T. \qquad (6.11\text{–}5)^*$$

Equation (6.11–2)* also yields, for a perfect gas at constant pressure,

$$V = \alpha'' T. \qquad (6.11\text{–}6)^*$$

α' and α'' are defined in terms of the ice point pressures and volumes of a perfect gas so that the ice point temperature is 273.15°K. Thus

$$\alpha' = \frac{P_0}{273.15}; \qquad \alpha'' = \frac{V_0}{273.15}. \qquad (6.11\text{–}7)^*$$

These results show that, *without reference to any particular process* such as the one considered in Section 6.6, the thermodynamic temperature scale can be defined in terms of the pressure of a perfect gas at constant volume or the volume of a perfect gas at constant pressure. Equations (6.11–5)* and (6.11–6)* are the equivalent of equation (6.4–4), which defines temperature in terms of the efficiency of a perfect heat engine.

6.12 Final Relations among Heat Capacities

Equations (6.10–1) and (6.10–2) can now be used to obtain a relationship between C_P and C_V which is more useful than those given by equations (5.3–11) and (5.3–12). It is

$$C_P = C_V + T\left(\frac{\partial P}{\partial T}\right)_V \left(\frac{\partial V}{\partial T}\right)_P; \qquad (6.12\text{–}1)$$

the proof of this relationship is treated in Problem 6.12-1.

Problem 6.12-1. By use of (5.3–11) and (6.10–2) derive equation (6.12–1). Show that the same relationship results from (5.3–12) and (6.10–1). Also show that

$$C_P - C_V = -T\frac{(\partial V/\partial T)_P{}^2}{(\partial V/\partial P)_T}. \qquad (6.12\text{–}2)$$

Likewise the saturated heat capacity is given by

$$C_{\text{sat}} = C_P - T\left(\frac{\partial V}{\partial T}\right)_P \left(\frac{\partial P}{\partial T}\right)_{\text{sat}}. \qquad (6.12\text{–}3)$$

The effect of volume on the heat capacity at constant volume is obtained by differentiation of equation (5.3–2),

$$C_V = \left(\frac{\partial E}{\partial T}\right)_V, \qquad (5.3\text{–}2)$$

with respect to volume. Noting that the order of partial differentiation is immaterial, this procedure yields

$$\left(\frac{\partial C_V}{\partial V}\right)_T = \left[\frac{\partial(\partial E/\partial V)_T}{\partial T}\right]_V. \tag{6.12–4}$$

Substituting for $(\partial E/\partial V)_T$ the value given by (6.10–1),

$$\left(\frac{\partial C_V}{\partial V}\right)_T = T\left(\frac{\partial^2 P}{\partial T^2}\right)_V. \tag{6.12–5}$$

Likewise it can be shown that

$$\left(\frac{\partial C_P}{\partial P}\right)_T = -T\left(\frac{\partial^2 V}{\partial T^2}\right)_P. \tag{6.12–6}$$

Problem 6.12-2. By differentiating (5.3–4) and then using (6.10–2), derive equation (6.12–6).

Problem 6.12-3. Show that $(\partial C_V/\partial V)_T$ and $(\partial C_P/\partial P)_T$ are zero for a perfect gas.

Problem 6.12-4. Show that, for a van der Waals gas, C_V is a function of temperature only.

Problem 6.12-5. The critical temperature of SO_2 is 157°C, and its critical pressure is 78 atm. Using the modified Berthelot equation (4.5–3), calculate the difference between the heat capacity of SO_2 at 2 atm, and at 1 atm, at 25°C.

6.13 Calculation of the Change of Entropy with Temperature

Now that temperature has been satisfactorily defined, equation (6.8–4) can be used to calculate the change in entropy which occurs when any system passes from one temperature to another at constant volume. This equation is

$$\left(\frac{\partial S}{\partial T}\right)_V = \frac{C_V}{T}. \tag{6.8–4}$$

Integration between the limits T_A and T_B, at which the system has the entropies S_A and S_B, yields

$$S_B - S_A = \int_{T_A}^{T_B} \frac{C_V}{T}\,dT \tag{6.13–1}$$

$$= \int_{T_A}^{T_B} C_V\,d\ln T. \tag{6.13–2}$$

Similarly, for the entropy change in a process at constant pressure equation (6.9–5),

$$\left(\frac{\partial S}{\partial T}\right)_P = \frac{C_P}{T}, \tag{6.9–5}$$

yields

$$S_B - S_A = \int_{T_A}^{T_B} \frac{C_P}{T}\,dT. \tag{6.13–3}$$

$$= \int_{T_A}^{T_B} C_P\,d\ln T. \tag{6.13–4}$$

For a perfect monatomic gas the molal heat capacities at constant volume and pressure are given by

$$\tilde{C}_V = \frac{3R}{2} \tag*{(6.13–5)*}$$

and

$$\tilde{C}_P = \frac{5R}{2}. \tag*{(6.13–6)*}$$

In this case equations (6.13–2) and (6.13–4) yield

$$\tilde{S}_B - \tilde{S}_A = \frac{3}{2}R\ln\frac{T_B}{T_A} \tag*{(6.13–7)*}$$

and

$$\tilde{S}_B - \tilde{S}_A = \frac{5}{2}R\ln\frac{T_B}{T_A}. \tag*{(6.13–8)*}$$

6.14 Entropy Changes on Expansion at Constant Temperature

Equation (6.8–8),

$$\left(\frac{\partial P}{\partial T}\right)_V = \left(\frac{\partial S}{\partial V}\right)_T, \tag{6.8–8}$$

allows calculation of the change of entropy on expansion at constant temperature to be made in a simple and straightforward manner if an equation of state is known which gives the pressure in terms of the temperature and volume. If S_A and S_B are the entropies before and after an expansion from V_A to V_B,

$$S_B - S_A = \int_{V_A}^{V_B} \left(\frac{\partial P}{\partial T}\right)_V dV. \tag{6.14–1}$$

Likewise, if the equation of state gives the volume in terms of the pressure, equation (6.9–8) yields

$$S_B - S_A = -\int_{P_A}^{P_B} \left(\frac{\partial V}{\partial T}\right)_P dP. \tag{6.14–2}$$

Application of equations (6.14–1) and (6.14–2) to a mole of a perfect gas yields

$$\tilde{S}_B - \tilde{S}_A = R \ln \frac{V_B}{V_A} \qquad (6.14\text{–}3)^*$$

and

$$\tilde{S}_B - \tilde{S}_A = R \ln \frac{P_A}{P_B}, \qquad (6.14\text{–}4)^*$$

which are, of course, identical.

6.15 General Expressions for Entropy Change. Reversible Adiabatic Processes

In general, where temperature and volume are considered the independent variables, the entropy change is

$$dS = \left(\frac{\partial S}{\partial T}\right)_V dT + \left(\frac{\partial S}{\partial V}\right)_T dV. \qquad (6.15\text{–}1)$$

Substitution from equations (6.8–4) and (6.8–8) yields

$$dS = \frac{C_V}{T} dT + \left(\frac{\partial P}{\partial T}\right)_V dV. \qquad (6.15\text{–}2)$$

If temperature and pressure are the main variables, the corresponding relation is

$$dS = \frac{C_P}{T} dT - \left(\frac{\partial V}{\partial T}\right)_P dP. \qquad (6.15\text{–}3)$$

Problem 6.15-1. Derive equation (6.15–3).

When a thermally isolated system undergoes a reversible process doing work only against pistons, the process occurs at constant entropy. Such a process is spoken of as a reversible adiabatic process. Application of equation (6.15–3) yields

$$\left(\frac{\partial T}{\partial P}\right)_S = T\frac{(\partial V/\partial T)_P}{C_P}, \qquad (6.15\text{–}4)$$

and equation (6.15–2) yields

$$\left(\frac{\partial T}{\partial V}\right)_S = -T\frac{(\partial P/\partial T)_V}{C_V}. \qquad (6.15\text{–}5)$$

These two equations (particularly the former) are used in measuring heat capacities by adiabatic expansion.

Problem 6.15-2. An apparatus consists of two cylinders connected by a bar of copper. The first cylinder is sealed; the second can do work against a piston. The entire assembly is thermally insulated from the outside. At the start each cylinder contains a mole of a perfect gas at a temperature of 27°C and a pressure of 25 atm. The heat capacity at constant pressure of the gas is 7.0 cal mole^{-1} deg^{-1}. The cylinders and the copper bar have negligible heat capacity. The gas in the second cylinder is allowed to expand reversibly and slowly to 1 atm, so that the temperature of the two cylinders remains the same.

(a) Calculate the work done and the final temperature of the system.

(b) Calculate the entropy changes in each of the cylinders, and from them the entropy change in the entire isolated system. (*Ans.* $\Delta S_{\text{total}} = 0$.)

(c) State what conclusions you can draw about the reversibility of the entire process.

Problem 6.15-3. In an apparatus identical with that described in Problem 6.15-2, the gas in the second cylinder is expanded very slowly against a constant pressure of 1 atm. Assume that the rate of expansion is slow enough that the temperature of the sealed cylinder is at all times the same as that of the one in which the gas does work. As before, the starting temperature is 27°C, and the final pressure of the second cylinder is 1 atm; the same amounts of the same gas are used as in Problem 6.15-2. (*Note.* The desired expansion may be accomplished by using a piston with an appropriate amount of friction against the cylinder walls.)

(a) Calculate the work done and the final temperature of the system.

(b) Calculate the entropy changes in each of the cylinders, the entropy change in the surroundings, and the total entropy change of sytem and surroundings.

(c) State what conclusions may be drawn about the reversibility of the process.

Problem 6.15-4. In the apparatus of Problem 6.15-2, the gas in the second cylinder is expanded rapidly and reversibly to 1 atm, during which process the gas in the first, (sealed) cylinder remains at its original temperature and pressure. In a second step heat is conducted along the copper bar connecting the cylinders until the temperatures of the two cylinders become identical; during this step the pressure of the gas in the second cylinder is kept at 1 atm by suitable motion of its piston.

(a) Calculate the work done and the final temperature of the expanded gas in the first step.

(b) Calculate the work done in the second step and the final temperature of the system.

(c) Calculate the entropy change of the isolated system.

(d) State what conclusions may be drawn about the reversibility of the process.

Problem 6.15-5. A mole of a perfect gas, for which $\tilde{C}_P = 7.0$, is confined at 27°C and 25 atm in a copper cylinder whose heat capacity is 20 cal deg^{-1}; the cylinder is thermally isolated from its surroundings. The gas is allowed to expand reversibly to 1 atm. Calculate (a) the final temperature, (b) the work done, and (c) the entropy change of the system.

6.16 Change in Entropy during Reversible Phase Changes

When a substance undergoes a reversible change in phase at constant temperature, such as vaporization, fusion, or transition, it is an experimental fact that the pressure remains constant. According to equation (5.2–3), the heat withdrawn from the surroundings is given by

$$q = \Delta H = H_{\text{B}} - H_{\text{A}}. \qquad (6.16\text{–}1)$$

The entropy change is thus

$$\Delta S = S_B - S_A = \frac{\Delta H}{T}. \tag{6.16–2}$$

6.17 Relation of Maximum Work at Constant Temperature to Entropy. The Helmholtz Free Energy

It is not only against pressure that a system may do work. For example, in a reversible electrolytic cell operating at constant temperature, work is done against the opposing electrical forces. Applying the first law to such a reversible system,

$$dE = T\,dS - w_{max}, \tag{6.17–1}$$

$$w_{max} = -(dE - T\,dS). \tag{6.17–2}$$

Integrating at constant temperature for a change from state A to state B,

$$w_{max} = -(\Delta E - T\,\Delta S), \tag{6.17–3}$$

where ΔE means $E_B - E_A$ and ΔS means $S_B - S_A$. Since the temperature is constant, (6.17–3) may be replaced by

$$w_{max} = -\Delta(E - TS). \tag{6.17–4}$$

In order to formalize calculations, it is convenient to define a quantity, A, called the Helmholtz free energy or sometimes the work content, as

$$A = E - TS. \tag{6.17–5}$$

Thus, for any constant temperature process,

$$\Delta A = A_B - A_A = -w_{max}. \tag{6.17–6}$$

This is the third of the arbitrarily defined thermodynamic quantities.

Equation (6.17–6) can be used as a criterion of the reversibility of a process. Suppose that a process such as the vaporization of water is proceeding at 100°C. If the maximum work is being done, the process is reversible. If less than the maximum work is being done, the process is not reversible. Thus the second law states that, for the actual work done in a process at constant temperature,

$$w \leqq -\Delta A, \tag{6.17–7}$$

where the equality sign is for the reversible process and the inequality for any actual process. (*Note.* This is not a unique criterion for reversibility, although for all practical cases it is adequate. The strict criteria are discussed in Chapter 9.)

Thus, if water, at 100°C, is vaporized into an evacuated container until a pressure of 1 atm is reached, the maximum work has not been done and the process is irreversible. Vaporization against a constant pressure of 1 atm yields the maximum work for the change and is the reversible process designated by

$$H_2O(l) \rightarrow H_2O(g, 1 \text{ atm}).$$

In this process the only work done is expansion work (work against pressure).

The more general use of the function A can be seen by considering the electrolytic cell

$$\text{Pt}, H_2(g, 1 \text{ atm}), \text{HCl}(g, 10^{-3} \text{ atm}), \text{AgCl}(s), \text{Ag}(s).$$

This cell is set up by using as electrolyte an aqueous solution whose partial pressure of hydrogen chloride is 10^{-3} atm. Consider that the cell is opposed by an electromotive force exactly opposite to its own and is arranged so that the hydrogen and the hydrogen chloride have their pressures balanced by pistons on which are exerted pressures of exactly 1 atm and 10^{-3} atm respectively; the cell operates reversibly, with the atmosphere acting as a reversible piston on the silver and silver chloride. At 25°C, the opposing emf required to reduce the current to zero is 0.0266 v. When a very small current is drawn from the cell, the maximum electrical work and the maximum work against pistons will be done. This is the maximum work obtainable from the process under *any* circumstance. The total work is the sum of the two and is equal to $-\Delta A$. Let the amount of chemical reaction occurring be

$$H_2(g, 1 \text{ atm}) + 2\text{AgCl}(s) = 2\text{Ag}(s) + 2\text{HCl}(g, 10^{-3} \text{ atm}).$$

Two faradays of electricity must pass through the circuit to produce this amount of reaction. The results of this large transference of electricity can be obtained by proportion from results obtained when only infinitesimal amounts pass. The maximum work is given by

$$w_{\max} = -\Delta A = -(2A_{\text{Ag}} + 2A_{\text{HCl}} - A_{\text{H}_2} - 2A_{\text{AgCl}}). \qquad (6.17\text{–}8)$$

(The symbol Δ has the same significance as in Section 5.10).

The electrical work is calculated from the emf opposing the cell. In joules, it is

$$w_e = 2 \times 96493.1\mathscr{E}, \qquad (6.17\text{–}9)$$

where 96,493.1 is Faraday's equivalent expressed in coulombs per equivalent. The factor 2 is inserted because two equivalents of electricity pass in the reaction. This result is converted to calories upon division by 4.1840. Thus the electrical work in calories is

$$w_e = 2 \times 23062.4\mathscr{E} = 46124.8 \times 0.0266 = 1227 \text{ cal}, \qquad (6.17\text{–}10)$$

where 23062.4 is Faraday's equivalent in calories per volt equivalent.

The mechanical work is obtained by subtracting the work done on the hydrogen and silver chloride pistons from the work done by the hydrogen chloride and silver pistons; in each case this is the constant pressure on the substance times the volume produced or consumed. Thus the mechanical work w_m is given by

$$w_m = 2(P\tilde{V})_{\mathrm{HCl}} + 2(P\tilde{V})_{\mathrm{Ag}} - (P\tilde{V})_{\mathrm{H_2}} - 2(P\tilde{V})_{\mathrm{AgCl}} = \Delta PV, \qquad (6.17\text{–}11)$$

where $(P\tilde{V})_{\mathrm{HCl}}$, etc., represent the $P\tilde{V}$ products for hydrogen chloride, etc. Thus

$$w_{\max} = 2 \times 23062.4\mathscr{E} + \Delta PV. \qquad (6.17\text{–}12)$$

Under the circumstances each of the gases may be assumed to be perfect, and the PV products of the solids may be neglected. Thus in this particular case

$$\Delta PV = RT. \qquad (6.17\text{–}13)^*$$

Combining (6.17–12) and (6.17–8),

$$-\Delta A = 2 \times 23062.4\mathscr{E} + \Delta PV, \qquad (6.17\text{–}14)$$

and, by use of (6.17–3) along with (6.17–12),

$$-(\Delta E + \Delta PV) + T\,\Delta S = 2 \times 23062.4\mathscr{E} = w_e. \qquad (6.17\text{–}15)$$

Using equation (5.2–4),

$$-\Delta H + T\,\Delta S = w_e. \qquad (6.17\text{–}16)$$

Inspection of equation (6.17–16) reveals several interesting facts. If there were no entropy change the electrical work would be equal to $-\Delta H$, that is, to the heat liberated in the spontaneous reaction at constant pressure. In the absence of entropy change the entire heat of reaction is convertible into electrical work. If, on the other hand, there is a positive entropy change, more electrical work is done than corresponds to $-\Delta H$, the extra work being obtained at the expense of an entropy increase. The extra energy $T\,\Delta S$ is drawn from the bath. If the entropy change is negative, only part of the heat of reaction is converted into work, while the rest goes to the bath as $T\,\Delta S$. If ΔH were zero, electrical work could be obtained at the expense of an entropy increase only.

The electrical work can be reduced to zero by suitable changes in the equilibrium pressures in the cell. The chemical reaction will be then occurring reversibly when the potential opposing the cell is zero. In this case,

$$-\Delta H + T\,\Delta S = 0 \tag{6.17–17}$$

or

$$\Delta S = \frac{\Delta H}{T}. \tag{6.17–18}$$

That is, the entropy change in a chemical reaction occurring reversibly and doing only expansion work is given by the same expression as that given in section 6.16 for reversible phase changes.

It is obvious that a reaction will be able to produce electrical work against an opposing electromotive force only if it is able to occur spontaneously with no electromotive force. Thus, according to equation (6.17–16), a criterion that a chemical reaction can occur at constant pressure and temperature is that

$$-\Delta H + T\,\Delta S \geqq 0. \tag{6.17–19}$$

The equality sign expresses the unattainable limit when the process occurs under its reversible conditions. (See note following equation 6.17–7. This also is not a unique criterion of equilibrium.)

6.18 The Gibbs (or Lewis) Free Energy

In equation (6.17–16) the maximum electrical work was equated to the quantity $(-\Delta H + T\,\Delta S)$. In addition, it has been shown above that this quantity must be greater than zero for any spontaneous chemical reaction at constant pressure and temperature. At constant temperature,

$$-\Delta H + T\,\Delta S = -\Delta(H - TS). \tag{6.18–1}$$

In view of this condition, the quantity $(H - TS)$ is important in formalizing calculations, and it is designated by the letter F; it is called the Gibbs (or Lewis) free energy. It is the fourth of the arbitrary thermodynamic properties that we have defined. Thus

$$F = E + \sum_i P_i V_i - TS = H - TS. \tag{6.18–2}$$

The summation sign has been inserted for the same reason as in equation (5.2–7); it applies only if parts of the system are at different pressures.

Then, at constant temperature and pressure, according to (6.17–16),

$$w_e = -\Delta F = -\Delta H + T\,\Delta S, \tag{6.18–3}$$

and thus the use of the quantity F is at once apparent. It is also apparent that this is the only physical significance of the quantity. The reader is reminded that the principal use of the quantity H is the calculation (through ΔH) of the heat withdrawn from the surroundings when no electrical work is done, and that, when the maximum electrical work is done, the heat is $T\,\Delta S$.

In the previous example,

$$\Delta F = 2\mu_{Ag} + 2\mu_{HCl} - \mu_{H_2} - 2\mu_{AgCl}, \tag{6.18–4}$$

where μ_{Ag}, etc., are the molal free energies. The symbols μ_{Ag}, etc., are used rather than F_{Ag}, etc., for reasons of uniformity which will appear presently.

Our criterion for the possibility of a spontaneous process at constant temperature and pressure is thus that $-\Delta F > 0$ or that ΔF is negative. For any process occurring under equilibrium conditions, ΔF is zero. Thus, for any process at constant temperature and pressure to occur,

$$\Delta F \leqq 0, \tag{6.18–5}$$

or, for an infinitesimal process for which the temperature and pressure are constant,

$$dF \leqq 0. \tag{6.18–6}$$

The reader is reminded that this is not a unique criterion of equilibrium (see note following equation 6.17–19).

When a chemical reaction occurs spontaneously at constant temperature and pressure, *the entropy change in the bath is* $(-\Delta H/T)$. *The entropy change in the chemical system is* ΔS. According to Section 6.7 and equation (6.7–3), the entropy change in the isolated system is the sum of the two and

$$-\frac{\Delta H}{T} + \Delta S \geqq 0. \tag{6.18–7}$$

The equality refers to a reversible process, and the inequality to an actual process. This is illustrated by Problem 6.7–9. Thus, for a process at constant temperature and pressure, $(-\Delta F/T)$ measures the entropy change in the isolated system, and

$$-\frac{\Delta F}{T} \geqq 0. \tag{6.18–8}$$

This relation is equivalent to (6.18–5), but it has been reached by a different argument.

6.19 The Gibbs Free Energy as a Function of Pressure and Temperature

The Gibbs free energy as defined by equation (6.18–2) is obviously a property of the system, since it is a sum of quantities which are properties of the system. For any infinitesimal reversible change doing no electrical work, if the pressure is the same in each part of the system ($\sum_i P_i V_i = PV$),

$$dF = dE + P\,dV + V\,dP - T\,dS - S\,dT. \qquad (6.19\text{–}1)$$

Consider a reversible change in which only expansion work is done. From the first law,

$$q = dE + w, \qquad (6.19\text{–}2)$$

where for this process q is $T\,dS$ and w is $P\,dV$. Therefore

$$T\,dS = dE + P\,dV. \qquad (6.19\text{–}3)$$

Using this relation in (6.19–1), one obtains

$$dF = V\,dP - S\,dT. \qquad (6.19\text{–}4)$$

Of the pairs of variables P and T or V and T, either of which uniquely defines the system, the former is the most natural, since, from equation (6.19–4),

$$\left(\frac{\partial F}{\partial P}\right)_T = V \qquad (6.19\text{–}5)$$

and

$$\left(\frac{\partial F}{\partial T}\right)_P = -S. \qquad (6.19\text{–}6)$$

Problem 6.19-1. Making use of the fact that order of partial differentiation is immaterial, prove that

$$\left(\frac{\partial S}{\partial P}\right)_T = -\left(\frac{\partial V}{\partial T}\right)_P. \qquad (6.9\text{–}8)$$

This relation has already been derived in a less straightforward fashion in Section 6.9.

Problem 6.19-2. Proceeding as we did in writing (6.19–1), derive

$$dA = -P\,dV - S\,dT, \qquad (6.19\text{–}7)$$

and then, noting that, for A, the natural variables are V and T, show that

$$\left(\frac{\partial A}{\partial T}\right)_V = -S \qquad (6.19\text{–}8)$$

and

$$\left(\frac{\partial A}{\partial V}\right)_T = -P. \qquad (6.19\text{–}9)$$

Problem 6.19-3. Using the results of Problem 6.19-2, show that

$$\left(\frac{\partial S}{\partial V}\right)_T = \left(\frac{\partial P}{\partial T}\right)_V, \tag{6.8–8}$$

which is a more straightforward derivation than used in Section 6.8.

Problem 6.19-4. Prove

(a)
$$\left[\frac{\partial(F/T)}{\partial T}\right]_P = -\frac{H}{T^2} \tag{6.19–10}$$

by direct differentiation and substitution of the values of F and $(\partial F/\partial T)_P$; and

(b)
$$\left[\frac{\partial(F/T)}{\partial(1/T)}\right]_P = H$$

by a similar process (first differentiating with respect to $1/T$).

Problem 6.19-5. (a) By differentiating the identity

$$F = H - TS \tag{6.18–2}$$

directly with respect to T at constant P, and noting that

$$\left(\frac{\partial H}{\partial T}\right)_P = T\left(\frac{\partial S}{\partial T}\right)_P, \tag{6.9–4}$$

derive equation (6.19–6).

(b) Similarly rederive equation (6.19–10) by differentiation of the quantity $(H/T) - S$.

Problem 6.19-6. Prove that for a perfect gas

$$\left(\frac{\partial F}{\partial P}\right)_T = \frac{nRT}{P}, \tag{6.19–11}$$

and thence that the free energy change when the pressure of the gas is changed from P_A to P_B at constant temperature is given by

$$F_B - F_A = nRT \ln \frac{P_B}{P_A}. \tag{6.19–12}$$

Problem 6.19-7. Using the data of Section 6.17, calculate the pressure of hydrogen chloride for which the reaction H_2(g, 1 atm) + 2AgCl(s) = 2Ag(s) + HCl(g, P) is at equilibrium under no opposing electromotive force. Assume that the gases are perfect. (Note that the emf of the cell can be brought to zero by reduction of the hydrogen chloride partial pressure and that $dF = V\,dP$.)

Problem 6.19-8. Assuming that in the reaction of Problem 6.19-7 the pressure of hydrogen is kept one thousand times that of the hydrogen chloride, calculate the pressures of hydrogen and hydrogen chloride necessary for equilibrium under zero applied electromotive force. Assume that both gases are perfect. (Note that variation of the pressures of the other gas can also bring the emf to zero, and apply $\int V\,dP$ to each gas.)

Problem 6.19-9. The entropy of nitrogen is 45.8 cal mole^{-1} deg^{-1} at 25°C, and its heat capacity at constant pressure may be taken at 7.0 cal mole^{-1} deg^{-1}. Assuming that the gas is perfect, calculate (a) ΔS, (b) ΔF, and (c) ΔA for a process in which a mole of nitrogen is heated from 25°C to 200°C at 1 atm.

Problem 6.19-10. Using the virial coefficients given in Appendix 2, Table A2–4, calculate the changes in (a) enthalpy, (b) entropy, (c) Gibbs free energy, and (d) Helmholtz free energy which accompany the expansion of 1 mole of nitrogen from 50 atm to 1 atm at 25°C. (*Hint.* The rate of change of the virial coefficients with temperature may be evaluated graphically. Evaluate integrals of the type $\int f(V)\,\mathrm{d}V$ by parts where necessary.)

6.20 Energy Change in the General Reversible Process

Consider any infinitesimal process made to occur reversibly. The galvanic cell of Section 6.17 with proper opposing forces constitutes a fairly general example of such a process. Gases entering or leaving the system must do so with the aid of pistons which exactly balance their pressures so that the maximum mechanical work is done *by* the system or the minimum done *on* it. Likewise the maximum electromotive force which the cell can generate must be balanced against an equal electromotive force, if the process is spontaneous. Otherwise, the minimum electromotive force must be used to make the reaction occur, if it is one that would not occur spontaneously. For an infinitesimal reversible process,

$$\mathrm{d}E = T\,\mathrm{d}S - \sum_i P_i\,\mathrm{d}V_i - w_e. \tag{6.20–1}$$

This equation says that the system gains energy as a result of taking heat from a bath in amount $T\,\mathrm{d}S$ (first term on the right) and loses it by doing work. Work is done against pistons on each of which is exerted a pressure P_i to produce corresponding volume changes $\mathrm{d}V_i$, etc. This gives rise to the second term on the right. Work is also done against the opposing electromotive force. This is denoted by w_e and is the last term on the right of equation (6.20–1).

As an example, for an infinitesimal amount of reaction, the chemical equation in Section 6.17 can be written

$$\delta\mathrm{H_2(g, 1\ atm)} + 2\delta\mathrm{AgCl(s)} = 2\delta\mathrm{Ag(s)} + 2\delta\mathrm{HCl(g, 10^{-3}\ atm)} + 1227\delta\ \mathrm{cal}, \tag{6.20–2}$$

where each chemical symbol stands for the molal free energy of the chemical compound in question and δ is a very small fraction. Corresponding to this equation, w_e is 1227δ cal, since, according to equation (6.18–3),

$$w_e = -\delta\,\Delta F, \tag{6.20–3}$$

where ΔF is the free energy change in the chemical equation of Section 6.17; or

$$w_e = -(2\delta\mu_{\mathrm{Ag}} + 2\delta\mu_{\mathrm{HCl}} - \delta\mu_{\mathrm{H_2}} - 2\delta\mu_{\mathrm{AgCl}}), \tag{6.20–3a}$$

where μ_{Ag}, etc., are the molal contributions of the respective compounds.

Let dn_{Ag} and dn_{HCl} denote the number of gram atoms of silver and moles of hydrogen chloride (at the specified pressure) that are formed in the system. And let $-dn_{H_2}$ and $-dn_{AgCl}$ denote the number of moles of hydrogen at the specified pressure and the corresponding number of moles of AgCl that are used up in the cell reaction, and then

$$\begin{aligned} dn_{Ag} &= 2\delta, \\ dn_{HCl} &= 2\delta, \\ -dn_{H_2} &= \delta, \\ \text{and} \qquad -dn_{AgCl} &= 2\delta. \end{aligned} \tag{6.20–4}$$

Substituting in (6.20–3), using μ_i and dn_i respectively to denote molal free energies and changes in numbers of moles for the substances present,

$$w_e = -\delta\Delta F = -\sum_i \mu_i \, dn_i . \tag{6.20–5}$$

Although we have used a simple example for illustration, equation (6.20–5) can be written quite arbitrarily because the independent variables are still the same. However, owing to the effects of enthalpy and entropy of mixing, the μ_i cannot be specifically assigned to any molecular species as soon as there is more than one species in any phase. Thus a meaning must be given to μ_i where solutions are involved. This we shall now do for the completely general case. To do so we consider the chemical reaction

$$\text{aA} + \text{bB} + \cdots = \text{lL} + \text{mM} + \cdots,$$

where the substances A, B, etc., L, M, etc., can be gases, liquids, solids, or components of solutions.

Substituting for w_e in equation (6.20–1) the arbitrary value $\Sigma\mu_i \, dn_i$ to obtain an equation which is to be regarded as defining the μ_i,

$$dE = T\,dS - \sum P_i \, dV_i + \sum \mu_i \, dn_i . \tag{6.20–6}$$

It follows that

$$\left(\frac{\partial E}{\partial S}\right)_{V_i, n_i, \text{etc.}} = T, \tag{6.20–7}$$

$$\left(\frac{\partial E}{\partial V_i}\right)_{S, n_i, \text{etc.}} = -P_i, \tag{6.20–8}$$

and

$$\left(\frac{\partial E}{\partial n_i}\right)_{S, V_i, n_j \neq n_i, \text{etc.}} = \mu_i . \tag{6.20–9}$$

The general definition of the Lewis free energy is given in Section 6.18 as

$$F = E + \sum P_i V_i - TS, \tag{6.20–10}$$

so that, in general,

$$dF = dE + \sum P_i \, dV_i + \sum V_i \, dP_i - T \, dS - S \, dT. \tag{6.20–11}$$

Problem 6.20-1. As an exercise in handling summations derive equation (6.20–11) in the form

$$dF = dE + P_1 \, dV_1 + P_2 \, dV_2 + \cdots + V_1 \, dP_1 + V_2 \, dP_2 + \cdots - T \, dS - S \, dT$$

by taking the differential of (6.20–10).

Using this relation to eliminate dE from equation (6.20–6),

$$dF = \sum V_i \, dP_i - S \, dT + \sum \mu_i \, dn_i. \tag{6.20–12}$$

Thus

$$\left(\frac{\partial F}{\partial P_i}\right)_{T,n_i,\text{etc.}} = V_i, \tag{6.20–13}$$

$$\left(\frac{\partial F}{\partial T}\right)_{P_i,n_i,\text{etc.}} = -S, \tag{6.20–14}$$

and

$$\left(\frac{\partial F}{\partial n_i}\right)_{T,P_i,n_j \neq n_i,\text{etc.}} = \mu_i. \tag{6.20–15}$$

Equations (6.20–13) and (6.20–14) are exactly equivalent to (6.19–5) and (6.19–6); (6.20–15) shows that the quantities μ_i are, in reality, derivatives of the free energy with the respect to the number of moles of the several molecular species. In equation (6.18–4) these quantities appeared as molal quantities. (Were it not for almost universal usage, $\bar{F}$ would be the appropriate symbol. Since these quantities are most frequently referred to, as below, as *chemical potentials*, it is better to retain Gibbs's symbol for them.) For pure substances, $\mu \equiv \tilde{F}$.

Let us consider equation (6.20–12) (at constant P and T) to apply to the free energy change of a process corresponding to an equation like (6.20–2) but in which the products and reactants are in solution. The equation is

$$\mathrm{a}\,\delta\mathrm{A} + \mathrm{b}\,\delta\mathrm{B} + \cdots = \mathrm{l}\,\delta\mathrm{L} + \mathrm{m}\,\delta\mathrm{M} + \cdots + w_e \tag{6.20–16}$$

Thus limited, equation (6.20–12) becomes

$$dF = \sum \mu_i \, dn_i = \delta \, \Delta F, = -w_e \tag{6.20–17}$$

where ΔF is the free energy change for the general reaction

$$\text{aA} + \text{bB} + \cdots = \text{lL} + \text{mM} + \cdots.$$

Equation (6.20–17) is thus derivable directly from equation (6.20–15) for a process at constant T and P.

6.21 The Partial Molal Free Energy or Chemical Potential of Gibbs

Suppose that, in the cell used as example in the previous section, the hydrogen is mixed with one tenth its volume of nitrogen and the hydrogen chloride mixed with one thousand times its volume of nitrogen. In practice this would be the case if the hydrogen contained the nitrogen as impurity while nitrogen was slowly bubbled through the electrolyte with the dissolved hydrogen chloride. The reaction occurring for infinitesimal passage of current is generalized in equation (6.20–16). We wish to know the increase or decrease in free energy when 1 mole of hydrogen or of hydrogen chloride is added to the gas mixture of which it is a component, keeping the composition constant. This can be ascertained by using infinite volumes of the mixtures or adding a small fraction of a mole to a finite quantity and calculating the proportionate increase per mole. If the latter is done, for strict accuracy one must pass to the limit of $\delta F/\delta n_i$ as δn_i approaches zero for the substance in question.

The limit of this ratio, however, is exactly μ_i:

$$\mu_i = \lim_{\delta n_i \to 0} \frac{\delta F}{\delta n_i} \tag{6.21–1}$$

Since it is a partial derivative, μ_i is often called a partial molal free energy. Corresponding to it are the partial molal volume, partial molal energy, partial molal heat content, and partial molal entropy. These quantities are discussed fully in Chapter 8. The following problems are illustrative of the relations between the partial molal quantities. They may be postponed until Chapter 8 is reached, but to do so is neither necessary nor desirable.

Problem 6.21-1. Show that

$$\left(\frac{\partial \mu_i}{\partial T}\right)_{P_i, n_i} = -\bar{S}_i, \tag{6.21–2}$$

where

$$\bar{S}_i = \left(\frac{\partial S}{\partial n_i}\right)_{T, P, n_j \neq n_i, \text{ etc.}}$$

and is called the *partial molal entropy*.

Problem 6.21-2. Show that

$$\left(\frac{\partial \mu_i}{\partial P}\right)_{T,n_i} = \bar{V}_i, \tag{6.21–3}$$

where

$$\bar{V}_i = \left(\frac{\partial V}{\partial n_i}\right)_{T,P,n_j \neq n_i,\text{ etc.}}$$

Problem 6.21-3. Show that, for a perfect gas expanding from P_A to P_B, at constant temperature,

$$\mu_B - \mu_A = RT \ln \frac{P_B}{P_A}. \tag{6.21–4}*$$

6.22 Introduction to the Study of Equilibria in Chemical Reactions. The Activity

It is desirable at this point to give the reader an idea of the uses of the quantities and equations just given. To this end, we give here a brief development and outline of material to be fully discussed in later chapters. The problems may be postponed until Chapter 12 is completed. One of the chief objectives of thermodynamics is to ascertain the conditions under which a reaction is at equilibrium. Logically these conditions are found by using the following considerations.

It has been seen that, for the process

$$2AgCl(s) + H_2(g, 1\text{ atm}) = 2Ag + 2HCl(g, 10^{-3}\text{ atm}),$$

the free energy change, ΔF, is -1227 cal. Equilibrium under zero applied emf is obtained if the pressure of hydrogen is reduced so as to decrease the free energy of 1 mole of hydrogen by 1227 cal. Another way to obtain equilibrium is to increase the pressure of hydrogen chloride so that the free energy of 2 moles of hydrogen chloride is increased by 1227 cal. (See Problem 6.19-7.) In actual practice this procedure is formalized. The resulting system will now be discussed.

It would be an awkward task to give tables of the values of the free energy of a substance for all pressures or concentrations required. The task becomes simpler if, instead of the free energy, a function related to it is used. This function is called the activity. The absolute activity, λ, is related to the partial molal free energy by the relation

$$\mu = RT \ln \lambda. \tag{6.22–1}$$

In Chapter 23 it is shown how this can be calculated from statistical mechanics. All other thermodynamic quantities are then obtained as its temperature derivatives. Actually it is more convenient to use relative activities, a, which represent the difference between the partial molal free energy of the substance under specified conditions and in some reference state at the same temperature. Thus

$$\mu - \mu^\circ = RT \ln \frac{\lambda}{\lambda^\circ} = RT \ln a, \tag{6.22–2}$$

where μ and μ° are the partial molal free energies in some particular state and in the standard state respectively, λ and λ° are the corresponding absolute activities, and a is the relative activity. For gases the reference state is usually the hypothetical ideal gas at 1 atm. In this case the quantity is frequently termed the fugacity, f; with such a reference state,

$$\mu - \mu^\circ = RT \ln f \tag{6.22–3}$$

If the quantity f/P is tabulated against the pressure for a real gas, very few entries suffice since at low pressures f/P is nearly unity.

Problem 6.22-1. Using the Berthelot equation and the critical constants of Appendix 2 calculate the ratio of the activities of H_2 at 1 atm and 200 atm at 90°K. (*Hint.* Evaluate

$$\int_{P=1}^{P=200} \tilde{V}\, dP$$

analytically.)

6.23 Introduction to the Use of Activity. The Equilibrium Constant

In the general chemical reaction

$$\text{aA} + \text{bB} = \text{lL} + \text{mM},$$

the difference between the free energy change, ΔF, for specified states of A, B, L, and M, and that for each in its standard state, ΔF° is, according to (6.22–2),

$$\Delta F - \Delta F^\circ = RT \ln \frac{a_L{}^l a_M{}^m}{a_A{}^a a_B{}^b}, \tag{6.23–1}$$

where a_A, etc., refer to the specified states.

Problem 6.23-1. Derive equation (6.23–1) in detail by considering the quantities $(\mu_A - \mu_B{}^\circ)$, etc.

This result is given here and discussed below (in a preliminary way) as an illustration of the use of the quantities given. Its detailed use is described in Chapter 12, after methods for determination of the activity have been given.

To illustrate the meaning of (6.23–1) it is desirable to consider the cell reaction for the cell which has already been discussed in Section 6.17.

If the gases are taken to be perfect, and the relative activities are taken with reference to the ideal gases at 1 atm, equation (6.23–1) becomes

$$\Delta F - \Delta F^\circ = RT \ln \frac{P_{\mathrm{HCl}}^2}{P_{\mathrm{H_2}}}, \tag{6.23–2)*}$$

where P_{HCl}, etc., are the partial pressures in the cell.

Problem 6.23-2. Derive equation (6.23–2). Assume perfect gases; use equation (6.22–3), and note that, by (6.21–4)*, $\mu - \mu^\circ = RT \ln P$ for a perfect gas.

For equilibrium under no applied electromotive force, ΔF must be zero. The ratio involving the pressures of hydrogen and hydrogen chloride under those circumstances is then given by

$$RT \ln \left[\frac{P_{\mathrm{HCl}}^2}{P_{\mathrm{H_2}}}\right]_{\mathrm{equilib.}} = -\Delta F^\circ, \tag{6.23–3)*}$$

where P_{HCl}, etc., are now the partial pressures in a cell where $\mathscr{E}$ is zero (i.e., where the reaction is at equilibrium).

or

$$\left[\frac{P_{\mathrm{HCl}}^2}{P_{\mathrm{H_2}}}\right]_{\mathrm{equilib.}} = e^{-\Delta F^\circ/RT}. \tag{6.23–4)*}$$

But ΔF° is the free energy change when the gases in the cell are each at unit activity and is a constant. Thus

$$\left[\frac{P_{\mathrm{HCl}}^2}{P_{\mathrm{H_2}}}\right]_{\mathrm{equilib.}} = K. \tag{6.23–5)*}$$

The constant so defined is the equilibrium constant for the cell reaction, first deduced by Guldberg and Waage.[4]

Problem 6.23-3. Calculate the equilibrium constant for the reaction $2\mathrm{AgCl(s)} + \mathrm{H_2(g)} = 2\mathrm{Ag(s)} + 2\mathrm{HCl(g)}$ at 25°C from the data given in Section 6.17, assuming both gases to be perfect.

Problem 6.23-4. If with a pressure of hydrogen equal to 1 atm the emf of the cell under discussion is 0.2224 v, calculate the partial pressure of hydrogen chloride above the cell.

[4] C. M. Guldberg and P. Waage, *Études sur les Affinités Chimiques*, Brogger and Christie, Christiania, 1867.

Equilibria between Two or More Phases of a Pure Substance

CHAPTER 7

7.1 Coexistent Phases

It is not easy to give a more concise definition of a *phase* than that given by Gibbs himself in his abstract of his famous monograph,[1] "The Equilibrium of Heterogeneous Substances." The following is his definition:

In considering the different homogeneous bodies which can be formed out of any set of component substances, it is convenient to have a term which shall refer solely to the composition and thermodynamic state of any such body without regard to its size or form. The word phase has been chosen for this purpose. Such bodies as differ in composition or state are called different phases of the matter considered, all bodies which differ only in size and form being regarded as different examples of the same phase.

Two or more phases are said to be coexistent when they exist together in equilibrium with bounding surfaces whose curvature is negligibly small. (It will be shown in Chapter 15 that the free energy of a small droplet depends on its size.)

7.2 Equilibria between Coexistent Phases

The equilibria which can be established between the phases of a pure substance under varying conditions of temperature and pressure are the

[1] *The Collected Works of J. Willard Gibbs*, Vol. 1, Longmans, Green, New York, 1928, p. 358.

simplest examples of coexistent phases. The phases under consideration will be the one or more possible crystalline forms, the liquid, and the gas.

For a single phase obviously pressure and temperature may be varied at will within certain limits (a liquid is, of course, limited to temperatures below the critical temperature). The system existing as a single phase is thus said to have two degrees of freedom. The condition for equilibrium between two phases (say liquid and vapor), under no applied force other than the pressure, is that the work done against the atmosphere in a transition between them is the maximum; that is, as in Section 6.18,

$$\Delta F = 0. \tag{7.2–1}$$

This means that for equal masses of two phases A and B in equilibrium the free energies must be equal. Taking the gram mole as the unit of mass and denoting the free energy of the two phases by $\tilde{F}_A$ and $\tilde{F}_B$ respectively, the condition for equilibrium is

$$\tilde{F}_A = \tilde{F}_B \quad (\text{or } \mu_A = \mu_B). \tag{7.2–2}$$

Since there are no other variables, both $\tilde{F}_A$ and $\tilde{F}_B$ are functions only of the common pressure and temperature of phase A and phase B; thus equation (7.2–2) yields a relation between P and T after substitution. Thus only one of the variables (P or T) is independent and the system has only one degree of freedom. If a third phase C is present (say one of the possible crystalline forms), a second independent relationship between pressure and temperature results from the equality of free energies:

$$\tilde{F}_B = \tilde{F}_C. \tag{7.2–3}$$

This relation removes the last degree of freedom, so that another relation,

$$\tilde{F}_C = \tilde{F}_D \tag{7.2–4}$$

cannot be satisfied, and further phases are not allowed. Thus a special case of the Gibbs phase rule has been derived. The general case in which more than one substance is present is discussed in Chapter 9.

7.3 Change of Equilibrium Pressure with Temperature for Two Coexistent Phases

If two phases A and B are to remain in equilibrium for any change in temperature and pressure, their molal free energies must stay equal. Thus

$$d\tilde{F}_A = d\tilde{F}_B \quad (\text{or } d\mu_A = d\mu_B). \tag{7.3–1}$$

Since both $\tilde{F}_A$ and $\tilde{F}_B$ are functions of P and T alone, (7.3–1) is equivalent to

$$\left(\frac{\partial \tilde{F}_A}{\partial T}\right)_P dT + \left(\frac{\partial \tilde{F}_A}{\partial P}\right)_T dP = \left(\frac{\partial \tilde{F}_B}{\partial T}\right)_P dT + \left(\frac{\partial \tilde{F}_B}{\partial P}\right)_T dP. \quad (7.3\text{–}2)$$

Substituting the values of the partial derivatives from equations (6.20–13) and (6.20–14),

$$-\tilde{S}_A\, dT + \tilde{V}_A\, dP = -\tilde{S}_B\, dT + \tilde{V}_B\, dP, \quad (7.3\text{–}3)$$

where $\tilde{S}_A$ and $\tilde{S}_B$ are the molal entropies of A and B respectively and $\tilde{V}_A$ and $\tilde{V}_B$ are the corresponding volumes. Thus

$$\frac{dP}{dT} = \frac{\tilde{S}_B - \tilde{S}_A}{\tilde{V}_B - \tilde{V}_A} = \frac{\Delta S}{\Delta V}; \quad (7.3\text{–}4)$$

making use of equation (6.16–2) for the entropy change associated with a phase change,

$$\frac{dP}{dT} = \frac{\tilde{H}_B - \tilde{H}_A}{T(\tilde{V}_B - \tilde{V}_A)} = \frac{\Delta H}{T\,\Delta V}. \quad (7.3\text{–}5)$$

This equation is known as the Clapeyron equation.[2] It allows the pressure at which a vapor is in equilibrium with a liquid or solid to be calculated, if the heat of vaporization and the molal volumes of the liquid and vapor are known. It also allows the effect of pressure on melting points or transition points to be calculated.

Problem 7.3-1. Calculate the rate of change of vapor pressure with temperature for 1-butene at 266.7°K from the following information.[3] The heat of vaporization is given by the formula $\Delta\tilde{H} = 6595.1 + 4.500T - 0.0359T^2$. At 266.7°K the molal volume of the liquid is 0.090 liter/mole, the molar volume of the vapor is 21.08 liters, and the vapor pressure is 755 mm Hg.

Problem 7.3-2. Calculate the second virial coefficient of gaseous 1-butene at 242.2°K from the data of Problem 7.3-1 and the following information.[3] The molar volume of the liquid at 242.2°K is 0.086 liter. The vapor pressure p at 242.2°K is 258.9 mm Hg, and dp/dT is 12.662 mm Hg/deg.

Problem 7.3-3. Calculate the change in freezing point, per atmosphere, of water at its freezing point, obtaining data where necessary.

Problem 7.3-4. Calculate the change in freezing point of benzene per atmosphere at its freezing point from the following data. The heat of fusion of benzene is 2340 cal mole^{-1} at the freezing point, 5.5°C. The density of liquid benzene is 0.894 and that of solid benzene is 1.014 at this temperature.

[2] Clapeyron, *J. école polytech.* (*Paris*), **14,** No. 23, 1953 (1834).
[3] *J. Am. Chem. Soc.*, **68,** 52 (1946).

7.4 Equilibrium between Two Phases under Different Pressures

Suppose that a piston exerts a pressure P_A on a liquid A which is contained in a cylinder while the liquid is confined to a portion of a cylinder by a membrane permeable to the vapor. The other portion of the cylinder is also closed by a piston which exerts a pressure P_B on the vapor B of the same substance. The arrangement is shown in Fig. 7.4–1. Both portions

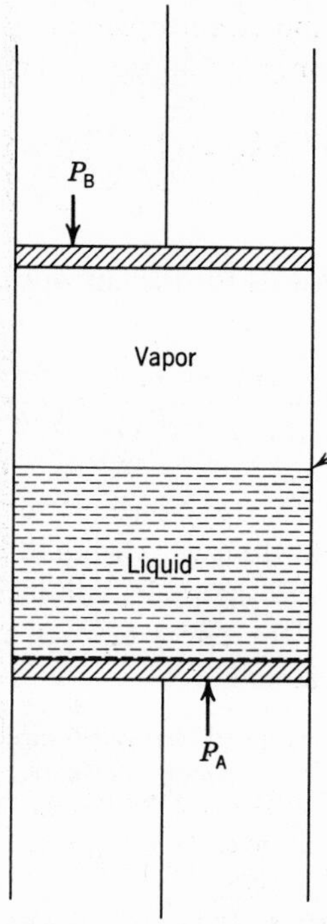

Fig. 7.4–1. Vapor-liquid equilibrium with phases under different pressures.

of the cylinder are at the same temperature, T.

The condition for equilibrium is

$$\left(\frac{\partial \tilde{F}_A}{\partial T}\right)_P dT + \left(\frac{\partial \tilde{F}_A}{\partial P_A}\right)_T dP_A = \left(\frac{\partial \tilde{F}_B}{\partial T}\right)_P dT + \left(\frac{\partial \tilde{F}_B}{\partial P_B}\right)_T dP_B. \qquad (7.4\text{–}1)$$

Substituting for the partial derivatives as in the last section,

$$-\tilde{S}_A\, dT + \tilde{V}_A\, dP_A = -\tilde{S}_B\, dT + \tilde{V}_B\, dP_B, \qquad (7.4\text{–}2)$$

where $\tilde{S}_A$, $\tilde{S}_B$, $\tilde{V}_A$, and $\tilde{V}_B$ are the appropriate molal entropies and volumes. If the temperature is constant, equation (7.4–2) reduces to

$$\frac{dP_B}{dP_A} = \frac{\tilde{V}_A}{\tilde{V}_B}. \qquad (7.4\text{–}3)$$

Problem 7.4-1. Show that application of equation (7.4–3) to the equilibrium between a liquid and a vapor which is a perfect gas yields

$$\frac{d \ln p}{dP} = \frac{\tilde{V}_l}{RT} \qquad (7.4\text{–}4)^*$$

for the change in vapor pressure p with applied pressure (P) on the liquid whose molal volume is $\tilde{V}_l$.

Problem 7.4-2. Calculate the change in vapor pressure of water, per atmosphere, at the freezing point from the data used for Problem 7.3–3.

If the temperature is varied while the pressure on the liquid remains constant, equation (7.4–2) yields

$$\left(\frac{\partial P_B}{\partial T}\right)_{P_A} = \left(\frac{\tilde{H}_B - \tilde{H}_A}{T\tilde{V}_B}\right). \qquad (7.4\text{–}5)$$

This equation shows how the vapor pressure of a liquid changes with temperature when the pressure on the liquid remains constant instead of being equal to that of the vapor.

Problem 7.4-3. Derive equation (7.4–5).

Problem 7.4-4. Show that, if the vapor is a perfect gas, equation (7.4–5) becomes

$$\left(\frac{\partial \ln p}{\partial T}\right)_{P_A} = \frac{\Delta H_{vap}}{RT^2}, \qquad (7.4\text{–}6)$$

where p is the vapor pressure of the liquid and $\Delta\tilde{H}_{vap}$ the molal heat of vaporization.

7.5 Transitions of Higher Order

When liquid helium is cooled below its boiling point with the pressure equal to the vapor pressure, it does not freeze but instead goes into a second liquid phase at 2.18°K. At this temperature there is no true heat of transition, but instead the equivalent of a heat of transition is removed as sensible heat over a temperature range. Thus there is an abnormal rise in the heat capacity in the neighborhood of 2.18°K. Figure 7.5–1 shows the molal heat capacity of helium plotted as a function of the temperature between 1.7° and 2.4°K. The shape of this curve, which looks like a Greek lambda, has caused the maximum point to be known as the *lambda point*, and such transitions to be known as *lambda* transitions. There are also transitions in solid phases (e.g., methane at 20.4°K) in the neighborhood of which the heat capacity curve has the same shape. It by no means follows that there is any simple physical connection between the various lambda transitions any more than there is a simple physical relation between the common type of transitions such as melting and vaporization. Transitions of this sort, in which there is no heat of transition but a discontinuity in the heat capacity, are known as *second-order* transitions. The more usual phase change, with a heat of transition, is known as a *first-order* transition.

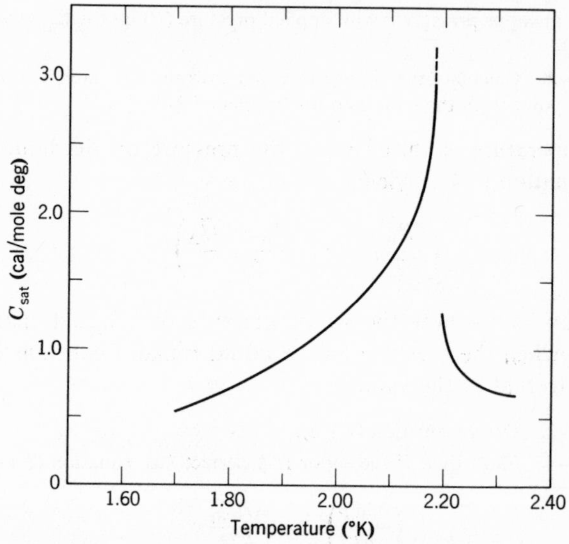

Fig. 7.5–1. Heat capacity of liquid helium from 1.7° to 2.4°K.

For a lambda-type transition, there is no latent heat, and therefore ΔS is zero. Since equations (7.3–4) and (7.3–5) involve the total derivatives, they may be written

$$\frac{\mathrm{d}T}{\mathrm{d}P} = \frac{T(\tilde{V}_{\mathrm{B}} - \tilde{V}_{\mathrm{A}})}{(\tilde{H}_{\mathrm{B}} - \tilde{H}_{\mathrm{A}})} = \frac{T\,\Delta V}{\Delta H} = \frac{\Delta V}{\Delta S}. \tag{7.5–1}$$

If ΔH were exactly zero in a transition and ΔV were finite, the rate of change in transition temperature with pressure would be infinite; such a transition would have an infinite range of transition temperatures along the vertical direction of a container due merely to the small variation of pressure with height. Such a situation has not been observed. For lambda-type transitions, $\mathrm{d}P/\mathrm{d}T$ remains non-zero and finite, so that ΔV

must be zero. Thus the derivative dP/dT obtained from equation (7.3–4) or (7.3–5) is indeterminate; that is,

$$\frac{dP}{dT} = \frac{\Delta S}{\Delta V} = \frac{0}{0}. \qquad (7.5\text{–}2)$$

Figure 7.5–2 gives a plot of P against T, where P is the pressure necessary

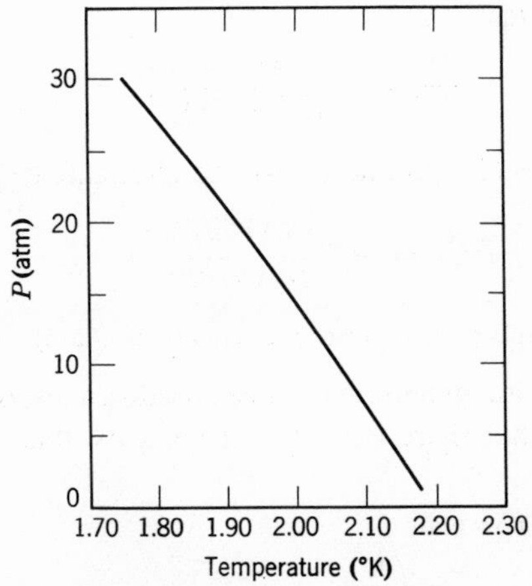

Fig. 7.5–2. Lambda point pressure of liquid helium.

to maintain liquid helium at the lambda point at the temperature T. For any chosen pressure the heat capacity curve is like that shown in Fig. 7.5–1, so that ΔS and ΔV remain zero along the curve separating the two forms of helium. Thus $d\Delta S$ and $d\Delta V$ are both zero along this curve. Then, for small changes in P and T,[4]

$$d\Delta S = \left(\frac{\partial \Delta S}{\partial T}\right)_P dT + \left(\frac{\partial \Delta S}{\partial P}\right)_T dP = 0 \qquad (7.5\text{–}3)$$

and

$$d\Delta V = \left(\frac{\partial \Delta V}{\partial T}\right)_P dT + \left(\frac{\partial \Delta V}{\partial P}\right)_T dP = 0. \qquad (7.5\text{–}4)$$

From the first of these equations there results

$$\frac{dP}{dT} = -\frac{\partial \Delta S/\partial T}{\partial \Delta S/\partial P} = \frac{\Delta C_P}{T(\partial \Delta V/\partial T)_P}, \qquad (7.5\text{–}5)$$

[4] P. Ehrenfest, *Koninkl. Ned. Akad. Wetenschap. Proc.*, **36**, 153 (1933); *Leiden Comm. Suppl.*, **75b**.

after substitution, using equation (6.9–5) and (6.9–8), which are

$$\left(\frac{\partial S}{\partial T}\right)_P = \frac{C_P}{T} \tag{6.9–5}$$

and

$$\left(\frac{\partial S}{\partial P}\right)_T = -\left(\frac{\partial V}{\partial T}\right)_P. \tag{6.9–8}$$

Equation (7.5–4) yields

$$\frac{dP}{dT} = -\frac{(\partial \Delta V/\partial T)_P}{(\partial \Delta V/\partial P)_T}. \tag{7.5–6}$$

Combining equations (7.5–5) and (7.5–6) to eliminate dP/dT yields

$$\Delta C_P = -T\frac{(\partial \Delta V/\partial T)_P{}^2}{(\partial \Delta V/\partial P)_T}. \tag{7.5–7}$$

Problem 7.5-1. Complete the derivation of equations (7.5–5), (7.5–6), and (7.5–7).

The lambda transition of helium has been used as a test of these equations on the assumption that there is no latent heat, as illustrated in Problem 7.5–2.

Problem 7.5-2. (a) Show that

$$\left(\frac{dP}{dT}\right)_\lambda = \frac{\Delta C_P}{T\tilde{V}\,\Delta\alpha}. \tag{7.5–8}$$

where α is the coefficient of expansion, $1/V(\partial V/\partial T)_P$, and $\Delta\alpha$ is the difference between the coefficients of expansion on either side of the lambda point.

(b) For the lambda transition of helium, dP/dT is -80.8 atm/deg. From the graph of $\tilde{C}_{PI}$ against T it is found that $\tilde{C}_{PII} - \tilde{C}_{PI}$ is 1.9 cal g^{-1} deg^{-1}, where $\tilde{C}_{PII}$ is the limit of the heat capacity of the low temperature form at the lambda point and $\tilde{C}_{PI}$ is the limit of the heat capacity when the lambda point is approached from the high temperature scale. The limit of the coefficient of expansion, α_I, approached from the high temperature side, is 0.0222 deg^{-1}. Using equation (7.5–8), show that α_{II}, the limit of the coefficient of expansion approached from the low temperature side at the lambda point, is -0.0426 deg^{-1}. (This turns out to be the value observed experimentally.)[5,6]

Problem 7.5–2 illustrates the importance of the assumption that ΔC_P is finite at the lambda point. Since

$$\Delta C_P = \frac{1}{T}\left(\frac{\partial \Delta S}{\partial T}\right)_P, \tag{7.5–9}$$

it follows that $(\partial \Delta S/\partial T)$ is not zero when ΔC_P is finite. Were there no

[5] W. H. Keesom, *Koninkl. Ned. Akad. Wetenschap. Proc.*, **36**, 147 (1933); *Leiden Comm. Suppl.*, **75a**.

[6] *Warning*: At the time of writing, this interpretation of the lambda point of helium is being questioned.

discontinuity, the derivative would be zero and the previous equations would not apply. When this situation exists, the transition is called, by definition, a third-order transition.

Figure 7.5–3 shows the heat capacity of methane in the neighborhood

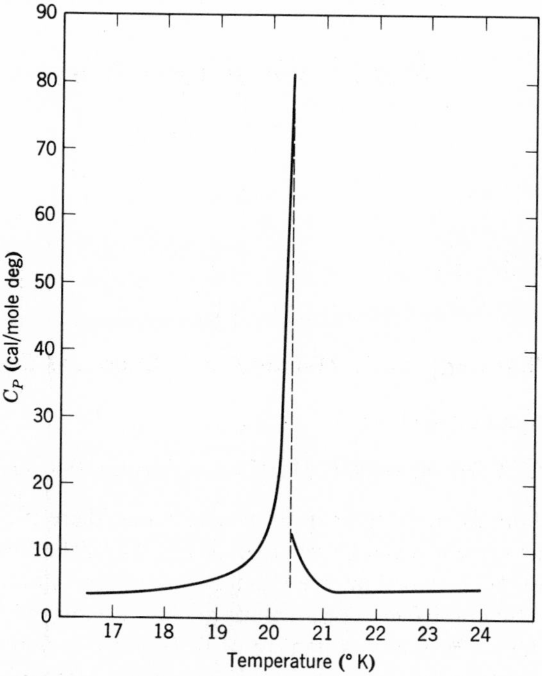

Fig. 7.5–3. Heat capacity of solid methane near 20°K.

of 20.4°K. That there is a discontinuity in the heat capacity curve at the point T is apparent.

Problem 7.5-3. Using the subscripts A and B to refer to the varieties of methane above and below the lambda point,

$$\tilde{C}_{PA} - \tilde{C}_{PB} = 68 \text{ cal deg}^{-1} \text{ mole}^{-1}.$$

The effect of pressure on the lambda point temperature is expressed by

$$\left(\frac{dP}{dT}\right)_\lambda = -181 \text{ atm deg}^{-1}.$$

Taking the lambda point temperature as 20.4°K, show that the change in $(\partial\tilde{V}/\partial T)_P$ across the lambda point is expressed by

$$\left(\frac{\partial\tilde{V}_A}{\partial T}\right)_P - \left(\frac{\partial\tilde{V}_B}{\partial T}\right)_P = 0.76 \text{ cm}^3 \text{ deg}^{-1} \text{ mole}^{-1}.$$

Partial Molal Quantities

CHAPTER 8

8.1 The Thermodynamic Meaning of a Chemical Equation

When an equation such as

$$HCl\ (0.096\ m) + NH_3\ (0.107\ m) = NH_4Cl\ (0.015\ m) \qquad (8.1\text{–}1)$$

is written without further explanation, it means that there is no change in mass in a reaction which can be regarded as a result of the four processes: (a) 1 mole of HCl is withdrawn from a very large (strictly speaking, infinite) quantity of 0.096 molal solution; (b) 1 mole of ammonia is withdrawn from a very large quantity of 0.107 molal solution; (c) the two are allowed to react; and (d) the resulting ammonium chloride is added to a very large quantity of 0.015 molal solution. From the standpoint of the very large amounts of solution, this is a *differential process*. In order to find the change of any property (for example, volume) associated with equation (8.1–1), it is necessary to obtain for each substance the property (volume) change which occurs when a mole of substance is withdrawn from or added to a very large amount of the solution specified in each case. For HCl, this is obviously not the molar property (volume) of gaseous HCl at the pressure of the reaction, nor is it likely to prove to be the molar property (volume) of pure liquid HCl. It must be determined by some process similar to that described just above.

In the example above, a very large amount of each solution was required so that a mole of a substance could be withdrawn or added without changing the composition of the solution, since otherwise the solution could not be specified exactly. The same information can be obtained by measurement of the property (volume) change δV which occurs when a very small number of moles δn is withdrawn from a finite amount of solution; since the volume is an extensive property, the change in volume per mole is $\delta V/\delta n$. If the composition is not to be altered, δn must be made to approach zero. The quantity sought is then $\lim_{\delta n \to 0} (\delta V/\delta n)$, which is the first derivative of V with respect to n. The chemical potentials, μ_i, discussed at the end of the last chapter, are examples of such quantities.

8.2 Partial Molal Quantities

The derivative referred to above was in fact a partial derivative, since the process described was one in which the amount of only one component was changed, the amounts of all others being held constant. The partial molal volumes, $\bar{V}$, are defined by equations of the form

$$\bar{V}_1 = \left(\frac{\partial V}{\partial n_1}\right)_{n_2, n_3, \cdots, P, T}. \qquad (8.2\text{–}1)$$

In general, for any extensive property G, the partial molal property with respect to component 1 is

$$\bar{G}_1 = \left(\frac{\partial G}{\partial n_1}\right)_{n_2, n_3, P, T}. \qquad (8.2\text{–}2)$$

The partial molal property is obviously an intensive property.

The obvious way to obtain partial molal quantities is to plot the total property of a solution for various amounts of one component, with a fixed amount of the others, against the number of moles of the first component. The partial molal quantity is the slope of the curve. As an example of this procedure, Fig. 8.2–1 shows the volume of sulfuric acid solutions containing 1000 g of water plotted against the number of moles of sulfuric acid present (molality). A tangent at 4.0 molal has a slope of 41 cm^3 $mole^{-1}$, which is the partial molal volume of H_2SO_4 at this concentration (the molar volume of pure sulfuric acid is 53.5 cm^3 $mole^{-1}$ at this temperature).

It is now possible to specify the change in a given property in the reaction described by equation (8.1–1). The change produced in the property G when a small amount of HCl is withdrawn from a very large amount of solution is given by $-\bar{G}_{HCl}\, \delta n_{HCl}$, and similarly for the other substances, so that

$$\delta G = \bar{G}_{NH_4Cl}\, \delta n_{NH_4Cl} - \bar{G}_{HCl}\, \delta n_{HCl} - \bar{G}_{NH_3}\, \delta n_{NH_3}. \qquad (8.2\text{–}3)$$

Since a very large amount of each solution was present, equation (8.2–3) may be put on the basis of the numbers of moles appearing in equation (8.1–1),

$$\Delta G = \bar{G}_{NH_4Cl} - \bar{G}_{HCl} - \bar{G}_{NH_3}, \tag{8.2–4}$$

which is the same equation as would be used if the reaction involved pure substances except for the substitution of partial molal properties for molar properties. It should be noted that this change in G is that due to the chemical reaction alone and does not include any transfer or removal of solvent.

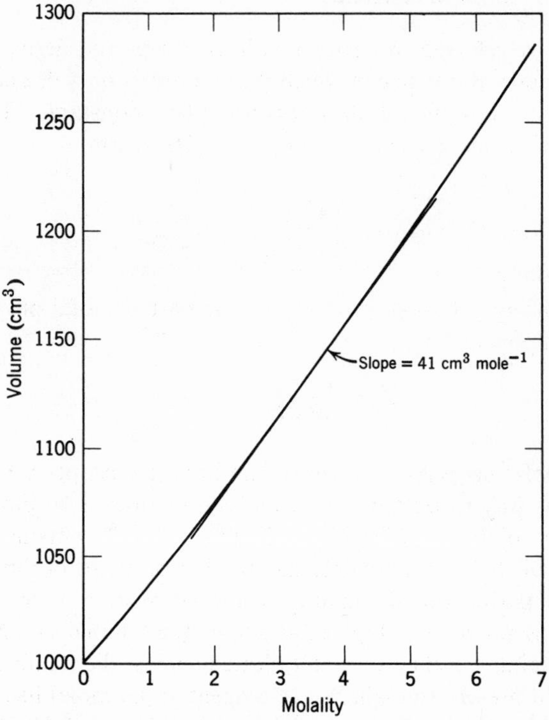

Fig. 8.2–1. Volumes of aqueous sulfuric acid containing 1000 g of water at 20°C.

Relationships between partial molal quantities may readily be obtained. From the general equation for partial derivatives, a change dG in any extensive property caused by changes in the amounts of various components is given by

$$\begin{aligned} dG &= \left(\frac{\partial G}{\partial n_1}\right)_{n_2,n_3} dn_1 + \left(\frac{\partial G}{\partial n_2}\right)_{n_1,n_3} dn_2 + \cdots \\ &= \bar{G}_1\, dn_1 + \bar{G}_2\, dn_2 + \cdots. \end{aligned} \tag{8.2–5}$$

The total property G is obtained by integration of (8.2–5). The equation may be integrated readily if the condition is imposed that the composition of the solution remain constant, so that all the $\bar{G}$'s are constant. At constant composition, let

$$n_2 = \alpha n_1, \quad n_3 = \beta n_1, \cdots, \tag{8.2–6}$$

whence

$$dn_2 = \alpha\, dn_1, \quad dn_3 = \beta\, dn_1, \cdots, \tag{8.2–7}$$

and, from (8.2–5),

$$dG = (\bar{G}_1 + \alpha\bar{G}_2 + \beta\bar{G}_3 + \cdots)\, dn_1. \tag{8.2–8}$$

Since $\bar{G}_1$, $\bar{G}_2$, $\bar{G}_3$, etc., are all constants for fixed composition, pressure, and temperature, the quantity in parentheses is a constant. Upon integration, equation (8.2–8) becomes

$$G = \bar{G}_1 n_1 + \alpha\bar{G}_2 n_1 + \beta\bar{G}_3 n_1 + \cdots, \tag{8.2–9}$$

whence

$$G = \bar{G}_1 n_1 + \bar{G}_2 n_2 + \bar{G}_3 n_3 + \cdots. \tag{8.2–10}$$

The integration described corresponds to a physical process in which the solution is compounded by successive additions of infinitesimal amounts of each component, care being taken that all components are added in the original ratio each time. The equation is quite general, since by suitable choice of α, β, etc., any desired composition may be obtained in the manner specified.

Problem 8.2-1. Table 8.2–1 gives the partial molal volumes of ethanol and water at 20°C. Use these data to calculate the volumes and densities of (a) a solution containing 2 moles of water and 8 moles of ethanol; (b) a solution containing 50 g of water and 50 g of ethanol. Make graphical interpolation in the table where necessary. The results of (a) and (b) may be compared with the densities given in Table 8.3–4.

Table 8.2-1

Partial Molal Volumes in Ethanol-Water Solutions at 20°C

Mole Per Cent Ethanol	Partial Molal Volume of Water	Partial Molal Volume of Ethanol
0	18.05	54.20
10	18.11	53.10
20	17.67	55.40
40	17.01	57.10
60	16.21	57.97
80	15.37	58.30

If the general equation (8.2–10) is differentiated without the imposition of any special conditions, then

$$dG = \bar{G}_1\, dn_1 + n_1\, d\bar{G}_1 + \bar{G}_2\, dn_2 + n_2\, d\bar{G}_2 + \cdots. \tag{8.2–11}$$

However, $d\bar{G}$ was already given by equation (8.2–5), which is also perfectly general. Equating the two expressions,

$$n_1 \, d\bar{G}_1 + n_2 \, d\bar{G}_2 + \cdots = 0. \tag{8.2–12}$$

This equation is a form of the Duhem equation. It will prove very useful in the determination of partial molal properties.

It is frequently useful to talk of a *partial specific property*, which is defined as the rate of change of a property per *gram* of substance added, the amounts of all other substances being held constant. The partial specific properties follow the same rules and equations as the partial molal properties, except that number of grams must be substituted for number of moles whenever partial specific properties are substituted for partial molal properties. As will become apparent in the problems below, data are frequently given in such form that the partial specific properties are more readily determined than the corresponding partial molal properties. In some cases partial specific properties may themselves be used in further calculations; in other cases they provide a convenient stepping-stone to the partial molal properties. The partial molal property is equal to the partial specific property times the molecular weight of the substance.

In principle, all partial molal properties can be determined by the method outlined in this section. The following section gives detailed directions for specific techniques which are useful in determination of partial molal properties. It will be found essential for the reader who is either measuring or using partial molal properties, but it may be omitted by the more general reader without loss.

8.3 Determination of Partial Molal Properties

In the example of the preceding section, the partial molal volume of sulfuric acid was obtained from the slope of a curve in which the volume of solution containing 1000 g of water was plotted against the number of moles of acid present. This type of procedure, which follows directly the definition of a partial molal quantity given in equation (8.2–2), will be discussed below as the "direct method." There are many other methods for the calculation of partial molal properties from the properties of a solution, and only a few will be considered below. A generalized treatment of this subject is given by Young and Vogel.[1] Appendix 3 contains their tables of the relationships between the partial molal quantities and the slopes of graphs in which a variety of functions of the property in question are plotted against various functions of concentration.

The discussions to follow will be concerned primarily with the determination of partial molal properties for binary solutions. Most of the methods can be

[1] T. F. Young and O. G. Vogel, *J. Am. Chem. Soc.*, **54**, 3025 (1932).

generalized readily to treat solutions of more components for which sufficient data are available. It may be assumed, in the absence of a direct statement to the contrary, that a method or equation described for calculation of $\bar{G}_1$ may be applied to the calculation of $\bar{G}_2$ by interchange throughout of the labels 1 and 2.

8.3–1 The Direct Method and Its Extensions

In the direct method it is necessary first to obtain the value of the property considered for a set of solutions containing a fixed amount of one component. For solutions whose concentrations are expressed as molality, an obvious choice is that amount containing 1000 g of water, as illustrated previously. For concentrated solutions, the measured properties are frequently given as functions of mole fractions; in this case, the value of the property per mole of solute is $G/\tilde{N}_2 n_{\text{total}}$, and the moles of solvent per mole of solute is the mole ratio $r_1 = n_1/n_2 = \tilde{N}_1/\tilde{N}_2$, with similar expressions for the solvent. The determination of partial molal properties by such direct plots is severely limited in accuracy by the difficulty of drawing tangents.

The difficulties of this method are removed if the property G can be expressed as an analytical function of the number of moles of solute and solvent, $G = f(n_1, n_2)$, in which case the partial molal properties may be obtained by differentiation of this function. The same result is obtained from an equation giving the value of the property as a function of the number of moles of one component for solutions containing a fixed amount of the other. In this case, one partial molal property is obtained by differentiation of the function, and the other by use of equation (8.2–10).

Example. The data for sulfuric acid solutions used in Section 8.2 may be represented within its accuracy from 1 to 6 molal by the empirical equation

$$V = 1001.8 + 35.35n_2 + 0.863n_2^2 \qquad (n_1 = 55.51)$$

(at very low concentrations, by the theory of electrolytes, a term in $n_2^{1/2}$ should be included). By differentiation of this equation,

$$\bar{V}_2 = 35.35 + 1.726n_2 \qquad (n_1 = 55.51),$$

since, by equation (8.2–10),

$$V = n_1\bar{V}_1 + n_2\bar{V}_2,$$

$$\bar{V}_1 = \frac{V - n_2\bar{V}_2}{55.51} = 18.047 - 0.0152n_2^2 \qquad (n_1 = 55.51).$$

Upon application of these equations for $\bar{V}_2$ and $\bar{V}_1$, one obtains, at 4 molal, $\bar{V}_2 = 42.05$, $\bar{V}_1 = 17.80$.

Problem 8.3-1. (a) Using the equations given in the example above, obtain the partial molal volumes of sulfuric acid and water at 2.0 and 3.0 molal.

(b) Use the partial molal volumes obtained in (a) to calculate the volume of each solution which contains 1000 g of water, and from these results obtain the densities of 2.0 and 3.0 molal sulfuric acid. Compare the results with those obtained directly from the analytic equation for V.

Problem 8.3-2. Table 8.3–1 lists the specific heat capacity at constant pressure for solutions of NaBr in water at 25°C, from the measurements of Randall and Rossini[2] below 1 molal and those of Bender and Kaiser[3] above 1 molal. Plot the total heat capacity for the amount of solution containing 1000 g of water against the molality and obtain $\bar{C}_{P2}$ at 1, 3, and 5 molal by construction of tangents. Evaluate $\bar{C}_{P1}$ at these concentrations by difference.

Table 8.3-1
Specific Heat of Sodium Bromide Solutions at 25°C

Molality	Specific Heat (cal g^{-1} deg^{-1})	Molality	Specific Heat (cal g^{-1} deg^{-1})
0.00	0.9979	1.00	0.8953
0.10	0.9857	2.205	0.8078
0.20	0.9741	3.8495	0.7247
0.35	0.9576	5.9985	0.6534
0.50	0.9420	8.3735	0.6028
0.75	0.9177		

In practice it may not be convenient to obtain an equation or set of equations representing the data accurately over the entire range of concentration. In such cases, an approximate function may be used and the difference between this function and the actual property evaluated at each concentration. Suppose a function f is chosen such that

$$G = f(n_2) + \delta \qquad \text{(at constant } n_1\text{)}. \tag{8.3–1}$$

By differentiation of equation (8.3–1), one obtained for the partial molal property

$$\bar{G}_2 = \left(\frac{\partial f}{\partial n_2}\right)_{n_1} + \left(\frac{\partial \delta}{\partial n_2}\right)_{n_1}. \tag{8.3–2}$$

The first of the two derivatives may be obtained analytically and the second graphically. Another possibility is to take

$$\frac{G - f'(n_2)}{n_2} = \delta' \qquad \text{(at constant } n_1\text{)}, \tag{8.3–3}$$

in which case differentiation gives

$$\bar{G}_2 = \left(\frac{\partial f'}{\partial n_2}\right)_{n_1} + n_2\left(\frac{\partial \delta'}{\partial n_2}\right)_{n_1} + \delta'. \tag{8.3–4}$$

In either case, $\bar{G}_1$ may be obtained by use of equation (8.2–10) as in the examples above.

The functions f and f' may be given any convenient form. If in equation (8.3–3) $f'(n_2) = n_1\bar{G}_1$, the quantity δ' is the "apparent molal property" to be

[2] M. Randall and F. D. Rossini, *J. Am. Chem. Soc.*, **51**, 323 (1929).
[3] P. Bender and A. D. Kaiser, *J. Am. Chem. Soc.*, **76**, 3084 (1954).

discussed below. If, on the other hand, the function f of equation (8.3–1) is chosen to be $(n_1\tilde{G}_1 + n_2\tilde{G}_2)$, where $\tilde{G}_1$ and $\tilde{G}_2$ are the molal volumes for the two constituents, then

$$G = n_1\tilde{G}_1 + n_2\tilde{G}_2 + \Delta; \tag{8.3–5}$$

and, upon differentiation,

$$\bar{G}_2 = \tilde{G}_2 + \left(\frac{\partial \Delta}{\partial n_2}\right)_{n_1}. \tag{8.3–6}$$

This is the procedure described below as the "method of molar excesses."

In all the examples above, the derivatives required could be obtained from a plot of the deviation functions (δ, δ', Δ) against n_2 at constant n_1. Other less direct methods are available, some of which are described below; others are listed in Appendix 3.

8.3–2 Method of Intercepts

A method for determination of partial molal properties which is slightly different in principle from those discussed above is the so-called method of intercepts. In this case the value of the property in question, per mole of total

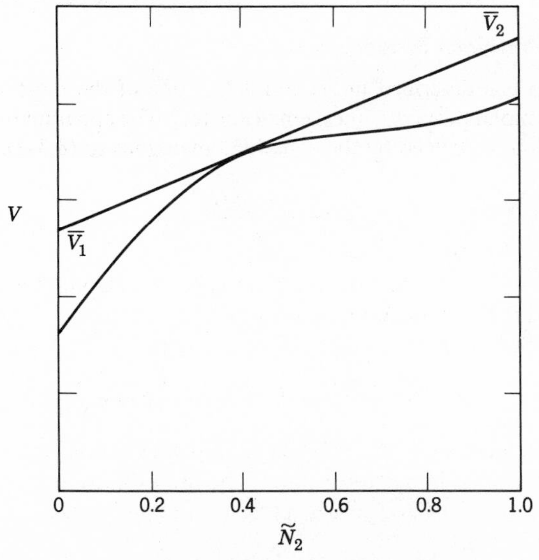

Fig. 8.3–1. Method of intercepts.

solution, is plotted against the mole fraction of one of the components. If a tangent is drawn at any composition, the intercept of this line at $\tilde{N}_1 = 1$ will be $\bar{G}_1$ and at $\tilde{N}_2 = 1$ will be $\bar{G}_2$. Such a plot is shown in Fig. 8.3–1, for the case of volume, where the intercepts are $\bar{V}_1$ and $\bar{V}_2$ respectively.[4]

[4] G. N. Lewis and M. Randall, *Thermodynamics*, McGraw-Hill, New York, 1923, p. 38.

Problem 8.3-3. Prove that when the quantity $G/(n_1 + n_2)$, hereafter abbreviated g', is plotted against $\tilde{N}_2$, the intercept at $\tilde{N}_2 = 0$ is indeed $\bar{G}_1$. You may proceed as follows:

(a) The slope of the curve is $dg'/d\tilde{N}_2$. Show that the value of the intercept is obtained by subtracting $\tilde{N}_2(dg'/d\tilde{N}_2)$ from g'.

(b) Evaluate $dg'/d\tilde{N}_2$. Observe that $dg'/d\tilde{N}_2 = (\partial g'/\partial n_2)_{n_1}/(\partial \tilde{N}_2/\partial n_2)_{n_1}$.

(c) Perform the subtraction indicated in part (a) and simplify the result.

By an exactly analogous procedure, partial specific properties will be obtained if the value of the property per gram of solution is plotted against the weight fraction of one component. These may be converted to the corresponding partial molal quantities upon multiplication by the appropriate molecular weight. Such a procedure is especially advantageous for a property such as volume, which is more often reported on a weight basis than on a molar basis. The method of intercepts requires only a simple plot and usually is substantially more accurate than the simplest method described above. Its accuracy is still severely limited by the precision with which tangents may be drawn.

Problem 8.3-4. Prove that the specific quantity and the weight fraction may be substituted in the method of intercepts to yield partial specific quantities which may be multiplied by the appropriate molecular weights to give the partial molal quantities.

8.3–3 Apparent Molal Properties

Of the functions described in Section 8.3–1, one of the most widely used is the "apparent molal property" mentioned above. The apparent molal property[5] (ϕ_2) of the solute is defined by the equation, analogous to (8.3–3),

$$\phi_2 = \frac{G - n_1\tilde{G}_1}{n_2}, \qquad (8.3\text{–}7)$$

where $\tilde{G}_1$ is the molal property for pure solvent.[6] Upon substitution of ϕ_2 for δ' and $n_1\tilde{G}_1$ for f' in equation (8.3–4),

$$\bar{G}_2 = \phi_2 + n_2\left(\frac{\partial \phi_2}{\partial n_2}\right)_{n_1} = \phi_2 + \left(\frac{\partial \phi_2}{\partial \ln n_2}\right)_{n_1}, \qquad (8.3\text{–}8)$$

with a similar expression for $\bar{G}_1$. $(\partial\phi_2/\partial n_2)_{n_i}$ or $[\partial\phi_2/(\partial \ln n_2)]_{n_1}$ may be determined by the methods given in Section 8.3–1. The use of apparent molal properties is especially convenient for nearly perfect solutions[6] where $\bar{G}_1 \approx \tilde{G}_1$. It is

[5] Apparent molal properties may be determined for a great variety of extensive properties. Where confusion might result, the symbol ϕ can be given a suitable subscript to denote the property being considered.

[6] The perfect solution is defined in Section 11.2, where its properties are fully discussed. As shown there, the partial molal volumes (and some other properties) of a component of a perfect solution are the same as the corresponding molal properties of the pure component. In such cases, the apparent molal property is also equal to the partial molal property, as will be seen by use of equation (8.2–10) in equation (8.3–7), with $\bar{G}_1 = \tilde{G}_1$.

of interest to note that any convenient constant could be substituted for $\tilde{G}_1$ in equation (8.3–7) without altering the validity of equation (8.3–8), (or if $\bar{G}_1$ is required, for $\tilde{G}_2$). Thus, in the case of limited solubility, the method could still be used to obtain the partial molal volume of the solvent by substitution of an arbitrary number for $\tilde{G}_2$.

Problem 8.3-5. Prove equation (8.3–8), and show that its validity is unaltered i any arbitrary constant c is used in place of $\tilde{G}_1$ in equation (8.3–7).

A number of interesting methods for the use of apparent molal properties are given by Young and Vogel[1] and summarized in the tables of Appendix 3. In particular, the apparent molal property ϕ_2 may be plotted against the mole fraction of solvent, $\tilde{N}_1$. The slope is $d\phi_2/d\tilde{N}_1$, and the partial molal quantity $\bar{G}_1$ is given by

$$\bar{G}_1 = \tilde{G}_1 + \tilde{N}_2{}^2\left(\frac{d\phi_2}{d\tilde{N}_1}\right). \tag{8.3–9}$$

Problem 8.3-6. Prove equation (8.3–9). (*Hint.* The mole fraction of component 1 in the solution may be varied, among other ways, by changing n_1 with n_2 fixed. $d\phi_2$ and $d\tilde{N}_1$ may then be obtained by differentiation. Note that $\bar{G}_2 = (\partial G/\partial n_2)_{n_1}$. See also Young and Vogel.[1])

Problem 8.3-7. Prove that

$$\bar{G}_1 = \tilde{G}_1 + \left(\frac{d\phi_2}{dr_1}\right), \tag{8.3–10}$$

where $r_1 = n_1/n_2$, so that the partial molal properties may be obtained from a plot of ϕ_2 against r. (*Hint.* This relationship may be proved in the same fashion as equation (8.3–9).)

8.3–4 Use of Partial Specific Properties

It was pointed out in Section 8.2 and again in the discussion of the method of intercepts that partial specific properties follow the same rules as partial molal properties, except for the use of mass instead of the number of moles. Their use is illustrated in the problems below.

Problem 8.3-8. The specific gravities of aqueous copper sulfate solutions at 18°C are given in Table 8.3–2. Calculate the partial molal volumes of $CuSO_4$ and water in solutions containing 8, 10, and 12 weight per cent $CuSO_4$. The specific volume of water at 18°C is 1.0014 cm^3/g. Determine the partial specific volume of water by the method of intercepts. From it obtain the partial specific volume of solute and thereafter the corresponding partial molal volumes. Since $\bar{V}_2$ is small in this case, the accuracy of its determination will not be very great.

Problem 8.3-9. In transference measurements it is necessary to know the increase of volume which occurs in an electrode chamber during electrolysis. In a given experiment the anode chamber contains originally 30 g of water and 0.03600 equivalents of $CuSO_4$. During the passage of current, an additional 0.00400 equivalent of copper ion is gained because that much more copper is dissolved from the electrode by passage of current than is transferred out of the electrode chamber (the necessary SO_4^{2-} ion is supplied from another part of the cell). (*Note.* In the process described, a small amount of water is transported by the hydrated ions; this may be neglected here.)

(a) Calculate the volume change in the electrode chamber from the densities given in Problem 8.3–8 for the electrolyte alone.

(b) Repeat the calculation by use of the partial molal or partial specific properties determined in Problem 8.3–8, interpolating where necessary.

Table 8.3-2

Specific Gravity of Copper Sulfate Solutions at 18°C

Weight Per Cent $CuSO_4$	Specific Gravity	Weight Per Cent $CuSO_4$	Specific Gravity
0.	1.0000	8.950	1.0923
1.279	1.0126	10.23	1.1063
2.557	1.0254	11.51	1.1208
3.836	1.0384	12.79	1.1354
5.114	1.0516	14.06	1.1501
6.393	1.0649	14.70	1.1585
7.671	1.0785		

8.3–5 Method of Molar Excesses

The method of molar excesses was first proposed by Sosnick[7] as especially applicable to nearly ideal solutions (i.e., solutions where $\bar{G}_i \approx \tilde{G}_i$). If one writes

$$G = n_1\tilde{G}_1 + n_2\tilde{G}_2 + \Delta, \tag{8.3–5}$$

then

$$\bar{G}_2 = \tilde{G}_2 + \left(\frac{\partial \Delta}{\partial n_2}\right)_{n_1} \tag{8.3–6}$$

and

$$\bar{G}_1 = \tilde{G}_1 + \left(\frac{\partial \Delta}{\partial n_1}\right)_{n_2}. \tag{8.3–11}$$

Since Δ is an extensive property, the derivatives of equations (8.3–6) and (8.3–11) may be evaluated by any method suitable for determination of $\bar{G}$, such as the direct method or the method of intercepts. Young and Vogel[1] list a variety of graphical methods using the function Δ (see Appendix 3). Sosnick[7] describes the use of an analytical function for Δ together with a deviation plot, for further improvement in accuracy. The function Δ is, of course, the change in the specified property which occurs when the solution is compounded from the pure components. In specific cases it is known as the "heat of mixing,"

[7] B. Sosnick, *J. Am. Chem. Soc.*, **49**, 2255 (1927).

"volume change of mixing," etc; these quantities are discussed more fully in Chapter 11. It is frequently possible to design an experiment wherein Δ is determined directly. In the problems below it must be obtained by use of equation (8.3–5).

Problem 8.3-10. Table 8.3–3 gives the specific volumes at 25°C of mixtures of BrF_3 and BrF_5 as calculated from the data of Stein, Vogel, and Ludewig.[8] From these obtain the "excess volumes," Δv, for use in equations like (8.3–6) and (8.3–11). Calculate $\bar{V}_1$ and $\bar{V}_2$ at 20, 50, and 80 mole per cent BrF_5. (Note that it is convenient to calculate first the partial specific volumes, for which purpose the concentrations must be expressed as weight per cent. The method of intercepts may be used to obtain the partial derivatives.)

Table 8.3–3
Specific Volume of BrF_3, BrF_5 Mixtures at 25°C

Mole Fraction of BrF_5	Specific Volume (ml/g)	Mole Fraction of BrF_5	Specific Volume (ml/g)
0.0000	0.35676	0.5685	0.38476
0.1009	0.36172	0.6711	0.38989
0.1610	0.36472	0.6965	0.39123
0.3074	0.37184	0.7220	0.39223
0.3868	0.37588	0.8472	0.39837
0.4532	0.37895	0.8691	0.39960
0.4618	0.37928	1.0000	0.40644

Problem 8.3-11. Stein, Vogel, and Ludewig[8] described their density measurements by the equation $d = f(\tilde{N}_2) = 2.8030 - 0.3884\tilde{N}_2 + 0.0641\tilde{N}_2^2 - 0.0183\tilde{N}_2^3$, where $\tilde{N}_2$ is the mole fraction of BrF_5. They gave the equation

$$\bar{V}_2 = \frac{\tilde{M}}{f} - \frac{\tilde{N}_1(\tilde{N}_1\tilde{M}_1 + \tilde{N}_2\tilde{M}_2)}{f^2}\left(\frac{df}{d\tilde{N}_2}\right).$$

Using this equation, calculate $\bar{V}_2$ at the same compositions as in Problem 8.3–10; compare the results of the two methods.

Problem 8.3-12. Derive the relationship for $\bar{V}_2$ given in Problem 8.3–11.

8.3–6 Calculation of Partial Molal Properties of One Component from Those of the Other

In some applications it will be found that partial molal quantities can be determined conveniently for only one of the components. In such cases the second may be determined by use of equation (8.2–10) but frequently may be calculated with greater accuracy by using (8.2–12). For a binary solution the

[8] L. Stein, R. C. Vogel, and W. H. Ludewig, *J. Am. Chem. Soc.*, **76**, 4287 (1954).

latter equation becomes, after division by the total number of moles,

$$\tilde{N}_1\, d\bar{G}_1 = -\tilde{N}_2\, d\bar{G}_2 \qquad (8.3\text{–}12)$$

or

$$d\bar{G}_1 = -\frac{\tilde{N}_2}{\tilde{N}_1}\, d\bar{G}_2\,, \qquad (8.3\text{–}13)$$

which may be integrated to

$$\bar{G}_1'' - \bar{G}_1' = -\int_{\bar{G}_2'}^{\bar{G}_2''} \frac{\tilde{N}_2}{\tilde{N}_1}\, d\bar{G}_2\,. \qquad (8.3\text{–}14)$$

The equations above may also be used to check independent calculations of $\bar{G}_1$ and $\bar{G}_2$. If equation (8.3–13) is divided by $d\tilde{N}_1$, the result is

$$\frac{d\bar{G}_1}{d\tilde{N}_1} = -\frac{\tilde{N}_2}{\tilde{N}_1}\frac{d\bar{G}_2}{d\tilde{N}_1}\,. \qquad (8.3\text{–}15)$$

This relationship between the slopes of a $\bar{G}_1$ vs. $\tilde{N}_1$ plot and those of a $\bar{G}_2$ vs. $\tilde{N}_1$ plot must be satisfied at all concentrations of a binary solution.

Problem 8.3-13. The densities of aqueous solutions of ethyl alcohol and water have been the subject of extensive and precise investigations, for obvious reasons. Table 8.3–4 gives some typical data at 20°C.

(a) By means of the method of intercepts, calculate the partial specific volume and the partial molal volumes of water and alcohol at 10, 20, 40, 60, and 80 mole per cent alcohol.

(b) By means of suitable graphs, show that the partial molal volumes follow equation (8.3–15) in the 40 mole per cent solution.

Table 8.3–4
Density of Ethyl Alcohol Solutions at 20°C

Alcohol (wt. %)	Density (g/ml)	Alcohol (wt. %)	Density (g/ml)	Alcohol (wt. %)	Density (g/ml)
0	0.99823	35	0.94494	70	0.86766
5	0.98938	40	0.93518	75	0.85567
10	0.98187	45	0.92472	80	0.84344
15	0.97514	50	0.91384	85	0.83095
20	0.96864	55	0.90258	90	0.81797
25	0.96168	60	0.89113	95	0.80424
30	0.95382	65	0.87948	100	0.78934

8.4 Relative Partial Molal Quantities

The applications of partial molal quantities up to this point have been made for properties, such as volume and heat capacity, which can be specified absolutely. This cannot be done for some of the thermodynamic properties, notably the enthalpy and free energy. Instead, these may be specified with respect to some chosen reference state. The use of *standard states* will be considered in detail in Chapter 10; for the present it will be sufficient to choose as reference state the infinitely dilute solution at the same temperature.

A *relative partial molal property* may then be defined as *the difference between the partial molal property in a given solution and its value in the reference state.* For the enthalpy this quantity is given the special symbol $\bar{L}$, so that for the ith component

$$\bar{L}_i \equiv \bar{H}_i - \bar{H}_i^\circ, \tag{8.4–1}$$

where $\bar{H}_i$ is the partial molal enthalpy at some specified concentration, and $\bar{H}_i^\circ$ the partial molal enthalpy in the reference state (infinite dilution). These relative quantities can be determined experimentally, whether or not the corresponding absolute quantity can be.

If relative partial molal quantities are used, the enthalpy change of a chemical reaction such as that of equation (8.1–1),

$$\text{HCl}\,(0.096\,m) + \text{NH}_3\,(0.107\,m) = \text{NH}_4\text{Cl}\,(0.015\,m), \tag{8.1–1}$$

may be expressed in terms of measurable quantities. From equation (8.2–4), the change in enthalpy per mole is

$$\Delta H = \bar{H}_{\text{NH}_4\text{Cl}} - \bar{H}_{\text{HCl}} - \bar{H}_{\text{NH}_3}. \tag{8.4–2}$$

The terms on the right may then be replaced by use of (8.4–1) to give

$$\begin{aligned}\Delta H &= \bar{L}_{\text{NH}_4\text{Cl}} - \bar{L}_{\text{HCl}} - \bar{L}_{\text{NH}_3} + \bar{H}^\circ_{\text{NH}_4\text{Cl}} - \bar{H}^\circ_{\text{HCl}} - \bar{H}^\circ_{\text{NH}_3}\\ &= \Delta L + \Delta H^\circ.\end{aligned} \tag{8.4–3}$$

The heat of reaction for a given set of solutions is thus the difference in relative partial molal enthalpies plus the constant term, ΔH°, which is the heat of reaction obtained when each substance is in its standard state. Conversely, equation (8.4–3) indicates that the change in relative partial molal enthalpy may be determined by measurements of heat of reaction at various concentrations.

Relative partial molal enthalpies of individual substances may be obtained from measurements of *heats of dilution.* The dilution of an aqueous solution containing a mole of a substance A may be written

$$\text{A} \cdot n\text{H}_2\text{O} + n'\text{H}_2\text{O} = \text{A} \cdot n''\text{H}_2\text{O}, \tag{8.4–4}$$

where $n'' = n + n'$. The enthalpy of each solution contains contributions from both solute and solvent, and the heat of dilution is

$$\Delta H = \bar{H}_2'' + n''\bar{H}_1'' - (\bar{H}_2 + n\bar{H}_1) - n'\bar{H}_1^\circ. \tag{8.4–5}$$

The terms on the right side of (8.4–5) are obtained by application of

(8.2–10) to each solution in turn. In equation (8.4–5) the subscripts 1 and 2 refer to solvent and solute respectively, the unprimed terms refer to the original solution, and the doubly primed terms to the final solution. The standard state is pure water for the solvent and the infinitely dilute solution for the solute. Upon replacement of the enthalpies, using equation (8.4–1),

$$\Delta H = \bar{L}_2'' + \bar{H}_2^\circ + n''\bar{L}_1'' + n''\bar{H}_1^\circ - (\bar{L}_2 + \bar{H}_2^\circ + n\bar{L}_1 + n\bar{H}_1^\circ) - n'\bar{H}_1^\circ. \tag{8.4–6}$$

The terms corresponding to the standard states cancel, so that

$$\Delta H = \bar{L}_2'' - \bar{L}_2 + n''\bar{L}_1'' - n\bar{L}_1. \tag{8.4–7}$$

Equation (8.4–7) may be further simplified if the amount of solvent added is so large that the final solution is infinitely dilute. Then the products are in their standard states, so that $\bar{L}_2''$ and $\bar{L}_1''$ are both zero, by equation (8.4–1). The heat of infinite dilution per mole of solute, $\Delta\tilde{H}^*$, is then

$$\Delta\tilde{H}^* = -\bar{L}_2 - n\bar{L}_1. \tag{8.4–8}$$

If n_2 moles of solute are used, the procedure above gives for the heat of infinite dilution

$$\Delta H^* = -n_2\bar{L}_2 - n_1\bar{L}_1, \tag{8.4–9}$$

where n has been replaced by n_1, the number of moles of solvent in the original solution. Equation (8.4–9) is of the same form as (8.2–10), so that the relative partial molal quantities are given by

$$\bar{L}_1 = -\left(\frac{\partial \Delta H^*}{\partial n_1}\right)_{n_2}; \qquad \bar{L}_2 = -\left(\frac{\partial \Delta H^*}{\partial n_2}\right)_{n_1}. \tag{8.4–10}$$

They may be obtained from the heat of dilution by the methods of Section 8.3.

The procedure for determination of the relative partial molal quantities is as follows. The heat absorbed (per mole of solute) is obtained for successive dilutions of concentrated solutions to concentrations as low as practical. A particular solution is chosen as a reference, and the heat absorbed when this solution is diluted to each of the lower concentrations is found by summation of the observed heats. The heats of dilution thus obtained are plotted against a suitable function of concentration, and the heat of infinite dilution of the reference solution obtained by extrapolation. The heats of infinite dilution (per mole of solute) for each of the other solutions are then obtained by difference. The relative partial molal enthalpy of the solvent may then be obtained from the slope of a graph in which the heats of infinite solution are plotted against the moles of solvent present, or by one of the other methods of Section 8.3. The relative partial molal enthalpy of solute may then be obtained by use of equation (8.4–8). Problem 8.4–1 illustrates the procedure.

Problem 8.4-1. Table 8.4–1 gives the heat absorbed when a mole of NaCl in aqueous solution is diluted from the initial to the final concentration listed.

(a) Obtain the heat absorbed per mole of NaCl when a 0.1 molar solution is diluted to each of the lower concentrations. (*Note.* Below 0.01 molar the heat effect is not altered appreciably by changes of concentration less than several per cent, so the various concentrations differing by only 1 or 2% may be considered equivalent.)

(b) Plot the heat quantities obtained in part (a) against the square root of the concentration and obtain the heat absorbed when the 0.1 molar solution is made infinitely dilute. With the aid of this value, obtain the heat of infinite dilution of each of the other solutions.

(c) Calculate the relative partial molal enthalpies of water and NaCl at 0.05, 0.0125, and 0.005 molar solutions from a plot of the heats of infinite dilution against the moles of solvent per mole of solute, or by other methods. The densities of the solutions may be taken as unity.

Table 8.4–1

Heat of Dilution of NaCl at 25°C†

Initial Concentration (moles/liter)	Final Concentration (moles/liter)	Heat of Dilution (cal/mole NaCl)
0.1	0.00308	−61.5
0.1	0.00605	−52.9
0.05	0.00154	−54.9
0.05	0.00302	−48.7
0.025	0.000770	−45.6
0.025	0.001515	−39.9
0.0125	0.000385	−33.1
0.0125	0.000754	−30.5

† From A. L. Robinson, *J. Am. Chem. Soc.*, **54,** 1311 (1932).

Problem 8.4-2. Table 8.4–2 gives the relative partial molal enthalpy of sucrose and water at various concentrations at 20°C. Calculate the heat absorbed when a 5 molal sucrose solution is diluted to 3 molal with pure water.

The *relative partial molal free energy* is seldom tabulated, being more frequently expressed in terms of the *activity* (see Section 6.22). Calculation and use of the activity function are discussed in Chapter 11. The *partial molal heat capacity*, although it can be evaluated absolutely, is frequently tabulated as the relative quantity. It may, of course, be obtained from the relative partial enthalpy by differentiation, since

$$\tilde{C}_P - \tilde{C}_P^{\circ} = \left(\frac{\partial \bar{L}}{\partial T}\right)_P. \qquad (8.4\text{–}11)$$

The relative partial molal heat capacity is frequently denoted by the symbol J.

Table 8.4–2

Relative Partial Molal Enthalpies of Aqueous Sucrose Solutions at 20°C†

Molality	Relative Partial Molal Enthalpy of Sucrose $\bar{L}_2$	Partial Molal Enthalpy of Water $\bar{L}_1$
0.1	25.6	−0.02
0.2	50.7	−0.10
0.5	123.7	−0.56
1.0	237.0	−2.82
2.0	432.6	−13.29
3.0	586.6	−44.3
4.0	699.2	−69.3
5.0	787.1	−120.3

† Calculated from the equations given by F. T. Gucker, Jr., H. B. Pickard, and R. W. Planck, *J. Am. Chem. Soc.*, **61**, 459 (1939).

8.5 Uses of Partial Molal Properties

The use of partial molal properties in the calculation of the properties of a solution is apparent in equation (8.2–10) and was illustrated for volumes in Problem 8.2–1. Their use for calculation of the property change associated with a chemical reaction was described in Section 8.2 and again for the special case of relative partial molal properties in Section 8.4. It should be evident that for any process involving solutions the partial molal quantity may (and must) be substituted for ordinary molal quantities. As illustrated in previous sections, a reaction must always be so written as to represent properly all processes occurring.

In addition to their use in connection with chemical reactions, partial molal properties can be utilized to calculate the change in a property which occurs when a solution is diluted, or two solutions are mixed. In the first case, an equation of the same form as (8.4–5) may be written for the change upon dilution of any extensive property, with suitable extension to the case where the number of moles of solute is not unity. The situation is only slightly different if two solutions are mixed to form a third. Let a process be represented by

$$A \cdot nH_2O + A \cdot n'H_2O = 2A \cdot n''H_2O. \tag{8.5–1}$$

The corresponding change in the property, G, is then

$$\Delta G = 2\bar{G}_2'' + n''\bar{G}_1'' - (\bar{G}_2 + n\bar{G}_1) - (\bar{G}_2' + n\bar{G}_1'), \tag{8.5–2}$$

with the same notation as in (8.4–5). Equation (8.5–2) is unaltered if relative partial molal quantities are used and can readily be extended to solutions with any number of moles of solute.

The problems below illustrate several applications of partial molal quantities.

Problem 8.5-1. Table 8.5–1 gives the partial molal volumes of mixtures of BrF_3 and BrF_5 from the data of Stein, Vogel, and Ludewig.[8] Use the partial molal volumes to calculate the volume of a solution containing 2 moles of BrF_3 and 3 moles of BrF_5 and compare with a value obtained by use of the specific volumes in Table 8.3–3.

Table 8.5–1

Partial Molal Volumes of BrF_3 and BrF_5 at 25°C

Mole Fraction of BrF_5	$\bar{V}_{BrF_3}$	$\bar{V}_{BrF_5}$
0.0	48.85	69.17
0.1	48.83	69.50
0.2	48.78	69.80
0.3	48.69	70.07
0.4	48.56	70.31
0.5	48.38	70.53
0.6	48.15	70.72
0.7	47.86	70.87
0.8	47.50	70.99
0.9	47.07	71.07
1.0	46.54	71.09

Problem 8.5-2. Use the data of Table 8.5–1 to calculate the volume change which occurs when a solution containing 2 moles each of BrF_3 and BrF_5 is mixed at 25°C with a mole of pure BrF_3.

Problem 8.5-3. One hundred grams of an ethanol-water solution containing 20 mole per cent ethanol is mixed at 20°C with 100 g of a solution containing 60 mole per cent of ethanol in water.

(a) Calculate the composition of the final solution obtained, and write a reaction to represent the process.

(b) Utilize the data of Table 8.2–1 to calculate the volume change in the process. The result of (b) may be checked by use of the density data of Table 8.3–4, if desired.

A word of caution is required at this point about the physical interpretation of partial molal quantities. Except for ideal solutions, a property such as the volume may depend in a rather complicated way on the composition and the properties of the components. Thus the addition of a mole of one component to a large amount of solution does not cause merely an increase of volume. Molecular interactions within the solution involving an indeterminate number of molecules of both components may be altered. The use of partial molal properties to represent this increase is a helpful mathematical artifice, but except for nearly ideal solutions one may assume no simple connection between the molal property of a pure substance and its partial molal property in solution.

8.6 Derivatives of Partial Molal Quantities

The dependence of partial molal quantities upon temperature and pressure may readily be seen by differentiation. If a partial molal quantity $\bar{G}_1$ is differentiated with respect to temperature,

$$\left(\frac{\partial \bar{G}_1}{\partial T}\right) = \left(\frac{\partial}{\partial T}\right)_{n_1,n_2,\cdots,P}\left(\frac{\partial G}{\partial n_1}\right)_{n_2,\cdots,P,T} = \left(\frac{\partial}{\partial n_1}\right)_{n_2,\cdots,P,T}\left(\frac{\partial G}{\partial T}\right)_{n_1,n_2,\cdots,P,} \tag{8.6–1}$$

since the order of partial differentiation is immaterial. The partial molal enthalpy may be considered as a specific example. Then

$$\begin{aligned}\left(\frac{\partial}{\partial T}\right)_{n_1,n_2,\cdots,P}\left(\frac{\partial H}{\partial n_1}\right)_{n_2,\cdots,P,T} &= \left(\frac{\partial}{\partial n_1}\right)_{n_2,\cdots,P,T}\left(\frac{\partial H}{\partial T}\right)_{n_1,n_2,\cdots,P} \\ \left(\frac{\partial \bar{H}_1}{\partial T}\right)_{n_1,n_2,\cdots,P} &= \left(\frac{\partial C_P}{\partial n_1}\right)_{n_2,\cdots P,T} = \bar{C}_{P_1}\end{aligned} \tag{8.6–2}$$

since $(\partial H/\partial T)_P = C_P$.

Thus the temperature derivative of a partial molal quantity $\bar{G}$ is the partial molal quantity corresponding to $(\partial G/\partial T)$, and similarly for the pressure derivative. These derivatives may then be written directly by insertion of the partial molal notation into the corresponding derivatives for molal quantities.

Problem 8.6-1. Gucker, Pickard, and Planck[9] give for the partial molal heat capacities of aqueous sucrose solution

$$\bar{C}_{P_2} = 151.50 + 2.260\, m - 0.1398\, m^2,$$

$$\bar{C}_{P_1}{}^{\circ} - \bar{C}_{P_1} = 0.018016(1.130\, m^2 - 0.0932\, m^3).$$

(a) Calculate the heat capacity of a solution containing 1 mole of sucrose dissolved in 200 g of water. You may take the specific heat of pure water as 0.9977 cal deg^{-1}.

(b) The relative partial molal enthalpy of sucrose, in the solution of part (a) at 20°, may be taken from Table 8.4–2. Assuming that the relative partial heat capacity of the sucrose is constant between 20° and 30°C, calculate the relative partial molal enthalpy of sucrose in this solution at 30°C. The value calculated from the equations of Gucker et al.[9] is 871 cal mole^{-1}.

[9] F. T. Gucker, Jr., H. B. Pickard, and R. W. Planck, *J. Am. Chem. Soc.*, **61**, 459 (1939).

Generalized Thermodynamics

(The Methods of J. Willard Gibbs, Part I)

CHAPTER 9

9.1 Introduction. Definitions and Fundamental Relations

A number of relationships between the several thermodynamic properties have been derived in previous chapters, notably in Chapter 6, by various means. All the essential relationships may be obtained directly from the fundamental thermodynamic equation developed by Gibbs for so-called *open systems*, to be discussed below. In fact, Gibbs so developed most of the important thermodynamic relationships, but he did so in an abstract form which has often hampered the utilization of his methods. This chapter will examine the methods of Gibbs; it will, in addition, complete the development of the *phase rule*, whose application to one-component systems was discussed in Chapter 7. The notation used will be that employed previously in this book, which is generally different from that employed by Gibbs.

In Chapter 6 an important equation for the infinitesimal energy change during a reversible chemical process occurring in an electrical cell was deduced from the second law; namely,

$$dE = T\,dS - \Sigma P_i\,dV_i + \Sigma \mu_i\,dn_i. \qquad (6.20\text{–}6)$$

If the balancing pressures on the several products and reactants are all equal, the equation becomes

$$dE = T\,dS - P\,dV + \Sigma\mu_i\,dn_i. \tag{9.1–1}$$

This equation is, formally, the fundamental equation of Gibbs, but at this point its meaning is somewhat different. As it stands, it refers to matter appearing and being consumed in the most general chemical process,

$$aA + bB = lL + mM,$$

which, when written to be mathematically consistent with (9.1–1) for the infinitesimal process, becomes

$$\Sigma\tilde{A}_i\,dn_i = 0. \tag{9.1–2}$$

In (9.1–2) $\tilde{A}_i$ stands for the gram molecular weight of each of the chemicals and dn_i for the number of moles of each of the substances (dn_i is negative for each of the reactants). Gibbs,[1] however, referred merely to entry of masses of chemicals into the system. Gibbs therefore wrote equation (9.1–1) without reference to a cell. His reasoning amounted to the following but was more abstract. In a process involving a fixed quantity of matter, which can be made reversible without application of any forces other than the pressure on the system (regarded as constant throughout), the change in energy is given by

$$dE = T\,dS - P\,dV. \tag{6.8–1}$$

In the systems considered previously, energy, but not matter, could be transferred from system to surroundings. Such systems are called *closed systems*. In an *open* system matter may enter or leave the system. If matter can enter the system, the relationship cannot hold. However, if there are one or more new applied *potentials* (the term is due to Gibbs) which can make the process described by equation (9.1–2) reversible, an equation similar to (6.17–1) can be applied. The energy change is now clearly a function of the number of moles of substance, quite apart from its dependence on S and V. The independent variables are thus S, V, and the number of the moles (i.e., all the quantities n_i). To make (6.8–1) applicable an extra term is thus required which can be taken to represent work done reversibly against these potentials so that the equation becomes

$$dE = T\,dS - P\,dV + \sum_i M_i\,dn_i, \tag{9.1–3}$$

[1] *The Collected Works of J. Willard Gibbs*, Vol. 1, Longmans, Green, New York, 1928, p. 63, eq. 38.

where the quantities M_i are given by

$$M_i = \left(\frac{\partial E}{\partial n_i}\right)_{S,V} \tag{9.1–3a}$$

The first term on the right side of equation (9.1–3) represents heat drawn from the thermostat; the second, work done on pistons; and the third, entry of energy carried by the entering chemical species. The last is regarded by Gibbs as a hypothetical type of work done on the system in addition to that done by pistons against mechanical forces. The difficulty of understanding this concept has undoubtedly made developments from it difficult to understand.

Gibbs's idea becomes much more concrete if two or more of his *open systems* are so connected that the total mass leaving one group of systems is equal to that entering the other group; the assembly is thus a closed system. We shall now consider the application of equation (9.1–3) to such a system. Clearly, if the system is reversible, without the application of an opposing electromotive force, the potentials on the system must be such that the last term on the right side of equation (9.1–3) is zero; that is,

$$\sum_i M_i \, dn_i = 0, \tag{9.1–4}$$

since equation (9.1–3) must reduce to equation (6.8–1). A special case of a process occurring in a closed system at equilibrium is the transfer of a chemical substance from one phase to another where there is equilibrium between the phases. In this case, since the amount leaving one phase must equal that entering the other for each chemical species, the chemical process corresponding to equation (9.1–2) is

$$\tilde{A}_i'' \, dn_i'' + \tilde{A}_i' \, dn_i' = 0 \tag{9.1–2a}$$

or

$$\tilde{A}_i'' \, dn_i'' = -\tilde{A}_i' \, dn_i', \tag{9.1–2b}$$

where $\tilde{A}_i''$ denotes one gram molecular weight of the chemical added to one phase, and $\tilde{A}_i'$ denotes one mole of the same chemical added to the other phase. Similarly, equation (9.1–4) becomes

$$M_i'' \, dn_i'' + M_i' \, dn_i' = 0, \tag{9.1–4a}$$

where the primes and double primes denote each of the two phases. Thus

$$M_i'' = M_i'. \tag{9.1–4b}$$

This is obviously equivalent to stating that the partial molal free energies (chemical potentials) are equal in the two phases. This principle was used in Chapter 7 in discussing equilibria between two phases of a pure substance. In that case the partial molal free energies were equal to the molal ones.

Comparing (9.1–3), applied to a closed system, with (9.1–1), it is seen that M_i is identical with μ_i with perfect generality, since, when the system is closed, $-\Sigma_i M_i \, dn_i$ equals the electrical work. If the process described by equation (9.1–2) is reversible without application of these potentials, equation (9.1–4) may be written

$$\sum \mu_i \, dn_i = 0. \tag{9.1–4c}$$

Equation (9.1–1) may now be regarded as applying to an open system and integrated, keeping the pressure and temperature constant as well as the μ_i's. The μ_i's may be kept constant, as discussed in Section 8.2, by adding the various species in the correct ratio. The result of the integration is

$$E = TS - PV + \Sigma \mu_i n_i . \tag{9.1–5}$$

No constant of integration needs to be included. The meaning of a constant of integration can be seen if the equation is integrated between definite limits at constant T, P and constant composition (i.e., constant μ_i). The resulting equation is

$$E - E^* = T^*(S - S^*) - P^*(V - V^*) + \sum \mu_i^*(n_i - n_i^*). \tag{9.1–5a}$$

E^*, V^*, and the n_i^* refer to values of E, V, and the n_i at the start of the process in question. The μ_i's and T and P have been starred to denote that they are the constant values holding throughout the integration. The ratios of the n_i^*'s are, of course, the same as the ratios of the n_i's, since the process is at constant composition. Thus the constant of integration is

$$\text{Constant} = E^* - T^*S^* + P^*V^* - \sum \mu_i^* n_i^* .$$

Clearly, the zeros of the variables may be chosen to make the constant equal to zero. Differentiation of equation (9.1–5) yields, with perfect generality,

$$dE = T\,dS + S\,dT - P\,dV - V\,dP + \Sigma \mu_i \, dn_i + \Sigma n \, d\mu_i .$$

Thus, according to equation (9.1–1),

$$S\,dT - V\,dP + \Sigma n_i \, d\mu_i = 0, \tag{9.1–6}$$

and, for any process at constant temperature and pressure,

$$\Sigma n_i \, d\mu_i = 0. \tag{9.1–7}$$

This equation has been deduced in Chapter 8 for the general partial molal quantity of which μ_i is an example.

Problem 9.1-1. Apply equation (9.1–7) to a solution containing 1 mole of ethyl alcohol and 1 mole of water.

Ans. $d\mu_{H_2O} + d\mu_{C_2H_6O} = 0.$

Problem 9.1-2. (a) Give a relation between the partial molal free energies of sulfuric acid and the SO_4^{2-} and H^+ ions for the process

$$H_2SO_4\ (1\ m) = 2H^+ + SO_4^{2-},$$

where the ions exist in equilibrium amounts.

(b) Apply (9.1–7) to a 1 *m* solution of sulfuric acid in equilibrium with its ions made from 1 mole of sulfuric acid.

Ans. $55.51\ d\mu_{H_2O} + d\mu_{H_2SO_4} = 0.$

Gibbs defined the quantity F as

$$F = E + PV - TS. \tag{9.1–8}$$

Since the pressure is supposed to be the same in all parts of the system, this equation is identical with equation (6.20–10). Differentiating perfectly generally,

$$dF = dE + P\,dV + V\,dP - T\,dS - S\,dT.$$

Substituting for dE from equation (9.1–1),

$$dF = V\,dP - S\,dT + \sum \mu_i\,dn_i. \tag{9.1–9}$$

For a uniform pressure throughout the system this is identical with equation (6.20–12). Regarding F as a function of P, T, and all the n_i, the following partial derivatives can be written at once:

$$\left(\frac{\partial F}{\partial P}\right)_{T,n_i} = V, \tag{9.1–10}$$

$$\left(\frac{\partial F}{\partial T}\right)_{P,n_i} = -S, \tag{9.1–11}$$

and

$$\left(\frac{\partial F}{\partial n_i}\right)_{T,P} = \mu_i. \tag{9.1–12}$$

These equations are identical with (6.20–13), (6.20–14), and (6.20–15).

If equation (9.1–9) is integrated at constant temperature, pressure, and composition (all the μ_i constant), there results the equation

$$F = \Sigma\mu_i n_i + \text{constant}, \tag{9.1–13}$$

where the constant clearly represents the free energy of the system at the start of the process; if this is chosen as zero, the constant may be dropped. For a closed system this equation becomes

$$\Delta F = \Sigma n_i \mu_i, \tag{9.1–13a}$$

where the summation is now taken over the substances present in the closed system and ΔF refers to a chemical reaction. Clearly, if the process in the closed system is reversible without the application of an outside potential (i.e., chemically reversible), $\Sigma \mu_i \, dn_i$ is zero, by equation (9.1–4c), and the integration yields

$$\Delta F = 0$$

for the closed system. If electrical work is obtained from a reversible cell, $\Sigma n_i \mu_i$ is clearly negative in equation (9.1–13a), since this term is equal to $-w_e$, the negative of the electrical work. Thus, for any process to occur at constant temperature and pressure in a closed system with the opposing electromotive force removed, the change in free energy must be negative; that is,

$$\Delta F = \sum n_i \mu_i \leqq 0. \tag{9.1–13b}$$

The equality refers to a process at equilibrium, the inequality to any process that may occur spontaneously at a finite rate. By substitution of equation (6.18–3) into (9.1–13a) one obtains, for a closed system,

$$\Sigma \mu_i n_i = -\mathcal{N} \mathcal{F} \mathcal{E}, \tag{9.1–14}$$

where $\mathcal{N}$ is the number of equivalents of electricity involved in the chemical process, and $\mathcal{F}$ is the Faraday equivalent in the proper units.

Referring to an open system, Gibbs gives the definition of A as

$$A = E - TS, \tag{6.17–5}$$

just as was done in Section 6.17. By differentiating A perfectly generally, one obtains

$$dA = dE - T\,dS - S\,dT.$$

Substituting for dE from equation (9.1–1), there results

$$dA = -P\,dV - S\,dT + \Sigma \mu_i \, dn_i. \tag{9.1–15}$$

Regarding A as a function of $V, T,$ and the several n_i, the following relations are evident.

$$\left(\frac{\partial A}{\partial V}\right)_{T,n_i} = -P, \tag{9.1–16}$$

$$\left(\frac{\partial A}{\partial T}\right)_{V,n_i} = -S, \tag{9.1–17}$$

and

$$\left(\frac{\partial A}{\partial n_i}\right)_{V,T,n_j \neq n_i} = \mu_i. \tag{9.1–18}$$

Gibbs defines H for an open system as

$$H = E + PV.$$

Differentiating,

$$\mathrm{d}H = \mathrm{d}E + P\,\mathrm{d}V + V\,\mathrm{d}P. \tag{9.1–19}$$

Substituting from (9.1–1),

$$\mathrm{d}H = T\,\mathrm{d}S + \sum \mu_i\,\mathrm{d}n_i + V\,\mathrm{d}P; \tag{9.1–20}$$

so that

$$\left(\frac{\partial H}{\partial S}\right)_{P,n_i} = T, \tag{9.1–21}$$

$$\left(\frac{\partial H}{\partial P}\right)_{S,n_i} = V, \tag{9.1–22}$$

and

$$\left(\frac{\partial H}{\partial n_i}\right)_{S,P,n_j \neq n_i} = \mu_i. \tag{9.1–23}$$

Finally, from equation (9.1–1) itself the following relations are evident.

$$\left(\frac{\partial E}{\partial S}\right)_{V,n_i} = T, \tag{9.1–24}$$

$$\left(\frac{\partial E}{\partial V}\right)_{T,n_i} = -P, \tag{9.1–25}$$

and

$$\left(\frac{\partial E}{\partial n_i}\right)_{T,V,n_j \neq n_i} = \mu_i. \tag{9.1–26}$$

Equations (9.1–1), (9.1–9), and (9.1–20) involve the variables S, V, P, T, and as many n_i as there are independently variable substances in the system. Let us call this last number C. These variables are written down because they all appear as differentials in the equations in question. Equation (9.1–6) needs also the quantities μ_i as variables, since the differentials $\mathrm{d}\mu_i$ appear and there are C of them. There are thus in all $2C + 4$ variables that are regarded as independent in one or the other of the equations. Through (9.1–5) these variables can be used to express the value of E. To obtain expressions for H, A, and F the additional variable E is needed. Thus there are $2C + 5$ fundamental quantities. Equations (9.1–24), (9.1–25), and (9.1–26) give $C + 2$ relations among these variables, and equation (9.1–5) gives another, making $C + 3$

relations in all; thus only $C + 2$ of the variables are independent. These can be the variables used in (9.1–1), (9.1–9), (9.1–15), (9.1–20), or (9.1–6), as listed below in that order along with the dependent variable in each case:

$$E,\ S,\ V,\ n_i;$$
$$F,\ P,\ T,\ n_i;$$
$$A,\ V,\ T,\ n_i;$$
$$H,\ S,\ P,\ n_i;$$
and
$$P,\ T,\ \mu_i.$$

The first quantity in each of the first four sets is the dependent variable, and there is an equation giving its value as a function of the others. Differentiation in each case yields an equation involving the $C + 2$ partial derivatives with respect to the independent variables. These partials can then be equated to the other $C + 2$ variables. Equation (9.1–6) needs special attention, since it involves one less variable than the others. It can be expressed in the form

$$\mathrm{d}P = \left(\frac{S}{V}\right)\mathrm{d}T + \Sigma\left(\frac{n_i}{V}\right)\mathrm{d}\mu_i. \tag{9.1–27}$$

The equation has as independent variables T and the C variables, μ_i, making $C + 1$ in all, while P appears as a dependent variable. Such an equation reduces the $C + 2$ independent variables by one, this corresponding to the fact that the quantities (S/V) and (n_i/V), which are the partial derivatives of P with respect to T and the μ_i respectively, are independent of the total volume (S, n, and V are each proportional to the total mass of the system). This is obviously required since P, T, and μ_i are all intensive properties (i.e., do not depend on the total amount of material).

9.2 The Phase Rule

All the equations necessary for discussion of equilibrium between coexisting phases have now been derived. The concept of a phase has been defined in Chapter 7. In Section 7.2 the equilibria between phases of a pure substance have been discussed; the principle derived there can now be extended to the general case of any number of substances. When only one substance is present, there is said to be only one component. Otherwise the number of components is defined as the smallest number of pure substances from which all the phases can be constructed.

Where no chemical reaction can occur which converts a substance or group of substances into other substances, the number of components is simply the number of chemical species in the system; otherwise the number of components may be less than the number of chemical species. For example, a liquid solution of ethylene in ethane existing in equilibrium with a vapor of ethane, ethylene, and hydrogen is a three-component system in the absence of a catalyst. In the presence of platinum black, the reaction

$$C_2H_4 + H_2 = C_2H_6 \tag{9.2–1}$$

can occur reversibly. If a given mixture is required, it can always be obtained by adding ethylene and hydrogen; the required ethane is then produced by the chemical reaction as it attains equilibrium; or ethane may be taken and hydrogen withdrawn (i.e., a negative amount added) while the reaction (9.2–1) occurs under equilibrium conditions. Finally, ethylene and ethane can be added as reaction (9.2–1) comes to equilibrium. Under these circumstances the system has two components only, since any composition possible may be attained by using two of the species.

According to equation (9.1–4b), when a system of C components exists as P phases in equilibrium, any one of the C partial molal free energies $\mu_i, \cdots, \mu_c$ is the same in every phase. Alternatively, for the process of transfer of any component of molecular formula X from any one phase (say phase A) to any other (say phase B), represented by the chemical equation

$$\text{X (in phase A)} = \text{X (in phase B)}, \tag{9.2–2}$$

the free energy change is zero, and thus

$$\Delta F = \mu_x^{\text{B}} - \mu_x^{\text{A}} = 0, \tag{9.2–3}$$

where μ_x^{A} and μ_x^{B} are the partial molal free energy in the two phases respectively. The system of independent variables T, P, and the μ_i is thus the most convenient for the discussion of the possible equilibria which may be established between the phases in which the system may exist. If there is one phase present, one equation, like (9.1–27) or (9.1–7), may be written down and used to reduce the number of variables in the system. The number of variables is then $C + 1$; this means that $C + 1$ of the $C + 2$ quantities may be fixed independently to establish the state of the system. The number of variables, F, which must be assigned values and which alone can be assigned values to define, unequivocally, the state of the system, is called the number of *degrees of freedom*. For a homogeneous one-component system the value of F is thus equal to 2. If there are two phases, two equations like (9.1–27) apply, one to each phase; in this case the number of degrees of freedom is C. Since for every new phase there will be an additional equation like (9.1–27), the number of degrees of freedom is given in general by

$$\mathrm{F} = C + 2 - P \tag{9.2–4a}$$

or

$$P + \mathrm{F} = C + 2. \tag{9.2–4b}$$

This is the celebrated phase rule of Gibbs.

The system ethane, ethylene, and hydrogen has three components in the absence of a catalyst. When there is only one phase (liquid, solid, or vapor), it is seen from equation (9.2–4) that there are four degrees of freedom which can and must be specified to define the state of the system. If P, T, and the μ_i are chosen as the independent variables, only two of the μ_i are needed since the value of the third is given by an equation like (9.1–27). In fact, it is just this equation that reduces the degrees of freedom by one. However, as a rule the variables chosen are the pressure, temperature, and the percentages of two of the components, the third being determined by difference. It is only the percentage composition that determines the intensive properties of the phase, and this is exactly what equation (9.1–27) says. For a liquid mixture in equilibrium with its vapor ($P = 2$) there are three degrees of freedom. These could be the temperature and the percentage of two of the components in the liquid (or vapor, but not both), the percentage of the third component being determined by difference. Or they could be pressure and percentage of two components in the liquid. They could also be the pressure and percentage of one of the components in both phases; the equilibrium conditions themselves then set the ratios between the percentages of the other components in both phases. Five phases is the maximum number that can be present; for example, liquid, vapor, solid ethane, solid ethylene, and solid hydrogen.

If the reaction given in equation (9.2–1) can occur reversibly owing to the presence of a catalyst, the number of components is reduced to two, and only four phases could be present as a maximum; for example, liquid, vapor, and two solid phases (e.g., solid ethane and solid ethylene or solid ethane and solid hydrogen). The reason for this is readily seen; if the variables T, P, and the μ_i are used, one less μ_i can be specified independently, where there is equilibrium in reaction (9.2–1), since the equilibrium conditions then require that

$$\Delta F = \mu_{C_2H_6} - \mu_{C_2H_4} - \mu_{H_2} = 0, \tag{9.2–5}$$

$\mu_{C_2H_6}$ etc., being the partial molal free energies of the components.

Problem 9.2-1. (a) What is the maximum number of phases which can coexist in a system consisting of silver and gold?

(b) If a system of silver and gold is desired in which the vapor pressure and composition of any of the phases is uniquely determined by the temperature, how many phases must be present?

(c) Give examples to illustrate (a) and (b) above.

Problem 9.2-2. The substance N_2O_4 can dissociate into NO_2 according to the reaction

$$N_2O_4 = 2NO_2.$$

(a) How many components are there in a system in which N_2O_4 and NO_2 occur together in CCl_4 (i) if there is equilibrium in the above reaction, (ii) if the reaction is very slow?

(b) How many phases must be present to make the vapor pressure of the system solely a function of the temperature (i) if there is equilibrium between N_2O_4 and NO_2, (ii) if there is not equilibrium?

(c) What is the maximum number of phases which can be present in either case?

(d) Give an example for each of the situations mentioned above.

Problem 9.2-3. (a) Phenol and water form two immiscible phases. Does the temperature uniquely determine the vapor pressure of the system? Explain.

(b) Under what circumstances can ice be present as well as the two liquid phases and the vapor phase? What must happen if the temperature is varied and the two liquid phases are to be retained as well as the ice?

The conditions for chemical and phase equilibrium have previously been considered in terms of the change in free energy which occurs when a definite amount of reaction or phase change occurs without alteration in chosen variables of state. For example, if a mole of water is vaporized under constant pressure and temperature,

$$\Delta F \overline{\leq} 0, \tag{6.18–5}$$

where the equality refers to equilibrium, and the inequality to a spontaneous process. Gibbs considers the effect of a slight displacement from equilibrium conditions of state for a system already at equilibrium. In the case above, it is evident that the change in Gibbs free energy must always be positive. By definition, a system can depart from equilibrium only by a non-spontaneous process, for which (at essentially constant temperature and pressure) the change in free energy must be positive. Thus the equilibrium condition corresponds to a *minimum* in the Gibbs free energy.

By exactly similar arguments it may be shown that the *Helmholtz free energy* (A) is a minimum for a system at equilibrium under essentially constant *temperature* and *volume*. For a system at constant *entropy* and *volume* (isolated systems) the *energy* must be a minimum at equilibrium; for a system at constant *energy* and *volume* the entropy must be a maximum. (These conditions may be proved as in Chapter 6; Gibbs proves them in a somewhat more abstract fashion.)

Gibbs examines also the necessary conditions for *stability* of a given phase. These conditions follow from the statements above concerning the minima in energy, enthalpy, etc., in states of equilibrium under various external conditions. His arguments are rather abstract, and we shall not attempt to describe them in detail here; the reader is referred to Gibbs' work for the proofs.[2] The arguments show that C_P, C_V, and the isothermal compressibility, $-(1/V)(\partial V/\partial P)_{T,n_i}$, of a stable phase must always be greater than zero. For a solution $(\partial\mu_i/\partial n_i)_{n_j,P,T}$ must be positive for stability.

Truly unstable phases, for which these quantities are negative, are completely hypothetical, since they must go over spontaneously to a stable phase (or phases). However, many states are *metastable*. Such states may retain their identity for small changes of the variables of state, but not for large ones, or they may exist only until a suitable initiation process (e.g., nucleation in a supersaturated solution) has taken place. These metastable states obey the conditions above. The process by which they go over to stable states may be taken as an analogy to the behavior of the hypothetical unstable state. For example, liquid may frequently be cooled below its freezing point by removal of heat and is then metastable. Usually there is a point of maximum supercooling, beyond which further attempted cooling will be accompanied by transition to a mixture of liquid and solid at the freezing point. For such a situation it is possible to have a highly irreversible process with a negative value of q accompanied by a positive ΔT. Thus, in a purely formal way, the "heat capacity" is negative at the point of instability.

The condition placed on $(\partial\mu_i/\partial n_i)$ shows that a solution must be unstable (i.e., split into two phases) if the partial molal free energy of any component does not increase as the amount of that component is increased. Thus, if the addition of a component to a mixture fails to increase the vapor pressure of that component above the mixture, this "solution" must contain or split into two distinct phases.

[2] Gibbs, *op. cit.*, Vol. I, pp. 100 ff.

Imperfect Gases. Fugacity and Entropy Diagrams

CHAPTER 10

10.1 Introduction

The treatment of physical changes or of chemical equilibria has been shown earlier to be reasonably simple for perfect gases (see, for example, Problem 6.19–6 and Section 6.22). The corresponding calculations for real gases may become quite involved. Consideration of real gases can be considerably simplified by use of the activity instead of the pressure (see Section 6.22), in which case many of the thermodynamic equations reduce to forms like those used for perfect gases. An alternative approach is the calculation of entropy, enthalpy, and other properties of the real gas over a sufficient range of temperature and pressure to permit construction of an entropy diagram from which the properties of the gas may thereafter be read. Although this alternative is the one usually chosen for physical changes in a pure substance, it is impractically cumbersome for chemical changes. Entropy diagrams are quite valuable to engineers and are discussed in this chapter mainly for that reason.

10.2 Activity of Pure Gases. Fugacity

Application of the equation

$$\left(\frac{\partial F}{\partial P}\right)_T = V \qquad (6.19\text{–}5)$$

to a mole of a perfect gas gives

$$\left(\frac{\partial \tilde{F}}{\partial P}\right)_T = \frac{RT}{P}. \qquad (10.2\text{–}1)^*$$

The difference in free energy accompanying an isothermal change in pressure is obtained by integration of (10.2–1)*; it is

$$\tilde{F}_2 - \tilde{F}_1 = RT \ln \frac{P_2}{P_1}. \qquad (10.2\text{–}2)^*$$

For an imperfect gas a similar equation may be arbitrarily written, at constant temperature,

$$\tilde{F}_2 - \tilde{F}_1 = RT \ln \frac{f_2}{f_1}, \qquad (10.2\text{–}3)$$

where f_1 and f_2 are the *fugacities* of the imperfect gas at P_1 and P_2. Since the change in free energy may always be calculated, by use of equation (6.19–5), equation (10.2–3) serves to define the fugacity ratio f_2/f_1. Comparison with equation (10.2–2)* shows that the fugacity of a perfect gas must be proportional to its pressure; for convenience the two will be set equal to each other. The definition of fugacity for the real gas is then completed by setting the condition that

$$\frac{f}{P} \rightarrow 1 \quad \text{as} \quad P \rightarrow 0, \qquad (10.2\text{–}4)$$

since the real gas approaches the properties of the ideal gas as the pressure approaches zero. This is equivalent to choosing as a standard state the (hypothetical) ideal gas at a pressure of one atmosphere. The matter of standard states in general need not be discussed at this point; it is discussed in detail in Section 11.4.

With the fugacity defined by equations (10.2–3) and (10.2–4), it is possible to replace the statement of the equilibrium constant given in equation (6.23–3) by one of the same form which does not assume the gases to be perfect. For convenience, the reaction previously considered will be used as an example. This is

$$H_2(g) + 2AgCl(s) = 2Ag(s) + 2HCl(g). \qquad (10.2\text{–}5)$$

Comparison of the free energy change in any specified state with that in the standard state of unit fugacity then yields, upon use of (10.2–3), for each of the gases

$$\Delta F - \Delta F^\circ = RT \ln \frac{f_{\mathrm{HCl}}^2}{f_{\mathrm{H_2}}}, \qquad (10.2\text{–}6)$$

where as before any (slight) changes in the fugacities of the solid phases have been neglected. If the specified state is that of chemical equilibrium, $\Delta F = 0$, and

$$\Delta F^\circ = -RT \ln \frac{f_{\mathrm{HCl}}^2}{f_{\mathrm{H}_2}} = -RT \ln K. \tag{10.2–7}$$

Equation (10.2–7) is a general statement of the relationship between ΔF° and K.

Problem 10.2-1. Prove equation (10.2–6) in detail.

In equation (10.2–6) the small changes in free energy of the solid phases with pressure were neglected in comparison with the (usually) much larger changes in free energy of the gases. At high pressures, this may no longer be justifiable. The definition of fugacity given in equation (10.2–3) may be extended to include the free energy and fugacity of condensed phases. In this case it is evident that the fugacity of the condensed phase is the same as that of the vapor with which it is in equilibrium.

Problem 10.2-2 Prove the statement immediately above, noting that the free energies of two phases in equilibrium are identical.

The change in the fugacity of solid or liquid with pressure may then be calculated by combination of equations (10.2–3) and (6.19–5). It is

$$RT \ln \frac{f_2}{f_1} = \int_{P_1}^{P_2} \tilde{V}\, \mathrm{d}P. \tag{10.2–8}$$

If the variation of volume with pressure is known, the integration of equation (10.2–8) may be performed.

Problem 10.2-3. The density of solid silver is 10.5 g/cm³ at 25°C, 1 atm. Neglecting the change of density with pressure, calculate the ratio of the fugacity of silver at 100 atm. to that at 1 atm.

10.3 Calculation of the Fugacity of a Pure Gas

A general relationship among fugacity, free energy, and the variables of state is obtained by combination of equations (10.2–3) and (6.19–5). It is

$$\ln \frac{f_2}{f_1} = \frac{\tilde{F}_2 - \tilde{F}_1}{RT} = \frac{1}{RT} \int_{P_1}^{P_2} \left(\frac{\partial \tilde{F}}{\partial P}\right)_T \mathrm{d}P = \frac{1}{RT} \int_{P_1}^{P_2} \tilde{V}\, \mathrm{d}P. \tag{10.3–1}$$

Equation (10.3–1) states explicitly the manner in which the fugacity of a gas depends on its pressure and molar volume at a given temperature. For its application the dependence of volume upon pressure must be known, either as an equation of state or in the form of tables of data, both of which were discussed in Chapter 4. Upon integration of (10.3–1) between two particular pressures one obtains the ratio of the corresponding fugacities. To get individual fugacities, it is necessary to rearrange the equation in terms of the ratio of fugacity to pressure (f/P) and apply equation (10.2–4), by extrapolation if necessary. A simple example of this procedure is given in Problem 10.3-1.

Problem 10.3-1. Show that, if the equation of state for a gas is $P(\tilde{V} - b) = RT$, where b is a constant, the fugacity of the gas is given by

$$\ln \frac{f}{P} = \frac{bP}{RT}.$$

Hint. Solve the equation of state for $\tilde{V}$, and substitute into (10.3–1). After integration, rearrange to get f_2/P_2 and allow P_1 to go to zero, whereupon $f_1/P_1 \rightarrow 1$. Note that this is a special case of (10.3–5).

It is convenient to incorporate the extrapolation of f/P to zero pressure explicitly into equation (10.3–1); this may be done whether or not the P-V-T data are in the form of an equation of state. The volume may always be written

$$\tilde{V} = \frac{RT}{P} - \alpha, \tag{10.3–2}$$

where α is a function of pressure and temperature. Upon substitution for $\tilde{V}$ from (10.3–2), equation (10.3–1) becomes

$$\ln \frac{f_2}{f_1} = \int_{P_1}^{P_2} \frac{dP}{P} - \frac{1}{RT} \int_{P_1}^{P_2} \alpha \, dP$$

$$= \ln \frac{P_2}{P_1} - \frac{1}{RT} \int_{P_1}^{P_2} \alpha \, dP. \tag{10.3–3}$$

Upon rearrangement of (10.3–3) one obtains

$$\ln \frac{f_2}{P_2} = \ln \frac{f_1}{P_1} - \frac{1}{RT} \int_{P_1}^{P_2} \alpha \, dP. \tag{10.3–4}$$

If P_1 is allowed to approach zero, whereupon f_1/P_1 approaches unity, this equation becomes

$$\ln \frac{f_2}{P_2} = -\frac{1}{RT} \int_{0}^{P_2} \alpha \, dP. \tag{10.3–5}$$

Tne function α, which represents the deviation of the molar volume from that of an ideal gas, may be obtained from an equation of state or directly from P-V-T data. If the latter, the integration must be performed graphically, with the function α extrapolated to zero pressure;

this procedure is facilitated by the fact that at sufficiently low pressures α must approach a constant value.

Problem 10.3-2. Evaluate the function α for the general equation of state $P\tilde{V}/RT = 1 + B'P + C'P^2 + \cdots$, and show that it approaches a constant value as P approaches zero.

The compressibility factor $Z(= P\tilde{V}/RT)$ is, of course, a measure of gas imperfection. It is related to α as follows:

$$Z = \frac{P\tilde{V}}{RT} = 1 - \frac{\alpha P}{RT}, \tag{10.3–6}$$

$$\frac{\alpha}{RT} = \frac{1 - Z}{P}. \tag{10.3–7}$$

Upon use of this expression for α/RT in equation (10.3–5) one obtains an equivalent expression for f/P,

$$\ln \frac{f_2}{P_2} = -\int_0^{P_2} \frac{1}{P}(1 - Z)\,\mathrm{d}P. \tag{10.3–8}$$

Equation (10.3–8) is immediately applicable to data of state given in terms of the compressibility. The ratio $(1 - Z)/P$ always approaches a constant value at low pressures, just as α does.

The calculation of fugacity may be carried out as follows:

1. If the molar volume $\tilde{V}$ or the compressibility factor Z is given explicitly in terms of pressure by an equation of state, (10.3–5) or (10.3–8) may be used to obtain a corresponding equation for f/P as a function of pressure.
2. If the equation of state cannot be solved to give volume or compressibility as a function of pressure, it may be used for computation of the pressures corresponding to a given set of values of $\tilde{V}$ or Z. The integrals of (10.3–5) and (10.3–8) may then be evaluated graphically.
3. If the P-V-T data are given in tabular form, they may be used to compute α or Z for each of the pressures given; equation (10.3–5) or (10.3–8) may then be integrated graphically.

The van der Waals equation is a special case. It may be used to replace $\mathrm{d}P$ in equation (10.3–1). If the resulting equation is integrated and one of the pressures allowed to approach zero as before, the result is

$$\ln f = \ln \frac{RT}{\tilde{V} - \mathrm{b}} + \frac{\mathrm{b}}{\tilde{V} - \mathrm{b}} - \frac{2\mathrm{a}}{RT\tilde{V}} \tag{10.3–9}$$

Problem 10.3-3. Prove equation (10.3–9). Note that it is necessary to start from the equation

$$\Delta F = RT \ln \frac{f}{f'} = \int_{P'}^{P} \tilde{V}\, dP.$$

Solve the van der Waals equation for P and obtain dP(T constant). Substitute this into the equation for fugacity, and perform the integration. Solve the resulting equations for $\ln f/P$. Then, if P' is allowed to approach zero, $f'/P' \to 1$, $1/\tilde{V}' \to 0$, and $P'\tilde{V}' \to RT$.

It is sometimes useful to obtain an estimate of the fugacity of a gas. If the deviations from perfect gas behavior are not large, the fugacity is given approximately by

$$\frac{f}{P} \approx \frac{P}{P_i}, \qquad (10.3\text{–}10)^{**}$$

where P is the pressure of the gas at some molar volume $\tilde{V}$, and P_i is the pressure it would exert if it were ideal ($P_i = RT/\tilde{V}$). Equation (10.3–10)** may be proved as follows. Assume that the pressure is low enough that the *moderate pressure gas equation* (4.4–4) is obeyed.

$$P\tilde{V}(1 - \beta P) = RT. \qquad (4.4\text{–}4)$$

Then the function α is given by

$$\alpha = \frac{-RT\beta}{1 - \beta P}. \qquad (10.3\text{–}11)^{**}$$

Upon substitution of this value of α into (10.3–5), integration, and simplification of the resulting integral by use of (4.4–4), one obtains

$$\frac{f}{P} = \frac{P\tilde{V}}{RT}, \qquad (10.3\text{–}12)^{**}$$

which may be rewritten in the form of (10.3–10)**.

Problem 10.3-4. Prove equation (10.3–10)** in the manner indicated.

A superior method for the estimation of fugacity, especially in regions where data of state are not available, utilizes the law of corresponding states (see Chapter 4). Newton[1] calculated the fugacities of a large number of gases over a wide range of temperature and pressure, using experimental data in equations like (10.3–5) and (10.3–8). The activity coefficients (f/P) were then plotted against reduced temperature (T/T_c) and pressure (P/P_c). A curve derived for the average represented the individual points within a few per cent, at pressures up to ten times the critical pressure. The student is referred to the original publication for details on the preparation and use of these graphs.

[1] R. Newton, *Ind. Eng. Chem.*, **27**, 302 (1935).

A comparison of several methods for calculation or estimation of fugacities is given in Table 10.3–1. The experimental data used were those of Otto, Michels, and Wouters[2] for nitrogen at 25°C. The separate columns give the fugacity at each pressure as calculated or estimated by the method indicated in each case. The entries from experimental data were derived by graphical integration, through equation (10.3–5), and are certainly the most accurate above 75 atm. At 75 atm and below, the values of α obtained from the experimental data are slightly erratic; the "smoothing" effect introduced by use of the series equation probably improves the accuracy of the calculation, since this equation is an excellent representation of the experimental data in this range.

Table 10.3–1

Calculation of Fugacity of Nitrogen Gas at 25°C

Pressure (atm)	From Experimental Data	From Series Equation†	From Van der Waals' Equation‡	From Equation (10.3–10)**	From Newton's Graphs
25	24.95	24.89	24.6	24.94	25.0
50	49.78	49.65	48.4	49.85	50.0
75	74.62	74.30	71.5	74.92	75.0
100	99.55	99.19	94.2	100.4	100.0
125	124.7	124.3	116.8	127.1	125.0
150	150.1	149.6	139.2	153.8	151.0
175	176.0	175.5	161.9	182.0	177.0
200	202.5	202.0	185.1	211.5	203.0
225	229.5	229.3	209.7	242.3	230.0
250	257.4	257.6	235.3	274.2	258.0

† The series equation referred to is the analytical expression $P\tilde{V}/RT = 1 - 2.002 \times 10^{-4} P + 2.422 \times 10^{-6} P^2 + 4.63 \times 10^{-12} P^4$, which is a slightly abbreviated form of the equation used by Otto, Michels, and Wouters[2] in the representation of their data.

‡ The van der Waals constants used are given in Appendix 2.

Problem 10.3-5. Using the van der Waals constants listed in Appendix 2, calculate the fugacity of nitrogen gas at 298°K for molar volumes ($\tilde{V}$) of 5, 1, 0.5, and 0.25 liter. Calculate the pressures and compare the respective values. (See also Table 10.3–1.)

Problem 10.3-6. Values of $P\tilde{V}/RT$ for CO_2 at 40.11°C are given in Table 10.3–2. Calculate the quantity α for each of the pressures given. By graphical integration of

[2] J. Otto, A. Michels, and H. Wouters, *Physik. Z.*, **35**, 97 (1934).

equation (10.3–5) or its equivalent (10.3–8) obtain values of the fugacity at 96.6, 284, 681, and 1553 atm.

Table 10.3–2
Compressibility of Carbon Dioxide at 40.11°C†

P (atm)	$P\tilde{V}/RT$	P (atm)	$P\tilde{V}/RT$
24.08	0.8888	192.0	0.3938
46.04	0.7682	284.0	0.5383
72.7	0.5612	436.7	0.7960
96.58	0.2711	681.1	1.1187
111.9	0.2751	1056.9	1.6249
138.9	0.3111	1533.0	2.2551

† Calculated from the data of A. Michels, *Proc. Roy. Soc.* (*London*), **153A**, 201 (1935).

Problem 10.3-7. At 25°C the P-V-T data for carbon monoxide may be represented approximately by an equation $P\tilde{V}/RT = 1 - 0.00023\ P + 0.000002\ P^2$ (see Problem 4.4–2). This equation represents the data within 1% up to about 200 atm. By use of this equation calculate f/P and f for CO at 200 atm, 25°C.

Problem 10.3-8. Noting that $[\mathrm{d}\ln(f/P)]/\mathrm{d}P = -\alpha/RT$, calculate at 25°C the value of $P\tilde{V}/RT$ for nitrogen gas at 100, 140, 200, 250 atm. Use the data in the second column of the Table 10.3–1. (*Note.* This procedure should always be used as a check on the accuracy of calculation of fugacities.)

10.4 Fugacity in Gaseous Mixtures

In a chemical reaction it seldom happens that only one material is present in the gaseous phase. The fugacities required for use in calculation of chemical equilibria, for example, will usually be those of several different gases present together in a mixture. The necessary calculations for their determination may be made by generalization of the procedures described in Section 10.3. Unfortunately, the data required for this sort of calculation are seldom available; usually some approximate relationship between the properties of the mixture and those of the pure components must be used.

The equations necessary for calculation of the individual fugacities in a gas mixture are obtained by minor adjustments of equations (10.2–3) and (10.2–4). Since two or more components are present, the partial molal free energy of each must be used, as in equation (6.22–3). The fugacity is thus defined by the equation

$$\mu_i = \mu_i^\circ + RT \ln f_i, \tag{10.4–1}$$

where the standard state is chosen to have unit fugacity. The mixture approaches ideal behavior as the total pressure approaches zero, just as for a one-component system. Thus the ratio f_i/P_i approaches unity as the total pressure of the system goes to zero. The partial pressure of a given component is defined as the total pressure times the mole fraction of that component. Consequently equation (10.2–4) becomes

$$\frac{f_i}{P_i}\left(=\frac{f_i}{\tilde{N}_i P}\right) \to 1 \quad \text{as} \quad P \to 0. \tag{10.4–2}$$

The limiting process described by equation (10.4–2) must be carried out at constant composition.

The fugacities of the components in a gas mixture may now be evaluated by procedures similar to those used for pure gases. Denoting the total free energy of the gas mixture by the symbol F;

$$\left(\frac{\partial F}{\partial P}\right)_{n_1,n_2,T} = V;$$

$$\left(\frac{\partial^2 F}{\partial n_1\,\partial P}\right)_{n_2T} = \left(\frac{\partial \mu_1}{\partial P}\right)_{n_1,n_2,T} = \left(\frac{\partial V}{\partial n_1}\right)_{n_2,P,T} = \bar{V}_1. \tag{10.4–3}$$

At constant composition and temperature, from equations (10.4–1) and (6.21–3),

$$\mathrm{d}\mu_1 = \bar{V}_1\,\mathrm{d}P = RT\,\mathrm{d}\ln f_1. \tag{10.4–4}$$

A new variable, α_1', is defined by the equation

$$\alpha_1' = \frac{RT}{P} - \bar{V}_1. \tag{10.4–5}$$

The values of $\bar{V}_1$ required may be obtained by the methods of Chapter 8. Upon substitution of $\bar{V}_1$ into equation (10.4–4) and subsequent integration between any two pressures, P' and P, one obtains

$$RT\ln\frac{f_1}{P_1} - RT\ln\frac{f_1'}{P_1'} = -\int_{P'}^{P}\alpha_1'\,\mathrm{d}P. \tag{10.4–6}$$

Note that at constant composition $P_1/P_1' = P/P'$. If P' is allowed to approach zero, the second term on the left side vanishes. The result is

$$\ln\frac{f_1}{\tilde{N}_1 P} = -\frac{1}{RT}\int_0^P \alpha_1'\,\mathrm{d}P, \tag{10.4–7}$$

where P_1 has been replaced by its equivalent, $\tilde{N}_1 P$. (Note that the "partial pressure," P_i, of a component in a gas mixture is taken, by definition, to be equal to the total pressure times the mole fraction of the component considered.) For a mixture of perfect gases, $\bar{V}_1 = RT/P$, $\alpha_1' = 0$, and $f_1 = \tilde{N}_1 P$ under all conditions.

In the application of this method to mixtures of real gases, it is necessary first to obtain $\bar{V}_1$ or its equivalent from the data of state. As before, the calculation may be made directly from the compressibility factor $Z = PV/(n_{\text{total}})RT$. Then

$$\ln\frac{f_1}{\tilde{N}_1 P} = -\int_0^P \frac{1}{P}\left(\frac{\partial}{\partial n_1}\right)_{n_2}[n_{\text{total}}(1 - Z)]\,\mathrm{d}P. \tag{10.4–8}$$

This technique is especially useful when Z is nearly unity.

A possible equation of state for a binary gas mixture is a simplified virial equation:

$$\frac{PV}{(n_1 + n_2)RT} = 1 + B'P. \tag{10.4–9}**$$

The constant B' may be represented as

$$B' = \tilde{N}_1^2 B'_{11} + 2\tilde{N}_1\tilde{N}_2 B'_{12} + \tilde{N}_2^2 B_{22}, \tag{10.4–10}$$

where B'_{11} and B'_{22} are the corresponding virial coefficients for the pure components and B'_{12} is an "interaction" term. The assumption that $B'_{12} = (B'_{11} + B'_{22})/2$ yields the widely used approximation of Lewis and Randall: $f_i/P_i = f_i^\circ/P$, where f_i° is the fugacity of the pure ith component at the total pressure P. Unfortunately, this assumption is seldom justified, as will be seen from the problems to follow.

Problem 10.4-1. Show by use of equation (10.4–8) that the approximation $f_i/P_i = f_i^\circ/P$ follows from the assumption that B'_{12} is a linear average of B'_{11} and B'_{22}.

Problem 10.4-2. Table 10.4–1 gives $P\tilde{V}/RT$ at 50°C for 1 mole of methane–ethane mixture of the composition given at pressures from 0 to 60 atm.

(a) Evaluate α_1' (or its equivalent) for methane in a mixture containing 0.6 mole methane, 0.4 mole ethane. (*Hint.* A plot of Z vs. $\tilde{N}_2$ gives $P\bar{V}/RT$ by the method of intercepts.)

(b) By graphical integration, evaluate f_1/P_1 and f_1 for 20, 30, 40, 50, 60 atm for the mixture which is 60 mole % methane. You may assume α_1' to be a linear function of pressure.

(c) Evaluate f/P for pure methane at the same pressures, and compare with the results of part (b).

(d) State qualitatively how f_1/P_1 for methane in a 20 mole % mixture should differ from the results of (b) and (c).

Table 10.4–1

Compressibility of Methane–Ethane Mixtures at 50°C†

P (atm)	100% CH_4	80% CH_4	60% CH_4	40% CH_4	20% CH_4	0% CH_4
0	1.0000	1.0000	1.0000	1.0000	1.0000	1.0000
10	0.9871	0.9801	0.9717	—	—	0.9381
20	0.9746	0.9606	0.9433	0.9226	0.9002	0.8707
30	0.9625	0.9416	0.9151	0.8829	0.8456	0.7963
40	0.9510	0.9229	0.8870	0.8421	0.7872	0.7108
50	0.9398	0.9051	0.8591	0.8006	0.7242	0.6067
60	0.9295	0.8876	0.8318	0.7586	0.6571	0.4662

† A. Michels and G. W. Nederbragt, *Physica*, **6**, 656 (1939).

Problem 10.4-3. Using the data of Problem 10.4–2, (a) obtain approximate equations $PV/(n_1 + n_2)RT = 1 + B'P$ for each composition.

(b) Taking the B's for pure methane and ethane as B'_{11} and B'_{22}, evaluate an apparent B'_{12} (in an expression $B' = \tilde{N}_1^2 B'_{11} + 2\tilde{N}_1\tilde{N}_2 B'_{12} + \tilde{N}_2^2 B'_{22}$) for each composition. Note that the values of B' obtained in part (a) are approximate only, since the compressibility is not a linear function of the pressure; thus equation (10.4–10) may not be applied exactly.

(c) Draw any conclusion you can with regard to the fugacities of these gases in the pure state and in mixtures.

In the absence of sufficient data, the fugacities of the components in a gas mixture may be estimated if the constants of a suitable equation of state may be estimated. An empirical method for estimation of the constants required for application of the equations of van der Waals, Berthelot, and Dieterici to mixtures was given in Section 4.10. These constants may be used for the estimation of P-V-T data for mixtures, and the methods described above then applied. Since these equations cannot be explicitly solved for V_1, an analytical expression for the fugacity cannot be obtained.

A better method of estimation is based on the indication of theory that the virial coefficients for a mixture are expressible as power series in mole fractions with coefficients B_{ij}, etc., as in equation (10.4–10). Methods for doing so for specific theoretical approaches are given by Hirschfelder et al.[3]

10.5 Entropy Diagrams

The state of pure material or of a mixture of definite composition is determined by specification of two variables such as temperature, pressure, volume, entropy, enthalpy, or energy. If two of these are taken as coordinates, any others may be represented by families of lines, each representing definite values of the chosen variable. One of the more useful of the various ways of doing this is demonstrated by the temperature-entropy (T–S) diagram, a small portion of which is shown in Fig. 10.5–1. On this diagram are plotted lines of constant pressure (P), volume (V), enthalpy (H). The central "dome" compasses the region within which liquid and gas can coexist. It includes in addition lines of constant "quality" (i.e., fraction of vapor in the mixture). Specification of any two of the variables determines a point on the diagram from which the values of the others may be read by interpolation.

Figures 10.8–1 and 10.8–2 show more complete entropy diagrams for helium and hydrogen, as constructed by student groups using methods similar to those described below.

Problem 10.5-1. Construct a T–S diagram from 100° to 1000°K for a perfect gas ($\tilde{C}_P = \frac{5}{2}R$) showing: constant pressure lines at 1, 2, 5, and 10 atm; constant volume lines at 2, 8, and 16 liters; and constant enthalpy lines at 0, 1000, 2500, and 4000 cal.

[3] J. O. Hirschfelder, C. F. Curtiss, and R. B. Bird, *Molecular Theory of Gases and Liquids*, Wiley, New York, 1954.

Take $\tilde{S} = 0$ and $\tilde{H} = 0$ at $P = 1$ atm, $T = 100°$K. (*Hint.* Draw the constant pressure lines first, then use the perfect gas law to place points for each volume on as many of these as possible. Note that for the perfect gas the members of each family of lines are all parallel.)

The entropy may be obtained as a function of temperature and pressure by integration of equation (6.15–3):

$$dS = \frac{C_P}{T}\,dT - \left(\frac{\partial V}{\partial T}\right)_P dP. \tag{6.15–3}$$

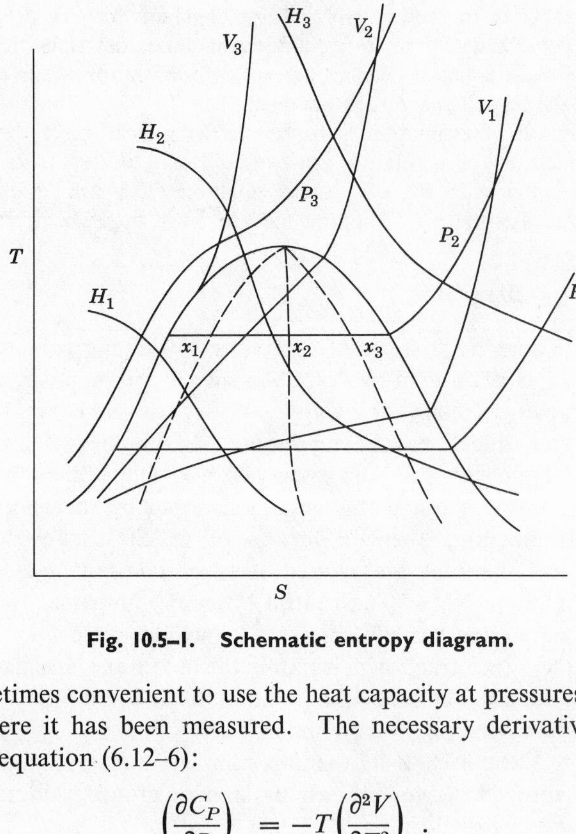

Fig. 10.5–1. Schematic entropy diagram.

It is sometimes convenient to use the heat capacity at pressures other than those where it has been measured. The necessary derivative has been given by equation (6.12–6):

$$\left(\frac{\partial C_P}{\partial P}\right)_T = -T\left(\frac{\partial^2 V}{\partial T^2}\right)_P. \tag{6.12–6}$$

Finally, we shall eventually need equation (6.10–2) for the change of enthalpy, and it is here rewritten:

$$\left(\frac{\partial H}{\partial P}\right)_T = V - T\left(\frac{\partial V}{\partial T}\right)_P. \tag{10.5–1}$$

Problem 10.5-2. (a) Substitute a virial equation of the form $P\tilde{V}/RT = \mathrm{A} + \mathrm{B}'P + \mathrm{C}'P^2$ into equation (6.15–3), and show from this what quantities (including derivatives) are needed if such an equation is to be used to get the variation of entropy with pressure at constant temperature.

(b) State in what respect the information of Problem 10.3–7 is insufficient to permit determination of the change of entropy with pressure for CO at 25°C.

Problem 10.5-3. Appendix 2 gives the necessary constants for representation of the data of state of nitrogen by an equation of the form

$$\frac{P\tilde{V}}{RT} = 1 + \mathrm{B}'P + \mathrm{C}'P^2 + \mathrm{D}'P^4.$$

(At low pressures the term in P^4 may be neglected.)

(a) Obtain the derivatives $\mathrm{dB}'/\mathrm{d}T$ and $\mathrm{dC}'/\mathrm{d}T$ for nitrogen at 25°C from the data of Appendix 2. (*Note.* This may be done graphically or, if the student prefers, analytically after first determining the functional dependence of the constants on temperature.)

(b) Express the derivative $(\partial S/\partial P)_T$ as a function of pressure for nitrogen at 25°C.

(c) Obtain the change in entropy which occurs when nitrogen is compressed at 25°C from 1 atm to 50 atm, and compare with the corresponding entropy change for a perfect gas.

Problem 10.5-4. Use the methods and data of Problem 10.5–3 to calculate (a) the enthalpy change which occurs when nitrogen is expanded isothermally at 25°C from 50 atm to 1 atm; (b) the difference at 25°C between the heat capacity of nitrogen at 50 atm and 1 atm.

The experimental data required for construction of an entropy diagram for a gaseous substance with respect to an arbitrary standard state are:

1. The heat capacity of the gas as a function of temperature at some given pressure.
2. Data of state for the material over the temperature and pressure considered.

The following additional data are required for inclusion of the liquid phase:

1. The heat capacity of the saturated liquid as a function of temperature.
2. The heat of vaporization of the liquid and the vapor pressure at some pressure and temperature.
3. The density of the liquid at various temperatures and pressures.

The absolute entropy of the gas, in the ideal state, may be calculated from spectroscopic and molecular data as described in later chapters. If this is done, the entropy diagram may be put on an absolute basis. The entropy of the real gas may be calculated by use of a suitable modification of equation (6.15–3). The calculation may be made graphically from P-V-T data or analytically from suitably accurate equations of state derived therefrom.

Detailed calculation of the information required for construction of an entropy diagram may be made by using only the equations given above together with the entropy of vaporization and the definitions of the quantities involved. However, it is frequently convenient to use various derived relationships instead; in addition, there are many possible techniques for obtaining the derivatives and integrals required. The choice among the various possible procedures frequently depends on the nature of the data available. Examples of possible procedures are given below for purposes of illustration; the student may find alternative procedures desirable in specific cases.

10.6 Calculation of Entropy and Enthalpy for the Vapor Phase

Data of state are frequently reported in terms of the compressibility factor Z $(= P\tilde{V}/RT)$ tabulated as a function of the Amagat density, ρ_a. ($\rho_a = \tilde{V}_0/\tilde{V}$, where $\tilde{V}_0$ is the molal volume at 1 atm, 0°C.) (*Note.* The student is referred to Section 4.3 for previous discussion of volume and density in Amagat units.) A method for handling data in this form has been described in detail by Wooley, Scott, and Brickwedde.[4]

It will be assumed that the entropy of the substance (in the ideal gas state) is known at 1 atm pressure; the symbol $\tilde{V}_i$ will be used for the volume of the ideal gas at 1 atm. The entropy of the real gas at any given volume $\tilde{V}$ may be obtained by calculation of (1) the entropy change which occurs when the ideal gas goes from volume $\tilde{V}_i$ to volume $\tilde{V}$ and (2) the difference between the entropy of the real gas and the ideal gas. The entropy change in the first step is

$$\Delta S_1 = R \ln \frac{\tilde{V}}{\tilde{V}_i}. \tag{10.6–1}$$

Since the entropy of the real gas approaches that of the ideal gas at sufficiently high molar volumes, the difference required for the second step is

$$\Delta S_2 = \left[\int_{\tilde{V}}^{\tilde{V}^*} \left(\frac{\partial P}{\partial T}\right)_V \mathrm{d}\tilde{V}\right]_{\text{ideal gas}} + \left[\int_{\tilde{V}^*}^{\tilde{V}} \left(\frac{\partial P}{\partial T}\right)_V \mathrm{d}\tilde{V}\right]_{\text{real gas}}, \tag{10.6–2}$$

where $\tilde{V}^*$ is a molar volume so large that deviation of the actual gas from ideal behavior may be neglected. Since for the ideal gas $P\tilde{V} = RT$ and for the real gas $P\tilde{V} = ZRT$, equation (10.6–2) becomes

$$\begin{aligned}\Delta S_2 &= -\int_{\tilde{V}^*}^{\tilde{V}} \frac{R}{\tilde{V}} \mathrm{d}\tilde{V} + \int_{\tilde{V}^*}^{\tilde{V}} \frac{R}{\tilde{V}}\left[Z + T\left(\frac{\partial Z}{\partial T}\right)_V\right] \mathrm{d}\tilde{V} \\ &= -\int_{\tilde{V}^*}^{\tilde{V}} \frac{R(1-Z)}{\tilde{V}} \mathrm{d}\tilde{V} + \int_{\tilde{V}^*}^{\tilde{V}} \frac{RT}{\tilde{V}} \left(\frac{\partial Z}{\partial T}\right)_V \mathrm{d}\tilde{V}. \end{aligned} \tag{10.6–3}$$

[4] H. W. Wooley, R. B. Scott, and F. G. Brickwedde, *J. Res. Natl. Bur. Standards*, **41**, 379 (1948).

For convenience in integration, equation (10.6–3) may now be expressed in terms of the Amagat density, $\rho_a = \tilde{V}_0/\tilde{V}$. For simplicity the subscript a will be omitted hereafter. The equations are equally valid if ρ is taken to represent the density in any other units. The necessary substitutions are

$$\tilde{V} = \frac{\tilde{V}_0}{\rho}; \qquad d\tilde{V} = -\frac{\tilde{V}_0}{\rho^2}\,d\rho; \qquad \left(\frac{\partial Z}{\partial T}\right)_V = \left(\frac{\partial Z}{\partial T}\right)_\rho. \tag{10.6–4}$$

Thus

$$\Delta S_2 = \int_{\rho^*}^{\rho} \frac{R(1-Z)}{\rho}\,d\rho - \int_{\rho^*}^{\rho} \frac{RT}{\rho}\left(\frac{\partial Z}{\partial T}\right)_\rho d\rho. \tag{10.6–5}$$

By combination of equations (10.6–1) and (10.6–5), the final equation for the entropy is

$$\tilde{S} = \tilde{S}(\text{ideal}, P = 1) + R\ln\frac{\tilde{V}}{RT} + \int_0^{\rho} \frac{R(1-Z)}{\rho}\,d\rho - \int_0^{\rho} \frac{RT}{\rho}\left(\frac{\partial Z}{\partial T}\right)_\rho d\rho, \tag{10.6–6}$$

where the V_i of equation (10.6–1) has been replaced by RT/P_0, with $P_0 = 1$ atm, and ρ^* has been allowed to approach zero. Unless the compressibility has been given as an analytic function of the Amagat density, the evaluation of $(\partial Z/\partial T)_\rho$ and the subsequent integrations must be made graphically.

When a series of the calculations described by equation (10.6–6) have been performed, the entropy is given as a function of the temperature and Amagat density ρ. The corresponding volumes may be calculated from the definition of ρ given in equation (10.6–4) and the entropy at particular molal volumes then obtained by interpolation. From these data *constant volume lines* may be placed on the diagram.

Points for *constant pressure lines* may be obtained as follows. The pressures corresponding to the volumes previously used can be obtained from the compressibility data at enough temperatures to permit construction of constant volume lines on a P–T plot. The values of T and V corresponding to each pressure may then be marked on the T–S diagram and the points joined to give constant pressure lines.

Enthalpies may be calculated by methods similar to those used for the entropy and constant enthalpy lines drawn as were the constant pressure lines. Spectroscopic data give $\tilde{H} - \tilde{E}_0^0$ for the ideal gas, where $\tilde{E}_0^0$ is the energy of the crystal at 0°K. Since the enthalpy of the ideal gas is independent of pressure, it is necessary to calculate only the enthalpy change suffered by the real gas upon compression to volume $\tilde{V}$ from a very large molar volume. From equation (6.9–2),

$$dH = T\,dS + V\,dP. \tag{10.6–7}$$

Thus

$$\left(\frac{\partial H}{\partial V}\right)_T = T\left(\frac{\partial S}{\partial V}\right)_T + V\left(\frac{\partial P}{\partial V}\right)_T$$

$$= T\left(\frac{\partial P}{\partial T}\right)_V + V\left(\frac{\partial P}{\partial V}\right)_T \qquad (10.6\text{–}8)$$

and

$$\tilde{H} = \tilde{H}_{\text{ideal}} + \int_{\tilde{V}^*}^{\tilde{V}} T\left(\frac{\partial P}{\partial T}\right)_V \mathrm{d}\tilde{V} + \int_{\tilde{V}^*}^{\tilde{V}} \tilde{V}\left(\frac{\partial P}{\partial V}\right)_T \mathrm{d}\tilde{V}. \qquad (10.6\text{–}9)$$

Upon replacement of P by $ZRT/\tilde{V}$ in the derivatives and simplification, one obtains

$$\tilde{H} = \tilde{H}_{\text{ideal}} + \int_{\tilde{V}^*}^{\tilde{V}} \frac{RT^2}{\tilde{V}}\left(\frac{\partial Z}{\partial T}\right)_V \mathrm{d}\tilde{V} + \int_{\tilde{V}^*}^{\tilde{V}} RT\,\mathrm{d}Z. \qquad (10.6\text{–}10)$$

Using the substitutions of equation (10.6–4),

$$\tilde{H} = \tilde{H}_{\text{ideal}} - RT\int_{\rho^*}^{\rho} \frac{T}{\rho}\left(\frac{\partial Z}{\partial T}\right)_\rho \mathrm{d}\rho + RT\int_{Z^*}^{Z} \mathrm{d}Z. \qquad (10.6\text{–}11)$$

Finally, letting ρ^* approach zero, so that Z^* approaches unity,

$$\tilde{H} = \tilde{H}_{\text{ideal}} + RT\left[(Z-1) - \int_0^{\rho} \frac{T}{\rho}\left(\frac{\partial Z}{\partial T}\right)_\rho \mathrm{d}\rho\right]. \qquad (10.6\text{–}12)$$

The operations described by equation (10.6–12) yield the enthalpy as a function of T and ρ. Lines of constant density can be plotted on a T–H diagram, and the densities and temperatures for desired values of enthalpy may be read therefrom and entered as points on the T–S diagram. These points may then be connected to give constant enthalpy lines.

A second method for construction of the vapor phase portion of the entropy diagram utilizes an intermediate calculation of the fugacity of the vapor. Equation (10.2–3) may be written

$$\tilde{F} - \tilde{F}^\circ = RT\ln f, \qquad (10.6\text{–}13)$$

where $\tilde{F}^\circ$ is the free energy in a hypothetical standard state where the gas has unit fugacity and behaves as an ideal gas. If equation (10.6–13) is differentiated with respect to temperature at constant pressure, the result is

$$\left[\frac{\partial(\tilde{F} - \tilde{F}^\circ)}{\partial T}\right]_P = R\ln f + RT\left(\frac{\partial \ln f}{\partial T}\right)_P$$

$$= -\tilde{S} + \tilde{S}^\circ \qquad (10.6\text{–}14)$$

after substitution from equation (6.19–6). This may be solved for the entropy:

$$\tilde{S} = \tilde{S}^\circ - R \ln f - RT \left(\frac{\partial \ln f}{\partial T} \right)_P, \tag{10.6–15}$$

where S° is the entropy of the ideal gas at unit pressure and fugacity.

The procedure then starts, as before, with the entropy of the ideal gas at 1 atm. By use of the methods of Section 10.3, the fugacity is obtained as a function of pressure at each temperature; usually $\ln f$ will be obtained directly. For each of a set of pressures, the derivatives $[(\partial \ln f)/\partial T]_P$ are obtained graphically and the entropies then evaluated by use of equation (10.6–15). From these results a set of constant pressure lines may be plotted on the T–S diagram. The P–V–T data, or equation of state, may then be used to locate points at specified molar volumes for the construction of constant volume lines. The enthalpy may be obtained by use of equation (6.19–10):

$$\left(\frac{\partial (\tilde{F}/T)}{\partial T} \right)_P = -\frac{\tilde{H}}{T^2}, \tag{6.19–10}$$

which becomes, after application of (10.6–13),

$$R \left(\frac{\partial \ln f}{\partial T} \right)_P = -\frac{\tilde{H} - \tilde{H}^\circ}{T^2}. \tag{10.6–16}$$

Thus

$$\tilde{H} = \tilde{H}^\circ - RT^2 \left(\frac{\partial \ln f}{\partial T} \right)_P. \tag{10.6–17}$$

Equation (10.6–17) gives the enthalpy at each pressure and temperature with respect to the ideal gas at the same temperature. The enthalpy of the ideal gas is obtained as described previously. Between the two the enthalpy is given as a function of temperature and pressure; constant enthalpy lines may then be drawn by interpolation.

One of the advantages in the use of fugacity is that it permits averaging of directly measured thermodynamic properties with those obtained from P–V–T data. The enthalpy of the gas may be obtained with respect to the ideal gas by use of the Joule–Thomson coefficient and the heat capacity. From equation (5.7–5), at constant temperature

$$d\tilde{H} = -\mu \tilde{C}_P \, dP. \tag{10.6–18}$$

Upon integration of equation (10.6–18),

$$\tilde{H} - \tilde{H}^\circ = -\int_0^P \mu \tilde{C}_P \, dP, \tag{10.6–19}$$

since the enthalpy of the real gas at zero pressure is the same as that of the ideal gas at any pressure. But, from equation (10.6–17),

$$\tilde{H} - \tilde{H}^\circ = -RT^2 \left(\frac{\partial \ln f}{\partial T}\right)_P . \tag{10.6–17}$$

Equations (10.6–17) and (10.6–19) give two independent values of the enthalpy at the pressure P. Because of experimental errors, the enthalpy as evaluated by the two methods will tend to differ slightly. The values can then be averaged, suitable weight being given to the uncertainty expected in each. Moreover, the enthalpy values obtained by this averaging process may be used with equation (10.6–17) to obtain a new set of fugacities; the integration constant required may be taken at the high temperature end where the fugacity approaches the pressure. The fugacities thus obtained may be used in a final calculation of the entropies. As far as we are aware, such a procedure has never been systematically applied.

10.7 Entropy and Enthalpy in Regions Containing Liquid

Each constant pressure line for the vapor phase must terminate at the temperature where the liquid has the corresponding vapor pressure, except in the case of pressures above the critical pressure of the substance. Connection of these points of termination forms the right side of the "dome" in Fig. 10.5–1, which is known as the "saturated vapor line"; this line marks the boundary between the gas phase and the liquid-vapor region. Immediately to the left of this boundary line is the region in which liquid and gas can coexist and where for a pure substance the pressure is a function of temperature only. Thus in this region the constant pressure lines (isobars) are parallel to the $\tilde{S}$ axis. The temperatures at which each constant pressure line intersects the dome may be obtained from a plot of the vapor pressure against temperature.

The left-hand boundary of the dome is known as the saturated liquid line; it makes the boundary between liquid and the two-phase region. The entropy of the liquid at each pressure can be obtained by subtraction of the entropy of vaporization from the entropy of the corresponding saturated vapor. The entropy of vaporization, $\Delta\tilde{S}_{\text{vap}}$, may be obtained from the Clapeyron equation (7.3–4):

$$\frac{dP}{dT} = \frac{\Delta S_{\text{vap}}}{\tilde{V}_g - \tilde{V}_l}, \tag{7.3–4}$$

using the density of liquid and vapor to get the respective molal volumes. Alternatively, the entropy of saturated liquid at the boiling point may be obtained, by using $\Delta\tilde{S}_{\text{vap}} = \Delta\tilde{H}_{\text{vap}}/T$. Then, if the heat capacity of the saturated liquid is known, the entropy of other points on the saturated liquid line may be obtained by integration:

$$\tilde{S} - \tilde{S}_0 = \int_{T_0}^{T} \frac{\tilde{C}_{\text{sat}}}{T}\,\mathrm{d}T. \qquad (10.7\text{–}1)$$

$\tilde{C}_{\text{sat}}$ is the heat capacity of saturated liquid, which is frequently available in the literature.

Problem 10.7-1. Derive the relation

$$C_{\text{sat}} = C_P - \frac{RT^2}{P}\left[\frac{Z}{T} + \left(\frac{\partial Z}{\partial T}\right)_P\right]\left(\frac{\partial P}{\partial T}\right)_{\text{sat}}. \qquad (10.7\text{–}2)$$

(*Hint.* See equation (6.12–3).)

In most cases the available data will not be sufficient to permit continuation of the above procedures to the critical temperature. The entropy at the critical temperature may be obtained by extrapolation of a set of constant "quality" lines such as shown in Fig. 10.5–1. If x is the fraction of vapor in the liquid-vapor mixture,

$$\tilde{S}_{\text{mix}} = \tilde{S}_{\text{l}} + x(\tilde{S}_{\text{g}} - \tilde{S}_{\text{l}}). \qquad (10.7\text{–}3)$$

All constant quality lines must terminate at the temperature and entropy of the critical point.

The volumes and enthalpies in the two-phase region may be obtained by an equation analogous to (10.7–3). The enthalpies of the liquid may be obtained at each temperature by subtraction of the heat of vaporization from the enthalpy of the saturated vapor.

The entropy and enthalpy of liquid at pressures above the vapor pressure may be obtained by integration of equations (6.9–8) and (10.5–1), respectively:

$$\left(\frac{\partial \tilde{S}}{\partial P}\right)_T = -\left(\frac{\partial \tilde{V}}{\partial T}\right)_P \qquad (6.9\text{–}8)$$

and

$$\left(\frac{\partial \tilde{H}}{\partial P}\right)_T = \tilde{V} - T\left(\frac{\partial \tilde{V}}{\partial T}\right)_P, \qquad (10.5\text{–}1)$$

if the necessary data on liquid density are available.

10.8 Verification and Uses of Entropy Diagrams

The methods of construction of the entropy diagram described have depended mainly on data of state and have employed relatively little

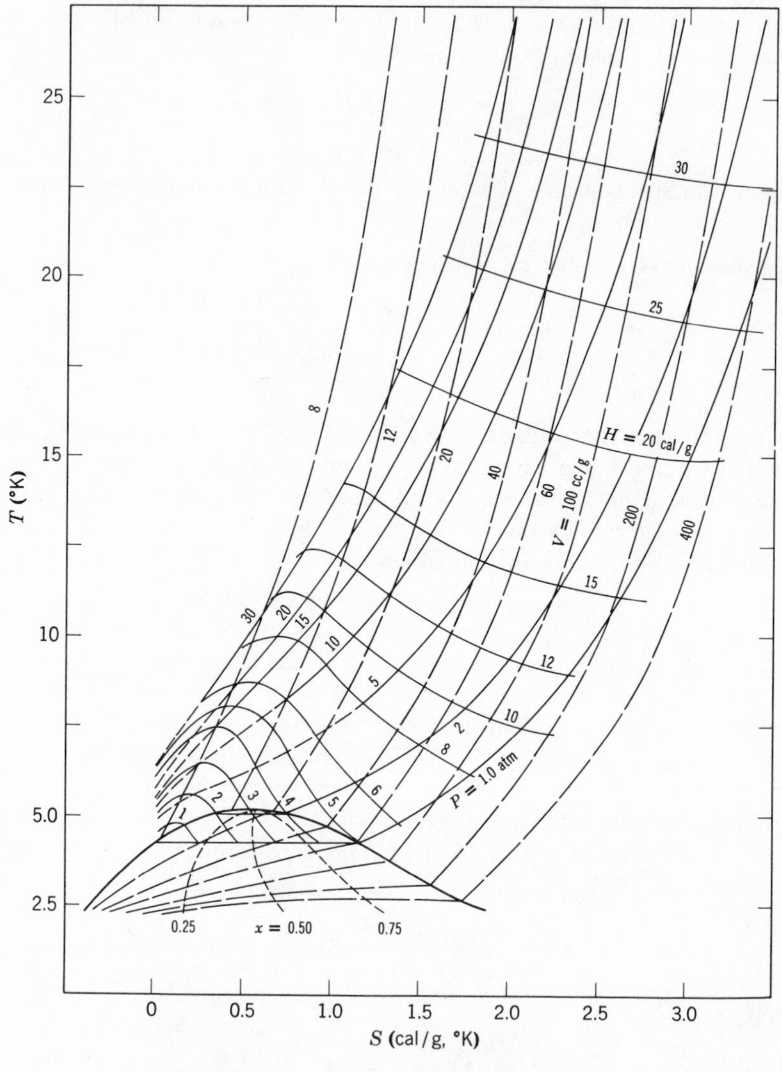

Fig. 10.8–1. Entropy diagram for helium.

thermal data. Verification of the accuracy of the diagram may be obtained by comparison with any other thermal data available. Two typical calculations are:

1. The heat capacity of the vapor at pressures other than atmospheric may be obtained from either enthalpy or entropy data taken from the *T–S* diagram and compared with measured values.

2. The Joule-Thomson coefficient, $\mu = (\partial T/\partial P)_H$, may be obtained from a suitable plot of the enthalpy data for comparison with experiment.

The uses of entropy diagrams are manifold since the changes in entropy,

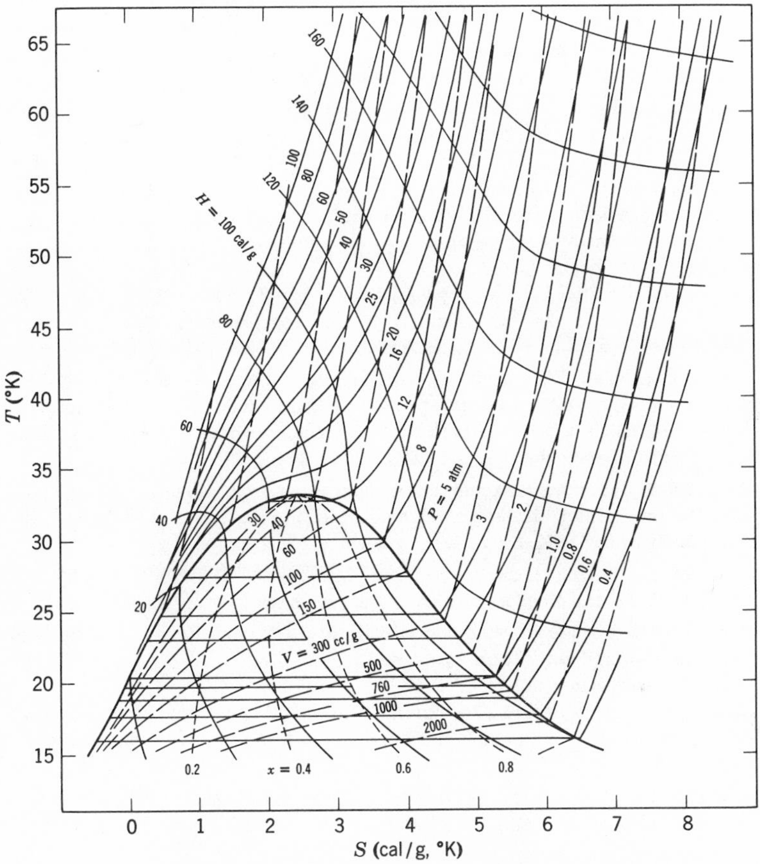

Fig. 10.8–2. Entropy diagram for hydrogen.

enthalpy, volume, and of the other variables for a process involving the pure material may be read from the diagram. Some of the possible uses will be illustrated by the following problems, which refer to Figs. 10.8–1 and 10.8–2.

Problem 10.8-1. Hydrogen gas, originally at 65°K and 100 atm, is allowed to expand adiabatically to 1 atm through a valve. Calculate the final temperature of the gas.

Problem 10.8-2. In a Joule-Thomson liquefier hydrogen gas is precooled at 100 atm to 65°K, and then further cooled by heat exchange with effluent hydrogen gas before expansion through a valve to 1 atm. At the valve a fraction (x) is liquefied, while the remainder ($1 - x$) serves to cool incoming hydrogen gas below 65°K.

(a) Calculate the fraction liquefied (x). Note that the entire process occurs at constant enthalpy. Assume that the unliquefied portion leaves at 65°K, 1 atm.

(b) Calculate the entropy change per mole of gas entering suffered by the portion of the gas liquefied.

(c) Calculate the entropy change per mole of gas entering suffered by the unliquefied portion and then the total entropy change per mole of gas entering.

Problem 10.8-3. In the liquefier described in Problem 10.8–2, about 25% of the hydrogen is liquefied. Answer (a), (b), and (c) for the liquefier on this assumption.

(a) Calculate the final temperature reached when 1 mole of hydrogen gas, originally at 100 atm, 65°K, is cooled by heat exchange with 0.75 mole of hydrogen gas at 1 atm, the low pressure gas being warmed from 20° to 65°K in the process.

(b) Calculate the entropy change suffered by each gas stream in (a) and thus the total entropy change in the heat exchanger.

(c) By use of the total entropy change calculated in Problem 10.8–2, obtain the entropy change at the expansion valve. Draw any conclusions you can about the relative sources of irreversibility in the liquefier.

Problem 10.8-4. Calculate the fraction of helium liquefied by a Joule-Thomson liquefier in which helium gas is precooled to 14°K at 30 atm and then expanded to 1 atm through a valve after heat exchange with the unliquefied portion of the gas. Assume that the portion not liquefied leaves at 13.5°K, 1 atm.

Problem 10.8-5. Estimate the temperature decrease and the entropy increase which occur when helium expands through a valve adiabatically from 30 atm to 1 atm if the gas was originally at (a) 20°K, (b) 15°K.

Problem 10.8-6. Calculate the temperature decrease which occurs when helium originally at 30 atm is expanded adiabatically and reversibly from (a) 25°K, (b) 20°K.

Problem 10.8-7. A mole of helium originally at 10°K and 30 atm is expanded adiabatically and reversibly to 1 atm.

(a) Estimate the fraction liquefied.

(b) Taking the density of liquid helium at 1 atm as 0.124 g/cm^3 and other data from Fig. 10.8–2, compare the volume of liquid obtained with the original volume of compressed gas.

Problem 10.8-8. From the entropy diagram for helium, estimate the heat capacity of helium gas near 13°K at (a) 1 atm, (b) 20 atm.

Solutions. The Activity of Non-electrolytes

CHAPTER 11

11.1 Introduction

The relative activity was defined by equation (6.22–2):

$$\mu_i = \mu_i^\circ + RT \ln a_i. \tag{6.22–2}$$

This may also be written in differential form (at constant T and P) as

$$\mathrm{d}\mu_i = RT\,\mathrm{d}\ln a_i. \tag{6.22–2a}$$

According to equation (10.2–3) this is equivalent to

$$a_i = \frac{f_i}{f_i^\circ}, \tag{11.1–1}$$

where the superscript refers as before to some arbitrary standard state for which the relative activity is chosen to be unity. For a liquid or solid the fugacity of each component is equal to its fugacity in the vapor phase with which the substance is at equilibrium (Section 10.2). In general, the standard state for a liquid solution is chosen such that the activities of solvent and solute approach their concentrations as the solution approaches infinite dilution. Some of the properties of the activity may be written immediately from the definitions.

From equation (6.21–3),

$$\left(\frac{\partial \mu_i}{\partial P}\right)_{T,n_i,\cdots} = \bar{V}_i, \tag{6.21–3}$$

from equation (6.21–2),

$$\left(\frac{\partial \mu_i}{\partial T}\right)_{P,n_i,\cdots} = -\bar{S}_i, \tag{6.21–2}$$

and, by differentiation of (6.19–10) with respect to composition,

$$\left[\frac{\partial(\mu_i/T)}{\partial T}\right]_{P,n_i,\cdots} = \frac{-\bar{H}_i}{T^2}. \tag{11.1–2}$$

Upon substitution of the activity from equation (6.22–2) these become

$$\left(\frac{\partial \ln a_i}{\partial P}\right)_{T,n_i,\cdots} = \frac{\bar{V}_i - \bar{V}_i^\circ}{RT}, \tag{11.1–3}$$

and

$$\left(\frac{\partial \ln a_i}{\partial T}\right)_{P,n_i,\cdots} = \frac{-(\bar{H}_i - \bar{H}_i^\circ)}{RT^2} \equiv \frac{-\bar{L}_i}{RT^2}. \tag{11.1–4}$$

Problem 11.1-1. Prove equations (11.1–3) and (11.1–4).

At constant temperature and pressure one may write, for a binary solution, from equation (8.3–12)

$$\tilde{N}_1\,\mathrm{d}\mu_1 = -\tilde{N}_2\,\mathrm{d}\mu_2. \tag{11.1–5}$$

In terms of the activity, this becomes

$$\tilde{N}_1\,\mathrm{d}\ln a_1 = -\tilde{N}_2\,\mathrm{d}\ln a_2. \tag{11.1–6}$$

If the activity is replaced by fugacity, the form of the equation is unchanged. If, however, it is then divided by $\mathrm{d}\tilde{N}_1 = -\mathrm{d}\tilde{N}_2$, it may be rearranged to

$$\left(\frac{\partial \ln f_1}{\partial \ln \tilde{N}_1}\right)_T = \left(\frac{\partial \ln f_2}{\partial \ln \tilde{N}_2}\right)_T. \tag{11.1–7}$$

Finally, to the approximation that the vapors may be considered perfect, one may substitute vapor pressures for fugacities and obtain the relationship

$$\left(\frac{\partial \ln p_1}{\partial \ln \tilde{N}_1}\right)_T = \left(\frac{\partial \ln p_2}{\partial \ln \tilde{N}_2}\right)_T. \tag{11.1–8)*$$

These equations make possible the correlation of the partial vapor pressures of a two-component system. Qualitatively, they state that, if one component follows Raoult's law over the entire composition range, the other must also do so; positive or negative deviations on the part of one component require deviations of the same sign by the other. The approximate equation (11.1–8)* is frequently obeyed much more closely than would be expected for non-ideal vapors. This is a consequence of the fact that similar deviations from perfect gas behavior, such as often exist for substances of similar character, tend to cancel each other out.

Problem 11.1-2. Derive equations (11.1–7) and (11.1–8)*. Prove the statements concerning Raoult's law in the paragraph following (11.1–8)*.

Problem 11.1-3. Table 11.1–1 gives the vapor pressures of ethyl alcohol above solutions of the alcohol in chloroform at 35°C. By use of equation (11.1–8)* calculate approximately the vapor pressure of chloroform above solutions containing 10, 30, and 50 mole per cent ethyl alcohol. The vapor pressure of pure chloroform is 295.11 mm at 35°C. Note that $(d \log P_2)/(d \log \tilde{N}_2) \rightarrow 1$ as $\tilde{N}_2 \rightarrow 0$. The actual vapor pressures of $CHCl_3$ are 275.42, 250.11, and 217.65 mm Hg.

Table 11.1–1

Vapor Pressures of Ethanol above Ethanol–Chloroform Mixtures at 35°C†

Mole Fraction of Ethanol	P_{ethanol} (mm Hg)	Mole Fraction of Ethanol	P_{ethanol} (mm Hg)
0.01	5.85	0.30	48.42
0.02	10.71	0.40	54.09
0.05	21.22	0.50	59.33
0.10	31.42	0.60	65.68
0.20	42.04	0.70	72.23

† From the data of G. Scatchard and C. L. Raymond, *J. Am. Chem. Soc.*, **60**, 1278 (1938).

11.2 The Perfect Solution

With solutions as with gases, it is useful to consider a limiting case of ideal behavior, which is known as the *perfect solution*. The perfect solution may be defined in a number of ways; a simple way is to state that it follows Raoult's law at all concentrations and over a finite range of pressures and temperatures. That is,

$$f_i \equiv f_i^\circ \tilde{N}_i, \qquad (11.2\text{–}1)$$

where fugacity is used instead of vapor pressure to avoid any complication due to non-ideality of the vapor. An equivalent statement is that

$$a_i \equiv \tilde{N}_i, \qquad (11.2\text{–}1)$$

where the standard state for each component is taken as the pure material.

For a perfect solution, the *heat of mixing* and *volume change upon mixing* of the components are both zero. The *entropy change* which occurs when a perfect solution is prepared from the pure components is

$$\Delta S_{\text{mix}} = -R(n_1 \ln \tilde{N}_1 + n_2 \ln \tilde{N}_2 + \cdots). \qquad (11.2\text{–}3)$$

If these requirements are given as the definition of the perfect solution, equation (11.2–1) may be derived from them. The partial molal volumes and enthalpies of the components of a perfect solution are identical with the molal properties of the pure components.

Problem 11.2-1. Prove that the heat and volume change of mixing of a perfect solution is zero, and that the entropy of mixing follows equation (11.2–3). These proofs are most easily accomplished by use of equations (11.1–3) and (11.1–4).

Problem 11.2-2. Prove that $\bar{V}_i$ and $\bar{H}_i$ for a perfect solution are identical at any composition with the molar volume and heat content of the pure component at the same temperature.

Problem 11.2-3. From the results of Problem 11.2–2 show that the heat of vaporization and entropy of vaporization of any component from a perfect solution are the same as those for pure component, provided that the vapors are perfect gases.

Problem 11.2-4. The entropy of liquid or *o*-xylene at 25°C is 59.3 cal mole^{-1} deg^{-1} and that of *m*-xylene is 60.3 cal mole^{-1} deg^{-1}. Assuming that they form ideal solutions, calculate the entropy of mixing and the total entropy of solutions containing 20, 40, 60, and 80 mole per cent *o*-xylene in *m*-xylene.

The partial molal free energies and entropies of components of a perfect solution may readily be derived. The partial molal free energy of the *i*th component is

$$\mu_i = \mu_i^{\circ} + RT \ln \tilde{N}_i, \qquad (11.2\text{–}4)$$

where μ_i is the partial molal free energy (chemical potential) in the solution and μ_i° is its value in the standard state. At constant temperature and pressure equation (11.2–4) may also be written in differential form

$$d\mu_i = RT\, d \ln \tilde{N}_i. \qquad (11.2\text{–}4a)$$

Similarly the partial molal entropies are

$$\bar{S}_i = \bar{S}_i^{\circ} - R \ln \tilde{N}_i. \qquad (11.2\text{–}5)$$

Problem 11.2-5. Prove equations (11.2–4) and (11.2–5).

The equilibria between a pure solid phase and a perfect solution may be treated quite simply. As discussed in Chapter 7, the condition for equilibrium between phases of a pure substance is that the molal free energies of the phases be equal. When the phases consist of solutions, the free energy change for the transfer of an infinitesimal quantity of any component from one phase (′) to another (″) at constant temperature and pressure, $(\mu_i' - \mu_i'')\, dn_i$, must also be zero. That is, the partial molal free energies (chemical potentials), μ_i' and μ_i'', in the two phases must be equal. In this case,

$$\mu_i = \tilde{F}_i, \qquad (11.2\text{–}6)$$

where μ_i is the partial molal free energy of the component in solution, and $\tilde{F}_i$ the molal free energy of the pure solid component. If the composition of the solution is changed slightly, and the temperature altered simultaneously so as to maintain equilibrium, then

$$\mathrm{d}\mu_i = \mathrm{d}\tilde{F}_i. \tag{11.2–7}$$

The free energy of the solid phase depends only on temperature, whereas that of the solution depends also upon concentration. Thus

$$\left(\frac{\partial \mu_i}{\partial T}\right)_{\tilde{N}_i,P} \mathrm{d}T + \left(\frac{\partial \mu_i}{\partial \tilde{N}_i}\right)_{T,P} \mathrm{d}\tilde{N}_i = \left(\frac{\partial \tilde{F}_i}{\mathrm{d}T}\right)_P \mathrm{d}T. \tag{11.2–8}$$

The two temperature derivatives are given by equations (6.21–2) and (6.19–6). The other is obtained by rearrangement of (11.2–4a):

$$\left(\frac{\partial \mu_i}{\partial \tilde{N}_i}\right)_{T,P} = \frac{RT}{\tilde{N}_i}. \tag{11.2–9}$$

Upon substitution for the derivatives in (11.2–8), one obtains

$$-\bar{S}_i\,\mathrm{d}T + \frac{RT}{\tilde{N}_i}\,\mathrm{d}\tilde{N}_i = -\tilde{S}_i\,\mathrm{d}T, \tag{11.2–10}$$

whereupon

$$\frac{\mathrm{d}T}{\mathrm{d}\tilde{N}_i} = \frac{RT}{\tilde{N}_i(\bar{S}_i - \tilde{S}_i)}. \tag{11.2–11}$$

Since the process is at equilibrium,

$$\bar{S}_i - \tilde{S}_i = \frac{\bar{H}_i - \tilde{H}_i}{T} = \frac{\Delta\tilde{H}_f}{T}, \tag{11.2–12}$$

so that

$$\frac{\mathrm{d}T}{\mathrm{d}\tilde{N}_i} = \frac{RT^2}{\tilde{N}_i\,\Delta\tilde{H}_f}. \tag{11.2–13}$$

If the heat of fusion is known as a function of temperature, equation (11.2–13) may be integrated. In particular, if $\Delta\tilde{H}_f$ is assumed constant,

$$\frac{T_i^\circ - T}{T_i^\circ T} = -\frac{R}{\Delta\tilde{H}_f}\ln \tilde{N}_i\,. \tag{11.2–14}$$

If equation (11.2–14) is applied to equilibrium between pure solid solvent and solution, then the freezing point depression may be calculated from

$$\frac{T_1^\circ - T}{T_1^\circ T} = -\frac{R}{\Delta\tilde{H}_1}\ln \tilde{N}_1, \tag{11.2–15}$$

where T_1° is the freezing point of pure solvent, T is the freezing point of a solution in which the mole fraction of solvent is $\tilde{N}_1$, and $\Delta\tilde{H}_1$ is the heat of fusion of pure solvent.

Equation (11.2–14) can be applied equally well to the equilibrium between pure solid solute and solutions. Upon change of subscripts and rearrangement,

$$\ln \tilde{N}_2 = -\frac{\Delta H_2}{RTT_2^\circ}(T_2^\circ - T), \qquad (11.2\text{–}16)$$

where $\tilde{N}_2$ is the solubility of the solute (as mole fraction), T_2° is the melting point of pure solute, and $\Delta\tilde{H}_2$ the heat of fusion of pure solute.

Problem 11.2-6. Methane melts at 90.5°K and has a heat of fusion of 232 cal mole^{-1}. Estimate the solubility of methane in liquid nitrogen at 78°K, assuming that the two substances form an ideal solution and neglecting the variation in heat of fusion with temperature.

At the eutectic temperature of a binary system forming perfect solutions, equations (11.2–15) and (11.2–16) must be satisfied simultaneously. Since in addition $(\tilde{N}_1 + \tilde{N}_2) = 1$, these equations may be used to estimate the eutectic temperature and composition. (It should be noted that these equations apply only if the solid phases are pure materials. The slightly more complicated situation which exists when solid solutions are formed is discussed below.)

Problem 11.2-7. *o*-Dichlorobenzene and *m*-dichlorobenzene melt at 17.5° and −24.5°C respectively. Their heats of fusion are 2090 and 2040 cal mole^{-1}. Assuming that these two materials form an ideal solution, estimate the temperature and composition of their eutectic.

11.3 The Dilute Solution

The concept of the perfect solution, while similar in many ways to that of the perfect gas, differs in an essential respect. Although, in a solution, concentration of the solute plays a role analogous to that of pressure in a gas, it is not necessary that any actual solution approach perfect solution behavior as the concentration of the solute approaches zero. Ideal behavior will be observed only if the forces between adjacent molecules are zero or identical. In a gas it is always possible to separate the molecules sufficiently (at very low pressures) to make intermolecular forces effectively zero. In a liquid this is not possible, and the forces can be made substantially identical only by choosing components of very similar structure. It is obvious that the forces between a benzene molecule and an alcohol molecule will never be the same as those between two benzene molecules, regardless of how dilute the mixture is. Thus any non-ideal solution can only partially approach perfect solution behavior at low concentrations. The extent to which it can do so will be incorporated in the definition of a dilute solution.

The *dilute solution* will be defined as one for which the solute follows Henry's law (within the accuracy of measurements) for a finite range of temperature and pressure. This may be stated exactly for a binary solution as

$$f_2 = \mathrm{k}_2 \tilde{N}_2. \qquad (11.3\text{–}1)$$

(Approximate forms of this law may be obtained by substitution of pressure for fugacity and of other concentration units for mole fraction.) It may readily be shown, by application of equation (11.1–7), that the solvent in such a solution must obey Raoult's law. The activity of each component may be chosen equal to its mole fraction in the region for which Henry's law is obeyed. The *heat of dilution* of a solution obeying Henry's law is zero; thus the *enthalpy* of each component is the same as in its standard state. The partial molal *free energy* and *entropy* are given by equations (11.2–4) and (11.2–5). The standard state for solute, however, has the properties of the infinitely dilute solution rather than those of the pure solute. Thus no general statement can be made concerning *heat* or *entropy of mixing* of the pure components.

Problem 11.3-1. Prove that, if the solute of a binary solution follows Henry's law, the solvent must follow Raoult's law.

Problem 11.3-2. Prove that there is no heat effect upon dilution of a solution obeying Henry's law.

It can be shown theoretically that any solute must obey Henry's law at sufficiently high dilution; in some cases, this may be below the concentration ranges generally employed experimentally.

A number of the familiar approximate relations of physical chemistry may be readily derived for the dilute solution by the same general procedures followed for perfect solutions in Section 11.2. One of these is the *elevation of the boiling point* of a solvent produced by addition of a non-volatile solute. At the boiling point of the solution, the partial molal free energy of the solvent in the solution (μ_1) must be equal to its molal free energy in the gas phase ($\tilde{F}_1$). If additional solute is added, the free energy of solvent in the solution will be reduced; at constant temperature the pressure of solvent vapor must be reduced. On the other hand, at constant pressure equilibrium can be reestablished by alteration of the temperature. In either case, the condition that equilibrium be maintained when a small change is made in the composition is

$$\mathrm{d}\tilde{F}_1 = \mathrm{d}\mu_1. \qquad (11.3\text{–}2)$$

At constant pressure, $\tilde{F}_1$ is a function of temperature only, whereas μ_1

depends on both temperature and composition. Thus, as in equation (11.2–8), one may write

$$\left(\frac{\partial \tilde{F}_1}{\partial T}\right)_P \mathrm{d}T = \left(\frac{\partial \mu_1}{\partial T}\right)_{P,\tilde{N}_2} \mathrm{d}T + \left(\frac{\partial \mu_1}{\partial \tilde{N}_2}\right)_{P,T} \mathrm{d}\tilde{N}_2. \qquad (11.3\text{–}3)$$

The first two derivatives are already familiar. The last may be derived from the fact that the solvent must obey Raoult's law. Thus equation (11.2–9) holds, and, since $\mathrm{d}\tilde{N}_1 = -\mathrm{d}\tilde{N}_2$,

$$\left(\frac{\partial \mu_1}{\partial \tilde{N}_2}\right)_{P,T} = -\left(\frac{\partial \mu_1}{\partial \tilde{N}_1}\right)_{P,T}$$

$$= -\frac{RT}{\tilde{N}_1}. \qquad (11.3\text{–}4)^{**}$$

Then

$$-\tilde{S}_1\,\mathrm{d}T = -\bar{S}_1\,\mathrm{d}T - \left(\frac{RT}{\tilde{N}_1}\right)\mathrm{d}\tilde{N}_2,$$

or

$$\frac{\mathrm{d}T}{\mathrm{d}\tilde{N}_2} = \frac{RT}{\tilde{N}_1(\tilde{S}_1 - \bar{S}_1)}. \qquad (11.3\text{–}5)^{**}$$

Finally, since the process is at equilibrium under constant pressure, the entropy change may be replaced by $\Delta H/T$; and, since the solvent obeys Raoult's law, the change in heat content, ΔH, is the heat of vaporization of pure solvent. Thus

$$\frac{\mathrm{d}T}{\mathrm{d}\tilde{N}_2} = \frac{RT^2}{\tilde{N}_1\,\Delta H_{\mathrm{vap}}}. \qquad (11.3\text{–}6)^{**}$$

Upon substitution for $\tilde{N}_1$, equation (11.3–6)** may be integrated. At high dilutions, however, $\tilde{N}_1$ may be set equal to unity throughout, in which case the equation reduces to the familiar one for boiling point elevation.

Problem 11.3-3. By integration of equation (11.3–6)** for the case where variation in $\tilde{N}_1$ may not be neglected, show that

$$\frac{T^\circ - T}{TT^\circ} = \frac{R}{\Delta H}\ln(1 - \tilde{N}_2). \qquad (11.3\text{–}7)^{**}$$

Show that as infinite dilution is approached the elevation of the boiling point becomes directly proportional to the mole fraction of added solute. Neglect the variation of heat of vaporization with temperature.

By an exactly analogous procedure, it may be shown that at sufficiently high dilutions the depression of the freezing point of a solvent by addition of solute is directly proportional to the mole fraction of the solute; in this case it is not necessary that the solute be non-volatile.

Problem 11.3-4. By the procedure outlined above, derive the equation.

$$\frac{dT}{d\tilde{N}_2} = -\frac{RT^2}{\tilde{N}_1\,\Delta\tilde{H}_f}, \tag{11.3–8}**$$

which gives the proportionality between freezing point depression and solute mole fraction for a dilute solution in which the solid phase is pure solvent.

Problem 11.3-5. Derive the expression below for the freezing point lowering when the solid phase formed is a perfect solid solution:

$$\frac{dT}{d\tilde{N}_2} = -\frac{RT^2}{\tilde{N}_1\,\Delta\tilde{H}_f}(1-\alpha), \tag{11.3–9}**$$

where α is the ratio between mole fraction of solute in the solid solution ($\tilde{N}_2'$) and the solute mole fraction ($\tilde{N}_2$) in the equilibrium liquid solution. Note that this expression reduces to equation (11.3–8)** as $\alpha \to 0$ and is valid, in practice, only for $\tilde{N}_2 \ll \tilde{N}_1$. (*Hint*. The partial molal free energy of solvent in the solid solution is given by an expression analogous to equation (11.2–9)).

Problem 11.3-6. A sample of dimethylamine started to freeze 0.10° below the melting point (180.97°K) of the pure material. Calculate the mole per cent of impurity, assuming that no solid solutions are formed. The heat of fusion of pure dimethylamine is 1420 cal mole^{-1}.

Problem 11.3-7. The heat of fusion of metallic lead is 1240 cal mole^{-1} at the melting point, 327.5°C. Calculate the freezing point of a solution containing 1 mole per cent of an impurity which does not dissolve in solid lead.

For completeness we shall now calculate the *osmotic pressure* of a solution. This quantity is related to the partial molal free energy of the solvent and has played an important part in theory of solutions. In a system composed of a dilute solution and pure solvent, at constant temperature, the partial molal free energy of the solvent component is lower in the solution than in the pure solvent, as illustrated by equation (11.2–4). If the two liquids are connected by a membrane permeable only to the solvent, the difference in free energy will cause a flow of solvent from the pure phase into the solution. Equilibrium may be established if the pressure over the solution is altered to make equal the free energy of solvent in the two phases. This excess of pressure is called the *osmotic pressure* of the solution. The change in free energy of the solvent produced by slight simultaneous changes in pressure and composition is

$$d\mu_1 = \left(\frac{\partial \mu_1}{\partial P}\right)_{\tilde{N}_2,T} dP + \left(\frac{\partial \mu_1}{\partial \tilde{N}_2}\right)_{P,T} d\tilde{N}_2. \tag{11.3–10}$$

If the change in pressure is so chosen as to counterbalance exactly the change in composition, $d\mu_1 = 0$ and

$$\left(\frac{\partial \mu_1}{\partial P}\right)_{\tilde{N}_2,T} dP = -\left(\frac{\partial \mu_1}{\partial \tilde{N}_2}\right)_{P,T} d\tilde{N}_2. \tag{11.3–11}$$

But, from equation (6.21–3),

$$\left(\frac{\partial \mu_1}{\partial P}\right)_{\tilde{N}_2,T} = \bar{V}_1;$$

and, from equation (11.3–4)**,

$$\left(\frac{\partial \mu_1}{\partial \tilde{N}_2}\right)_{P,T} = -\frac{RT}{\tilde{N}_1}\,.$$

Thus

$$\frac{\mathrm{d}P}{\mathrm{d}\tilde{N}_2} = \frac{RT}{\tilde{N}_1\bar{V}_1}\,. \qquad (11.3\text{–}12)^{**}$$

For the dilute solution, $\bar{V}_1$ can be replaced by $\tilde{V}_1$, the molar volume of pure solvent. Equation (11.3–12)** may then be integrated to give $P - P^\circ$, where P is the total pressure at equilibrium and P° is the vapor pressure of pure solvent. This increase in pressure is the *osmotic pressure* of the solution. If the integration is performed over a concentration range sufficiently small that variation of $\tilde{N}_1$ from unity may be neglected, the (approximate) result is

$$\pi = P - P^\circ = \frac{\tilde{N}_2 RT}{\tilde{V}_1}\,. \qquad (11.3\text{–}13)^{**}$$

This is one of the forms of the osmotic pressure equation of van't Hoff.

Problem 11.3-8. Calculate the osmotic pressure of 0.1, 0.3, and 0.5 molal sucrose solutions at 25°C, using the molar volume of pure water, 18.05 cm³ mole⁻¹, in each case. (This approximation is valid for these solutions within 0.2%.) The actual values are 2.59, 7.61, and 12.75 atm. Give reasons for the discrepancies.

11.4 Activity Coefficients and Standard States of Non-electrolytes

The treatment of solutions up to this point has been based on a standard state of unit activity (so defined) without reference to the nature of that state. This introduced no difficulty, and the standard state could have been defined as any real or hypothetical state of the system. However, in order to systematize calculations, it is desirable to choose a small number of convenient standard states. In doing so, it is convenient to pick real or hypothetical states which are as nearly identical as possible at all temperatures, and in which the system is as nearly ideal as possible. By equation (11.1–1) the activity is dimensionless.

1. Gaseous Systems. The standard state of a gas is the (hypothetical) ideal gas at unit pressure (and fugacity). This standard state has already been used in Section 10.6. The activity (f/f°) of the gas in any other state is therefore numerically equal to its fugacity. The entropy and enthalpy of the real gas, with respect to their values in the standard state, have been given in terms of the fugacity by equations (10.6–15) and (10.6–17). In more general terms, the entropy, enthalpy and free energy are given by

$$\tilde{S} - \tilde{S}^\circ = -\int_0^1 \left[\left(\frac{\partial \tilde{V}}{\partial T}\right)_P - \frac{R}{P}\right] \mathrm{d}P - \int_1^P \left(\frac{\partial \tilde{V}}{\partial T}\right)_P \mathrm{d}P, \tag{11.4–1}$$

$$\tilde{H} - \tilde{H}^\circ = -\int_0^P \left[T\left(\frac{\partial \tilde{V}}{\partial T}\right)_P - \tilde{V}\right] \mathrm{d}P, \tag{11.4–2}$$

and

$$\mu - \mu^\circ = -\int_0^1 \left(\frac{RT}{P} - \tilde{V}\right) \mathrm{d}P - \int_1^P \tilde{V}\, \mathrm{d}P. \tag{11.4–3}$$

Equations (11.4–1) to (11.4–3) are derived by considering the same sort of process as in Section 10.6, in which the real gas is expanded to a pressure low enough that it behaves ideally, and the (hypothetical) ideal gas is thereafter recompressed to 1 atm.

2. *Liquid* (*or Solid*) *Solvent.* The standard state for the solvent is the pure liquid or solid. Since the solvent approaches Raoult's law at infinite dilution, for any solution

$$a_1 \rightarrow \tilde{N}_1 \quad \text{as} \quad \tilde{N}_1 \rightarrow 1. \tag{11.4–4}$$

In any region where Raoult's law is obeyed, the activity will be equal to the mole fraction. Or, in another form,

$$\frac{a_1}{\tilde{N}_1} \rightarrow 1 \quad \text{as} \quad \tilde{N}_1 \rightarrow 1. \tag{11.4–5}$$

The ratio $a_1/\tilde{N}_1$ is called the *activity coefficient* of the solvent and is given the symbol γ_1. It is defined by the equation

$$\gamma_1 \equiv \frac{a_1}{\tilde{N}_1}. \tag{11.4–6}$$

3. *Solute.* The fugacity, and thus the activity of solute, in the dilute solution are proportional to the mole fraction of the solute, according to Henry's law. The *standard state* is the hypothetical solution of unit concentration whose properties are obtained by extrapolation of those of the dilute solution. The choice of concentration units is a matter of convenience; the concentration is customarily expressed in terms of mole fraction for concentrated solutions and in terms of molality (moles solute per 1000 g of solvent) for dilute solutions.

For an ideal solution the activity of the solute is at all times equal to the concentration. For a real solution the activity will approach the concentration as the latter approaches zero (i.e., as the solution approaches Henry's law behavior). We thus write for the activity coefficient γ_2

$$\frac{a_2}{\tilde{N}_2} \to 1 \quad \text{as} \quad \tilde{N}_2 \to 0 \tag{11.4–7}$$

or

$$\frac{a_2}{m} \to 1 \quad \text{as} \quad m \to 0, \tag{11.4–8}$$

depending on our choice of concentration units for the standard state.

In most systems the solution becomes saturated with respect to one of the components at a relatively modest concentration. In such systems it is usually convenient to consider the material present in smaller concentration as the solute and to follow the conventions given above. For completely miscible liquids the designation of solute and solvent is quite arbitrary; in such cases the standard states of both components may be taken as their pure liquids, and this is frequently done.

11.5 Calculation of Activities for Non-electrolytes

Four simple methods of obtaining activity coefficients are given separately in this section.

1. *Definitions and Calculation from Vapor Pressure Data.* The activity of the solvent can be calculated directly from equation (11.1–1), with f_1 the fugacity of solvent vapor above the solution and f_1° the fugacity of vapor above the pure solvent. The equation for the activity is then

$$a_1 = \frac{f_1}{f_1^\circ}. \tag{11.5–1}$$

If the vapor obeys the perfect gas law, one may write

$$a_1 = \frac{p_1}{p_1^\circ}, \tag{11.5–2)*$$

where p_1 is the partial vapor pressure of solvent above the solution, and p_1° is the vapor pressure of pure solvent.

The corresponding equation for the activity of the solute is

$$a_2 = \frac{f_2}{f_2^\circ}. \tag{11.5–3}$$

The fugacity in the standard state (f_2°) must be evaluated by the extrapolation indicated in equation (11.4–7) or (11.4–8). The result is

$$f_2 = \mathrm{k}_2, \tag{11.5–4}$$

where k_2 is the Henry's law constant for the solute, defined by the equation

$$k_2 = \lim_{c_2 \to 0} \frac{f_2}{c_2} \cdot \qquad (11.5\text{–}5)$$

Consequently, the final expression for the activity of solute is

$$a_2 = \frac{f_2}{k_2} \cdot \qquad (11.5\text{–}6)$$

The pressure may usually be used as an approximation to the fugacity in equation (11.5–6).

Problem 11.5-1. Prove equation (11.5–6). (*Hint.* At all concentrations, $a_2 = f_2/f_2^\circ$; note that $a_2/c_2 \to 1$ as $c_2 \to 0$, and apply (11.5–5).)

If the pure solute were chosen as standard state, the activity of the solute could be calculated in the same way as that of the solvent. Solute activities determined in this manner may be converted to the standard state described by equation (11.5–6) if the activity coefficient can be extrapolated to infinite dilution. The limit is then the ratio of the activities of the two possible standard states for the solute.

A word of caution is required with regard to the common practice of treating any vapor as a perfect gas. This is certainly justified if the vapor pressure is low but is often quite inaccurate at 1 atm. For pure water at 100°C and 1 atm, the vapor differs by 0.6% from the perfect gas law. For benzene vapor at its normal boiling point and 1 atm. the fugacity is almost 2% less than the pressure.

Problem 11.5-2. Table 11.5–1 contains equilibrium data on the system ethanol-chloroform at 35°C. Calculate the activities of ethanol (a_1) and chloroform (a_2) for the different solutions, assuming that the vapors behave as ideal gases. Calculate the vapor pressure of the (hypothetical) state in which $a_2 = 1$, and compare with the vapor pressure of pure chloroform, which is 295.11 mm Hg.

Table 11.5–1

Vapor–Liquid Equilibria for Ethanol–Chloroform Mixtures at 35°C†

Mole Fraction of Chloroform in Liquid	Mole Fraction of Chloroform in Vapor	Total Vapor Pressure
0.0000	0.0000	102.78
0.0100	0.0414	106.20
0.0200	0.0832	109.83
0.0500	0.2000	121.58
0.1000	0.3588	143.23
0.2000	0.5754	190.19
0.3000	0.6844	228.88
0.4000	0.7446	257.17
0.5000	0.7858	276.98

† From the data of G. Scatchard and C. L. Raymond, *J. Am. Chem. Soc.*, **60**, 1278 (1938).

2. *Calculation of Activity from Distribution between Solvents.* If a solute is distributed between two immiscible solvents, its fugacity at equilibrium must be the same above both solvents, and its activity in one solvent must be directly proportional to its activity in the other. The proportionality constant, by equation (11.4–7), will be the limiting ratio of the equilibrium concentrations in the two solvents as the concentrations approach zero. This method is particularly applicable if the solute forms a nearly ideal solution in one solvent, or if its activity may be measured much more easily in one solvent than in the other.

3. *Activity of Solutions Which May Be Used as Electrodes* (*from Cell Measurements*). If two electrodes of the same pure metal in the same physical condition are placed in contact with an electrolyte, there may be a transfer of material, but there is no change in free energy. If two copper electrodes are in contact with a cupric sulfate solution, the over-all reaction will be

$$\text{Cu (on electrode 1)} = \text{Cu (on electrode 2)}; \qquad \Delta F = RT \ln \frac{a_2}{a_1} = 0, \tag{11.5–7}$$

since the activity of copper must be the same in two identical electrodes. By equation (6.20–5), the electrical work (in this case $\mathcal{N}\mathcal{F}\mathcal{E}$) is given by

$$w_e = -\Delta F = \mathcal{N}\mathcal{F}\mathcal{E}. \tag{11.5–8}$$

The electromotive force of the cell is thus

$$\mathcal{E} = -\Delta F/\mathcal{N}\mathcal{F}, \tag{11.5–9}$$

and must also be zero. If the two electrodes are not physically identical, the activities will be different, and the electromotive force of the cell provides a measurement of their difference.

In a metallic solution, the more electropositive metal will be the only one to enter into the cell reaction. Consider a cell involving electrodes which are solutions of gold in lead in contact with a lead salt as electrolyte. In this cell the reaction will be

$$\text{Pb (in solution at } \tilde{N}_1'\text{)} = \text{Pb (in solution at } \tilde{N}_1\text{)}, \tag{11.5–10}$$

so that the free energy change is

$$\Delta F = RT \ln \frac{a_1}{a_1'} = -\mathcal{N}\mathcal{F}\mathcal{E}, \tag{11.5–11}$$

and the corresponding voltage is

$$\mathcal{E} = -\frac{RT}{\mathcal{N}\mathcal{F}} \ln \frac{a_1}{a_1'} \cdot \tag{11.5–12}$$

If the first electrode is pure lead, its activity will be unity, and

$$\mathscr{E} = -\frac{RT}{2\mathscr{F}} \ln a_1, \qquad (11.5\text{–}13)$$

since two faradays of electricity accompany the transfer of one gram atom of lead. Kleppa[1] has made measurements of the system lead-gold at and above 600°C, using one electrode of pure lead and the other a lead-gold alloy, with the electrolyte a fused salt containing some lead chloride. Table 11.5–2 gives some of the results of measurements at 600°C. Kleppa defines the standard states of both materials as the pure material, with modifications to the treatment that should be evident to the reader at this stage.

Table 11.5–2

Activity of Lead at 600°C from Cell Measurements

Atomic Fraction of Lead in Alloy Electrode	Emf at 600°C (millivolts)	a_{Pb} in Alloy Electrode
0.9665	1.40	0.9623
0.9345	2.75	0.9294
0.9008	4.25	0.8932
0.8205	8.81	0.7911
0.7393	14.14	0.6866
0.6715	18.86	0.6056
0.6054	25.19	0.5118
0.5078	35.15	0.3927
0.3697	53.20	0.2431
0.2702	74.25	0.1389
0.2135	91.20	0.0885

If the metal used as the solute is more electropositive than the solvent metal, as with the thallium amalgams, the solute ions must be in the electrolyte instead of those of the solvent metal, otherwise the solvent metal would be formed from the electrolyte at the expense of the solute metal. In this case it is preferable to use a reference alloy rather than the pure metal as the reference electrode. From equation (11.5–11), for a solute taking part in the cell reaction,

$$\ln a_2 = \ln a_2' - \frac{\mathscr{N}\mathscr{F}\mathscr{E}}{RT}, \qquad (11.5\text{–}14)$$

where a_2' is the activity of thallium in a reference electrode whose mole

[1] O. Kleppa, *J. Am. Chem. Soc.*, **71**, 3275 (1949).

fraction is $\tilde{N}_2'$. Upon conversion to common logarithms and subtraction of $\log \tilde{N}_2$, the mole fraction of thallium in the other electrode, this becomes

$$\log \frac{a_2}{\tilde{N}_2} = \log a_2' - \left(\frac{\mathcal{N}\mathcal{F}\mathcal{E}}{2.303\ RT} + \log \tilde{N}_2\right). \tag{11.5–15}$$

Since $\log a_2/\tilde{N}_2$ must approach zero as $\tilde{N}_2$ approaches zero (infinite dilution), it is evident that the quantity in parentheses must extrapolate to the finite value $\log a_2'$. If this function is plotted against the mole fraction of solute, the intercept at $\tilde{N}_2 = 0$ gives $\log a_2'$, and the activity coefficient at all other values of $\tilde{N}_2$ may be obtained by use of equation (11.5–15).

Problem 11.5-3. Table 11.5–3 gives the voltage at 600°C of the cell

$$Sn(l)\,|\,SnCl_2 \text{ in } LiCl_2(l)\,|\,\text{Sn–Au solution}(l)$$

from the data of Kleppa. X_{Sn} is the atomic fraction of tin in the second electrode. Calculate the activity and activity coefficient of the tin in each solution.

Table 11.5–3

Cell Voltages in a Tin–Gold System at 600°C†

X_{Sn}	Voltage (mv)	X_{Sn}	Voltage (mv)
0.9026	4.52	0.4982	72.18
0.8125	11.16	0.4426	93.90
0.6815	27.65	0.3596	131.70
0.5985	41.50	0.2941	166.55
0.5480	56.25	0.2589	189.80
0.5302	63.30	0.2223	217.50
0.5091	69.00		

† From the data of O. Kleppa, *J. Am. Chem. Soc.*, **72,** 3346 (1950).

4. *Calculation of the Activity of One Component from That of the Other.* A fundamental relationship between the activities of solvent and solute has already been derived from the Duhem equation and given as equation (11.1–6):

$$\tilde{N}_1\, d \ln a_1 = -\tilde{N}_2\, d \ln a_2. \tag{11.1–6}$$

This may be rearranged to the form

$$d \ln \frac{a_1}{\tilde{N}_1} = -\frac{\tilde{N}_2}{\tilde{N}_1}\, d \ln \frac{a_2}{\tilde{N}_2}, \tag{11.5–16}$$

which upon integration from $\tilde{N}_1 = 1 = a_1$ to some other mole fraction gives

$$\ln \frac{a_1}{\tilde{N}_1} = -\int_{\tilde{N}_2=0}^{\tilde{N}_2} \frac{\tilde{N}_2}{\tilde{N}_1}\, d \ln \frac{a_2}{\tilde{N}_2}. \tag{11.5–17}$$

Problem 11.5-4. Show that equation (11.5–16) follows from equation (11.1–6), and then prove equation (11.5–17). Note that $d\tilde{N}_2 = -d\tilde{N}_1$, so that $\tilde{N}_2 \, d \ln \tilde{N}_2 = -\tilde{N}_1 \, d \ln \tilde{N}_1$.

Equation (11.5–17) is useful for calculation of the activity of solvent from that of solute. The integration required may be performed graphically except for the point $\tilde{N}_2 = 1$, where $\tilde{N}_2/\tilde{N}_1$ becomes infinite. The reverse process is frequently more useful, since very often the activity of the solvent may be measured more readily than that of the solute. Unfortunately, the analogous equation for determination of a_2 cannot be integrated in this fashion, since the ratio $\tilde{N}_1/\tilde{N}_2$, which occurs in the integral, becomes infinite as the standard state is approached.

Problem 11.5-5. Write an equation for $\ln (a_2/\tilde{N}_2)$ analogous to (11.5–17), and prove the validity of the statement above.

Lewis and Randall[2] have devised a function h in terms of which the integration for $\ln (a_2\tilde{N}_1/\tilde{N}_2)$ may be performed. The result is

$$\ln \frac{a_2}{r} = -h - \int_0^{\tilde{N}_2/\tilde{N}_1} \frac{h}{r} \, dr, \tag{11.5–18}$$

where

$$h = \frac{1}{r} \ln a_1 + 1 \quad \text{and} \quad r = \frac{\tilde{N}_2}{\tilde{N}_1}. \tag{11.5–19}$$

Problem 11.5-6. Show that h goes to zero and that the ratio h/r remains finite as r approaches zero. Note that, as $r \to 0$, $a_1 \to \tilde{N}_1$.

Problem 11.5-7. Derive equation (11.5–18) from equation (11.5–16). (*Hint.* The proof of equation (11.5–16) may be accomplished readily if the function h is differentiated and $\ln a_1$ then eliminated by use of equations (11.1–6) and (11.5–19); upon subtraction of $d \ln r$ from both sides, the equation may then be integrated to give (11.5–18).

11.6 Change of Activity with Temperature. Calculation of Activity from Freezing Points

This section describes a very powerful method of obtaining activity coefficients.

If equation (6.22–2) is solved for $\ln a_i$ and then differentiated with respect to the temperature, one obtains equation (11.1–4):

$$\left(\frac{\partial \ln a_i}{\partial T}\right)_{P,n_i} = \left(\frac{\partial}{\partial T}\right)_P \left(\frac{\mu_i - \mu_i^\circ}{RT}\right) = -\frac{\bar{H}_i - \bar{H}_i^\circ}{RT^2} \equiv -\bar{L}_i/RT^2. \tag{11.1–4}$$

Equation (11.1–4) may be integrated, if the dependence of $\bar{L}_i$ on temperature

[2] G. N. Lewis and M. Randall, *Thermodynamics*, McGraw-Hill, New York, 1923.

is known, so as to give the activity as a function of temperature. Thus the activity of a component at a variety of temperatures may be obtained from its value at one temperature and a knowledge of the thermal properties of the solution.

Alternatively, equation (11.1–4) may be employed for determination of activities from measurement of the freezing points of solutions. In a system consisting of a solution and solid solvent, the partial molal free energy and activity of the solvent will be the same in both phases. Since the activity is a relative quantity, it must be referred to the same standard state for both parts of the system; in this case the standard state chosen is pure liquid solvent. The activities of solid and liquid are both unity at the normal freezing point, T_0, of the solvent. The activity of the solid phase at any other temperature may be derived by integration of (11.1–4); the result is also the activity of solvent in the solution which freezes at the second temperature.

The relative partial molal quantity required for the integration of (11.1–4) is the enthalpy of pure solid solvent with respect to the pure liquid. This is

$$\bar{L}_s = \tilde{H}_s - \tilde{H}_1^\circ = -\Delta H_f, \tag{11.6–1}$$

where $\tilde{H}_s$ is the enthalpy of the solid, $\tilde{H}_1^\circ$ that of the pure liquid at the same temperature, and $\Delta\tilde{H}_f$ the heat of fusion at this temperature. Upon substitution of (11.6–1) into (11.1–4), the activity of the solid is given by

$$\frac{\mathrm{d}\ln a_s}{\mathrm{d}T} = \frac{\Delta H_f}{RT^2}, \tag{11.6–2}$$

where a_s is the activity of solvent in the solid and in the solution which is in equilibrium with solid at temperature T.

The activity of the solid is obtained by integration of equation (11.6–2). It is convenient to make a change in variables before carrying out this integration. Let T be given by

$$T = T_0 - \theta, \qquad \mathrm{d}T = -\mathrm{d}\theta, \tag{11.6–3}$$

where θ is the *lowering of the freezing point*. Upon insertion of ΔH_f as a function of temperature, the right side of (11.6–2) may be written as a series in θ which converges rapidly for small values of θ. For most purposes the heat of fusion may be written as a linear function of temperature,

$$\Delta H_f = \Delta H_{T_0} - \Delta C_P\theta, \tag{11.6–4}$$

where ΔC_P is the heat capacity of the liquid less that of the solid. Upon substitution for T and ΔH_f, followed by expansion in series, equation (11.6–2) becomes

$$\frac{-\mathrm{d}\ln a_s}{\mathrm{d}\theta} = \left(\frac{1}{RT_0^2}\right)\left[\Delta H_{T_0} + \left(\frac{2\Delta H_{T_0}}{T_0} - \Delta C_P\right)\theta + \left(\frac{3\Delta H_{T_0}}{T_0^2} - \frac{2\Delta C_P}{T_0}\right)\theta^2 + \cdots\right]. \tag{11.6–5}$$

Problem 11.6-1. Prove equation (11.6–5).

Equation (11.6–5) may be written as a generalized series in θ. Since the activity of solvent is the same in the solid and in the solution, this becomes

$$-\mathrm{d}\ln a_1 = (A + B\theta + C\theta^2 + \cdots)\,\mathrm{d}\theta. \tag{11.6–6}$$

Upon integration between T_0 and T,

$$-\ln a_1 = A\theta + \tfrac{1}{2}B\theta^2 + \tfrac{1}{3}C\theta^3 + \cdots, \tag{11.6–7}$$

since $a_1 = 1$ and $\theta = 0$ at T_0, the normal freezing point.

The activity of solvent in a given solution *at its freezing point* is obtained by substituting into (11.6–7) the value of θ for the chosen solution. In order to obtain the activity at some other temperature, say T_0, it is necessary to apply equation (11.1–4), using the $\bar{L}_1$ appropriate to this concentration. This relative partial molal quantity is frequently small enough that the dependence of solvent activity on temperature may be neglected.

The activity of the solute may now be calculated by use of the Duhem equation. For the present the temperature correction to the solvent activity will be neglected, so that (11.6–7) will be taken to give the activity of solvent at all temperatures between T_0 and T. In this case the activity a_1 of solvent in a solution where its mole fraction is $\tilde{N}_1$ is given as a function of the freezing point lowering θ of that solution by equation (11.6–7). The calculation of solute activity will be illustrated for concentration expressed as molality.

For concentrations expressed as molality, equation (11.1–6) may be written

$$\mathrm{d}\ln a_2 = -\frac{\tilde{N}_1}{\tilde{N}_2}\,\mathrm{d}\ln a_1 = -\frac{1000}{\tilde{M}_1 m}\,\mathrm{d}\ln a_1, \tag{11.6–8}$$

where $\tilde{M}_1$ is the molar weight of the solvent. When equation (11.6–6) is used for a_1,

$$\mathrm{d}\ln a_2 = \frac{1000}{\tilde{M}_1 m}(\mathrm{A} + \mathrm{B}\theta + \mathrm{C}\theta^2 + \cdots)\,\mathrm{d}\theta. \tag{11.6–9}$$

The solute activity is obtained by integration of (11.6–9) from zero molality to the value m. This integration is simplified, as usual, by suitable transformation and change of variables. The constant A is given by (11.6–5) as $(\Delta H_{T_0}/RT_0^2)$. The first term of the series in (11.6–9) may be replaced in terms of the *freezing point lowering constant* λ:

$$\lambda = \frac{\tilde{M}_1 R T_0^2}{1000\ \Delta H_{T_0}}, \tag{11.6–10}$$

and the remaining terms written as $f(\theta)$. Equation (11.6–9) then becomes

$$\mathrm{d}\ln a_2 = \frac{\mathrm{d}\theta}{\lambda m} + \frac{1}{m} f(\theta)\,\mathrm{d}\theta, \tag{11.6–11}$$

where $f(\theta)$ is defined by

$$f(\theta) = \frac{1000}{\tilde{M}_1}(B\theta + C\theta^2 + \cdots). \tag{11.6–12}$$

Problem 11.6-2. Derive equation (11.6–11) from (11.6–8) by carrying out the substitutions indicated.

Equation (11.6–11) may be integrated over any range of concentration where $1/m$ is finite. In order to carry the integration to $m = 0$, it is necessary to subtract from both sides $\mathrm{d}\ln m = \mathrm{d}m/m$; when this has been done, the equation becomes

$$\mathrm{d}\ln\frac{a_2}{m} = \frac{\mathrm{d}\theta}{\lambda m} - \frac{\mathrm{d}m}{m} + \frac{1}{m} f(\theta)\,\mathrm{d}\theta. \tag{11.6–13}$$

The integration of (11.6–13) is simplified by use of a variable j, suggested by Lewis and Randall.[3] This variable is defined by the equation

$$j = 1 - \frac{\theta}{\lambda m}, \tag{11.6–14}$$

in terms of which

$$\frac{\mathrm{d}\theta}{\lambda m} = (1 - j)\frac{\mathrm{d}m}{m} - \mathrm{d}j. \tag{11.6–15}$$

Upon substitution of this quantity into equation (11.6–13) and integration of the equation, the resulting expression for a_2/m is

$$\ln\frac{a_2}{m} = -\int_0^m \frac{j}{m}\,\mathrm{d}m - j + \int_0^m \frac{1}{m} f(\theta)\,\mathrm{d}\theta, \tag{11.6–16}$$

[3] Lewis and Randall, *op. cit.*, p. 286.

since both ln (a_2/m) and j approach zero as $m \rightarrow 0$, in accordance with Section 11.4.

Problem 11.6-3. Show that $j \rightarrow 0$ as $m \rightarrow 0$, and then prove equations (11.6–15) and (11.6–16).

Equation (11.6–16) may be used for the calculation of solute activity from freezing point data, provided, as originally stipulated, that the effect of temperature on activity may be neglected, at least over the temperature range covered by the freezing point data. This is generally the case for non-electrolytes. The corrections necessary where the effect of temperature must be considered will be discussed in connection with the activity of electrolytes in Chapter 13.

Problem 11.6-4. Table 11.6–1 gives the lowering of the freezing point (θ) of benzene produced by the addition of *p*-cresol. Use the procedure above to calculate the activity a_1 and activity coefficient γ_1 of benzene in each solution. The freezing point of pure benzene is 5.53°C; its molal heat of fusion is 2350 cal. The heat capacity of liquid benzene may be taken as 31.8 cal mole^{-1} deg^{-1}, and that of solid as 32.3 cal mole^{-1} deg^{-1}.

Table 11.6–1

Freezing Point Lowering of *p*-Cresol in Benzene†

Molality of *p*-Cresol, m	Freezing Point Lowering, θ	θ/m	Molality of *p*-Cresol, m	Freezing Point Lowering, θ	θ/m
0.0861	0.420	4.878	0.9951	3.483	3.501
0.2341	1.100	4.699	1.143	3.773	3.301
0.2906	1.305	4.490	1.466	4.405	3.006
0.3867	1.663	4.300	1.691	4.780	2.827
0.6389	2.539	3.974	1.852	5.002	2.700

† C. R. Bury and H. O. Jenkins, *J. Chem. Soc.*, **146,** 688 (1934).

Problem 11.6-5. Utilizing the data of Problem 11.6–4, calculate the activity and activity coefficient of *p*-cresol at m = 0.0861, 0.3867, 1.143, and 1.852.

Systematic Calculation of Enthalpy (Heat Content), Free Energy, and Entropy Changes in Chemical Reactions. The Equilibrium Constant. Use of Tables. The Third Law of Thermodynamics

CHAPTER 12

12.1 Introduction

With the conclusion of the last chapter we have reached the goal of being able to predict the conditions in a chemical system at equilibrium. In this chapter we shall consider the methods of applying the thermodynamic functions enthalpy, free energy, and entropy most directly to the study of chemical equilibria. Lewis and Randall[1] did just this in 1923 with the help of barely adequate data. In many cases we shall use their methods; in other cases there are now more convenient ones. The calculations are frequently facilitated by the use of tables; examples of these tables and their use are given in this chapter.

Certain relationships derived in Chapter 6 will be amplified for special

[1] G. N. Lewis and M. Randall, *Thermodynamics*, McGraw-Hill, New York, 1923.

cases, not only in order to make this chapter as self-contained as possible but also to emphasize the simplicity of calculations with the use of the tables. Some of the quantities required are most easily obtained by use of the third law of thermodynamics. The physical basis of this law and its application are considered briefly in this chapter. Its meaning is considered later, in the discussion of statistical thermodynamics.

12.2 Enthalpy Change. Heat of Reaction at Constant Pressure

In considering the general equation for the change in a property in a chemical reaction

$$\mathrm{aA} + \mathrm{bB} = \mathrm{lL} + \mathrm{mM} + x \tag{12.2–1}$$

at constant pressure it is well to be more general than to consider merely reactions with the same constant pressure on the reactants and products. Instead the pressure is considered constant for any particular reactant or product. The constant pressures, P_{A}, etc., on the reactants are not regarded as equal and neither are the constant pressures on the products, P_{L}, etc.

If each term in equation (12.2–1) is now made to represent the enthalpy of the corresponding compound, it is clear that x is the negative of ΔH, the enthalpy change.

According to Section 5.2, equation (5.2–3), at constant pressure

$$q = \Delta H, \tag{12.2–2}$$

and ΔH is equal to the heat of reaction at constant pressure, as has already been pointed out in Section 5.10.

It is obviously desirable to tabulate the enthalpy of chemical compounds as a function of temperature, but it is clear that, if these enthalpies are to yield heats of reaction at constant pressure by substitution in equation (12.2–1), they must be referred to a common energy zero. One procedure is to use the *standard heat of formation*, which is defined as *the heat withdrawn from the surroundings when one mole of the material in the state specified is formed from its elements in their most common form and in their standard state at the temperature specified.* Thus the heats of formation at room temperature of graphite, gaseous hydrogen at zero pressure (or any pressure in the hypothetical perfect gas state), gaseous oxygen at zero pressure, monoclinic sulfur, crystalline silver, liquid mercury, liquid bromine, and solid iodine will always be zero. In practice, heats of formation are most commonly given at 25°C and 0°K, and sometimes at 18°C; for a few substances tables are available which cover an extended temperature range. Table 12.2–1 gives, among other things, the heats of

Table 12.2–1
Heat of Formation at 0°K; Free Energy, and Equilibrium Constant of Formation, Entropy, and Heat Capacity at 298.15°K (25°C)†

Substance	Description	State	$\Delta H_f°$ at 0°K (kcal/mole)	$\Delta H_f°$ at 298.15°K (25°C) (kcal/mole)	$\Delta F_f°$ at 298.15°K (25°C) (kcal/mole)	$\log_{10} K_f$ at 298.15°K (25°C)	$\tilde{S}°$ at 298.15°K (25°C) (cal/deg mole)	$\tilde{C}_P°$ at 298.15°K (25°C) (cal/deg mole)
O_2		g	0.	0.	0.	0.	49.003	7.017
O_3	Ozone	g		34.0	39.06	−28.631	56.8	9.12
H_2		g	0.	0.	0.	0.	31.211	6.892
H^+	Std. state, hyp. $m = 1$	aq		0.	0.	0.	0.	0.
OH^-	Std. state, hyp. $m = 1$	aq		−54.957	−37.595	27.5566	−2.519	−32.0
H_2O	Water	g	−57.107	−57.7979	−54.6357	40.04724	45.106	8.025
		l		−68.3174	−56.6902	41.55313	16.716	17.996
F		g	17.8	18.3	14.2	−10.41	37.917	5.436
F_2		g	0.	0.	0.	0.	48.6	7.52
HF		g		−64.2	−64.7	47.402	41.47	6.95
HF	Std. state, hyp. $m = 1$	aq		−78.66	−66.08	48.435	−2.3	−29.5
HF_2^-		aq		−153.6				
Cl		g	28.61	29.012	25.192	−18.4651	39.4569	5.2203
Cl^-	Std. state, hyp. $m = 1$	aq		−40.023	−31.350	22.9792	13.17	−30.0
Cl_2		g	0.	0.	0.	0.	53.286	8.11
HCl		g	−22.019	−22.063	−22.769	16.6896	44.617	6.96
	Hyp. $m = 1$	aq		−40.023	−31.350	22.9792	13.16	−30.0
Br^-		g		−55.3				
Br^-	Std. state, hyp. $m = 1$	aq		−28.90	−24.574	18.0124	19.29	−30.7
Br_2		l	0.	0.	0.	0.	36.4	
HBr		g		−8.66	−12.72	9.3269	47.437	6.96
	Std. state, hyp. $m = 1$	aq		−28.90	−24.574	18.0124	19.29	−30.7

I_2		g	15.640	14.876	4.63	−3.3937	62.280	8.81
		c	0.	0.	0.	0.	27.9	13.14
		aq		5.0				
HI		g	6.73	6.20	0.31	−0.227	49.314	6.97
	Std. state, hyp. $m = 1$	aq		−13.37	−12.35	9.052	26.14	−31.0
S		g		53.25	43.57	−31.9362	40.085	5.66
	Rhombic	c, II	0.	0.	0.	0.	7.62	5.40
	Monoclinic	c, I		0.071	0.023	−0.0169	7.78	5.65
SO_2		g		−70.96	−71.79	52.621	59.40	9.51
SO_3		g		−94.45	−88.52	64.884	61.24	12.10
H_2S		g		−4.815	−7.892	5.7847	49.15	8.12
	Std. state, hyp. $m = 1$	aq		−9.4	−6.54	4.797	29.2	
H_2SO_4		l		−193.91				32.88
SO_4^{2-}	Std. state, hyp. $m = 1$	aq		−216.90	−177.34	129.988	4.1	4.0
SO_3^{2-}	Std. state, hyp. $m = 1$	aq		−149.2	−118.8	87.08	10.4	
Ag	Solid	s	0.	0.	0.	0.	10.21	6.09
Ag_2O	Solid	s	−6.940	−7.306	−2.586	−1.8955	29.09	15.67
AgCl	Solid	s		−30.36	−26.22	19.222	22.97	12.14
AgBr	Solid	c, II		−23.78	−22.93	16.807	25.60	12.52
Hg	Liquid	l	0.	0.	0.	0.	18.5	6.65
Hg_2Cl_2	Solid	c		−63.32	−50.35	36.91	46.8	24.3

† The entries in this table are taken mainly from F. D. Rossini et al., "Selected Values of Chemical Thermodynamic Properties," *Natl. Bur. Standards Circ.*, No. **500** (1952); the last six entries are from F. D. Rossini et al., *Selected Values of Physical and Thermodynamic Properties of Hydrocarbons and Related Compounds*, Carnegie Press, Pittsburgh, 1953.

Table 12.2-1 (Continued)

Substance	Description	State	ΔH_f° at 0°K kcal/mole	ΔH_f° at 298.15°K. (25°C) kcal/mole	ΔF_f° at 298.15°K. (25°C) kcal/mole	$\log_{10} K_f$ at 298.15°K. (25°C)	$\tilde{S}^\circ$ cal/deg mole	$\tilde{C}_P^\circ$ cal/deg mole
Cu	Solid	c	0.	0.	0.	0.	7.96	5.848
$CuSO_4$	Solid	c		−184.0	−158.2	115.96	27.1	24.1
Zn	Solid	c	0.	0.	0.	0.	9.95	5.99
ZnO	Solid	c		−83.17	−76.05	55.744	10.5	9.62
$ZnSO_4$	Solid	c		−233.88	−208.31	152.688	29.8	28.
Mg	Solid	c	0.	0.	0.	0.	7.77	5.71
$Mg(OH)_2$	Solid	c		−221.00	−199.27	146.06	15.09	18.41
MgO	Solid	c		−143.84	−136.13	99.781	6.4	8.94
$MgSO_4$	Solid	c		−305.5	−280.5	153.83	21.9	23.01
C	Solid	Graphite	0.	0.	0.	0.	1.3609	2.066
		Diamond	0.5766	0.4532	0.6850	−0.5021	0.5829	1.449
CO		g	−27.2019	−26.4157	−32.808	24.048	47.30	6.965
CO_2		g	−93.969	−94.052	−94.2598	69.091	51.061	8.874
CH_4		g	−15.987	−17.889	−12.140	8.899	44.50	8.536
C_2H_2		g	54.329	54.194	50.000	−36.649	47.997	10.499
C_2H_4		g	14.522	12.496	16.282	−11.935	52.45	10.41
C_2H_6		g	−16.517	−20.236	−7.860	5.761	54.85	12.59
n-C_3H_8		g	−19.482	−24.820	−5.614	4.115	64.51	
n-Butane		g	−23.67	−30.15	−4.10	3.0052	74.12	23.29
n-Pentane		g	−36.91	−35.00	−2.00	1.4660	83.40	28.73
		l		−41.36	−2.25		62.92	
Neopentane	$(CH_3)_4C$	g	−31.30	−39.67	−3.64	2.668	73.23	
Benzene		g	24.000	+19.820	30.99	−22.714	64.34	19.52
Toluene		g	17.500	11.950	29.23	−21.424	76.42	24.80

formation at 0°K (column 4) and 298.15°K (column 5) for a variety of substances. Only where the element is not in its common form (e.g., where it is in a metastable state or in solution) will the heat of formation for an element be other than zero. In this table the symbol g means perfect gas state, and the symbols s and l mean solid and liquid respectively. The heats of formation in Table 12.2–1 may be substituted for enthalpies in equation (12.2–1) to obtain heats of reaction directly.

Problem 12.2-1. Show that heats of formation may be treated as enthalpies in obtaining heats of reaction. Noting that the heat of formation is the difference between the enthalpies of a compound and its elements, apply equation (12.2–1) and show that the enthalpies of the elements must cancel, except where one of the reactants or products is an element.

Problem 12.2-2. Calculate the heats of reaction at 298.15°K for each of the following reactions from Table 12.2–1.

(a) $F_2(g) + 2HCl(g) = 2HF(g) + Cl_2(g)$;
(b) $Ag(s) + HCl(g) = \frac{1}{2}H_2(g) + AgCl(s)$;
(c) $Hg_2Cl_2(s) + 2Ag(s) = 2Hg(s) + 2AgCl(s)$;
(d) $Hg_2Cl_2(s) + Cl_2(g) = 2HgCl_2(s)$;
(e) $2Zn(s) + O_2(g) = 2ZnO(s)$;
(f) $2Mg(s) + O_2(g) + 2H_2O(l) = 2Mg(OH)_2(s)$;
(g) $CuSO_4(s) + Zn(s) = ZnSO_4(s) + Cu(s)$;
(h) $Mg(OH)_2(s) + H_2SO_4(l) = MgSO_4(s) + 2H_2O(l)$;
(i) $CH_3CH_2CH_2CH_2CH_3(g) = (CH_3)_4C(g)$;
(j) $CO_2(g) + 4H_2(g) = CH_4(g) + 2H_2O(g)$;
(k) $3HC{\equiv}CH(g) = C_6H_6(\text{benzene, g})$.

If the compounds are present in solution, partial molal enthalpies are needed for the calculation of ΔH. In Chapter 8 a quantity called the partial molal relative enthalpy was defined using as reference states: (a) for the solute its partial molal enthalpy in infinitely dilute solution; (b) for the solvent the molal enthalpy of pure solvent. If ΔH_f represents the heat of formation of the pure substances, $\bar{L}_2$ and $\bar{L}_1$ represent the enthalpies of the solute and solvent in a solution, and $\tilde{L}_2$ represents the enthalpy of pure solute relative to the partial molal heat content in the infinitely dilute solution, for the solute the heat of formation required for Table 12.2–1, $\Delta H_f\ (m = x)$, is given by

$$\Delta H_f\ (m = x) = \Delta H_f - \tilde{L}_2 + \bar{L}_2. \qquad (12.2\text{–}3)$$

For the solvent,

$$\Delta H_f\ (m = x) = \Delta H_f + \bar{L}_1. \qquad (12.2\text{–}4)$$

For reasons which will be apparent when the free energy of a reaction is discussed, and because, if Henry's law is assumed, changes of concentration produce no heat effects, it is convenient to consider as reference state a hypothetical 1 molal solution whose properties are deduced from the very dilute solutions by assuming Henry's law at all temperatures. The state will be denoted by the abbreviation ($m = 1$, hyp.) It is not possible to determine the heat of formation or other thermodynamic properties of single ions. For convenience these have been chosen with respect to the corresponding properties for the hydrogen ion as zero, and they are so tabulated in Table 12.2–1. It is possible to show that these entries will give correct heats of reaction, etc., by the same general procedures as were used in Problem 12.2–1.

Problem 12.2-3. Calculate the heat of the following reactions from Table 12.2–1.

(a) $H_2(g) + Cl(g) = 2HCl$ ($m = 1$, hyp.).

(b) $Cl_2(g) + 2HBr$ ($m = 1$, hyp.) $= 2HCl$ ($m = 1$, hyp.) $+ Br_2(l)$.

(c) $AgCl + \frac{1}{2}H_2(g) = HCl$ ($m = 1$, hyp.) $+ Ag(s)$.

(d) $2HCl$ ($m = 1$, hyp.) $+ Mg(OH)_2(s) = MgCl_2(s) + 2H_2O(l)$.

12.3 Change of Heat of Reaction with Temperature

The two expressions for change of heat of reaction at constant volume and at constant pressure are respectively

$$\left(\frac{\partial \Delta E}{\partial T}\right)_V = \Delta C_V \tag{5.11–2}$$

and

$$\left(\frac{\partial \Delta H}{\partial T}\right)_P = \Delta C_P, \tag{5.11–1}$$

which were derived in Section 5.11. Because the constant pressure process is the important one, the latter of these two relations is the more important. To use it with facility the data necessary for evaluation of ΔC_P must be available in the form of equations or tables. The last column of Table 12.2–1 gives $\tilde{C}_P{}^\circ$ at 298.15°K, from which ΔC_P for a given reaction may be evaluated by use of equation (12.2–1). In the next section analytical relations and tables showing the variation of heat capacity with temperature will be considered in some detail; these are useful for evaluating ΔC_P over a temperature range.

For our present purposes, a general analytical relation for $\tilde{C}_P$ as a function of temperature will suffice. This is

$$\tilde{C}_P = a_0 + a_1 T + a_2 T^2 + a_3 T^3 + \cdots. \tag{12.3–1}$$

If Δa_0, Δa_1, Δa_2 are used to denote quantities for the constants a_0, a_1, a_2, etc., analogous to the quantity ΔC_P, that is, for the reaction

$$aA + bB \cdots = lL + mM + \cdots,$$

$$\Delta a = la_L + ma_M + \cdots - aa_A - ba_B - \cdots, \tag{12.3–2}$$

then ΔC_P is given by the equation

$$\Delta C_P = \Delta a_0 + \Delta a_1 T + \Delta a_2 T^2 + \Delta a_3 T^3 + \cdots. \tag{12.3–3}$$

The enthalpy change is found by integration of (5.11–1) after replacement of ΔC_P through use of (12.3–3). It is

$$\Delta H = \Delta H_0 + \int (\Delta a_0 + \Delta a_1 T + \Delta a_2 T^2 + \Delta a_3 T^3 + \cdots)\, dT$$

$$= \Delta H_0 + \Delta a_0 T + \frac{\Delta a_1 T^2}{2} + \frac{\Delta a_2 T^3}{3} + \frac{\Delta a_3 T^4}{4} + \cdots, \qquad (12.3\text{–}4)$$

where ΔH_0 is the constant of integration. If equation (12.3–3) were valid down to the absolute zero, ΔH_0 could be identified with the change in enthalpy at the absolute zero. This is never, *emphatically never*, the case. Equations such as (12.3–1) are never in practice series expressions of a form which faithfully reproduces the heat capacity at all temperatures even though, as is often the case, they may be valid from room temperature to a few thousand degrees Kelvin. The failure of such equations lies in the low temperature region, where effects discussed in later chapters come into play.

There is a definite value in giving tables of heat of formation as a function of the temperature and in using the values as enthalpies in equation (12.2–1) to calculate heats of reaction. In most cases such tables use, as reference state, the elements in their most common state at the temperature of the entry. This choice of reference states has the advantage that the heat of formation for an element substituted in (12.2–1) will be zero unless that element is in an unusual state. This advantage is, however, offset by the fact that subtraction of the heats of formation at two temperatures T_1 and T_2 gives

$$(\Delta H_f)_2 - (\Delta H_f)_1 = \int_{T_1}^{T_2} (\Delta C_P)_{\text{formation}}\, dT \qquad (12.3\text{–}5)$$

rather than

$$\tilde{H}_2 - \tilde{H}_1 = \int_{T_1}^{T_2} \tilde{C}_P\, dT \qquad (12.3\text{–}6)$$

for the compound in question, because the reference states of the elements change with temperature.

To have a table from which changes in enthalpy with temperature can be evaluated for each substance, the reference states must be chosen at one temperature, and this temperature is most conveniently taken as the absolute zero. For the construction of such a table, heat capacities must be known for each substance down to the absolute zero. A table could then be constructed to give the heat of formation of each substance (at some particular temperature) from its elements (always at absolute zero). Such a table could be used not only to obtain heats of reaction but also to get changes of enthalpy with temperature of individual substances, as in equation (12.3–6).

The procedure outlined immediately above has not been generally followed. Instead, tables have been prepared of the enthalpies of various substances each relative to its own enthalpy at absolute zero ($\tilde{H}^\circ - \tilde{H}_0^\circ$). Table 12.3–1 gives the enthalpies of a number of substances in the ideal gas state with respect to the ideal gas state at 0°K. For a single substance, the entries in Table 12.3–1 may be used to get the change in enthalpy with temperature directly. If heats of reaction are desired, combination of the entries as in equation (12.2–1) will give

$$-x = \Delta H^\circ - \Delta H_0^\circ. \qquad (12.3\text{–}7)$$

The constant ΔH_0° is the heat of reaction at absolute zero. It may be evaluated from heats of formation at 0°K, as in Table 12.2–1, or it may be obtained by comparison at a temperature where ΔH° is known, from heats of formation or otherwise.

Problem 12.3-1. Calculate the heats of the following reactions at the temperatures indicated.

(a) C_2H_4 (g) + H_2(g) = C_2H_6 (g) at 300°K.
(b) C_2H_6 (g) + H_2(g) = $2CH_4$(g) at 500°K.
(c) $2C_2H_6$(g) + 2C (graphite) = $3C_2H_4$ (g) at 800°K.

Problem 12.3-2. By plotting data from Table 12.3–1, calculate the heat capacity of C_2H_6 at 250°K.

Problem 12.3-3. Calculate the number of calories required to heat 1 mole of each of the following substances from 300° to 1500°K: (a) oxygen, (b) hydrogen, (c) graphite, (d) ideally gaseous ethane.

Problem 12.3-4. Calculate how much heat it takes to convert liquid benzene at 300°K to benzene vapor at very low pressure at 1000°K. The heat of vaporization of benzene is 8090 cal mole^{-1} at 300°K.

12.4 Heat Capacity of Substances as a Function of Temperature

The heat capacities of gases may be obtained by direct experimental methods or by calculation from spectroscopic data; the latter method is discussed in Chapters 17 to 20. The values of the heat capacity at various temperatures can be expressed analytically by equations of the form of (12.3–1). It is convenient to tabulate the heat capacity in the hypothetical perfect gas state (i.e., at zero pressure). Correction to other pressures may be made by use of equation (6.12–6). The constants in the equation

$$\tilde{C}_P^\circ = \mathrm{a} + \mathrm{b}T + \mathrm{c}T^2 + \mathrm{d}T^3, \qquad (12.4\text{–}1)$$

applying to gases at zero pressure over the temperature range 300°K to

Table 12.3-1
Enthalpies of Various Substances as Function of Temperature†.

$(\tilde{H}^\circ - \tilde{H}_0^\circ)$

Substance	Temperature (°K)											
	150	200	250	298.15	300	400	500	600	800	1000	1500	2000
$O_2(g)$	1,037.0	1,384.4	1,732.5	2.069.8	2,082.6	2,792.4	3,524.0	4,279.2	5,856.0	7,497.0	11,776.5	16,218
$H_2(g)$	1,038.5	1,360.6	1,694.3	2,023.8	2,036.5	2,731.0	3,429.5	4,129.5	5,537.4	6,965.8	10,694.2	14,671.6
$H_2O(g)$				2,367.7	2,382.0	3,194.0	4,025.5	4,882.2	6,689.6	8,608.0	13,848	19,630
C (graphite)	43.155	91.980	162.475	251.56	255.30	502.8	821.0	1,198.2	2,081.6	3,075.0	5,814	8,780
$CO(g)$		1,389.4	1,737.	2,072.6	2,085.6	2,783.6	3,490.0	4,209.6	5,700.0	7,257.0	11,358	15,636
$CO_2(g)$				2,238.1	2,254.0	3,194.8	4,223.0	5,322.6	7,689.6	10,222	17,004	24,140
$CH_4(g)$	1,192	1,591	1,995	2,397	2,413	3,323	4,365	5,549	8,321	11,560	21,130	
$C_2H_6(g)$	1,258	1,744	2,280	2,856	2,879	4,296	6,010	8,016	12,760	18,280	34,500	
$C_2H_4(g)$				2,525	2,544	3,711	5,117	6,732	10,480	14,760	27,100	
$C_2H_2(g)$				2,391.5	2,410.8	3,541.2	4,791.0	6,127	8,999	12,090	20,541	
$C_6H_6(g)$				3,401	3,437	5,762	8,750	12,285	20,612	30,163	57,350	

† All data are taken from Rossini et al, *Selected Values of Physical and Thermodynamic Properties.* With the exception of carbon, the substances are in the perfect gas state.

1500°K for a variety of substances, have been given by H. M. Spencer and collaborators.[2] Table 12.4–1 gives the required constants for a number of

Table 12.4–1

Heat Capacity of Various Substances[2]

$\tilde{C}_P{}^\circ = \text{a} + \text{b}T + \text{c}T^2 + \text{d}T^3$

Substance	a	b × 10^3	c × 10^7	d × 10^9
$H_2(g)$	6.9469	−0.1999	4.808	
$N_2(g)$	6.4492	1.4125	−0.807	
$O_2(g)$	6.148	3.102	−9.23	
C (graphite)	−1.265	14.008	−103.31	2.751
NO	7.020	−0.370	25.46	−1.087
CO	6.420	1.665	−1.96	
CO_2	5.152	15.224	−96.81	2.313
H_2O	7.256	2.298	2.83	
SO_2	6.147	13.844	−91.03	2.057
NH_3	6.189	7.887	−7.28	
HCl	6.7319	0.4325	3.697	
SO_3	3.603	36.310	−288.28	8.649
CH_4	4.171	14.450	2.67	−1.722

substances, as taken from these data. The absence of an entry in any of the columns means that the term multiplied by the constant in question is not to be included in the equation.

Problem 12.4-1. Calculate how much heat is required to raise the temperature of each of the following gases from 300° to 1500°K at zero pressure: (a) sulfur dioxide, (b) oxygen, (c) ethane. Compare (b) and (c) with the results of Problem 12.3–3.

For most solids and liquids the heat capacities must be tabulated directly. However, for certain monatomic crystalline metals $\tilde{C}_V$ can be tabulated in terms of θ/T, where θ is a constant for the metal, the theoretical meaning of which is discussed in Chapter 21. A table for $\tilde{C}_V$ in terms of θ/T is given in Appendix 4 (Table A.4–1). The values of θ for certain substances are given in Table 12.4–2. Table A.4–1 also includes values of $\tilde{E}/T$,

Table 12.4–2

Values of Debye θ for Metals

Substance	θ
Al	398
Cu	315
Ag	215
Pb	88

[2] H. M. Spencer and J. L. Justice, *J. Am. Chem. Soc.*, **56**, 2311 (1934); H. M. Spencer and J. N. Flanagan, *ibid.*, **64**, 2511 (1942); H. M. Spencer, *ibid.*, **67**, 1859 (1945); and H. M. Spencer, *Ind. Eng. Chem.*, **40**, 2153 (1948).

the element at 0°K being taken as reference state, and of the entropy. (Note that the function $\tilde{E}/T$ changes slowly with temperature and is thus convenient for interpolation.)

Problem 12.4-2. Calculate the heat capacity of Ag at constant volume at 100°K from Table A.4–1.

Problem 12.4-3. Calculate the amount of heat required to heat metallic copper from 90° to 300°K at constant volume.

For the conversion of $\tilde{C}_V$ into $\tilde{C}_P$, the equation derived in Problem 6.12–1, namely

$$C_P = C_V - T\frac{(\partial V/\partial T)_P{}^2}{(\partial V/\partial P)_T}, \tag{6.12–2}$$

may be used. This equation may be rewritten in terms of the coefficients of expansion and compressibility defined by

$$\alpha = \frac{1}{V}\left(\frac{\partial V}{\partial T}\right)_P \tag{12.4–2}$$

and

$$\beta = -\frac{1}{V}\left(\frac{\partial V}{\partial P}\right)_T. \tag{12.4–3}$$

Then (12.4–2) becomes

$$C_P = C_V + \frac{TV\alpha^2}{\beta}. \tag{12.4–4}$$

Problem 12.4-4. Calculate $(\tilde{C}_P - \tilde{C}_V)$ and $\tilde{C}_P$ for silver at 300°K, taking α equal to 5.8×10^{-5} and β equal to 0.80×10^{-6}. The density of metallic silver is 10.5 g/cm³. **Watch units.**

12.5 The Free Energy Change in a Chemical Reaction

In this section the general chemical reaction

$$\mathrm{aA + bB + \cdots = lL + mM + \cdots}$$

will be considered at constant temperature. It seems wise to consider the criterion of reversibility again. If A and B are in solution or are gases, the concentrations of A, etc., are kept constant by having large reservoirs from which A, etc., are withdrawn, and the concentrations of L, etc., are kept constant by having large reservoirs to which they may be added.

First let us apply the first law equation

$$\Delta E = q - w. \tag{5.1–4}$$

This becomes

$$\begin{aligned}\Delta E &= q - (\mathrm{l}P_\mathrm{L}V_\mathrm{L} + \mathrm{m}P_\mathrm{M}V_\mathrm{M}\cdots - \mathrm{a}P_\mathrm{A}V_\mathrm{A} - \mathrm{b}P_\mathrm{B}V_\mathrm{B}\cdots)\\ &= q - \Delta(PV).\end{aligned} \tag{12.5–1}$$

In this case the only work done is against the atmosphere, but let us suppose that it is done reversibly because the pressures are held constant by frictionless pistons. Actually, in practice, the pistons are the atmosphere or the gas ahead in some connecting line. If this work is later dissipated at a valve, the chemical system neither knows nor cares.

In general, the reaction is not reversible even though the work against the atmosphere is reversible. Thus q cannot be replaced by $T\,\Delta S$. The entropy change in the surroundings, however, is $-q/T$. The second law, as stated in Section 6.7, required that for an irreversible process

$$\int_A^B dS_s + \int_A^B dS_r > 0. \tag{6.7–3}$$

Thus

$$-\frac{q}{T} + \Delta S > 0, \tag{12.5–2}$$

or

$$q < T\,\Delta S. \tag{12.5–3}$$

Consequently

$$\Delta E < T\,\Delta S - \Delta(PV). \tag{12.5–4}$$

Problem 12.5-1. Suppose that a cell whose voltage is 0.222 v is shorted by 1000 ohms, its own resistance being negligible. Assuming an infinitely large cell, calculate (a) the current, (b) the heat dissipated in the resistance per equivalent of current drawn from the cell. Supposing that the resistance is outside the thermostat; calculate (c) the heat withdrawn from the thermostat. (d) What is the net thermal effect in the thermostat if the resistance is included in the thermostat? (e) Repeat (a), (b), (c), and (d), assuming that the cell resistance is 100 ohms. Assume that the heat of reaction is $-10{,}000$ cal per equivalent.

If the chemical reaction were made reversible, neither ΔE, ΔS, nor $\Delta(PV)$ would change, since the process would involve the same initial and final states; thus the inequality in equation (12.5–4) can be rewritten

$$\Delta E = T\,\Delta S - \Delta(PV) + \Delta F, \tag{12.5–5}$$

where ΔF is a quantity introduced solely in order to make the right-hand side of equation 12.5–4 equal to ΔE. Its identification will be made later. Equation (12.5–5) may be rearranged to give

$$\Delta F = \Delta E + \Delta(PV) - T\,\Delta S. \tag{12.5–6}$$

The quantity $-\Delta F$ is thereby just the amount by which $T\,\Delta S$ exceeded the heat withdrawn from the bath when the chemical reaction occurred doing only expansion work. When the process is reversible, the heat withdrawn from the bath is $T\,\Delta S$, since, in the reversible process,

$$q = T\,\Delta S, \tag{12.5–7}$$

and ΔS cannot change because the initial and final products are still the same. This extra heat withdrawn from the bath must have been converted into work other than that against pistons. If the reaction has been made reversible by an opposing electromotive force, this is the electrical work, so that

$$-\Delta F = w_e. \tag{12.5–8}$$

Only if ΔF is zero will the reaction be reversible without opposing electromotive forces. For the reaction to be spontaneous, it must be possible to obtain electrical work by making the process reversible; that is, $-\Delta F$ is then positive. Thus, for any process

$$\Delta F \overline{\leq} 0. \tag{6.18–5}$$

This is the same result as was deduced in Section 6.18. In Section 6.18 a cell was first set up and then the postulated electrical work evaluated as ΔF.

The definition

$$F = E + PV - TS \tag{6.18–2}$$

reproduces equation (12.5–6), and the introduction of the partial molal free energies (chemical potentials), μ_i, defined by equation (6.20–15) yields

$$\Delta F = \mathrm{l}\mu_{\mathrm{L}} + \mathrm{m}\mu_{\mathrm{M}} - \mathrm{a}\mu_{\mathrm{A}} - \mathrm{b}\mu_{\mathrm{B}}, \tag{12.5–9}$$

where μ_{A}, μ_{B}, μ_{L}, μ_{M} respectively represent the partial molal free energies of A, B, L, M. Thus, if we write $\mathcal{N}\mathcal{F}\mathcal{E}$ for the electrical work, (6.18–2) becomes

$$\Delta F = \Delta H - T\,\Delta S = -\mathcal{N}\mathcal{F}\mathcal{E}, \tag{12.5–10}$$

where $\mathcal{N}$ is the number of electrical equivalents involved in the reaction, and $\mathcal{F}$ is the Faraday constant. The statements in this section have in a sense been reiteration of those in Section 6.18. The repetition has been made partly because of the little understood role of the electrical work and partly because an effort has been made to make this chapter self-contained.

12.6 Effect of Concentration on the Free Energy and Electromotive Force

The value of ΔF for any chemical reaction must depend on the state of the chemicals involved. Table 12.2–1, column 6, gives the free energy change, at 298.15°K, of the reaction by which the compound in the specified standard state is formed from its elements in their most common state at the same temperature. The choice of standard states has been discussed in Sections 11.4 and 12.2. Location in the table of elements in states for which the given $\Delta F°$ is zero (as was done in Section 12.2 for heats of formation) will remove any doubt about the reference states employed. For gases the pressure of the (ideal) gas must be specified. In keeping with Section 11.4 the pressure of the standard state is taken as 1 atm.

From Table 12.2–1 it is found that the standard free energy of formation, $\Delta F_f°$ of hydrogen chloride is −22,769 cal at 298.15°K. Thus one may write

$$\tfrac{1}{2}H_2 \text{ (ideal g, 1 atm)} + \tfrac{1}{2}Cl_2 \text{ (ideal g, 1 atm)} = HCl \text{ (ideal g, 1 atm)}; \quad \Delta F° = -22{,}769 \text{ cal.} \tag{12.6–1}$$

It is also found that the free energy of formation of solid silver chloride at 298.15°K is −26,220 cal:

$$Ag(s) + \tfrac{1}{2}Cl_2\text{(ideal g, 1 atm)} = AgCl(s); \quad \Delta F° = -26{,}220 \text{ cal.} \tag{12.6–2}$$

The superscript on $\Delta F°$ denotes that all the compounds are in their standard states. Subtracting the second of these equations from the first,

$$\tfrac{1}{2}H_2\text{(ideal g, 1 atm)} + AgCl(s) = Ag(s) + HCl\text{(ideal g, 1 atm)}; \quad \Delta F° = 3451 \text{ cal.} \tag{12.6–3}$$

This is the same as the reaction studied in Section 6.17 except for alteration of the pressure of hydrogen chloride.

As in the example of Section 6.18 (see equation 6.18–4), the difference $(\Delta F - \Delta F°)$ between the free energy change for a reaction involving any states and that for one involving only standard states may be calculated if $(\mu - \mu°)$, the difference in free energy between the arbitrary state and the standard state, is known for each reactant and product. These differences are expressed quite generally in terms of their activities as

$$\mu - \mu° = RT \ln a. \tag{6.22–2}$$

Clearly

$$\Delta F - \Delta F° = \mathrm{l}(\mu_\mathrm{L} - \mu_\mathrm{L}°) + \mathrm{m}(\mu_\mathrm{M} - \mu_\mathrm{M}°) - \mathrm{a}(\mu_\mathrm{A} - \mu_\mathrm{A}°) - \mathrm{b}(\mu_\mathrm{B} - \mu_\mathrm{B}°). \tag{12.6–4}$$

Thus

$$\Delta F - \Delta F° = RT \ln \frac{a_\mathrm{L}{}^\mathrm{l} a_\mathrm{M}{}^\mathrm{m}}{a_\mathrm{A}{}^\mathrm{a} a_\mathrm{B}{}^\mathrm{b}}, \tag{6.23–1}$$

where a_A, a_B, a_L, and a_M are the activities of A, B, L, and M respectively. in the general reaction given at the head of Section 12.5. This equation can then be applied to the reaction between hydrogen and silver chloride. According to equation (6.23–1), for the reaction given as equation (12.6–3),

$$\Delta F - \Delta F° = RT \ln \frac{P_{HCl}}{P_{H_2}^{1/2}}, \tag{12.6–5)*}$$

where ΔF° at 298.15°K is given by (12.6–3) and P_{HCl} and P_{H_2} have been substituted for the activities. The other activities are unity. Equation (12.6–5) is equivalent to (6.23–2).

Similarly, an expression for the electromotive force of a cell in which a chemical reaction occurs is obtained by use of equation (12.5–10) in equation (6.23–1). This is

$$\mathscr{E} - \mathscr{E}^\circ = -\frac{RT}{\mathscr{N}\mathscr{F}} \ln \frac{a_L{}^l a_M{}^m}{a_A{}^a a_B{}^b} . \tag{12.6–6}$$

Problem 12.6-1. Using the datum in equation (12.6–3), calculate ΔF at 298.15°K for the reaction H_2 (ideal g, 1 atm) + 2AgCl(s) = Ag(s) + 2HCl(ideal g, 10^{-3} atm), and compare the value with that given as the electrical work in equation (6.17–10). Calculate the emf of a cell in which this process occurs reversibly, and compare with equation (6.17–10).

Problem 12.6-2. Using Table 12.2–1 to obtain ΔF° and assuming that silver and gold form a perfect solid solution, calculate ΔF for the process H_2(ideal g, 1 atm) + 2AgCl(s) = Ag(N_2 = 0.5 in Au) + HCl(ideal g, 1 atm), and the emf of a cell in which this process occurs at 298.15°K.

Problem 12.6-3. The potential of the cell Pt, H_2 |KOH(aq)| Pt, O_2 is 1.228 v at 298.15°K when each of the substances is in its standard state.

(a) Calculate the standard free energy for the reaction $H_2O(l) = H_2(g) + \frac{1}{2}O_2(g)$.

(b) A cell such as the one in this problem has an internal resistance of 0.05 ohm. Calculate the minimum voltage necessary for this cell to produce 0.2 mole of hydrogen per hour.

Problem 12.6-4. (a) From the data of Table 12.2–1, calculate at 25°C the standard free energy of the reaction $\frac{1}{2}H_2(g)$ + AgCl(s) = HCl(aq) + Ag(s), and from it the potential of the cell Pt, H_2 |HCl(aq)| AgCl, Ag, when each of the substances is in its standard state. (Note that the HCl is in solution.)

(b) The activity (a_2) of 2 molal HCl solution is 4.07. Using the information of part (a), calculate the emf, at 25°C, of the cell for 2 molal HCl, with a partial pressure of hydrogen of 730 mm Hg.

12.7 The Equilibrium Constant

A chemical reaction is at equilibrium when ΔF is zero. Thus, for the generalized reaction discussed in the last two sections, insertion into equation (6.23–1) of the activities obtained *when the reaction has the concentrations (or pressures) of its reactants and products such that it is at equilibrium under no applied electromotive force* yields

$$-\Delta F^\circ = RT \ln \left(\frac{a_L{}^l a_M{}^m}{a_A{}^a a_B{}^b}\right)_{\text{equilib.}} . \tag{12.7–1}$$

But ΔF° is a constant characteristic of the reference state, so that

$$\left(\frac{a_L{}^l a_M{}^m}{a_A{}^a a_B{}^b}\right)_{\text{equilib.}} = K; \tag{12.7–2}$$

K is another constant, called the equilibrium constant. Substituting (12.7–2) in (12.7–1), one obtains

$$\Delta F^\circ = -RT \ln K. \tag{12.7–3}$$

Upon application of (12.5–10), this becomes

$$\mathscr{E}^\circ = \frac{RT}{\mathscr{N}\mathscr{F}} \ln K. \tag{12.7–4}$$

This equation is obtained directly from (12.6–6) by setting $\mathscr{E}$ equal to zero at the equilibrium ratio of activities.

Problem 12.7-1. From the data of Problems 12.6–1 and 12.6–4, calculate the equilibrium constants, at 25°C, of the reactions

(a) $\frac{1}{2}H_2(g) + AgCl(s) = HCl(g) + Ag(s)$;
(b) $\frac{1}{2}H_2(g) + AgCl(s) = HCl(aq) + Ag(s)$.

Problem 12.7-2. Calculate the equilibrium constant, at 25°C, of the reaction $H_2O(l) = H_2(g) + \frac{1}{2}O_2(g)$, using the datum of Problem 12.6–3.

Problem 12.7-3. The standard potential, at 25°C, of the cell Pb, $PbSO_4$ | Ni $So_4(aq)$ | Ni is 0.09 v. Calculate the equilibrium constant of the reaction $Pb(s) + Ni\,SO_4(aq) = PbSO_4(s) + Ni$.

12.8 Change of Free Energy, Electromotive Force, and Equilibrium Constant with Temperature. The Gibbs–Helmholtz Equation

In Chapter 6 it was shown that

$$\left(\frac{\partial F}{\partial T}\right)_P = -S. \tag{6.19–6}$$

For a chemical reaction,

$$\left(\frac{\partial \Delta F}{\partial T}\right)_P = -\Delta S. \tag{12.8–1}$$

If ΔF is replaced by $(-\mathscr{N}\mathscr{F}\mathscr{E})$, by use of (12.5–10), this becomes

$$\left(\frac{\partial \mathscr{E}}{\partial T}\right)_P = \frac{\Delta S}{\mathscr{N}\mathscr{F}}\cdot \tag{12.8–2}$$

If (12.8–1) is used to replace ΔS in (12.5–10), the result is

$$\Delta F = \Delta H + T\left(\frac{\partial \Delta F}{\partial T}\right)_P\cdot \tag{12.8–3}$$

Similarly, substituting (12.8–2) into (12.5–10), one obtains

$$\mathscr{N}\mathscr{F}\mathscr{E} = -\Delta H + \mathscr{N}\mathscr{F}T\left(\frac{\partial \mathscr{E}}{\partial T}\right)_P\cdot \tag{12.8–4}$$

The last equation is known as the Gibbs-Helmholtz equation.

When applied to a chemical reaction, equation (6.19–10) becomes

$$\left[\frac{\partial(\Delta F/T)}{\partial T}\right]_P = -\frac{\Delta H}{T^2}. \qquad (12.8\text{–}5)$$

When equation (12.3–4) is used for ΔH, this equation becomes

$$\left[\frac{\partial(\Delta F/T)}{\partial T}\right]_P = -\frac{\Delta H_0}{T^2} - \frac{\Delta a_0}{T} - \frac{\Delta a_1}{2} - \frac{\Delta a_2}{3}T + \cdots. \qquad (12.8\text{–}6)$$

Upon integration between indefinite limits, there results

$$\frac{\Delta F}{T} = \frac{\Delta H_0}{T} - \Delta a_0 \ln T - \frac{\Delta a_1}{2}T - \frac{\Delta a_2}{6}T^2 + \cdots + I, \qquad (12.8\text{–}7)$$

where I is a constant of integration; multiplying by T,

$$\Delta F = \Delta H_0 - \Delta a_0 T \ln T - \frac{\Delta a_1}{2}T^2 - \frac{\Delta a_2}{6}T^3 + \cdots + IT. \qquad (12.8\text{–}8)$$

If the analytical expression for ΔC_P which formed the basis of equation (12.3–3) were a valid expansion of a function which correctly represented ΔC_P at all temperatures, I would be the value of $-\Delta S$ at the absolute zero. Since the expression was an empirical representation of ΔC_P over a limited temperature range only, I cannot be given any physical meaning.

If equation (12.8–7) is applied to the reference state,

$$R \ln K = -\frac{\Delta H_0^\circ}{T} + \Delta a_0 \ln T + \frac{\Delta a_1}{2}T + \frac{\Delta a_2}{6}T^2 + \cdots - I, \qquad (12.8\text{–}9)$$

where $R \ln K$ has been substituted for $-\Delta F^\circ/T$ according to equation (12.7–3); ΔH_0° is the enthalpy change in the chemical reaction where the products and reactants are each in their reference states; Δa_0, etc., and I are also for these same reference states.

Problem 12.8-1. For the reaction $N_2(g) + 3H_2(g) = 2NH_3(g)$ at 298.15°K, the equilibrium constant is 710 atm^{-2}, while the value for ΔH is $-21{,}880$ cal. Obtain an expression for the free energy change as a function of temperature, and evaluate the equilibrium constant at 700°K, using the data of Table 12.4–1.

Problem 12.8-2. Using the data of Tables 12.2–1 and 12.4–1, obtain an expression for the equilibrium constant as a function of temperature and calculate the equilibrium constant of the reaction $CO_2(g) + H_2(g) = CO(g) + H_2O(g)$: (a) at 298.15°K; (b) at 1000°K.

Problem 12.8-3. Calculate the equilibrium constant of the reaction $SO_2(g) + \frac{1}{2}O_2(g) = SO_3(g)$ at 800°K.

Problem 12.8-4. The electromotive force of the cell Pt | H_2, HCl(aq) | AgCl, Ag is given as a function of temperature by the expression[3]

$$\mathscr{E}^\circ = 0.22239 - 645.5 \times 10^{-6}(t - 25) - 3.284 \times 10^{-6}(t - 25)^2 + 9.948 \times 10^{-9}(t - 25)^3,$$

where t is the temperature in centigrade degrees.

(a) Calculate $\mathscr{E}^\circ$ for the cell at 50°C.

(b) Calculate ΔF°, ΔS°, and ΔH° for the reaction H_2(g) + 2AgCl(s) = 2HCl(aq) + Ag(s) at 50°C.

12.9 Methods of Obtaining Free Energies of Chemical Reactions

It is clear from Section 12.6 that the standard free energy change (ΔF°) of a chemical reaction may be obtained whenever a suitable reversible electromotive force cell can be set up. Equation (12.6–6) is used to calculate $\mathscr{E}^\circ$ from the measured value of $\mathscr{E}$ when the reactants and products have the known activities $a_A, \cdots, a_L$, etc. ΔF° is then given by equation (12.5–10) as

$$\Delta F^\circ = -\mathscr{N}\mathscr{F}\mathscr{E}^\circ. \tag{12.9–1}$$

Similarly, it is clear that, if the activities are known for a chemical reaction at equilibrium, ΔF° can be obtained at once by use of equation (12.7–3). Once ΔF° is known at one temperature, its value may be obtained at other temperatures by use of equation (12.8–7) if ΔH_0° and all the Δa's are known for the partial molal heat capacities corresponding to the standard states. The single value of ΔF° is used to solve for I; when the numerical value of I is substituted back in (12.8–7), a complete expression for the free energy results, as is illustrated by Problems 12.8–1 and 12.8–2.

However, the ultimate object of determining values of ΔF° for chemical reactions is to obtain tables of free energies of formation, of which Table 12.2–1 is an example. If the table is complete, ΔF° for any chemical reaction can be calculated, and thus the electromotive force of any reversible cell or the equilibrium conditions for any reaction can be calculated. If only the methods just outlined for determination of ΔF° were available, the direct determination of either the equilibrium conditions or the electromotive force of a reversible cell would be required at one temperature for all key reactions. In addition, values of ΔH at some one temperature and a knowledge of the values of the heat capacities of the chemicals involved are required, if ΔF° is to be obtained at other temperatures without direct measurement. The difficulty of studying chemical equilibrium or of setting up reversible cells would make construction of a complete table such as Table 12.2–1 impossible if there were not another method of obtaining ΔF° which entirely avoids such measurements.

[3] H. S. Harned and R. W. Ehlers, *J. Am. Chem. Soc.*, **54,** 1350 (1932); **55,** 2179 (1933).

It is at this point that the contribution of thermodynamics to the study of equilibria is seen most spectacularly. If all the heat $-\Delta H$ liberated in a reaction at constant pressure could always be converted into electrical work in a reversible cell, the term $T\,\Delta S$ in equation (12.5–6) would always be zero, and equation (12.7–3) would place ΔH equal to $-RT\ln K$. The whole problem could thus be solved by measurement of ΔH alone. At one time it was believed that ΔH had these properties; when it became evident that it had not, disappointment resulted. A feeling grew in some quarters that the *a priori* calculation of conditions of chemical equilibrium for any appreciable number of reactions of technical importance was an essentially hopeless task. What was obviously required was a way to determine ΔS by purely thermal measurement. This problem was essentially solved with the introduction of the *third law of thermodynamics;* its use will be discussed in the next section.

12.10 Determination of Entropy Changes in Chemical Reactions. The Third Law of Thermodynamics

If the energy levels of a gas have been determined spectroscopically or deduced in some other way, the entropy of the gas can be calculated with great accuracy. Such calculations can now be made for a great many substances. The basis of such calculations is related to the *third law of thermodynamics,* and statistical mechanics is used to derive the necessary formulas. This subject is discussed in Chapters 17 and 18. Once the entropy changes accompanying conversion of liquid or solid to the ideal gas state have been determined, the entropies of solids and liquids can also be calculated. Thus the difficulty mentioned at the end of the last section has proved unfounded and calculations of ΔF° can now be made from thermal data alone.

Problem 12.10-1. Pierce and Pace[4] calculated statistically the molar entropy of NF_3 to be 54.61 cal mole^{-1} deg^{-1} in the ideal gas state at 1 atm and the normal boiling point, 144.15°K. They obtained 2769 cal mole^{-1} as the molal heat of vaporization at the normal boiling point. Calculate the entropy of liquid NF_3 at 144.15°K.

If the energy levels of a gas cannot be satisfactorily determined, there is yet another way to get the entropy. The *third law of thermodynamics* states that the *entropy of any perfect crystalline substance is zero* and its C_P becomes zero asymptotically *at the absolute zero at all pressures.* By a perfect crystal is meant one in which there is no disorder; that is, there is a single unit cell which repeats itself throughout the crystal without any change in arrangement of the atoms within the cell, or without any

[4] L. Pierce and E. L. Pace, *J. Chem. Phys.*, **23**, 551 (1955).

change in relations of the unit cell. If there is disorder, as in a glass, or if the system fails to reach internal equilibrium, the law cannot hold.

This principle resulted from the speculations of G. N. Lewis, Richards, van't Hoff, Haber, Nernst, and Planck. It received the wide application it justly deserved in its use to determine the value of I in equation (12.8–7). This principle allows entropies to be calculated if heat capacities down to sufficiently low temperatures are known.

Problem 12.10-2. Using the data of Table 12.4–2 and Appendix 4, calculate the change in entropy between 0° and 298.15°K for solid silver at constant volume.

Problem 12.10-3. Table 12.10–1 gives the heat capacity of solid silver as a function of temperature. Calculate the entropy of solid silver at 298.15°K from these data. You may assume that the heat capacity is proportional to T^3 below 15°K. Compare with the results of Problem 12.10–2.

Table 12.10–1
Heat Capacity of Metallic Silver†

T (°K)	$\tilde{C}_P$	T (°K)	$\tilde{C}_P$	T (°K)	$\tilde{C}_P$
15	0.160	110	5.010	250	5.911
20	0.410	130	5.289	270	6.050
30	1.141	150	5.490	290	6.080
40	2.005	170	5.644	300	6.095
50	2.784	190	5.757		
70	3.904	210	5.837		
90	4.573	230	5.911		

† P. F. Meads, W. R. Forsythe, and W. F. Giauque, *J. Am. Chem. Soc.*, **63**, 1902 (1941).

Problem 12.10-4. For the general reaction involving solids, show how I can be evaluated if an equation of the type of (12.4–1) can be fitted to the data down to the absolute zero for each of the solids, and if the entropy of each of the solids is zero at the absolute zero.

It follows from the third law together with the second law that the coefficients of expansion of perfect crystalline substances must be zero at 0°K.

Problem 12.10-5. Prove that $(1/V)(\partial V/\partial T)_P$ is zero at 0°K.

Figure 12.10–1 is a graph of the heat capacity of hydrogen chloride from 16°K to the normal boiling point. The lower break in the curve represents the transition point between two crystalline forms, and the upper break represents the melting point. Table 12.10–2 summarizes the calculation of the entropy of the gas at the normal boiling point, using the equation

$$\tilde{S} = \int_0^{16} \tilde{C}_P \, d\ln T + \int_{16}^{T_t} \tilde{C}_P \, d\ln T + \frac{\Delta H_t}{T_t} + \int_{T_t}^{T_m} \tilde{C}_P \, d\ln T$$

$$+ \frac{\Delta H_m}{\tilde{T}_m} + \int_{T_m}^{T_v} \tilde{C}_P \, d\ln T + \frac{\Delta H_v}{T_v}, \qquad (12.10\text{–}1)$$

where T_t, T_m, and T_v represent temperatures of transition, fusion and

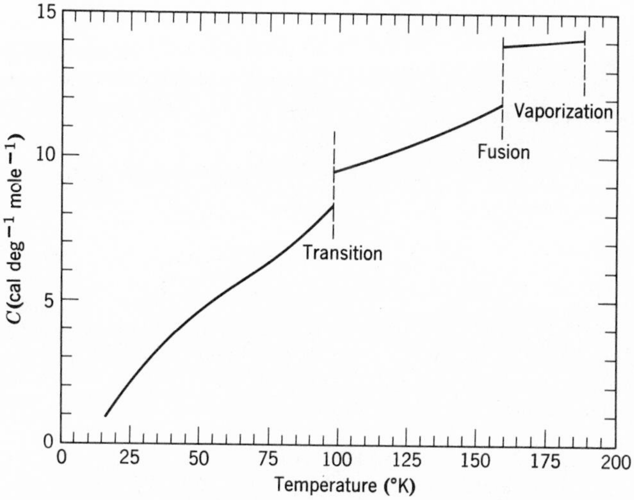

Fig. 12.10–1. Heat capacity of hydrogen chloride from 16° to 188°K.

vaporization, and ΔH_t, ΔH_m, and ΔH_v are the corresponding enthalpy increases on change of phase. The entropy of the crystalline solid is taken as zero at 0°K.

Table 12.10–2

Entropy of Hydrogen Chloride Gas

0° to 16°K (extrapolation)	0.30
16° to 98.36°K (graphical)	7.06
Transition (284.3/98.36)	2.89
98.36° to 158.91°K (graphical)	5.05
Fusion (476.0/158.91)	3.00
158.91° to 188.07° (graphical)	2.36
Vaporization (3860/188.07)	20.50
Gas (188.07°K, 1 atm)	41.2 ± 0.1 cal mole^{-1} deg^{-1}

The first term on the right side of equation (12.10–1) is obtained by extrapolation. For such a small contribution as this, it may usually be assumed that at low temperatures

$$\tilde{C}_P = aT^3. \tag{12.10–2}$$

Thus

$$\int_0^T \frac{\tilde{C}_P}{T}\,dT = \frac{aT^3}{3} = \frac{\tilde{C}_P}{3}. \tag{12.10–3}$$

The extrapolated part of the entropy (0.30 cal deg^{-1} mole^{-1}) can be verified by reference to Fig. 12.10–1. The remaining integrals on the right side of (12.10–1) are entropy increases expressed according to (6.13–3) and are evaluated graphically. The third, fifth, and seventh members on the right side of (12.10–1) represent respectively the entropies of transition, fusion, and vaporization at constant temperature expressed according to (6.16–2). The correction to the ideal gas state may be made using equation (11.4–1) with the necessary derivatives obtained from the Berthelot equation (4.5–3), using measured values of the critical constants. To obtain the entropy of the ideal gas at 1 atm and at high temperatures $\int_{T_v}^{T} \tilde{C}_P{}^\circ \, d\ln T$ must be evaluated.

Problem 12.10-6. Check the calculations in Table 12.10–2, using the original heat capacity data of Giauque and Wiebe,[5] which are given in Table 12.10–3, and the heats and temperatures of the phase changes which appear before the entries in Table 12.10–2 as denominator and numerator respectively of a fraction.

Table 12.10–3
Heat Capacity of Hydrogen Chloride

T (°K)	$\tilde{C}_P$ (cal mole^{-1} deg^{-1})	T (°K)	$\tilde{C}_P$ (cal mole^{-1} deg^{-1})	T (°K)	$\tilde{C}_P$ (cal mole^{-1} deg^{-1})
17.29	1.031	63.31	5.550	117.30	10.14
21.34	1.637	67.85	5.848	123.92	10.46
24.71	2.066	72.63	6.159	131.18	10.67
26.85	2.330	75.46	6.329	138.79	10.95
28.10	2.491	77.65	6.526	148.90	11.34
31.89	2.943	80.25	6.712	155.06	11.65
35.82	3.393	82.63	6.894	158.91	fusion
39.95	3.794	84.69	7.053	163.72	13.89
44.20	4.132	87.70	7.327	171.45	13.95
48.62	4.472	88.79	7.410	171.74	13.95
51.23	4.677	92.83	7.786	178.64	14.01
56.01	5.070	98.36	Transition	185.20	14.07
58.94	5.231	103.01	9.64	188.07	Vaporization

[5] W. F. Giauque and J. Wiebe, *J. Am. Chem. Soc.* **50**, 101 (1928).

Problem 12.10-7. For the reaction CH_3NH_2 (ideal g, 1 atm) + HCl (ideal g, 1 atm) = $CH_3NH_3Cl(s)$ at 298.15°K, $\Delta H°$ is −43,620 cal. The third law entropies of CH_3NH_2 (ideal g, 1 atm), HCl (ideal g, 1 atm), and CH_3NH_3Cl (solid) are respectively 58.22, 44.62, and 33.13 cal mole^{-1} deg^{-1}. Calculate $\Delta F°$ and K for the reaction at 298.15°K.

Problem 12.10-8. For the reaction $2Ag_2O(s) = 2Ag(s) + O_2(g)$ at 298.15°K, $\Delta H°$ is 14,610 cal, and the equilibrium constant is 79 atm. The entropies ($S°$) of Ag and O_2 are 10.21 and 49.00 cal mole^{-1} deg^{-1} at 298.15°K. Calculate the entropy ($S°$) of Ag_2O at this temperature and compare with the value given in Table 12.2–1.

Problem 12.10-9. For the reaction $NiCl_2(s) + H_2(g) = Ni(s) + 2HCl(g)$, Busey and Giauque[6] give the following data, all at 298.15°K: $\Delta H° = 28{,}888$, $\Delta F° = 16{,}400$. The entropy of metallic nickel is 7.14 cal mole^{-1} deg^{-1}. Using these data and Table 12.2–1, calculate (a) the entropy and (b) the heat of formation of solid $NiCl_2$ at 298.15°K.

By comparing entropies calculated using the third law with those obtained directly from equilibrium data and by study of coefficients of expansion at low temperatures,[7] this law has been verified. The relation of the law to certain consequences of the quantum mechanics will be discussed in Chapters 17 and 18, where it is shown that the statement of the law just given is a somewhat restricted one.

[6] R. H. Busey and W. F. Giauque, *J. Am. Chem. Soc.*, **75,** 1791 (1953).

[7] W. H. Keesom, F. P. G. A. J. van Ogt, and A. F. J. Jansen, *Proc. Roy, Soc. Amsterdam*, **29,** 786 (1926); H. Ebert, *Z. Physik*, **47,** 712 (1928); R. M. Buffington and W. M. Latimer, *J. Am. Chem. Soc.*, **48,** 2305 (1926).

Solutions of Electrolytes

CHAPTER 13

13.1 Properties of Dissociable Substances

In previous discussions of pure substances and solutions, the problem of association or dissociation of the materials did not arise. In the specification of entropy, enthalpy, volume, etc., of a given amount of material, it was generally necessary only to consider a suitably defined mass of substance without regard to possible dissociation or association of the material. Similarly, in the treatment of partial molal properties it was sufficient to speak of the property of a formula weight of solute without reference to the presence of ions or polymeric species in the solution, provided that a suitable means was available for determination of the desired property and its dependence on temperature or concentration.

The effect of polymerization may readily be seen upon consideration of a substance which forms a stable dimer in the gas phase at pressures low enough that the perfect gas law would otherwise apply. At pressures where dimerization was substantially complete, such a substance would occupy only half the volume predicted by the perfect gas law, but at sufficiently low pressure the substance would approach perfect gas behavior for the monomer. In some intermediate region the compressibility factor ($P\tilde{V}/RT$) would go from 1 to $\frac{1}{2}$ with increasing pressure. The description of the behavior of the gas can be simplified if the equilibrium between monomer and dimer is taken into account.

A more serious difficulty arises with respect to the vapor pressure from solution of a substance which dissociates. Hydrogen chloride is essentially undissociated in benzene, and its vapor pressure from benzene solutions will follow Henry's law (equation 11.3–1) at low concentrations. In aqueous solution, however, HCl is almost completely dissociated. Experiments show that at low concentrations its vapor pressure varies with the square of the molality, for reasons to be discussed below. The Henry's law constant as defined by equation (11.5–5) approaches zero, if the stoichiometric molality or mole fraction is used for the concentration. Thus the procedure described in Section 11.5 for determination of activity from vapor pressure data must be modified if it is to be applied to HCl. Likewise, the freezing point constant, λ, must be suitably altered to take into account the dissociation.

The difficulties may be resolved readily if the dissociation is specifically considered. In an aqueous solution, at least at high dilutions, hydrogen chloride is present primarily as hydrogen ions and chloride ions. As infinite dilution is approached, the acid must approach complete dissociation; that is, the concentration of each ion approaches the stoichiometric molality of the acid, and the fraction of the material present in undissociated form approaches zero. It is in this region also that perfect solution behavior must be approached. Consequently, as the concentration approaches zero, the ratio of activity to concentration approaches a constant value for each of the ions; the concentration used in the ratio is the stoichiometric concentration of the solution. The activity of undissociated acid may be defined in terms of the activities of the ions by writing the equilibrium constant for the dissociation:

$$\mathrm{HCl(aq)} = \mathrm{H^+} + \mathrm{Cl^-}; \qquad K = \frac{(a_{\mathrm{H^+}}a_{\mathrm{Cl^-}})}{(a_{\mathrm{HCl}})}. \tag{13.1–1}$$

It is evidently proportional to the product of the ion activities.

For the equilibrium with the gas phase, where the substance is undissociated, the reaction is

$$\mathrm{HCl(aq)} = \mathrm{HCl(g)}; \qquad K = \frac{f_{\mathrm{HCl}}}{a_{\mathrm{HCl}}}. \tag{13.1–2}$$

The fugacity (approximately, the vapor pressure) of HCl is thus proportional to the activity of the undissociated material, that is, to the product of the ion activities. At high dilutions, this product is proportional to the square of the stoichiometric concentration; accordingly, at high dilutions the vapor pressure of HCl from aqueous solutions is proportional to the square of the molality.

If the dissociation constant of equation (13.1–1) is sufficiently small, as for a weak organic acid, it is possible that the undissociated material may approach Henry's law behavior at a concentration where the effect of dissociation is still slight. Such systems may be treated as undissociated except at very low concentrations. If the dissociation constant is only moderately large, it may be evaluated and used in equation (13.1–1) to relate the activity of undissociated material to that of the ions. In such cases as aqueous solutions of HCl and other "strong" electrolytes the dissociation constant is sufficiently large that its evaluation is frequently impractical, and other methods must be used.

13.2 Activity in Solutions of Strong Electrolytes

If the dissociation constant of an electrolyte, for example that of equation (13.1–1), is large, whether or not it can be evaluated, it is useful to treat the solution as if all the solute were in the form of ions. The standard state for undissociated material is then chosen to make the dissociation constant unity. For a di-ionic salt this means that

$$a_2 \equiv a_+ a_-, \tag{13.2–1}$$

or, in general, for a salt A_xB_y, the activity a_2 becomes

$$a_2 = a_+{}^x a_-{}^y, \tag{13.2–2}$$

where a_2 is the activity of undissociated material at a given concentration; a_+ and a_- are the activities, and x and y the numbers of positive and negative ions respectively. As will become evident later, the individual activities cannot be determined separately, but only a product corresponding to a_2 above. The "mean ion activity" is defined by the general equation for a salt A_xB_y,

$$a_\pm = (a_2)^{1/\nu}, \tag{13.2–3}$$

where $\nu\ (= x + y)$ is the number of ions formed by the dissociation. For di-ionic salts this reduces to

$$a_\pm \equiv (a_2)^{1/2} \equiv (a_+a_-)^{1/2}. \tag{13.2–4}$$

For salts in which the numbers of positive and negative ions are not identical, the mean molality $m_\pm$ is defined by the equation

$$m_\pm \equiv [(m_+)^x(m_-)^y]^{1/\nu}. \tag{13.2–5}$$

The molalities of the individual ions are calculated from the stoichiometric molality, assuming complete ionization. The mean ion activity coefficient $\gamma_\pm$ is then defined by the equation

$$\gamma_\pm \equiv \frac{a_\pm}{m_\pm}, \tag{13.2–6}$$

or by an equation in the (undeterminable) individual ion activity coefficients

γ_+, equal to a_+/m_+, and γ_-, equal to a_-/m_-, of the same form as equation (13.2–5).

Problem 13.2-1. Derive the relationship

$$\gamma_\pm = (\gamma_+{}^x\gamma_-{}^y)^{1/\nu}, \tag{13.2–7}$$

where γ_+ and γ_- are the respective ion activity coefficients.

The standard state for the ions is chosen so that the activities of the ions approach their molalities as the solution approaches infinite dilution. That is,

$$\gamma_\pm \rightarrow 1 \quad \text{as} \quad m \rightarrow 0. \tag{13.2–8}$$

The properties of strong electrolytes in solvents of high dielectric constant differ from those of non-electrolytes in several essential respects beyond those due solely to dissociation. First, the deviations from ideal behavior are quite large. As a result it is necessary to go to extremely dilute solutions before ideal behavior is approached; in most cases it is practicable only to go to concentrations where the rate of approach is simple. Moreover, the partial molal heat contents, heat capacities, and other properties of the solute will differ much more from the properties of pure solute than they generally do with non-electrolytes. Second, it is possible to apply general, and now familiar, theoretical considerations to the deviations from ideal behavior in sufficiently dilute solutions. Third, the electrical properties of the ions make possible additional types of measurement.

Problem 13.2-2. Prove that

$$\text{(a)} \quad m_\pm = m(x^x y^y)^{1/\nu} \tag{13.2–9}$$

$$\text{(b)} \quad \mathrm{d} \ln m_\pm = \mathrm{d} \ln m \tag{13.2–10}$$

13.3 The Debye-Hückel Theory

The theory of Debye and Hückel, developed with the aid of statistical thermodynamics, leads to equations for dilute solutions which are useful for extrapolation of activity data of strong electrolytes. A thorough account of this theory and its various extensions is given by Harned and Owen.[1] Only that directly necessary for our purposes is given below. The purposes of this chapter require mainly use of the "limiting law," which is valid for very high dilutions. The activity coefficient of a single ion is given by the limiting law as

$$\log \gamma_A = -\frac{1.283 \times 10^6 |Z_A|^2}{(DT)^{3/2}} \sqrt{\Sigma C_i Z_i^2} \tag{13.3–1}$$

[1] H. S. Harned and B. B. Owen, *The Physical Chemistry of Electrolytic Solutions*, 2nd ed., Reinhold, New York, 1950, especially Chapters 2 and 3.

where γ_A is the ion activity coefficient, Z_A the charge on the ion, D the dielectric constant of the medium, and T the absolute temperature; C_i is the concentration of each ion of the solution in moles per liter, and Z_i is the charge on the ion. For concentration expressed as molality the sum in the square root is replaced by the ionic strength μ, defined by the equation

$$\mu = \tfrac{1}{2}\,\Sigma m_i Z_i^2 = \Sigma \frac{C_i Z_i^2}{2d_0}, \qquad (13.3\text{–}2)$$

where d_0 is the density of the solvent. Adding expressions of the form (13.3–1) and using equation (13.3–2), the measurable quantity $\gamma_{\pm}$ is given by

$$\log \gamma_{\pm} = -\frac{1.814 \times 10^6 |Z_A Z_B| \sqrt{d_0 \mu}}{(DT)^{3/2}}, \qquad (13.3\text{–}3)$$

where Z_A and Z_B are the charges on the positive and negative ion, respectively.

Problem 13.3-1. Show that, if the activity coefficients of individual ions are given by an equation $\log \gamma_A = -BZ_A^2\sqrt{\mu}$, the mean ion activity coefficient of a salt A_xB_y is given by $\log \gamma_{\pm} = -B\,|Z_A Z_B|\,\sqrt{\mu}$. Deduce equation (13.3–3) from equation (13.3–1).

A second approximation, which is valid to somewhat higher concentrations, is obtained by inserting into the denominator of equation (13.3–3) the term $1 + A\sqrt{\mu}$, where A is a constant dependent upon the distance of closest approach of the ions and is generally near unity.[2] For aqueous solutions at 25°C, substitution into equation (13.3–3) gives

$$\log \gamma_{\pm} = -0.506|Z_A Z_B|\sqrt{\mu}, \qquad (13.3\text{–}4)$$

and the higher concentration form

$$\log \gamma_{\pm} = -\frac{0.506|Z_A Z_B|\sqrt{\mu}}{1 + A\sqrt{\mu}}. \qquad (13.3\text{–}5)$$

Tables giving the entire temperature-dependent term of equation (13.3–1) as well as the dielectric constant as a function of temperature are given by Harned and Owen,[3] along with other tables useful in the various interionic attraction theories.

The problem below illustrates the nature of experimental data on activity coefficients and the predictions of the simpler theories. For details on both topics, the reader is referred to Harned and Owen.[1]

[2] See Harned and Owen, *op. cit.*, p. 39.
[3] Harned and Owen, *op. cit.*, Chapter 5.

Problem 13.3-2. (a) Calculate $\gamma_\pm$ in aqueous solution at 25°C for salts of the type of KCl, $ZnCl_2$, and $ZnSO_4$ from equations (13.3–4) and (13.3–5) at 0.001, 0.01, 0.005, 0.10, 0.50, 1.00, 2.00, and 4.00 molal. Take the constant A of equation (13.3–5) to be unity.

(b) Compare the values of $\gamma_\pm$ obtained in part (a) with those from actual measurement for several salts of each type. Tables of activity coefficients for a wide variety of substances may be obtained from Harned and Owen[1] or elsewhere.

(c) Prepare a graph for each type of electrolyte in which log $\gamma_\pm$ is plotted against $\mu^{1/2}$, plotting the theoretical results and at least two examples of actual measurements.

(d) Prepare a similar graph for salts of the KCl type in which $\gamma_\pm$ is plotted against $\mu^{1/2}$.

As can be seen from Problem 13.3–2, the activity coefficients of electrolytes differ greatly from unity even at moderate concentrations and are simply related to the concentration only at high dilution. The Debye-Hückel theory will be used mainly to permit proper extrapolation to the range of very high dilution.

13.4 Numerical Calculation of the Activity of Electrolytes

It is now possible to discuss the modifications necessary for application of the procedures of Section 11.5 to the calculation of the activity of electrolytes. The methods which apply specifically to electrolytes will be discussed in Chapter 14.

1. *Calculation from Vapor Pressure Data.* The activity of undissociated material is still defined by equation (11.5–6):

$$a_2 = \frac{f_2}{k_2}, \tag{11.5–6}$$

but in order to extrapolate to infinite dilution to get the Henry's law constant k_2, it is necessary to replace a_2 by $a_\pm$, as defined in equation (13.2–3). For simplicity this will be illustrated for a di-ionic electrolyte, and pressure will be substituted for fugacity; then

$$a_\pm{}^2 = m_\pm{}^2\gamma_\pm{}^2 = \frac{P_2}{k_2}. \tag{13.4–1}$$

Since $a_\pm \rightarrow m_\pm$ and $\gamma_\pm \rightarrow 1$ as $m \rightarrow 0$, the Henry's law constant k_2 may be evaluated by the extrapolation:

$$k_2 = \lim_{m\rightarrow 0} \frac{P}{(m_\pm)^2}. \tag{13.4–2}$$

At all concentrations $(P/m_\pm{}^2) = k_2\gamma_\pm{}^2$, and the extrapolation may thus be guided by the theoretical limiting slope of $\gamma_\pm$ as given by equation (13.3–1).

Unfortunately, most electrolytes are non-volatile at room temperature; the vapor pressures of even the more volatile electrolytes are very low at ordinary temperatures, even from rather concentrated aqueous solutions. For example, the vapor pressure of HCl over a 4 molal solution is only about 0.02 mm Hg at 25°C. As a result, the extrapolation outlined above is generally quite impractical. Equation (13.4–1) may still be used to obtain relative values of the activity in concentrated solutions, since it may be written

$$\left(\frac{a_\pm}{a_\pm{}'}\right)^2 = \frac{P_2}{P_2{}'}. \tag{13.4–3}$$

Individual values of the activity may be obtained if the numerical value can be obtained at one or more concentrations by some other method.

For non-volatile electrolytes, it is possible to obtain the activity of the solute from measurements in which the activity of the solvent is first determined from its vapor pressure, and the activity of solute calculated by methods analogous to these described in the last part of Section 11.5. This procedure requires vapor pressure measurements of high accuracy, and the method has generally been limited to concentrations above 0.1 molal.

Problem 13.4-1. The vapor pressures of HCl above aqueous solutions at 10°C are given in Table 13.4–1. Calculate (a) the ratio $a_2/a_2{}'$ at each concentration, taking $a_2{}'$ as the activity at 2 molal; (b) the ratios $a_\pm/a_\pm{}'$ and $\gamma_\pm/\gamma_\pm{}'$ at each concentration; (c) plot $\gamma_\pm/\gamma_\pm{}'$ against m and against $m^{1/2}$ from the lowest concentration given to 9 molal.

Table 13.4–1

Vapor Pressure of HCl above Aqueous Solutions at 10°C[4]

Molality	Vapor Pressure (mm Hg)	Molality	Vapor Pressure (mm Hg)
0.5	1.15×10^{-5}	9.0	0.571
1.0	5.33×10^{-5}	10.0	1.278
2.0	3.45×10^{-4}	11.0	2.78
3.0	1.32×10^{-3}	12.0	5.60
4.0	4.36×10^{-3}	13.0	11.00
5.0	0.0131	14.0	20.75
6.0	0.0366	15.0	38.0
7.0	0.0964	15.88	61.2
8.0	0.242		

[4] *Chem. & Eng. Data Series*, **1,** 10 (1956).

2. *Calculation from Distribution between Solvents.* The activity of an electrolyte may be calculated from the equilibrium concentrations obtained when the electrolyte is distributed between two immiscible solvents. It is necessary, of course, to know the activity of the substance in one of the solutions from some other measurement. The method is most useful where the electrolyte is distributed between water and a solvent (X), in which it does not dissociate. In this case we may set, by Henry's law,

$$(a_{\pm})^2 \text{ (in water)} = \mathrm{k} a_2 \text{ (in X)}, \qquad (13.4\text{–}4)$$

where

$$\mathrm{k} = \lim_{m \to 0} \frac{(m_{\pm})^2 \text{ (in water)}}{m_2 \text{ (in X)}}. \qquad (13.4\text{–}5)$$

In equations (13.4–4) and (13.4–5) the concentration (m_2) and activity (a_2) in solvent X are expressed in terms of molalities. If they were put on the basis of mole fraction, the only change would be in the constant k.

Problem 13.4-2. Prove equations (13.4–4) and (13.4–5).

3. *Calculation of Activity from Freezing Points.* The activity of solvent may be obtained from freezing points as in Section 11.6, and the activities a_1 and a_2 may be expressed just as in equations (11.6–6) to (11.6–13), provided, as before, that the temperature dependence of the activity may be neglected.[5]

Upon substitution using equation (13.2–3), equation (11.6–9) becomes

$$\nu \, \mathrm{d} \ln a_{\pm} = \frac{1000}{\tilde{M}_1 m} (\mathrm{A} + \mathrm{B}\theta + \mathrm{C}\theta^2 + \cdots) \, \mathrm{d}\theta, \qquad (13.4\text{–}6)$$

and equation (11.6–11) becomes

$$\nu \, \mathrm{d} \ln a_{\pm} = \frac{\mathrm{d}\theta}{\lambda m} + \frac{1}{m} f(\theta) \, \mathrm{d}\theta. \qquad (13.4\text{-}7)$$

After $a_{\pm}$ has been replaced by use of equation (13.2–6) and equation (13.2–10), this equation becomes

$$\nu \, \mathrm{d} \ln \gamma_{\pm} = \frac{\mathrm{d}\theta}{\lambda m} - \frac{\mathrm{d}m}{m} + \frac{1}{m} f(\theta) \, \mathrm{d}\theta \qquad (13.4\text{–}8)$$

[5] The calculation of a_2 from a_1 involves application of the Duhem equation; the justification for applying this equation as if only one solute species were present is given in Section 13.5.

Redefining the function j in more general terms,[6]

$$j = 1 - \frac{\theta}{\nu\lambda m}, \tag{13.4–9}$$

one obtains

$$\ln \gamma_{\pm} = -\int_0^m \frac{j}{m}\,dm - j + \int_0^m \frac{1}{\nu m} f(\theta)\,d\theta. \tag{13.4–10}$$

Problem 13.4-3. Prove equation (13.4–10), noting equation (13.2–10).

The graphical integration of the first term of equation (13.4–10) cannot be carried out by a plot of j/m against the molality, since it may be shown from the Debye-Hückel limiting law (equation 13.3–3) that the ratio (j/m) becomes infinite as m approaches zero. An appropriate and equivalent form is

$$\ln \gamma_{\pm} = -2\int_0^m \frac{j}{m^{1/2}}\,dm^{1/2} - j + \int_0^m \frac{1}{\nu m} f(\theta)\,d\theta. \tag{13.4–11}$$

Graphical integration of the first term on the right is facilitated by the prediction of the Debye-Hückel theory that the ratio $j/m^{1/2}$ must approach a calculable limit as m approaches zero. The limiting value for the ratio may be obtained as follows. Let equation (13.3–3) be written in the generalized form,

$$\ln \gamma_{\pm} = -\mathrm{B}m^{1/2}, \tag{13.4–12}$$

so that

$$d \ln \gamma_{\pm} = -\frac{\mathrm{B}}{2} m^{-1/2}\,dm. \tag{13.4–13}$$

This expression for $\gamma_{\pm}$ is now substituted into equation (13.4–8). At very low concentrations only the first two terms on the right side of equation (13.4–8) are important. Upon substitution from equations (13.4–13) and (13.4–9) and simplification, one obtains

$$\frac{\mathrm{B}}{2} m^{1/2}\,dm = j\,dm + m\,dj = d(jm). \tag{13.4–14}$$

Upon integration, this becomes

$$j = \frac{\mathrm{B}}{3} m^{1/2}. \tag{13.4–15}$$

Problem 13.4-4. Prove equation (13.4–15). Note that the constant obtained on ntegration of equation (13.4–14) is zero, since j must approach zero as m does.

[6] Note that equation (11.6–14) is a special case of equation (13.4–9), since for non-electrolytes $\nu = 1$. Note also that $j \to 0$ as $m \to 0$.

For 1 : 1 electrolytes in water at 25°C, the constant B is 1.165, so for this case

$$\lim_{m \to 0} \frac{j}{m^{1/2}} = 0.388. \qquad (13.4\text{–}16)$$

For other temperatures, solvents, or types of electrolytes, it is necessary to re-evaluate the constant of equation (13.4–16). It is interesting to note that Lewis and Linhart[7] deduced an equation of the form of (13.4–15) empirically before the development of the Debye-Hückel theory.

The graphical integration required for the first term of equation (13.4–10) may thus be "anchored" to the limiting ratio of equation (13.4–16). Further improvement in accuracy may be made, if the data warrant, by use of an equation for j derived from a more extended form of the Debye-Hückel theory. Harned and Owen[8] consider general ways of doing so, and they give several specific examples.

Equation (13.4–10) does not give exact values of $\gamma_{\pm}$, since in its derivation the effect of temperature on the activity of the solvent was neglected in order to simplify the procedure. The error in doing so is slight at low concentrations (e.g., below 0.1 molal), but it becomes quite appreciable at concentrations above 1 molal. The modifications in the procedure necessary to take account of the temperature effect are outlined below.

As was pointed out in Section 11.6, the activity a_1 obtained by substitution of a given value of θ into equation (11.6–7) is the activity of the solvent in a solution at its freezing point, $T_0 - \theta$. In order to apply the Duhem equation properly, it is necessary first to use equation (11.1–4) to correct all the solvent activities to a common reference temperature. The activity a_1' of solvent at some reference temperature T' is obtained by combining (11.6–7) with (11.1–4). The result is

$$\begin{aligned} \ln a_1' &= \ln a_1 - \int_T^{T'} \frac{\bar{L}_1}{RT^2}\, dT \\ &= -(A\theta + \tfrac{1}{2}B\theta^2 + \tfrac{1}{3}C\theta^3 + \cdots) - \int_T^{T'} \frac{\bar{L}_1}{RT^2}\, dT, \qquad (13.4\text{–}17) \end{aligned}$$

where $T = T_0 - \theta$ is the freezing point at a given concentration, $\bar{L}_1$ is the relative partial molal heat content of solvent at that concentration,

[7] For a discussion of their equation see G. N. Lewis and M. Randall, *Thermodynamics*, McGraw-Hill, New York, 1923, p. 342.

[8] Harned and Owen, *op. cit.*, Chapter 9.

and T' is the chosen reference temperature. Following the same general procedure as Lewis and Randall,[9] equation (13.4–17) may be abbreviated:

$$\ln a_1' = \ln a_1 - x, \tag{13.4–18}$$

where x, which has been used as a symbol for the integral of equation (13.4–17), is obviously a function of the molality. When (13.4–18) is used in equation (11.6–8) and the rest of the procedure carried out as before, the final (exact) expression for the mean ion activity coefficient of the solute at T' is

$$\ln \gamma_\pm = -2 \int_0^m \frac{j}{m^{1/2}} \, dm^{1/2} - j + \int_0^m \frac{1}{\nu m} f(\theta)\, d\theta + \frac{1000}{\tilde{M}_1} \int_0^m \frac{dx}{\nu m}, \tag{13.4–19}$$

where dx is the change in the variable x, defined above, which is associated with a change in molality dm. The necessary corrections for the effect of temperature on solvent activity thus reduce to the evaluation of the integral in equation (13.4–17) and its use in (13.4–19), the remainder of the calculation of activity being carried out exactly as before. Lewis and Randall[9] have described a formal method for calculation of the correction, and they give tables to facilitate the work.

The operations described by equation (13.4–19) give the activity of solute exactly at the reference temperature T', which could have been chosen as the freezing point of pure solvent, a "standard" temperature such as 25°C, or any other. The activity at other temperatures could then be obtained by repeating the calculation of the correction term for each of the other temperatures.

The effect of temperature on solute activity is obtained in general form by further use of equation (11.1–4) For the solute

$$\left(\frac{\partial \ln a_2}{\partial T}\right)_{P,n_1,\cdots} = -\frac{\bar{L}_2}{RT^2}. \tag{13.4–20}$$

However, from (13.2–3) and (13.2–6),

$$a_2 = (a_\pm)^\nu = (m_\pm \gamma_\pm)^\nu. \tag{13.4–21}$$

Using (13.4–21) in (13.4–20), since at constant composition $\ln m_\pm$ is constant,

$$\left(\frac{\partial \ln \gamma_\pm}{\partial T}\right)_{P,n_1,\cdots} = -\frac{\bar{L}_2}{\nu RT^2}, \tag{13.4–22}$$

[9] Lewis and Randall, *op. cit.*, pp. 348 ff.

which becomes upon integration

$$\ln \frac{\gamma_{\pm}'}{\gamma_{\pm}} = -\int_T^{T'} \frac{\bar{L}_2}{\nu RT^2}\, dT. \qquad (13.4\text{–}23)$$

The mean ion activity coefficient at T' may thus be obtained from that at T by use of (13.4–23), $\bar{L}_2$ having first been evaluated over the required temperature range by the methods of Chapter 8. Conversely, $\bar{L}_2$ may be determined from measurements of activities by use of (13.4–22).

Problem 13.4-5. Show that for water the freezing point lowering constant λ is 1.858 and that the function $f(\theta)$ defined by equation (11.6–12) is

$$f(\theta) = 5.6 \times 10^{-4}\theta - 3.1 \times 10^{-6}\theta^2. \qquad (13.4\text{–}24)$$

You may take $T_0 = 273.1$, $\Delta H_{T_0} = 1435$ cal mole^{-1}, $\Delta C_P = 9$ cal mole^{-1} deg^{-1}.

Problem 13.4-6. Table 13.4–2 gives the function j, defined by equation (13.4–9), for aqueous NaCl as a function of molality from the work of Scatchard and Prentiss.[10] Calculate the mean ion activity coefficient at 0.0135, 0.1037, 0.2232, 0.486, 0.801, and 1.277 m, neglecting the effect of temperature on the activity.

Note that the freezing point depression θ may be calculated from j by use of equation (13.4–9). The freezing point depression constant λ and the function $f(\theta)$ may be taken from Problem 13.4–5. Also note that the $f(\theta)$ is unimportant at the lower concentrations, and that the second term in equation (13.4–24) becomes appreciable only at the highest concentrations.

Table 13.4–2

Freezing Point Lowering for Aqueous NaCl Solutions[10]

m	j	m	j	m	j
0.000819	−0.0092	0.1258	0.0710	0.5307	0.0899
0.001866	0.0092	0.1577	0.0743	0.5916	0.0902
0.005120	0.0192	0.1870	0.0775	0.6486	0.0908
0.008605	0.0265	0.2232	0.0803	0.7252	0.0907
0.01354	0.0334	0.2739	0.0831	0.8012	0.0907
0.02265	0.0445	0.3549	0.0863	0.9013	0.0894
0.03349	0.0468	0.4155	0.0881	0.9985	0.0884
0.05492	0.0553	0.4337	0.0884	1.1540	0.0862
0.07784	0.0628	0.4860	0.0892	1.2774	0.0845
0.1037	0.0668				

Problem 13.4-7. The measurements of Harned and Cook[11] give the relative partial molal enthalpy of the solute in 3 molal aqueous KCl between 0° and 40°C as $\bar{L}_2 = -1025 + 25.4t + 0.066t^2$, where t is the temperature in centigrade degrees.

[10] G. Scatchard and S. S. Prentiss, *J. Am. Chem. Soc.*, **55**, 4355 (1933).
[11] H. S. Harned and M. A. Cook, *J. Am. Chem. Soc.*, **59**, 1290 (1937).

Taking their value of the mean ion activity coefficient of this solution at 0°, $\gamma_{\pm} = 0.539$, calculate the activity coefficient at 25° and 40°C.

Problem 13.4-8. The Table 13.4–3 gives the mean ion activity coefficient of NaCl at several molalities from 0° to 100°C, from the compilation of Robinson.[12]

(a) By plotting the data in an appropriate form, obtain $\bar{L}_2$ at each molality at 10°, 50°, 70°, and 90°.

(b) Estimate $\bar{C}_{P_2} - \bar{C}_{P_2}{}^\circ$ at 1.0 molal and 30°C.

(c) Assuming the error in individual activity coefficients to be ± 0.0005, estimate the error in $\bar{L}_2$ and $\bar{C}_{P_2} - \bar{C}_{P_2}{}^\circ$ at 30°C and 1 molal.

Table 13.4–3

Activity Coefficients of NaCl Solutions as Function of Temperature[12]

	$\gamma_{\pm}$				$\gamma_{\pm}$		
t(°C)	0.1 m	1.0 m	3.0 m	t(°C)	0.1 m	1.0 m	3.0 m
0	0.781	0.6375	0.660	60	0.766	0.654	0.726
10	0.781	0.649	0.691	70	0.762	0.648	0.721
20	0.779	0.654	0.7115	80	0.757	0.641	0.712
30	0.777	0.657	0.724	90	0.752	0.632	0.700
40	0.774	0.657	0.728	100	0.746	0.622	0.687
50	0.770	0.656	0.728				

13.5 Calculation of Solute Activity from That of the Solvent

The activity of an electrolyte in solution may be calculated from the activity of the solvent by use of the Duhem equation, just as was done for non-electrolytes. The procedure was illustrated in the calculation of activity from freezing point lowering, where the equations of Section 11.6 were used without special justification. Thus the Duhem equation was applied in the same form as for non-electrolytes:

$$\tilde{N}_1 \, d \ln a_1 = -\tilde{N}_2 \, d \ln a_2 , \tag{11.1–6}$$

as if all solute were present as undissociated material. In a solution of an electrolyte or other dissociable materials, the solute is present not only as undissociated material but also in the form of ions or other dissociation products. The detailed application of the Duhem equation to such a solution is illustrated below for a simple example.

Let an electrolyte or other dissociable material AB dissociate according to the equation

$$AB = A + B; \qquad K = \frac{(a_A)(a_B)}{(a_{AB})} . \tag{13.5–1}$$

[12] R. A. Robinson, *Trans. Faraday Soc.*, **35**, 1222 (1939).

The numbers of moles of the species A and B are given by the equation $n_A = n_B = n_2 - n_{AB}$, where n_2 is the total number of moles of solute, and n_{AB} is the number of moles of undissociated material. From the general form of the Duhem equation (8.2–12), one may write for an amount of solution containing n_1 moles of solvent

$$\begin{aligned} n_1 \, d \ln a_1 &= -n_{AB} \, d \ln a_{AB} - n_A \, d \ln a_A - n_B \, d \ln a_B \\ &= -n_{AB} \, d \ln a_{AB} - (n_2 - n_{AB}) \, d \ln a_A - (n_2 - n_{AB}) \, d \ln a_B . \end{aligned} \tag{13.5–2}$$

By differentiation of equation (13.5–1) one obtains

$$0 = d \ln K = d \ln a_A + d \ln a_B - d \ln a_{AB}, \tag{13.5–3}$$

so that

$$d \ln a_A + d \ln a_B = d \ln a_{AB}, \tag{13.5–4}$$

regardless of the magnitude of the equilibrium constant K. Upon substitution of equation (13.5–4) into (13.5–2), one obtains

$$n_1 \, d \ln a_1 = -n_2 \, d \ln a_{AB} . \tag{13.5–5}$$

This equation is of the same form as equation (11.1–6); thus the Duhem equation may be applied to the calculation of the activity of undissociated material in exactly the same manner as was used for non-electrolytes. This result can readily be generalized to solutions in which more than two species are produced by dissociation or other reaction.

For an electrolyte, equation (13.5–4) may be used to replace the activity of undissociated material by that of the ions. For the simple case illustrated above, if A and B are ions,

$$n_1 \, d \ln a_1 = -n_2 \, d \ln a_{A^+} - n_2 \, d \ln a_{B^-} \tag{13.5–6}$$

$$= -n_2 \, d \ln (a_\pm)^2. \tag{13.5–7}$$

This result is the same as would be obtained from equation (11.1–6) by the substitution of $(a_\pm)^\nu$ for a_2, without regard to the presence of the various dissociated and undissociated species of the electrolyte.

In the calculation of solute activity from that of the solvent (or the reverse), the Duhem equation is first set up in forms similar to (13.5–5) or (13.5–7). The equation is then integrated by any suitable procedure. The integration procedures required have been illustrated in the previous section and will not be considered further at this point.

It is clear that any method of measurement which determines a_2 either directly or indirectly can give only the mean ion activity, as defined by equation (13.2–3), and cannot be used to obtain the activities of individual ions. In the next chapter it will become evident that the same limitations apply to methods responsive to the ion activities themselves.

Problem 13.5-1. Derive equations similar to (13.5–5) and (13.5–7) for the general case of a dissociation:

$$A_{\nu_+}B_{\nu_-} = \nu_+A^{Z+} + \nu_-B^{Z-}.$$

using a method similar to that just given for the case of AB.

13.6 Activity Coefficients of Weak Electrolytes

The methods described above for determination of ion activity coefficients assumed throughout that the material being studied was completely dissociated. For this reason they cannot be applied to non-electrolytes without major modification. (Acetic acid, a typical non-electrolyte, is about 1.5% dissociated at 0.1 molal and only about 70% dissociated at 10^{-5} molal. Even for much stronger acids, such as dichloracetic acid, the concentration region where dissociation is substantially complete is impractically low for most measurements). While it is possible to modify the methods to take account (by use of a dissociation constant other than unity) of incomplete dissociation, the resulting procedures are quite cumbersome and have not generally been used. (The student may, if he wishes, develop the necessary modifications, starting with equation (13.2–2)).

It is possible to treat really weak electrolytes in the same fashion as non-electrolytes, provided that it is feasible to make the necessary extrapolations to zero concentration from a concentration region where dissociation is negligible. This procedure has rarely been used for weak electrolytes.

Electromotive Force of Cells

CHAPTER 14

14.1 Introduction

The investigation of the electromotive force of galvanic cells is one of the most fruitful sources of information about the thermodynamic properties of solutions of electrolytes. This field has been very thoroughly reviewed by Harned and Owen.[1] The present chapter will attempt to examine only the basic method of approach and some applications. The reader is referred to Harned and Owen's book for a fuller discussion of experimental observations, techniques of calculation, and theoretical implications. As in Chapter 13, direct reference will frequently be made to specific sections of this work.

In the preceding chapter the thermodynamic treatment of electrolytes was developed to a point which allows the electromotive force to be calculated for reversible cells. In this chapter representative examples of electromotive force cells are considered. For a reversible cell, the free energy change accompanying the passage of $\mathcal{N}$ faradays of electricity is, from Chapters 6 and 12,

$$\Delta F = -\mathcal{N}\mathcal{F}\mathcal{E} \tag{12.5–10}$$

where $\mathcal{F}$ is Faraday's equivalent and $\mathcal{E}$ the electromotive force of the cell. Equation (12.5–10) makes possible the calculation of thermodynamic properties of the cell materials from electromotive force measurements. In the special case where each of the substances involved in the cell reaction is in its standard state, one may write

$$\Delta F^\circ = -\mathcal{N}\mathcal{F}\mathcal{E}^\circ, \tag{14.1–1}$$

where $\mathcal{E}^\circ$ is the *standard potential* of the cell in question.

[1] H. S. Harned and B. B. Owen, *Physical Chemistry of Electrolytic Solutions*, 2nd ed., Reinhold, New York, 1950.

The dependence of electromotive force upon the pressures or concentrations of the reacting substances may be seen by reference to a specific example. For the cell Pt, $H_2 \mid HCl(aq) \mid AgCl$, Ag, the cell reaction is

$$\tfrac{1}{2}H_2(g) + AgCl(s) = H^+ + Cl^- + Ag(s). \tag{14.1–2}$$

The effects of changes in pressure or concentration were discussed in Section 6.23. In general, for any such change, noting equation (12.5–10),

$$-\mathcal{N}\mathcal{F}(\mathcal{E} - \mathcal{E}') = \Delta F - \Delta F' = RT \ln \frac{(a_{H^+})(a_{Cl^-})(a_{Ag})(f'_{H_2})^{1/2}(a'_{AgCl})}{(a'_{H^+})(a'_{Cl^-})(a'_{Ag})(f_{H_2})^{1/2}(a_{AgCl})}, \tag{14.1–3}$$

where the primed quantities refer to the initial state and unprimed qualities to the final state. If the initial state is chosen such that each substance is in its standard state of unit activity or fugacity, by equation (14.1–1),

$$-\mathcal{N}\mathcal{F}(\mathcal{E} - \mathcal{E}^\circ) = \Delta F - \Delta F^\circ = RT \ln \frac{(a_{H^+})(a_{Cl^-})(a_{Ag})}{(f_{H_2})^{1/2}(a_{AgCl})}. \tag{14.1–4}$$

Then, in general terms,

$$\mathcal{E} = \mathcal{E}^\circ - \frac{RT}{\mathcal{N}\mathcal{F}} \ln Q, \tag{14.1–5}$$

where the symbol Q has been used for an activity ratio of the type shown in equation (14.1–4). Equation (14.1–5) is the equivalent of (12.6–6).

14.2 Use of Cell Measurements in the Calculation of Thermodynamic Properties

For a cell of given composition, it may be shown readily by differentiation of equation (12.5–10) that

$$\Delta S = \mathcal{N}\mathcal{F}\left(\frac{\partial \mathcal{E}}{\partial T}\right)_P, \tag{14.2–1}$$

$$\Delta H = -\mathcal{N}\mathcal{F}\mathcal{E} + \mathcal{N}\mathcal{F}T\left(\frac{\partial \mathcal{E}}{\partial T}\right)_P, \tag{12.8–4}$$

and

$$\Delta C_P = \mathcal{N}\mathcal{F}T\left(\frac{\partial^2 \mathcal{E}}{\partial T^2}\right)_P. \tag{14.2–2}$$

Problem 14.2-1. Prove equation (14.2–2).

Accordingly, measurements of the electromotive force may be used in determination of the changes in free energy, enthalpy, entropy, and heat capacity accompanying the cell reaction. The potential of a reversible cell may readily be measured to less than a millivolt. This corresponds to an uncertainty of about 23 cal/mole in the free energy change of a reaction in which one faraday of electricity is transferred per mole. The determination of ΔS and ΔH is subject to comparatively greater uncertainty since these quantities are related to the temperature coefficient of the electromotive force. Even so, careful cell measurements frequently provide more accurate determinations of entropy and enthalpy change than those available from other types of measurement.

Equations (14.2–1), (12.8–4), and (14.2–2) may also be used to extend emf data to temperatures beyond those where they have been measured. These applications may be seen most readily in a cell such as that used in Section 6.17, where all reactants are either solid or gaseous. For the cell considered in Section 14.1, the cell reaction may equally well be written

$$\tfrac{1}{2}H_2(g) + AgCl(s) = HCl(g) + Ag(s), \qquad (14.2\text{–}3)$$

since the concentration of the hydrogen chloride is directly related to its partial pressure. For the reaction written as equation (14.2–3) the standard state of HCl is the ideal gas at 1 atm rather than the hypothetical 1 molal solution. The use of the equations given above is illustrated in Problem 14.2–2.

Problem 14.2-2. The emf for the cell whose reaction is equation (14.2–3) is −0.1622 v at 10°C when each of the substances is in its standard state.

(a) Calculate ΔF°_{283} for the reaction.

(b) The table below gives $\tilde{S}^\circ_{298}$ and $(\tilde{C}_P{}^\circ)_{298}$ for each of the substances involved. Assuming that $\Delta C_P{}^\circ$ for the reaction is independent of temperature, calculate ΔF° at 298°, 323°, and 373°K.

(c) Calculate $\mathscr{E}^\circ$ for the cell at 298° and 323°K.

	$\tilde{S}^\circ_{298}$	$(\tilde{C}_P{}^\circ)_{298}$
$H_2(g)$	31.23	6.9
$AgCl(s)$	22.97	12.1
$Ag(s)$	10.21	6.1
$HCl(g)$	44.66	6.8

At ordinary pressures the activities of pure solid phases may be considered independent of pressure and concentration. In this case, for the reaction given as equation (14.2–3), equation (14.1–4) becomes

$$\mathscr{E} = \mathscr{E}^\circ - \frac{RT}{\mathscr{F}} \ln \frac{f_{HCl}}{(f_{H_2})^{1/2}}. \qquad (14.2\text{–}4)$$

If the pressure of hydrogen is known, cell data may be used for determination of the vapor pressure of HCl from solutions. It should be observed that equation (14.2–4) contains nothing which refers explicitly to the properties of the solvent. Thus this equation and the corresponding $\mathscr{E}^\circ$ are both equally valid for aqueous and non-aqueous solutions of the acid, provided that the cell reaction is the same. This provides a convenient method for evaluation of the standard electromotive force, as illustrated in Problem 14.2–4.

Problem 14.2-3. The vapor pressure of HCl over a 1 molal aqueous solution is about 2×10^{-4} mm Hg at 25°C. Using the value of $\mathscr{E}^\circ$ calculated in Problem 14.2–2, calculate the emf of the cell Pt, H_2 (1 atm) | HCl (1 *m*) | AgCl, Ag at 25°C. The measured value is 0.2333 v.

Problem 14.2-4. The emf of the cell whose reaction is given by equation (14.2–3) has been measured in concentrated acetic acid.[2] The emf was 0.0099 v at 25°C when the partial pressure of HCl was 1.80×10^{-4} atm and the pressure of hydrogen was 0.917 atm. Calculate $\mathscr{E}^\circ$ for the cell at 25°C. You may assume that the fugacities of HCl and H_2 are equal to their pressures.

Problem 14.2-5. The standard emf of the cell described in Problem 14.2–4 is −0.1345 v at 50°C. According to the results of Harned and Ehlers,[3] the voltage at 50°C of the cell containing 0.131 molal HCl is +0.3320 v; for 1.231 molal HCl, +0.2054 v; and for 1.979 molal HCl, +0.1706 v; all corrected to 1 atm pressure on the hydrogen. Calculate the vapor pressure of HCl above each of the solutions at 50°C.

If the activity of one or more of the reactants is taken as that in solution, rather than in the gas phase, the appropriate partial molal properties must be used in place of the molal quantities of the pure material. The procedure is illustrated by Problem 14.2–6.

Problem 14.2-6. For the cell Pt, H_2 | HCl(aq) | AgCl, Ag, the standard emf may be represented by the equation[3]

$$\mathscr{E}^\circ = 0.22239 - 6.453 \times 10^{-4}(t - 25) - 3.284 \times 10^{-6}(t - 25)^2 + 9.95 \times 10^{-9}(t - 25)^3,$$

valid between 0° and 60°C, where t is the temperature in centigrade degrees.

(a) Write the cell reaction to which $\mathscr{E}^\circ$ applies.

(b) Evaluate for this reaction ΔF°, ΔH°, ΔS°, and $\Delta C_P{}^\circ$ at 25°C and 60°C.

(c) Using the values given in Problem 14.2–2 for the entropies and heat capacities of the other substances at 25°C, calculate $\bar{S}^\circ$ and $\bar{C}_P{}^\circ$ for aqueous HCl at 25°C.

14.3 Calculation of Solute and Solvent Activity from Electromotive Force Measurements

If the activity of the solute is taken as that in the solution, the voltage of the aqueous HCl cell is given by equation (14.1–4). This may be

[2] *J. Am. Chem. Soc.*, **77**, 3175 (1955).

[3] H. S. Harned and R. W. Ehlers, *J. Am. Chem. Soc.*, **55**, 2179 (1933).

simplified if the activities of the solid materials are chosen to be unity and all potentials corrected to unit fugacity of hydrogen. In this case,

$$\mathscr{E} = \mathscr{E}^\circ - \frac{RT}{\mathscr{F}} \ln (a_{H^+})(a_{Cl^-}). \tag{14.3–1}$$

Upon substitution from equations (13.2–4) and (13.2–6), this becomes

$$\mathscr{E} = \mathscr{E}^\circ - \frac{2RT}{\mathscr{F}} \ln m_\pm - \frac{2RT}{\mathscr{F}} \ln \gamma_\pm . \tag{14.3–2}$$

Equation (14.3–2) is the fundamental equation relating the activity coefficient $\gamma_\pm$ with the measured voltage $\mathscr{E}$, and the mean molality $m_\pm$ (computed from the stoichiometric molality m by means of equation 13.2–5). The activity coefficient for a given concentration is obtained directly from (14.3–2), once $\mathscr{E}^\circ$ has been determined.

The determination of $\mathscr{E}^\circ$ proceeds as follows. Putting the measured quantities in equation (14.3–2) on the left,

$$\mathscr{E} + \frac{2RT}{\mathscr{F}} \ln m_\pm = \mathscr{E}^\circ - \frac{2RT}{\mathscr{F}} \ln \gamma_\pm. \tag{14.3–3}$$

Since $\gamma_\pm$ approaches unity as the concentration approaches zero, the left side of the equation (denoted $\mathscr{E}^{\circ\prime}$ by Lewis and Randall) must approach $\mathscr{E}^\circ$ at infinite dilution; $\mathscr{E}^\circ$ may thus be obtained by a graphical or numerical extrapolation of this quantity. Since $\mathscr{E}^{\circ\prime}$ is a linear function of $\ln \gamma_\pm$, it is evident from the Debye-Hückel limiting law that $\mathscr{E}^{\circ\prime}$ must become a linear function of $\mu^{1/2}$ (i.e., of $m^{1/2}$) at sufficiently high dilution. The extrapolation method of Lewis and Randall,[4] developed empirically before the advent of the Debye-Hückel theory, consists in plotting $\mathscr{E}^{\circ\prime}$ against $m^{1/2}$ for linear extrapolation to zero concentration. The curve thus obtained becomes linear at sufficiently low concentrations. The direct empirical extrapolation may be improved somewhat if the linear portion is arbitrarily drawn with the proper limiting slope as given by the Debye-Hückel theory. Unfortunately, most electrolytes show small deviations from the limiting law even at concentrations of 0.001 molar, and at best only the points at the lowest concentrations are suitable for linear extrapolation. (This is, of course, the region where experimental errors are most likely.)

Hitchcock[5] observed that, at moderate concentrations, the activities of

[4] G. N. Lewis and M. Randall, *Thermodynamics*, McGraw-Hill, New York, 1923, p. 332.

[5] D. J. Hitchcock, *J. Am. Chem. Soc.*, **50**, 2076 (1928).

strong electrolytes could be represented quite well by an equation of the form

$$\ln \gamma_{\pm} = -A\mu^{1/2} + B'm, \tag{14.3–4}$$

where A is the appropriate limiting slope and B' an empirical constant. Thus a plot of the function

$$\mathscr{E} + \frac{2RT}{\mathscr{F}}(\ln m_{\pm}) - \frac{2RTA}{\mathscr{F}}\mu^{1/2},$$

which also extrapolates to $\mathscr{E}^\circ$ at infinite dilution, should vary linearly with molality. Harned and Owen[6] show that, for the cell considered above, this function is linear up to 0.1 molal and is thus an excellent extrapolation function. Other extrapolation functions have been suggested and used. Since these are all semiempirical, the test of their validity must rest with the data.

The general procedure for determination of solute activity will be as follows. After specification of the cell reaction, an equation similar to (14.3–1) is written and then transformed into the same form as (14.3–3). $\mathscr{E}^\circ$ is then evaluated by use of a suitable extrapolation method. Thereafter the mean ion activity coefficient of the solute may be calculated directly, and from it the activity of the solute at the desired concentrations. The activity of the solvent may then be evaluated by use of the Duhem equation in a form such as (11.5–17).

As indicated in Section 13.4, relative activities obtained from vapor pressure measurements may be used to calculate activities at concentrations higher than those for which cell measurements are available. In the case of HCl, both cell and vapor pressure measurements have been made at high concentrations.

It is again evident, from equation (14.3–1), that the activity of individual ions cannot be determined experimentally. The electromotive force depends on the product of ion activities, which may conveniently be expressed in terms of the mean ion activity. This happens because one electrode must always be measured with respect to another. It is possible to record "single electrode potentials" only by the artifice of arbitrarily setting one such potential (that of the H_2, H^+ electrode) equal to zero. This provides a convenient way of constructing a condensed table of standard cell potentials, in much the same way that construction of a table of heats or free energy of formation simplifies calculation of the standard enthalpy or free energy change for chemical reactions. By the same token it tells us no more about the potential of an isolated electrode than the heat of formation of a substance tells us about its absolute enthalpy.

[6] Harned and Owen, *op. cit.*, p. 328.

Problem 14.3-1. Table 14.3–1 gives the emf of the cell Pt, H_2 | HCl(aq) | AgCl, Ag at 10°C, from the measurements of Harned and Ehlers.[3,7]

(a) Plot the function $\mathscr{E} + (2RT/\mathscr{F}) \ln m_{\pm}$ vs. $m^{1/2}$ below 0.1 molal. Obtain $\mathscr{E}^\circ$ by extrapolation, and estimate the constant A of equation (14.3–4) from the slope of the plot at low ionic strengths.

(b) Calculate the slope A theoretically, and compare with the value estimated in part (a). Plot the function $\mathscr{E} + (2RT/\mathscr{F})(\ln m_{\pm}) - (2RTA/\mathscr{F})\mu^{1/2}$ vs. m, and obtain a better value of $\mathscr{E}^\circ$. (*Note.* The value deduced by Harned and Ehlers is 0.23126.) The dielectric constant of water is 78.5 at 25°C and 84.1 at 10°C.

(c) Evaluate $\gamma_{\pm}$ and $a_{\pm}$ for HCl at 0.001, 0.005, 0.01, 0.05, 0.1, 0.2, 0.5, 1.0, 2.0, and 4.0 molal from smooth plots of the type prepared in part (a).

Table 14.3–1

Electromotive Force of the Cell Pt, H_2 | HCl(aq) | AgCl,Ag at 10°C and Concentrations below 4.1 Molal[3,7]

Molality	Emf	Molality	Emf	Molality	Emf
0.003215	0.51436	0.02563	0.41718	0.9699	0.24218
0.003661	0.50800	0.04935	0.38685	0.1204	0.22924
0.005314	0.49054	0.0727	0.36904	1.4407	0.21787
0.005763	0.48679	0.0975	0.35568	1.7196	0.20590
0.00771	0.47258	0.20301	0.32162	1.9753	0.19582
0.008636	0.46771	0.31887	0.30002	2.3802	0.18157
0.011095	0.45601	0.4897	0.27896	2.9566	0.16267
0.01305	0.44843	0.6702	0.26270	4.0875	0.12972
0.01646	0.43766	0.7983	0.25324		

Problem 14.3-2. (a) Table 14.3–2 gives the emf of the cell considered in Problem 14.3–1 at 10°C and higher concentrations than those listed there, from the measurements of Akerlof and Teare.[8] Using the value of $\mathscr{E}^\circ$ given in Problem 14.3–1, calculate the mean ion activity coefficient of HCl at each of the concentrations listed.

Table 14.3–2

Electromotive Force of the Cell H_2, Pt | HCl(aq) | AgCl, Ag at 10°C and Concentrations above 3 Molal[8]

Molality	Emf	Molality	Emf
4.000	0.13305	10.000	−0.00554
5.000	0.10614	11.000	−0.02438
6.000	0.08111	12.000	−0.04159
7.000	0.05751	13.000	−0.05805
8.000	0.03504	14.000	−0.07354
9.000	0.01410	15.000	−0.09979

[7] H. S. Harned and R. W. Ehlers, *J.Am. Chem. Soc.*, **54**, 1350 (1932).

[8] G. Akerlof and J. W. Teare, *J. Am. Chem. Soc.*, **59**, 1855 (1937).

(b) Use the results of Problem 14.3–1 together with the vapor pressure data of Problem 13.4–1 to obtain activity coefficients at each of the concentrations above 4 molal for which vapor pressures are given. Use the data between 2 and 4 molal to evaluate the Henry's law constant k_2 of equation (13.4–2). A relatively easy and accurate way to do so is to plot $\log(P^{1/2}/m)$ and $\log \gamma_{\pm}$ against the molality on the same graph, since $\log k_2 = 2(\log P^{1/2}/m - \log \gamma_{\pm})$. The constant k_2 may be obtained at any concentration in the region specified; for greater accuracy an average value of k_2 should be obtained. Compare graphically the activity coefficients calculated in this way with those of part (a).

Problem 14.3-3. Use the results of Problems 14.3–1 and 14.3–2 to calculate the activity of water in aqueous HCl solutions at 10° and 1, 3, 6, and 12 molal HCl.

Problem 14.3-4. Derive an equation comparable to equation (14.3–3) for the cell H_2, Pt | H_2SO_4(aq) | Hg_2SO_4, Hg.

14.4 Determination of Activity from the Electromotive Force of Concentration Cells

The methods described in Section 14.3 require measurements on a cell which has electrodes reversible with respect to the cation and anion, respectively, of the solute being investigated, since the cell reactions involve both ions. This procedure is not always convenient. For a salt such as sodium chloride, it is obvious that a pure sodium electrode cannot be used in aqueous solution. This difficulty is overcome if the sodium is present as an amalgam sufficiently dilute to inhibit the reaction of sodium with water. It is, however, difficult to construct and maintain amalgam electrodes of sufficiently constant properties for use of the methods of Section 14.3.

An alternative procedure is the construction of a *concentration cell* in which the net result of electrolysis is the transfer of electrolyte from one solution to another. Such a cell may be made by opposing two cells of the type previously considered, such as

$$\text{Pt, H}_2 \,|\, \text{HCl}(m) \,|\, \text{AgCl, Ag} \,|\, \text{HCl}(m') \,|\, \text{H}_2\text{, Pt.} \qquad (14.4\text{–}1)$$

Hydrogen chloride is produced in the left side and removed on the right. The silver-silver chloride electrode suffers no net change and serves primarily as a conductor of the current. The cell reaction corresponding to (14.4–1) is

$$\text{HCl}(m') = \text{HCl}(m). \qquad (14.4\text{–}2)$$

We proceed as before, and the electromotive force is given by

$$\mathscr{E} = -\frac{RT}{\mathscr{F}} \ln \frac{(a_{\text{H}^+})(a_{\text{Cl}^-})}{(a'_{\text{H}^+})(a'_{\text{Cl}^-})} \cdot \qquad (14.4\text{–}3)$$

The standard potential is zero since there is no electromotive force when the hydrogen chloride is at unit activity in each compartment. Inserting the mean molalities and mean activity coefficients as before,

$$\mathscr{E} = -\frac{2RT}{\mathscr{F}} \ln \frac{(m_\pm)(\gamma_\pm)}{(m_\pm{}')(\gamma_\pm{}')}. \tag{14.4–4}$$

Upon separation of known and unknown quantities,

$$\mathscr{E} - \frac{2RT}{\mathscr{F}} \ln m_\pm = \frac{2RT}{\mathscr{F}} \ln m_\pm{}'\gamma_\pm{}' - \frac{2RT}{\mathscr{F}} \ln \gamma_\pm. \tag{14.4–5}$$

If in a series of measurements the concentration of solute on the left side of the cell (14.4–1) is varied, while the concentration (and thus the activity) of HCl on the right side is kept constant, the application of equation (14.4–5) becomes similar to that of (14.3–3). The two equations differ only in the replacement of $\mathscr{E}^\circ$ by the constant term $(2RT/\mathscr{F})m_\pm{}'\gamma_\pm{}'$. If $\mathscr{E}$ is determined as a function of m, with m' held constant at any convenient value, the constant term may be obtained by suitable extrapolation of the left side of (14.4–5) to zero concentration, and the activity at each concentration then evaluated as before.

Since the center electrode in (14.4–1) suffers no net change, its composition is not critical, for the only condition necessary is that it remain uniform throughout. Thus the method may readily be used with amalgam or other alloy electrodes.

Problem 14.4-1 Derive the reaction for a cell Ag, AgCl | $NaCl(m_2)$ | $NaHg_x$ | $NaCl(m_1)$ | AgCl, Ag, and show that the electromotive force of the cell is independent of the amalgam concentration.

The cells described above are usually called *concentration cells without liquid junction,* since the two solutions are separated by a metallic connection rather than a liquid-liquid interface. An alternative type of cell would be

$$\text{AgCl, Ag} \mid \text{HCl}(m) \mid \text{HCl}(m') \mid \text{AgCl, Ag}, \tag{14.4–6}$$

where the two liquid solutions are in direct contact. (Mixing may be prevented by a suitable porous diaphragm or simply by gravity.) This type of cell is known as a *concentration cell with liquid junction.* Here the transference of electrolyte between the chambers must be accounted for. The reactions are (per faraday)

$$\begin{aligned} \text{Ag} + \text{Cl}^-(m) &= \text{AgCl} + e^-, \\ t_-\text{Cl}^-(m') &= t_-\text{Cl}^-(m), \\ t_+\text{H}^+(m) &= t_+\text{H}^+(m'), \\ \text{AgCl} + e^- &= \text{Ag} + \text{Cl}^-(m'), \end{aligned} \tag{14.4–7}**$$

where t_- and t_+ are the fractions of the current carried by chloride and hydrogen ions respectively, assumed to be the same in both solutions. Noting that $t_- + t_+ = 1$, we may write the over-all cell reaction:

$$t_+\mathrm{Cl}^-(m) + t_+\mathrm{H}^+(m) = t_+\mathrm{Cl}^-(m') + t_+\mathrm{H}^+(m'),$$

or alternatively

$$t_+\mathrm{HCl}(m) = t_+\mathrm{HCl}(m'). \tag{14.4–8)**}$$

The equation corresponding to (14.4–3) is then

$$\mathscr{E} = -\frac{t_+RT}{\mathscr{F}} \ln \frac{(a'_{\mathrm{H}^+})(a'_{\mathrm{Cl}^-})}{(a_{\mathrm{H}^+})(a_{\mathrm{Cl}^-})}. \tag{14.4–9)**}$$

The determination of solute activities is made as with concentration cells without liquid junction, except that the transference number t_+ must be obtained in a separate experiment.

Equations (14.4–7)** to (14.4–9)** assumed that the fractions of the current carried by each ion were the same in both solutions and could thus be identified with a single set of *transference numbers*, t_- and t_+, available from a separate determination. The transference number generally varies with concentration, and the electromotive force of (14.4–9)** must be obtained by a suitable integration between m and m'.

Problem 14.4-2. (a) For an infinitesimal difference in concentration, show that equation (14.4–9)** becomes

$$\mathscr{E} = -t_+ \frac{RT}{\mathscr{F}} \, \mathrm{d} \ln (a_{\mathrm{H}^+})(a_{\mathrm{Cl}^-}). \tag{14.4–10}$$

(b) Show that, when the transference numbers vary with concentration, the cell (14.4–6) can be considered as a number of concentration cells with infinitesimal concentration differences placed in series; i.e.,

Ag, AgCl | HCl(m) | HCl(m + dm) | AgCl, Ag | HCl(m + dm) | HCl(m + 2dm) | AgCl, Ag | HCl (m + 2dm) | HCl (m + 3dm) |, etc.

(c) Show that the electromotive force of the cell (14.4–6) becomes

$$\mathscr{E} = -\frac{RT}{\mathscr{F}} \int_m^{m'} t_+ \, \mathrm{d} \ln a_{\mathrm{H}^+} a_{\mathrm{Cl}^-} = -\frac{RT}{\mathscr{F}} \ln \frac{(a'_{\mathrm{H}^+})^{t'_+}(a'_{\mathrm{Cl}^-})^{t'_+}}{(a_{\mathrm{H}^+})^{t_+}(a_{\mathrm{Cl}^-})^{t_+}} + $$
$$+ \frac{RT}{\mathscr{F}} \int_{t_+}^{t'_+} \ln a_{\mathrm{H}^+} a_{\mathrm{Cl}^-} \, dt_+,$$

where t_+ and t_+' are the transference numbers at the molalities m and m' respectively.

Concentration cells, with and without liquid junction, have been frequently used for determination of activity coefficients. For a fuller discussion the reader is referred to Harned and Owen.[1]

14.5 Use of Electrolytic Cells in Determinations of Equilibrium Constants

If a cell is set up in which the concentration of one of the reacting ions is controlled by a chemical equilibrium involving this ion, the electromotive force of the cell may be used for determination of the equilibrium constant. A simple example is the cell Pt, $H_2 \mid HA(m_1), MA(m_2), MCl(m_3) \mid$ AgCl, Ag, where M represents a metallic ion more electropositive than hydrogen (say sodium or potassium). In this case the cell reaction is still given by (14.1–2), and the electromotive force by (14.3–1). The activity of hydrogen ion may be replaced by use of the equilibrium constant,

$$K = \frac{(a_{H^+})(a_{A^-})}{(a_{HA})} . \tag{14.5–1}$$

Upon introduction of the equilibrium constant and substitution for the activities in terms of molalities and activity coefficients, (14.3–3) becomes

$$\frac{(\mathscr{E} - \mathscr{E}^\circ)\mathscr{F}}{RT} + \ln \frac{(m_{HA})(m_{Cl^-})}{(m_{A^-})} = -\ln K - \ln \frac{\gamma_{HA}\gamma_{Cl^-}}{\gamma_{A^-}} . \tag{14.5–2}$$

The quantity on the left may be plotted against the ionic strength and extrapolated to infinite dilution, where it reduces to $-\ln K$. Frequently the molalities of the several species present may be taken without correction for ionization of the acid or hydrolysis of the salt. If either of these is appreciable, the corrections may be applied by use of successive approximations to the equilibrium constant. Examples of the application of cell measurements to the determination of dissociation constants are given by Harned and Owen.[1]

Problem 14.5-1. Prove equation (14.5–2).

In the example cited above, the concentration of the hydrogen ion was primarily affected by the addition of other solutes. The cell potential may also be altered by the addition of a material which reacts with HCl, and the change in potential used for calculation of the fugacity of HCl, by means of equation (14.2–4). This situation is illustrated in Problem 14.5–2.

Problem 14.5-2. The emf of cells containing a hydrogen electrode and a silver-silver chloride electrode with the electrolyte a solution of methylamine in absolute alcohol, saturated with methyl ammonium chloride, has been measured.[2] The potential of the cell (written in the usual fashion) was $+0.6970$ v at 25°C when the pressure of hydrogen was 0.893 atm and the directly measured pressure of methylamine was 4.15×10^{-3} atm. The standard emf of the cell described by equation (14.2–4) is -0.1508 volts at 25°C.[2]

(a) Calculate the fugacity of HCl above the solution, and $\Delta F°$ for the reaction $CH_3NH_3Cl(s) = CH_3NH_2(g) + HCl(g)$.

(b) Calculate the dissociation pressure of pure $CH_3NH_3Cl(s)$ into $CH_3NH_2(g)$ and HCl(g) at 25°C.

14.6 Mixtures of Electrolytes. Non-aqueous Systems

Cell measurements are particularly useful in determination of the activity of one electrolyte in the presence of others. For example, the cell Pt, $H_2 \mid HCl \mid AgCl$, Ag may be used for determination of the activity product of $(H^+)(Cl^-)$ regardless of other electrolytes present. The one requirement is that the electrodes used be sensitive only to the particular pair of ions to be studied. Many cell measurements have been made on mixed electrolytes, particularly on HCl-halide systems; the activity coefficients obtained illustrate the dependence of ion activity on the presence of other ions. The activity coefficients of HCl have been measured in solutions containing both HCl and alkali halides. In one set of experiments the total molality (acid plus salt) was held constant, while the concentration of hydrogen ion was varied. It was found that the activity coefficient of HCl was almost independent of acid-salt ratio. The effect of added salts on the activity of a dissolved electrolyte, as shown by the solubility, has been subject to many investigations. Experiments of both types and theoretical treatments of them are discussed by Harned and Owen.[9]

Cell measurements may be used to advantage in the study of electrolytes in non-aqueous systems, or in systems where the solvent is a mixture of water and a non-aqueous liquid. Many such investigations have been made for common electrolytes. In solvents of low dielectric constant, deviations from ideal behavior are much larger than in water, as the Debye-Hückel theory predicts (see equation 13.3–1). Deviations from the simple extensions of this theory are also larger. The procedures used for calculation of activities are the same as those described in Sections 14.3 and 14.4, except that the extrapolation for $\mathscr{E}°$ is more difficult and it is usually necessary to use a rather complicated extrapolation function in order to obtain accuracy in determination of the standard potential.

Problem 14.6-1. Hutchison and Chandlee[10] have measured the emf of the cell $Pt,H_2 \mid H_2SO_4$ in glacial acetic acid $\mid Hg_2SO_4,Hg$ at 25°C. They obtained 0.181 volt for $\mathscr{E}°$.

(a) Write the cell reaction.

(b) Write an equation connecting the voltage with the mean ion activity coefficient of H_2SO_4.

(c) Evaluate the mean ion activity coefficient of H_2SO_4 at 0.501 molal from the observed voltage, which is 0.480 volt.

[9] Harned and Owen, *op. cit.*, Chapter 14.

[10] A. W. Hutchison and G. C. Chandlee, *J. Am. Chem. Soc.*, **53**, 2881 (1931).

Thermodynamics Involving Variables Other than Pressure, Temperature, and Composition

CHAPTER 15

15.1 Introduction

In the sets of variables listed in Section 9.1, the pressure *or* volume always appears, but never both. The product of these two variables is work. There are other variables not previously considered, analogous to the pressure, which together with an extensive variable yield work. These are magnetic field, electric field, applied tension among others. The effect of such variables on the thermodynamic properties of the system is readily seen upon application of the first law of thermodynamics.

The variables considered can be conveniently divided as in Section 5.9 into *intensive variables* (P, T, etc.), which do not depend on the amount of substance present, and *extensive variables* (V, etc.), whose value is proportional to the amount. In the general discussions of the next section the intensive variables, except T, will be given the general symbol X_i (e.g., P, the magnetic field $\mathscr{H}$); the corresponding extensive variables will be given the symbol x_i (V, the intensity of magnetization I, etc.). In any particular case only those variables whose contribution to the state of the system is significant need be considered.

15.2 General Relations among Thermodynamic Properties

The work done by a system may be defined, in general, for a differential change as

$$w = X_i \, dx_i, \tag{15.2–1}$$

where X_i is an intensive variable, and dx_i is the change in the corresponding extensive variable.

In accordance with the first law, for a reversible process *involving a closed system* in the sense of Section 9.1,

$$dE = T\,dS - \sum X_i \, dx_i, \tag{15.2–2}$$

or

$$dE = T\,dS - P\,dV - \sum X_i \, dx_i, \tag{15.2–3}$$

where the variables P and V have been withdrawn from the summation. For clarity we shall hereafter consider P separately from the other X_i. Proceeding as in Section 9.1, we may use equation (15.2–3) to define the partial derivatives:

$$\left(\frac{\partial E}{\partial S}\right)_{V,x_i} = T; \tag{15.2–4}$$

$$\left(\frac{\partial E}{\partial V}\right)_{S,x_i} = -P; \tag{15.2–5}$$

$$\left(\frac{\partial E}{\partial x_i}\right)_{S,V,x_j \neq x_i} = -X_i; \tag{15.2–6}$$

and

$$T\left(\frac{\partial S}{\partial x_i}\right)_{E,V,x_j \neq x_i} = X_i. \tag{15.2–7}$$

The definition of the enthalpy H given in Section 5.2 must be generalized so that the *enthalpy change is equal to the heat withdrawn from the surroundings for a process in which all intensive variables* (other than temperature) *are held constant.* At constant P and X, the work done is

$$w = P\,\Delta V + \sum X_i \, \Delta x_i, \tag{15.2–8}$$

and the heat withdrawn from the surroundings is

$$q = \Delta E + P\,\Delta V + \sum X_i \, \Delta x_i. \tag{15.2–9}$$

Then, as in Section 5.2,

$$q = (E_B + P_B V_B + \Sigma\, X_B x_B) - (E_A + P_A V_A + \Sigma\, X_A x_A), \tag{15.2–10}$$

since neither P nor the X's change in the process. The enthalpy is defined, quite generally, by the equation

$$H = E + PV + \sum X_i x_i , \qquad (15.2\text{–}11)$$

so that q again equals ΔH. Since H is an arbitrarily defined quantity, it would be possible to retain the original definition ($H = E + PV$); this has frequently been done in the past. If we did this, the simple relationship of q to ΔH would no longer hold when variables other than P and V are considered.

Upon differentiation of (15.2–11) and replacement of dE by use of (15.2–3), a differential change in enthalpy is given by

$$\mathrm{d}H = T\,\mathrm{d}S + V\,\mathrm{d}P + \sum x_i\,\mathrm{d}X_i . \qquad (15.2\text{–}12)$$

From this equation the derivative of the enthalpy with respect to X_i is

$$\left(\frac{\partial H}{\partial X_i}\right)_{S,P,X_j \neq X_i} = x_i . \qquad (15.2\text{–}13)$$

The Helmholtz free energy A is defined as before:

$$A = E - TS. \qquad (6.17\text{–}5)$$

Upon differentiation and replacement of dE, using equation (15.2–3), the differential change in Helmholtz free energy is

$$\mathrm{d}A = -S\,\mathrm{d}T - P\,\mathrm{d}V - \sum X_i\,\mathrm{d}x_i . \qquad (15.2\text{–}14)$$

Consequently

$$\left(\frac{\partial A}{\partial x_i}\right)_{T,V,x_j \neq x_i} = -X_i . \qquad (15.2\text{–}15)$$

Similarly, the Gibbs free energy, F, is defined so that $-\Delta F$ is the electrical work done in a reversible cell at constant values of P and X_i,

$$F = H - TS = E - TS + PV + \sum X_i x_i . \qquad (15.2\text{–}16)$$

Upon differentiation and replacement of dE, using equation (15.2–3),

$$\mathrm{d}F = -S\,\mathrm{d}T + V\,\mathrm{d}P + \sum x_i\,\mathrm{d}X_i . \qquad (15.2\text{–}17)$$

Then

$$\left(\frac{\partial F}{\partial X_i}\right)_{T,P,X_j \neq X_i} = x_i . \qquad (15.2\text{–}18)$$

The definitions of H and F are thus consistent with each other.

Equations (15.2–13) and (15.2–18) may be used to define the extensive variables x_i in terms of the enthalpy and Gibbs free energy, respectively. Equations (15.2–6) and (15.2–15) define the intensive variables X_i in terms of the energy and Helmholtz free energy. As in Section 6.17, the maximum work obtained from a constant temperature process is

$$w_{\max} = -\mathrm{d}A = -P\,\mathrm{d}V - \sum X_i\,\mathrm{d}x_i\,. \qquad (15.2\text{–}19)$$

Thus a force X_i (intensive variable) may be defined in terms of measurable quantities from: (a) the work required to cause an infinitesimal change in x_i at constant temperature and volume (equation 15.2–19); (b) the change in energy associated with a reversible adiabatic change (equation 15.2–6); or (c) the heat withdrawn from the surroundings in a reversible change at constant energy and volume (equation 15.2–7).

The condition for equilibrium at constant temperature and pressure was given in Chapter 6 as

$$\Delta F = 0. \qquad (6.18\text{–}5)$$

With the definitions given above, the same equation may be applied to any changes in which T, P, and the variables X_i are kept constant.

From equation (6.7–8), for a differential process,

$$\mathrm{d}S_s + \mathrm{d}S_r \gtreqqless 0. \qquad (15.2\text{–}20)$$

But, since $\mathrm{d}S_r = -q/T$, for a process in which there is a change from state A to state B for the working substance (or substances)

$$T\,\mathrm{d}S - q \gtreqqless 0. \qquad (15.2\text{–}21)$$

From the first law,

$$q = \mathrm{d}E + w = \mathrm{d}E + P\,\mathrm{d}V + \sum X_i\,\mathrm{d}x_i\,, \qquad (15.2\text{–}22)$$

so that

$$T\,\mathrm{d}S - \mathrm{d}E - P\,\mathrm{d}V - \sum X_i\,\mathrm{d}x_i \gtreqqless 0. \qquad (15.2\text{–}23)$$

At constant T, P, and X_i, from equation (15.2–16),

$$\mathrm{d}F = \mathrm{d}E - T\,\mathrm{d}S + P\,\mathrm{d}V + \sum X_i\,\mathrm{d}x_i \lesseqqgtr 0, \qquad (15.2\text{–}24)$$

where, as in equation (6.18–6), the inequality applies to a spontaneous process, and the inequality to a process at equilibrium with the added condition that the X_i are kept constant.

It is sometimes desirable to examine the conditions for equilibrium at constant temperature, volume, and x_i. In this case $q = \mathrm{d}E$, so that at equilibrium

$$\mathrm{d}A = \mathrm{d}E - T\,\mathrm{d}S = 0 \qquad (T,\ V,\ x_i \text{ constant}). \qquad (15.2\text{–}25)$$

Problem 15.2-1. For a process occurring at constant T, V, and x_i, show that $q = \mathrm{d}E$ and thus that $\mathrm{d}A < 0$ for a spontaneous process and that $\mathrm{d}A = 0$ for equilibrium.

An alternative way of stating the conditions for equilibrium is that (a) for a process at constant T, P, and X_i the Gibbs free energy F is a minimum at equilibrium, and that (b) for a process at constant T, V, and x_i the

Helmholtz free energy A is a minimum at equilibrium. The validity of the first statement may readily be seen as follows. Equation (15.2–24) has already shown that a spontaneous process at constant T, P, and X_i must result in a decrease in the Gibbs free energy F; such a spontaneous process proceeds in the direction of equilibrium. The system can depart from equilibrium only by a non-spontaneous process, for which by the argument the free energy change must be greater than zero. Consequently the equilibrium state at constant T, P, and X_i corresponds to a minimum in the Gibbs Free Energy. The same argument can be used to show that the equilibrium state at constant T, V, and x_i must correspond to a minimum in the Helmholtz Free Energy.

Problem 15.2-2. Show that the condition for equilibrium at constant T, V, and x_i is that the Helmholtz free energy A is a minimum.

Problem 15.2-3. Show that the condition for equilibrium at constant entropy, pressure, and X_i is that the change in enthalpy H is zero. (*Hint.* Apply equation (15.2–22) and compare with (15.2–11).)

15.3 Derived Thermodynamic Relationships

Application of the first and second laws to systems involving other variables yields many thermodynamic equations similar in form to those considered previously. Several examples are given below, and others will be considered in special cases.

The heat capacity may be defined for constant intensive variables (X_i) or extensive variables (x_i). The heat capacity is defined in general as in Section 5.3,

$$C = \lim_{\delta T \to 0} \frac{q}{\delta T}. \tag{5.3–1}$$

By the first law,

$$q = \mathrm{d}E + w = \mathrm{d}E + P\,\mathrm{d}V + \sum X_i\,\mathrm{d}x_i. \tag{15.3–1}$$

Upon differentiation of equation (15.2–11) at constant P and X_i,

$$\mathrm{d}H = \mathrm{d}E + P\,\mathrm{d}V + \sum X_i\,\mathrm{d}x_i = q. \tag{15.3–2}$$

Therefore

$$C_{P,X_i} = \left(\frac{\partial H}{\partial T}\right)_{P,X_i}. \tag{15.3–3}$$

Similarly, from equation (15.3–1), at constant volume and x_i,

$$q = \mathrm{d}E$$

and

$$C_{V,x_i} = \left(\frac{\partial E}{\partial T}\right)_{V,x_i}. \tag{15.3–4}$$

We proceed as in Sections 6.8 and 6.9, and application of the first and second laws to reversible processes gives

$$\left(\frac{\partial S}{\partial T}\right)_{V,x_i} = \frac{C_{V,x_i}}{T} \tag{15.3–5}$$

and

$$\left(\frac{\partial S}{\partial T}\right)_{P,X_i} = \frac{C_{P,X_i}}{T} \tag{15.3–6}$$

as the more general forms of equations (6.8–4) and (6.9–5).

Problem 15.3-1. Derive equations (15.3–5) and (15.3–6).

Relations between the various X_i and x_i may be obtained by use of equations (15.2–15) and (15.2–18). If only x_1 and x_2 are allowed to vary, since the order of differentiation is immaterial,

$$\left(\frac{\partial}{\partial x_2}\frac{\partial A}{\partial x_1}\right)_{T,V} = \left(\frac{\partial}{\partial x_1}\frac{\partial A}{\partial x_2}\right)_{T,V}. \tag{15.3–7}$$

Then, from equation (15.2–15),

$$\left(\frac{\partial X_1}{\partial x_2}\right)_{x_j \neq x_2,T,V} = \left(\frac{\partial X_2}{\partial x_1}\right)_{x_j \neq x_1,T,V}. \tag{15.3–8}$$

Similarly, from equation (15.2–18),

$$\left(\frac{\partial x_1}{\partial X_2}\right)_{Xj \neq X_2,T,P} = \left(\frac{\partial x_2}{\partial X_1}\right)_{X_j \neq X_1,T,P}. \tag{15.3–9}$$

Problem 15.3-2. Derive equation (15.3–9) in detail.

The various equations in Section 15.2 and 15.3 were derived for systems in which the number of moles of each substance present remained fixed. If this number does not remain fixed, as in an electrical cell, the equations must be suitably altered. Upon application of the procedure used to get equations (6.20–6), equation (15.2–3) becomes

$$\mathrm{d}E = T\,\mathrm{d}S - P\,\mathrm{d}V - \sum X_i\,\mathrm{d}x_i + \sum \mu_i\,\mathrm{d}n_i; \tag{15.3–10}$$

equation (15.2–17) becomes

$$\mathrm{d}F = -S\,\mathrm{d}T + V\,\mathrm{d}P + \sum x_i\,\mathrm{d}X_i + \sum \mu_i\,\mathrm{d}n_i; \tag{15.3–11}$$

and so on. These equations may be applied to an open system as in Section 9.1 and are the generalizations of equations (9.1–1) and (9.1–9) respectively. The considerations of Section 9.2 which led to the statement of the phase rule must now be generalized. For a system of C components, C + n variables are now required; these are the C partial molal free energies μ_i, the pressure P, the temperature T, and $n - 2$ other intensive variables X_i. A completely general statement of the phase rule is thus

$$P + \mathrm{F} = \mathrm{C} + n, \tag{15.3–12}$$

where n is the number of non-trivial intensive variables. Ordinarily, the intensive variables other than P and T are not altered in the course of a phase study. It should be evident from equations (15.3–11) and (15.3–12) that alteration in other variables must shift the phase equilibrium and permit additional phases to exist.

Problem 15.3-3. Because oxygen is paramagnetic, its properties are affected in a non-trivial manner by a magnetic field $\mathscr{H}$. Show that the vapor pressure of liquid oxygen must be altered by application of a magnetic field at constant T.

Problem 15.3-4. Show that the equilibrium in a mixture of gases, some of which are paramagnetic, must be shifted by application of a magnetic field at constant T.

15.4 Thermodynamics of Magnetism

When any material is placed in a magnetic field $\mathscr{H}$, the induction in the sample is given by

$$B = \mathscr{H} + 4\pi I, \tag{15.4–1}$$

where I is the intensity of magnetization per unit volume. For a diamagnetic substance, the (induced) magnetization is in opposition to the applied field and the induction in the sample is less than the applied field; that is, there are fewer lines of magnetic force per unit area within the sample than at a distance from it. For a paramagnetic or ferromagnetic substance, I is positive, and lines of force tend to concentrate within the substance. The induction is also defined as

$$B = \mu\mathscr{H} \qquad \left(\mu = 1 + \frac{4\pi I}{\mathscr{H}}\right). \tag{15.4–2}$$

The second portion of (15.4–2) defines the *permeability* μ, which is greater than unity for paramagnetic and ferromagnetic substances and less than unity for diamagnetic substances. (Note that the magnetic permeability μ has no relationship to the Joule-Thomson coefficient μ or the chemical potential μ, although historically the same symbol has been used for all three.)

For paramagnetic materials at low fields and high temperatures, the intensity of magnetization is proportional to the applied field. The *magnetic susceptibility* χ is defined by the equation

$$\chi = \frac{I}{\mathscr{H}}. \tag{15.4–3}$$

Where the magnetic susceptibility depends on the field strength, it is more convenient to define χ by the equation

$$\chi = \left(\frac{\partial I}{\partial \mathscr{H}}\right)_r, \tag{15.4–4}$$

where r is some quantity (temperature, entropy, etc.) held constant during the process of measurement. The subscript r must be specified to give χ a definite meaning; typically it is either T or S.

For thermodynamic purposes it is convenient to work with molar quantities. The *molar intensity of magnetization* $\tilde{I}$ and the *molar magnetic susceptibility* χ_m, are defined by the equations

$$\tilde{I} = I\tilde{V}, \qquad \chi_m = \chi\tilde{V}, \tag{15.4–5}$$

where $\tilde{V}$ is the volume containing a mole (or gram atom) of magnetic material.

The work done, per mole, in magnetization of a paramagnetic body is, by equation (15.2–1),

$$w = -\mathscr{H}\,\mathrm{d}\tilde{I}. \tag{15.4–6}$$

The work is in ergs per mole if $\mathscr{H}$ is in oersteds, and $\tilde{I}$ is as defined above. The negative sign indicates that work is done *on* the system when the intensity of magnetization is increased.

The effects produced by magnetic work are not so obvious as those produced by pressure-volume work, and for this reason they will be examined in detail. In later sections of this chapter, the work will be written directly from equation (15.2–1).

From elementary magnetostatics, the energy, per unit volume, of a uniformly magnetized body in a magnetic field $\mathscr{H}$ is

$$E = \frac{B\mathscr{H}}{8\pi} = \frac{\mathscr{H}^2}{8\pi} + \frac{I\mathscr{H}}{2}. \tag{15.4–7}$$

The last term in equation (15.4–7) is the energy due to magnetization of the body and is the potential energy of the body in the field. It is therefore the work *required* to magnetize the body to a field $\mathscr{H}$ in the absence of heat flow or other sources of energy. The same result is obtained by integration of equation (15.4–6). It is

$$-w = \int_0^I \mathscr{H}\,\mathrm{d}I = \int_0^{\mathscr{H}} \chi\mathscr{H}\,\mathrm{d}\mathscr{H} = \frac{\chi\mathscr{H}^2}{2} = \frac{I\mathscr{H}}{2}. \tag{15.4–8}$$

The work of magnetization thus goes into increasing the potential energy of the body.

The thermodynamic properties of magnetic materials may now be derived from the general equations of Sections 15.2 and 15.3 after identifying $-\mathscr{H}$ with X_i and I with x_i. According to equation (15.2–3),

$$\mathrm{d}E = T\,\mathrm{d}S - P\,\mathrm{d}V + \mathscr{H}\,\mathrm{d}I. \tag{15.4–9}$$

According to (15.2–12),

$$\mathrm{d}H = T\,\mathrm{d}S + V\,\mathrm{d}P - I\,\mathrm{d}\mathscr{H}, \tag{15.4–10}$$

and, according to (15.2–17),

$$\mathrm{d}F = -S\,\mathrm{d}T + V\,\mathrm{d}P - I\,\mathrm{d}\mathscr{H}. \tag{15.4–11}$$

Problem 15.4-1. Following the procedures of Sections 15.2 and 15.3, prove equations (15.4–9) and (15.4–10) explicitly.

From the equations of Section 15.3, the heat capacities are defined

$$C_{\mathscr{H}} = \left(\frac{\partial H}{\partial T}\right)_{\mathscr{H},P} = T\left(\frac{\partial S}{\partial T}\right)_{\mathscr{H},P}, \tag{15.4–12}$$

$$C_I = \left(\frac{\partial E}{\partial T}\right)_{I,V} = T\left(\frac{\partial S}{\partial T}\right)_{I,V}. \tag{15.4–13}$$

Problem 15.4-2. Prove equations (15.4–12) and (15.4–13).

The *entropy change of magnetization at constant pressure and temperature*, ΔS_{mag}, may be obtained as follows. From equation (15.4–11) one obtains

$$\left(\frac{\partial S}{\partial \mathscr{H}}\right)_{P,T} = \left(\frac{\partial I}{\partial T}\right)_{P,\mathscr{H}}. \tag{15.4–14}$$

ΔS_{mag} is obtained upon integration; it is

$$\Delta S_{\text{mag}} = \int_{\mathscr{H}_1}^{\mathscr{H}_2} \left(\frac{\partial I}{\partial T}\right)_{P,\mathscr{H}} \mathrm{d}\mathscr{H}. \tag{15.4–15}$$

Problem 15.4-3. A substance for which $\chi_m T = \tilde{I}T/\mathscr{H} = \tilde{C}_1$, a constant, is said to follow Curie's law.

(a) Show that for such a substance the molar entropy of isothermal magnetization from zero field is given by

$$\Delta S_{\text{mag}} = -\frac{\tilde{C}_1 \mathscr{H}^2}{2T^2}. \qquad (15.4\text{–}16)^{**}$$

(b) Obtain an expression for the entropy of magnetization of a substance whose susceptibility follows the Curie-Weiss law, $\chi_m = \tilde{C}_1/(T + \Delta)$, where $\tilde{C}_1$ and Δ are constants independent of $\mathscr{H}$ and T.

Problem 15.4-4. Calculate, in calories mole^{-1} deg^{-1}, the entropy of magnetization from 0 to 6000 oersteds at (a) 1°, (b) 2°, and (c) 4° for a substance which follows Curie's law with a constant $\tilde{C}_1$ of 2.0. Note that for $\mathscr{H}$ in oersteds the units of $\mathscr{H}^2$ are ergs cm^{-3}; the units of $\tilde{C}_1$ are cm^3 deg mole^{-1}.

At constant pressure, if magnetic field and temperature are varied, the change in entropy is

$$dS = \left(\frac{\partial S}{\partial \mathscr{H}}\right)_T d\mathscr{H} + \left(\frac{\partial S}{\partial T}\right)_{\mathscr{H}} dT \tag{15.4–17}$$

or, by considering the case where dS is zero;

$$\left(\frac{\partial S}{\partial \mathscr{H}}\right)_T = -\left(\frac{\partial S}{\partial T}\right)_{\mathscr{H}} \left(\frac{\partial T}{\partial \mathscr{H}}\right)_S . \tag{15.4–18}$$

Solving for $(\partial T/\partial \mathscr{H})_S$, and using equations (15.4–12) and (15.4–14),

$$\left(\frac{\partial T}{\partial \mathscr{H}}\right)_S = -\frac{T}{\tilde{C}_{\mathscr{H}}}\left(\frac{\partial \tilde{I}}{\partial T}\right)_{\mathscr{H}} . \tag{15.4–19}$$

Equation 15.4–19 gives the rate of change of temperature with magnetic field upon reversible adiabatic magnetization. It forms the basis of methods of cooling paramagnetic salts by *adiabatic demagnetization*. The susceptibility, and thus the intensity of magnetization in a field, of most paramagnetic salts increase with decreasing temperature; that is, $(\partial \tilde{I}/\partial T)_{\mathscr{H}}$ is negative. Since T and $\tilde{C}_{\mathscr{H}}$ must be positive, the temperature of the salt must increase upon adiabatic application of a magnetic field. Conversely, the salt will cool upon adiabatic demagnetization. The extent of cooling will depend on the field used, the intensity of magnetization, and the heat capacity of the salt. This method of cooling paramagnetic salts was predicted by Giauque[1] and Debye[2] and was first verified experimentally by Giauque.[3]

The heat capacity required in equation (15.4–19), $\tilde{C}_{\mathscr{H}}$, may be written arbitrarily as

$$\tilde{C}_{\mathscr{H}} = \tilde{C}_0 + \tilde{C}_{\text{mag}} , \tag{15.4–20}$$

where $\tilde{C}_0$ is the heat capacity at a given temperature in the absence of a magnetic field, and $\tilde{C}_{\text{mag}}$ is the increase or decrease due to the applied field. This last term is

$$\tilde{C}_{\text{mag}} = \int_0^{\mathscr{H}} \left(\frac{\partial \tilde{C}_{\mathscr{H}}}{\partial \mathscr{H}}\right)_T d\mathscr{H} . \tag{15.4–21}$$

From equations (15.4–12) and (15.4–14),

$$\left(\frac{\partial \tilde{C}_{\mathscr{H}}}{\partial \mathscr{H}}\right)_{P,T} = T\left(\frac{\partial^2 \tilde{I}}{\partial T^2}\right)_{\mathscr{H},P} . \tag{15.4–22}$$

[1] W. F. Giauque, *J. Am. Chem. Soc.*, **49,** 1864, 1870 (1927).
[2] P. Debye, *Ann. Physik*, **81,** 1154 (1926).
[3] W. F. Giauque and D. P. MacDougall, *Phys. Rev.*, **43,** 768 (1933).

The additional heat capacity is then obtained by integration:

$$\tilde{C}_{\text{mag}} = \int_0^{\mathscr{H}} T\left(\frac{\partial^2 \tilde{I}}{\partial T^2}\right)_{\mathscr{H},P} \mathrm{d}\mathscr{H}. \qquad (15.4\text{–}23)$$

As will be seen in Chapter 22, the heat capacity in zero field contains terms due both to ordinary crystal vibrations and to the presence of magnetic ions. The derivative in (15.4–23) may be either positive or negative.

Problem 15.4-5. (a) Show that, for a substance which follows Curie's law, $\chi_m T = \tilde{C}_1$, the effect, $\tilde{C}_{\text{mag}}$, of a field $\mathscr{H}$ on the heat capacity is given by

$$\tilde{C}_{\text{mag}} = \frac{\tilde{C}_1 \mathscr{H}^2}{T^2}. \qquad (15.4\text{–}24)^{**}$$

(b) Calculate, in cal mole^{-1} deg^{-1}, $\tilde{C}_{\text{mag}}$ at 6000 gauss, 2°K, for a substance which follows Curie's law with a constant $\tilde{C}_1 = 2.0$.

Problem 15.4-6. Evaluate at 1°K and (a) 0, (b) 1, and (c) 10 oersteds the rate of change of temperature (degs/oersted) for adiabatic magnetization of a substance for which $\chi_m T = 2.0$ and for which $\tilde{C}_0 = 5 \times 10^{-4} T^3$ cal deg^{-1} mole^{-1}. The effect of these small fields on the heat capacity may be neglected.

Problem 15.4-7. (a) Show that the rate of change of energy with field upon isothermal magnetization at constant pressure and volume is given by

$$\left(\frac{\partial \tilde{E}}{\partial \mathscr{H}}\right)_{P,T} = T\left(\frac{\partial \tilde{I}}{\partial T}\right)_{P,\mathscr{H}} + \mathscr{H}\left(\frac{\partial \tilde{I}}{\partial \mathscr{H}}\right)_{P,T}. \qquad (15.4\text{–}25)$$

(b) Show that a substance which follows Curie's law suffers no change in energy upon isothermal magnetization. (Note the analogy with a perfect gas, which suffers no energy change on isothermal compression.)

15.5 Gravitation and Centrifugal Force

Newton's law of gravitation states that the force of attraction between two bodies of mass M and m, whose centers of mass are separated by a distance r, is

$$f = \frac{GmM}{r^2} = Mg, \qquad (15.5\text{–}1)$$

where G is the universal gravitational constant equal to 6.661×10^{-8} cm^3 g^{-1} sec^{-2}, and g contains the mass of one of the bodies and the distance. In its most common application, the larger body is the earth, and g is the acceleration due to gravity at the specified location. The effect of gravity upon thermodynamic properties was first discussed by Gibbs.[4]

[4] *Scientific Papers of J. Willard Gibbs*, Longmans, Green, New York, 1926, pp. 144–150.

The potential energy per mole of a body in the earth's gravitational field is

$$E_{\text{pot}} = M \int_{\text{h}_0}^{\text{h}} g \, \text{dh}, \qquad (15.5\text{–}2)$$

where h is the distance of the body from the earth's center of mass. The zero of energy is taken at the surface of the earth, a distance h_0 from the center. The intensive variable (X_i) is defined by[5]

$$X_i \equiv \phi = \int_{\text{h}_0}^{\text{h}} g \, \text{dh}, \qquad (15.5\text{–}3)$$

and the mass M is chosen as the extensive variable x_i. A change in Gibbs free energy for a one-component system is given from equation (15.2–17) as

$$\text{d}F = -S \, \text{d}T + V \, \text{d}P + M \, \text{d}\phi. \qquad (15.5\text{–}4)$$

If a column of material is to be at equilibrium throughout, its temperature must be uniform, and the pressure of each horizontal segment must remain constant. Thus the molal free energy of the material must be independent of position, the change due to height being exactly balanced by the difference in pressure. In this case,

$$V \, \text{d}P = -M \, \text{d}\phi \qquad (15.5\text{–}5)$$

and

$$\frac{\text{d}P}{\text{d}\phi} = -\frac{M}{V}. \qquad (15.5\text{–}6)$$

However, $\text{d}\phi = g \, \text{dh}$, and $M/V = \rho$, where ρ is the density of the material. Therefore

$$\frac{\text{d}P}{\text{dh}} = -g\rho, \qquad (15.5\text{–}7)$$

which is the well-known equation for hydrostatic equilibrium. Equation (15.5–7) may be integrated for any system in which the density is a known function of the pressure.

Problem 15.5-1. Show that, for an isothermal column of a perfect gas, the variation of pressure with height is given by

$$\ln \frac{P_1}{P_2} = \frac{g\tilde{M}}{RT}(\text{h}_2 - \text{h}_1), \qquad (15.5\text{–}8)^*$$

if the variation of g with height may be neglected.

[5] In keeping with previous convention, the potential energy is regarded somewhat artificially as being built up by introduction of small amounts of mass dM at the potential ϕ.

For a multicomponent system, the partial molal free energy of each component must be constant at equilibrium. For such a system, with temperature constant as before,

$$d\mu_i = \bar{V}_i\, dP + \tilde{M}_i\, d\phi + \left(\frac{\partial \mu_i}{\partial \tilde{N}_i}\right) d\tilde{N}_i = 0. \qquad (15.5\text{–}9)$$

$$\bar{V}_i\, dP + \left(\frac{\partial \mu_i}{\partial \tilde{N}_i}\right) d\tilde{N}_i = -\tilde{M}_i\, d\phi. \qquad (15.5\text{–}10)$$

For a perfect solution of ideal gases,

$$P_i = P\tilde{N}_i, \qquad PV = \sum n_i RT; \qquad (15.5\text{–}11)^{**}$$

whence

$$\bar{V}_i = \left(\frac{\partial V}{\partial n_i}\right)_{n_j,P,T} = \frac{RT}{P} \qquad (15.5\text{–}12)^{**}$$

and

$$\frac{\partial \mu_i}{\partial \tilde{N}_i} = \frac{RT}{\tilde{N}_i}. \qquad (11.2\text{–}9)^{**}$$

Equation (15.5–10) then becomes

$$\frac{RT}{P}\, dP + \frac{RT}{\tilde{N}_i}\, d\tilde{N}_i = -\tilde{M}_i\, d\phi. \qquad (15.5\text{–}13)^{**}$$

Rewriting the left side of (15.5–13)**,

$$RT\, d\ln P + RT\, d\ln \tilde{N}_i \equiv RT\, d\ln P\tilde{N}_i, \qquad (15.5\text{–}14)$$

whence

$$RT\, d\ln P\tilde{N}_i = -\tilde{M}_i\, d\phi, \qquad (15.5\text{–}15)^{**}$$

or, in terms of the partial pressure P_i,

$$RT\, d\ln P_i = -\tilde{M}_i\, d\phi. \qquad (15.5\text{–}16)^{**}$$

Upon integration of equation (15.5–16)**,

$$\ln \frac{P_i}{P_i'} = \frac{\tilde{M}_i}{RT}(\phi' - \phi) = \frac{\tilde{M}_i g}{RT}(\mathrm{h}' - \mathrm{h}). \qquad (15.5\text{–}17)^{**}$$

It will be noted that for this special case the variation in pressure with height is the same for the component of a mixture as it would have been for the pure gas, as given in equation (15.5–8)*. It is evident from equation (15.5–17)** that the pressures of two gases of different molecular weights will vary differently with height, so that the composition of the mixture must be a function of height. Equation (15.5–10) may also be applied to other solutions, both ideal and non-ideal.

Problem 15.5-2. At sea level, air may be considered to contain 20.16 mole per cent of oxygen and 78.72 mole per cent of nitrogen, with a total pressure of 0.995 atm due to these constituents. Calculate the partial pressures of oxygen and nitrogen at 15,000 ft altitude in a column of air at equilibrium at a constant temperature of 20°C. You may assume ideal gas behavior and neglect the effect of minor constituents.

The treatment of material under a *centrifugal force* may be carried out by analogous procedures, if the variable ϕ is redefined so that $d\phi$ is the product of the centrifugal acceleration times an arbitrary infinitesimal change in distance from the center of rotation; that is,

$$d\phi = r\omega^2\, dr, \tag{15.5–18}$$

where ω is the angular velocity and r the distance from the center of rotation; $r\omega^2$ (= g′) is the centrifugal acceleration. Then

$$\phi = \int_0^r r\omega^2\, dr = \frac{r^2\omega^2}{2}. \tag{15.5–19}$$

If the definitions (15.5–18) and (15.5–19) are used, equations analogous to those for gravitational effects may be derived.

The application of large centrifugal fields produces a separation of a multicomponent system which is much greater than that caused by gravity. This fact led to the elegant work of Svedberg[6] and others in the investigation of large molecules with the aid of the *ultracentrifuge*, which is capable of producing accelerations more than 100,000 times that of gravity.

15.6 Tension and Electric Field. The Piezoelectric Effect

If a body is placed under stress, strains are set up in it which result in a change of energy. In general, the effects produced are complicated, and it is necessary to set up a *strain tensor* specifying the change in dimensions along each of a set of coordinates produced by the various components of the stress. In the simple example considered below, it is assumed that a tension $\mathscr{T}$ applied to a body in a given direction results in a change of length l in that direction, with other dimensions substantially unaffected. For the body under tension, the work done is

$$w = -\mathscr{T}\, dl. \tag{15.6–1}$$

The negative sign is used because work is done *on* the body to increase its

[6] The Svedberg and K. O. Pedersen, *The Ultracentrifuge*, Clarendon Press, Oxford, 1940.

length. Thus, from (15.2–3) after identifying $-\mathscr{T}$ with X and l with x, one may write

$$dE = T\,dS - P\,dV + \mathscr{T}\,dl, \tag{15.6–2}$$

and, from (15.2–17),

$$dF = -S\,dT + V\,dP - l\,d\mathscr{T}. \tag{15.6–3}$$

Problem 15.6-1. By use of the first law, calculate the heat absorbed when a bar of steel 0.5 cm in diameter is isothermally stretched 0.1 mm under an applied tension of 10,000 lb in^{-2}. Assume that there is no change in entropy, and neglect the small change in volume.

Problem 15.6-2. With the aid of equation (15.6–3) show that the vapor pressure of a gold wire is lowered by placing it under tension.

Similarly, if an electric field $\mathscr{E}$ is applied to a material, a polarization $\mathscr{P}$ results, with a corresponding increase $\mathscr{E}\,d\mathscr{P}$ in the energy of the system. For a body under the influence of both tension and electric field,

$$dE = T\,dS - P\,dV + \mathscr{T}\,dl + \mathscr{E}\,d\mathscr{P} \tag{15.6–4}$$

and

$$dF = -S\,dT + V\,dP - l\,d\mathscr{T} - \mathscr{P}\,d\mathscr{E}. \tag{15.6–5}$$

If temperature and external pressure are held constant,

$$dF = -l\,d\mathscr{T} - \mathscr{P}\,d\mathscr{E}. \tag{15.6–6}$$

Then, as in equation (15.3–9),

$$\left(\frac{\partial l}{\partial \mathscr{E}}\right)_{T,P,\mathscr{T}} = \left(\frac{\partial \mathscr{P}}{\partial \mathscr{T}}\right)_{T,P,\mathscr{E}}. \tag{15.6–7}$$

Equation (15.6–7) relates the change of length produced in a body by application of an electric field with the electric polarization produced by tension.

Problem 15.6-3. (a) Prove equation (15.6–7).

(b) Show that, if a body has a positive polarization induced by tension, it must stretch upon application of a uniform electric field.

15.7 Thermodynamics of Surfaces and Adsorbed Films

Up to this point we have treated primarily systems in which the properties of the materials were uniform throughout each phase. In many applications of thermodynamics the special properties of an interface between two phases are important. Commonly observed effects are the force required to pull a metal ring away from the surface of a liquid and the tendency of liquids to form spherical drops. Both of these effects are due to the *surface tension* of the liquid. If the ratio of surface to volume in any system becomes large, the effects due to the surface become quite pronounced, as with colloidal systems and adsorbed gases.

The properties of a material do not change discontinuously at the interface between two phases. Instead, there is a region in which the properties of the material change continuously from those of one phase to those of the other. The interfacial (or surface) region may be taken to include all parts of the system whose properties differ appreciably from those of the bulk phases on either side of it. Within this region, the hydrostatic pressure (stress on a volume element per unit area) depends on the location of the volume element and upon the direction of the stress vector. For instance, in a curved interface between phases A and B, the pressure in a direction normal to the interface varies continuously from P_A to P_B, while the pressure parallel to the phase boundaries (denoted $P - Q$) also varies independently of the variation in P (in the case of a planar interface, the variation in P is zero, but it does not follow that Q is zero also). Q is zero at the boundaries of the interface, but it may be positive or negative between them. If the direction of $P - Q$ is assumed to point out of the volume element, then Q must have an average value which is greater than zero, since the effect of these surface stresses is such that the interface is under compression (i.e., a negative net internal pressure). This follows from the observation that bulk phases tend to take up a configuration of minimum area. The surface tension (force per unit length) is then defined by integration of Q through the surface region, as

$$\gamma = \int_{\mathrm{r_a}}^{\mathrm{r_b}} -Q \, \mathrm{dr}, \tag{15.7–1}$$

where γ is the surface tension, $\mathrm{r_a}$ and $\mathrm{r_b}$ the (usually unknown) bounds of the interfacial region, and $-Q$ the (usually unknown) net internal pressure. The surface tension is then a *property* of the two-phase system considered; for example, systems such as liquid water–water vapor, water–air, and water–oil.

An immediate consequence of the surface tension is the existence of a pressure difference between two bulk phases separated by an interface, provided that the latter is curved. The surface area will be denoted by σ. The work done by the system in the expansion of the surface at constant volume is thus given by

$$w = -\gamma \, d\sigma. \tag{15.7–2}$$

The pressure difference between phases may then be obtained by equating the work of expansion of the surface to the $P - V$ work accompanying the necessary change in volume.

The thermodynamic functions are obtained at once by identifying $-\gamma$ with X_i and σ with x_i and substituting in equations (15.2–17) and (15.2–14). For a single component, the change in the Gibbs free energy is

$$dF = -S\,dT + V\,dP - \sigma\,d\gamma, \tag{15.7–3}$$

while the corresponding change in the Helmholtz free energy is

$$dA = -S\,dT - P\,dV + \gamma\,d\sigma. \tag{15.7–4}$$

The conditions for equilibrium between a bulk phase and a region where there is a surface (e.g., a droplet) is that, at constant temperature, material may be transferred reversibly between the two regions without change in the extent of the surface or in the volume of either region. That is, the Helmholtz free energy is a minimum ($dA = 0$). A region with a large surface-to-volume ratio must be under a pressure in excess of that in the bulk phase, as is seen immediately below.

The excess pressure inside a spherical droplet may be obtained as follows. At constant temperature, let the volume of the droplet be increased by a small amount dV, with a concomitant change in surface area $d\sigma$, and always at equilibrium with a bulk phase. Since $dA = 0$, by equation (15.7–4)

$$P\,dV = \gamma\,d\sigma. \tag{15.7–5}$$

However, $dV = 4\pi r^2\,dr$, and $d\sigma = 8\pi r\,dr$, where r is the radius of the drop. Upon replacement of dV and $d\sigma$ in (15.7–5), the equation may be solved for the excess pressure P due to the presence of the surface. This is

$$P = \frac{2\gamma}{r}. \tag{15.7–6}$$

Similarly, for a cylindrical surface,

$$P = \frac{\gamma}{r}. \tag{15.7–7}$$

Problem 15.7-1. Prove equation (15.7–7) by the procedure followed in proving (15.7–6). Why does equation (15.7–4) apply only to a one-component system?

Problem 15.7-2. Show that the excess pressure is zero for a perfectly plane surface. Note that a plane has infinite radius of curvature.

Problem 15.7-3. The surface tension of a water–air interface is 72.8 dynes cm^{-1} at 20°C. Calculate, in millimeters of mercury, the excess pressure required to form a spherical bubble of air in water at the end of a capillary whose diameter is (a) 0.1 cm, (b) 0.001 cm.

Problem 15.7-4. Show that the capillary rise of a liquid in a cylindrical glass tube is given by

$$h = \frac{2\gamma}{\rho g r}, \tag{15.7–8}$$

where h is the height of the rise, r the radius of the capillary, ρ the density, and γ the surface tension of the liquid. (*Hint*. Assume that the surface of the liquid in the capillary is spherical, and balance the pressure excess, above the surface, by hydrostatic head.)

As discussed in Section 7.4, the vapor pressure of a liquid is increased by application of pressure. The vapor pressure of a droplet is thus greater than that of bulk liquid owing to the excess pressure associated with the surface. For a liquid whose vapor is a perfect gas, the change in vapor pressure is given by

$$\frac{\mathrm{d}\ln p}{\mathrm{d}P} = \frac{\tilde{V}_l}{RT}. \qquad (7.4\text{–}4)^*$$

The vapor pressure of a droplet is then obtained by integrating equation (7.4–4)* between the pressure of the bulk material and that of the droplet.

Problem 15.7-5. By integration of equation (7.4–4)*, show that the vapor pressure of a spherical droplet is given by

$$\ln\frac{p}{p^0} = \frac{2\tilde{V}_l}{RT}\left(\frac{\gamma}{r}\right), \qquad (15.7\text{–}9)$$

where p^0 is the vapor pressure of bulk liquid, p that of the droplet, and $\tilde{V}_l$ the molal volume of the liquid. Assume that the vapor is an ideal gas and that the molal volume of the liquid is independent of the pressure. Note that the *excess* pressure in the droplet is given by (15.7–6).

An adsorbed film may be treated as a surface under pressure, which is now an *open system*. Its partial molal free energy is then obtained by differentiating equation (15.2–16) with respect to n_s at constant T, P, and γ, after identifying $-\gamma$ with X_i and σ with x, and is given by

$$\mu_s = \bar{E}_s - T\bar{S}_s + P\bar{V}_s - \gamma\bar{A} \qquad (15.7\text{–}10)$$

where the subscripts indicate the properties of the adsorbate and $\bar{A}$ is the area per mole adsorbed. At equilibrium the molal free energy change of the adsorbed phase will be equal to that of the gas phase, which is a function solely of P and T. Thus, for changes at constant coverage,

$$\mathrm{d}\mu_s = \mathrm{d}\mu_g \qquad (15.7\text{–}11)$$

or

$$-\bar{S}_s\,\mathrm{d}T + \bar{V}_s\,\mathrm{d}P - \frac{1}{\Gamma_s}\,\mathrm{d}\gamma = -\tilde{S}_g\,\mathrm{d}T + \tilde{V}_g\,\mathrm{d}P, \qquad (15.7\text{–}12)$$

where $\Gamma_s = 1/\bar{A}$. At constant temperature,

$$-\left(\frac{\partial P}{\partial \gamma}\right)_T = \frac{1}{(\tilde{V}_g - \bar{V}_s)\Gamma_s}. \qquad (15.7\text{–}13)$$

If the volume of the adsorbed phase is neglected and the gas treated as a perfect one, equation (15.7–13) becomes

$$-\left(\frac{\partial \ln P}{\partial \gamma}\right)_T = \frac{1}{RT\Gamma_s}. \qquad (15.7\text{–}14)^*$$

Integrating from zero coverage, where the surface tension is γ_0,

$$\gamma_0 - \gamma = \phi = RT\int_0^P \Gamma_s \, d\ln P. \qquad (15.7\text{–}15)$$

$(\gamma_0 - \gamma)$ is frequently called the "spreading pressure" and given the symbol ϕ.

Equation (15.7–15) is known as the Gibbs adsorption isotherm.[7] This equation can only be compared with experiment in the case of films that can be studied in a Langmuir trough.[8]

The equilibrium between an adsorbed and gaseous substance cannot be distinguished externally from the solution of a gas in a solvent. For simplicity, it will be assumed in the discussions below that the amount and the surface area of the adsorbent are held constant. The properties of the gaseous adsorbate and the adsorbed material will be denoted by the subscripts g (e.g., n_g) and s, respectively, as before.

For a given amount of adsorbent, the (partial) molal free energy of the adsorbed phase will be a function of temperature, pressure, and the amount adsorbed, n_s. Thus by differentiating equation (15.3–11) with respect to n_s at constant T, P, and ϕ, after identifying X with ϕ and A with x (μ for the adsorbent, dP, dT, and dn are constants),

$$d\mu_s = \bar{V}_s \, dP - \bar{S}_g \, dT + \left(\frac{\partial \mu_s}{\partial n_s}\right) dn_s, \qquad (15.7\text{–}16)$$

where the partial molal notation takes into account the fact that the properties of the adsorbed material are a function of its "concentration" (i.e., of the moles adsorbed on a given amount of adsorbent). At equilibrium, the partial molal free energy of adsorbed material is the same as that of the gas. Proceeding as before,

$$\tilde{V}_g \, dP - \tilde{S}_g \, dT = \bar{V}_s \, dP - \bar{S}_s \, dT + \left(\frac{\partial \mu_s}{\partial n_s}\right) dn_s. \qquad (15.7\text{–}17)$$

At constant n_s, equation (15.7–17) becomes

$$\left(\frac{\partial P}{\partial T}\right)_{n_s} = \frac{\tilde{S}_g - \bar{S}_s}{\tilde{V}_g - \bar{V}_s}. \qquad (15.7\text{–}18)$$

[7] *The Collected Works of J. Willard Gibbs*, Vol. I, Longmans, Green, New York, 1928, p. 230.

[8] I. Langmuir, *J. Am. Chem. Soc.*, **39**, 1848 (1917).

Neglecting the molar volume of the adsorbed phase, and assuming the gas to be perfect,

$$\left(\frac{\partial \ln P}{\partial T}\right)_{n_s} = \frac{\tilde{S}_g - \bar{S}_s}{RT} = \frac{\tilde{H}_g - \bar{H}_s}{RT^2} = \frac{q_{st}}{RT^2}. \qquad (15.7\text{–}19)^*$$

The heat quantity q_{st}, defined by equation (15.7–19), is known as the *isosteric heat* of adsorption. In equation (15.7–19) the amount of adsorbed material n_s can equally well be represented by the "coverage," θ, which is defined as the ratio of the amount adsorbed to that required for completion

Table 15.7–1

Isotherms of Ethanol Adsorbed on Silica Gel[9]

40°C		70°C	
Grams ethanol/grams silica gel	Pressure (mm Hg)	Grams ethanol/grams silica gel	Pressure (mm Hg)
0.1016	0.300	0.0970	1.440
0.1241	1.625	0.1051	2.665
0.1382	3.325	0.1076	3.200
0.1464	4.325	0.1134	4.96
0.1555	5.630	0.1160	5.91
0.1590	6.24	0.1266	11.66
0.1631	7.775	0.1384	18.18
0.1701	8.24	0.1499	24.70
		0.1662	53.27

Table 15.7–2

Adsorption of Neon[10] on TiO_2

29.00°K		31.50°K	
V_a (cm³(STP)/m²)	P (mm Hg)	V_a (cm³(STP)/m²)	P (mm Hg)
0.094	2.15	0.099	6.83
0.150	3.98	0.149	8.61
0.175	5.09	0.200	19.57
0.232	10.50	0.228	24.29
0.288	20.80	0.282	49.62
0.326	33.63	0.316	79.33
		0.328	90.76

of a monolayer of film. It should be noted that the total surface remains constant, and various values of θ represent the density of molecules in the phase (or phases) on the surface.

Problem 15.7-6. Table 15.7–1 gives the dependence of pressure upon amount adsorbed (isotherms) for ethanol on silica gel, from the data of Lambert and Foster.[9] Calculate the average isosteric heat of adsorption for the temperature range covered (a) for 0.1000 g ethanol/g silica gel and (b) for 0.1600 g ethanol/g silica gel.

Problem 15.7-7. Table 15.7–2 contains isotherms of neon adsorbed on titanium dioxide.[10] The amount adsorbed is given in cubic centimeters (STP) of gas per square centimeter of surface area. Calculate the isosteric heat of adsorption at 0.100, 0.230, and 0.326 cm^3/cm^2. Plot the results, and state what conclusions you can draw concerning the heat of adsorption at very low coverage.

[9] B. Lambert and A. G. Foster, *Proc. Roy. Soc.*, (*London*), **134A**, 246 (1932).
[10] *J. Am. Chem. Soc.*, **77**, 2168 (1955).

Energy Levels of Particles, Atoms, and Molecules. Atomic and Molecular Spectra.

CHAPTER 16

16.1 Introduction

It is evidently almost a hopeless task to calculate exactly the energy of one mole of a chemical compound from the mechanics of the elementary particles of which it is comprised. On the other hand, it is natural to wish to calculate the energies of atoms and molecules from the mechanical properties of the particles of which they are composed, namely the nuclei and electrons.

At first, even this smaller problem appeared unlikely to be solved exactly. A system consisting of a nucleus surrounded by electrons presents a mechanical problem similar to that faced by the astronomer in calculating celestial orbits, except on a micro scale. As is well known, even the "three-body" problem is not capable of exact solution. The astronomer calculates the behavior of groups of bodies from classical dynamics by use of approximate methods. The early physicists attempted to do the same for groups of nuclei and electrons in terms of classical dynamics and classical electrodynamics. The attempt failed, for no obviously apparent reasons. The real difficulty was that the microscopic systems lost mechanical energy by radiation whose nature was unknown.

It is by no means evident that the fundamental components of matter will in any way follow the laws of the integrated whole (Newton's laws), any more than one would expect one of the polypeptides of the body to understand the meaning of a court injunction. Yet exactly this assumption was made, largely because there was no other choice. The result was, of course, failure.

There is not space here to follow the patient attempts to explain the mechanics of the atoms and how these attempts led to the development of new mechanical laws for the elementary particles of matter. The end results are now known well enough that, with little apology, they may be summarized as a starting point for the larger problem, that of the calculation of energies of physicochemical systems on a microscopic scale. Such a summary is given in this chapter so that in the next chapter we may start calculation of the thermodynamic properties of large systems by means of statistical mechanics, without further detailed mechanical study of these systems.

16.2 Spectra and Energy Levels

Although energies of atoms and molecules are frequently very difficult to calculate, they can often be measured with high accuracy from absorption or emission spectra. The emission spectrum is basically the spectrum (series of images of the source) which appear when light emitted by the system is passed through a prism or is reflected from a grating. The absorption spectrum is manifested by the reduction in intensity of light from an external source, already resolved by a prism or grating, after passage through a cell containing the system in question (sometimes the order is reversed). The absorption takes place in such a way as to produce in the spectrum *lines* (slit images) of reduced intensity. The existence of lines either in emission or absorption was unpredictable by classical theory, which indeed predicted a continuous spectrum associated with a continuous set of energies. It became evident that the observed spectroscopic lines were due to the emission or absorption of light which occurred when an atom or molecule changed from one discrete energy state to another. This principle is known as the Rydberg-Ritz combination principle.

The observed wave length of a spectral line is related to its frequency by the relation

$$\nu = \frac{c}{\lambda}, \tag{16.2–1}$$

where c is the velocity of light in a vacuum (2.99790×10^{10} cm sec^{-1}), λ is the wave length measured in (or corrected to) a vacuum, and ν is the frequency.

It is customary to use the wave number $\tilde{\nu}$ in place of the frequency. The wave number is the frequency divided by the velocity of light and is thus the reciprocal of the wave length. Its units are cm^{-1}. Thus

$$\tilde{\nu} = \frac{\nu}{c} = \frac{1}{\lambda}. \tag{16.2–2}$$

The Rydberg-Ritz combination principle can now be written in the form of an expression for the wave number of any spectroscopic line:

$$\tilde{\nu} = \mathbf{T}_2 - \mathbf{T}_1, \tag{16.2–3}$$

where $\mathbf{T}_2$ and $\mathbf{T}_1$, which have the dimensions of wave numbers, are called the term values. For each atom or molecule one can obtain a set of term values ($\mathbf{T}_1$, $\mathbf{T}_2$, etc.) such that all the observed spectroscopic lines may be derived by subtraction. The term values (expressed as wave numbers) are related to the energy levels of the atom or molecule by the relation

$$E_i = hc\mathbf{T}_i, \tag{16.2–4}$$

where E_i is the energy of the molecule in a state corresponding to the term $\mathbf{T}_i$ and h, which has the value 6.6238×10^{-27} erg sec, is called the Planck constant. In spectroscopy, energies are frequently expressed in units of wave numbers, as are the term values, that is, units of hc ergs.

16.3 Energy Levels and Stationary States

The use of equation (16.2–4) to calculate energy levels of an atom or molecule implies that the atom or molecule can exist only in certain states characterized by their energy, and that for some reason the intermediate values are excluded (except possibly during the transition itself). Such states are called *stationary states*. When a molecule undergoes a transition from one stationary state to another, the energy lost (or gained) is emitted (or absorbed) as light of a single frequency ν given by

$$E_2 - E_1 = h\nu. \tag{16.3–1}$$

This relation is evidently a result of equations (16.2–3) and (16.2–4). Its use permits deduction of the energies of stationary states directly from spectra.

16.4 Empirical Expressions for Energy Levels. The Hydrogen Atom

After the recognition of the principles elucidated in the last two sections it was most natural to attempt to calculate values for the energy of stationary states from spectroscopic data and to express them by empirical relations. The first such relation results from an empirical expression proposed by Balmer for the visible spectrum of the hydrogen atom. This relation is

$$E_n = -\frac{hc\mathrm{R_H}}{n^2}, \tag{16.4–1}$$

where n is an integral number, and $\mathrm{R_H}$, which has the value 109,677.59 $\mathrm{cm^{-1}}$, is called the Rydberg constant for hydrogen. This relation, along with equation (16.3–1), predicts the visible spectrum of hydrogen as ordinarily observed with remarkable accuracy, but it does not account for the details of the spectrum observed under high resolution. For energies in $\mathrm{cm^{-1}}$, equation (16.4–1) becomes

$$E_n = -\frac{\mathrm{R_H}}{n^2}. \tag{16.4–2}$$

The lines in the visible spectrum of the hydrogen atom are referred to as the Balmer series. All these lines result from the atom undergoing a transition from a state with $n > 2$ to a state with $n = 2$. The wave lengths of these lines in Angstrom units are: (ϑ) 3797.90, (η) 3835.39, (ζ) 3889.05, (ϵ) 3970.07, (δ) 4101.74, (γ) 4340.47, (β) 4861.33, and (α) 6562.79. The Greek letter in brackets gives the conventional name of the line, denoted symbolically by H_α, H_β, etc.

Problem 16.4-1. (a) Find the value of n for the initial state for the α, β, and γ lines of the Balmer series.

(b) Calculate the energies of the initial and final states for the α line in $\mathrm{cm^{-1}}$, ergs, and calories per molecule.

The energy levels just discussed are due to electronic motion. Asymmetric diatomic molecules absorb light in the infrared, and the resulting absorption bands are resolvable into lines. The individual lines may be traced to levels whose energies, in $\mathrm{cm^{-1}}$, are given approximately by a formula

$$E_{K,v} = B_e K^2 + v\tilde{\nu}_0 + E_0\,. \tag{16.4–3}$$

In equation (16.4–3), B_e and $\tilde{\nu}_0$ are constants, K has values of $n + {}^1/_2$ (where n is an integer and v can have any integral value). E_0 is a constant which cancels when the expression is used to calculate the frequency of a spectroscopic line. The first term on the right side is associated with the energy of rotation of the molecule, and the second with its energy of vibration. Equation 16.4–3 is only an approximate expression for the energies of the levels associated with particular values of v and K. More exact values may be obtained from analysis of the spectrum of the substance considered, as shown in the following example.

Hydrogen chloride (HCl^{35}) absorbs light in the infrared, giving rise to an absorption band at wave lengths near 3.46×10^{-4} cm. This band consists of two sets of lines with a small central gap. Each of the lines is associated with an increase of v from zero to 1, accompanied by an increase or decrease of one unit in K (see equation 16.4–3). The lines of lower frequency form a group known as the P *branch*; for each of them K decreases by one unit. The lines of higher frequency are known as the R *branch*, and they correspond to an increase of K by one unit. The middle of the gap corresponds to the energy of a missing transition from $v = 0$, $K = {}^1/_2$ to $v = 1$, $K = {}^1/_2$.

Problem 16.4-2. The first three lines of the R branch in the infrared spectrum of HCl^{35} referred to above are at 2906.25, 2925.78, and 2944.87 cm^{-1}. The first three lines of the P branch are at 2865.09, 2843.56, and 2821.49 wave numbers. They all correspond to transitions in which v goes from zero to unity.

(a) Calculate B_e and $\tilde{\nu}_0$, taking the energy difference between $v = 0$, $K = {}^1/_2$ and $v = 1$, $K = {}^1/_2$ as that corresponding to 2885.90 cm^{-1}.

(b) Taking the energy of the level with $v = 0$, $K = {}^1/_2$ as zero, calculate from equation (16.4–3) the energy in cm^{-1} of the levels $v = 0$, $K = {}^3/_2$; $v = 0$, $K = {}^5/_2$; $v = 0$, $K = {}^7/_2$; $v = 1$, $K = {}^1/_2$; $v = 1$, $K = {}^3/_2$; $v = 1$, $K = {}^5/_2$; $v = 1$, $K = {}^7/_2$.

(c) Identify the changes in v and K accompanying the transitions which give rise to the first three lines in the P and R branches of the spectrum. The energies calculated in part (b) may be used as a guide.

(d) Taking the energy of the level with $v = 0$, $K = {}^1/_2$ as before, use the observed wave numbers to make an exact calculation of the energies of each of the levels listed in part (b).

16.5 Quantum Mechanics

As stated in Section 16.1, classical mechanics and electrodynamics cannot be used to calculate even approximately correct values of the energies of atoms and molecules. Indeed, they predict a continuous series of energy states. In order to make the calculation correctly it was necessary to develop an entirely new theory. The final form of this theory is called *quantum mechanics*. We shall proceed with a brief discussion of the theory in order to facilitate interpretation of the energy levels.

For the present purpose, this theory can be adequately described by (a) the wave equation and (b) the Heisenberg principle of uncertainty. The wave equation and its properties can be stated in various degrees of generality. We proceed below by a method which seems simplest to us, but is not necessarily the most logical, since we start with the assumption that there are energy states and at once write the amplitude equation for the individual states. This procedure is justified, since we shall be concerned only with energy levels and shall treat transitions between these states in an entirely arbitrary fashion.

The wave equation for a system of n particles in a *stationary state* is

$$-\frac{h^2}{8\pi^2}\left[\sum_{i=1}^{i=n}\frac{1}{\mathrm{m}_i}\left(\frac{\partial^2\psi_k}{\partial x_i^2}+\frac{\partial^2\psi_k}{\partial y_i^2}+\frac{\partial^2\psi_k}{\partial z_i^2}\right)+V\psi_k\right]=W_k\psi_k. \quad (16.5\text{–}1)$$

By considering only stationary states, the time variable has been eliminated from the most general equation. The resulting equation is often referred to as the amplitude equation. In equation (16.5–1), x_i, y_i, and z_i are the coordinates of the particles and m_i their masses, V is the potential energy of the system, which depends on the positions of all the particles; W_k is the (constant) total energy of the system; h is the Planck constant. The function ψ is called a *wave function*; it is a function of the coordinates of all the particles. In general, the wave equation will have many possible solutions ψ_k, each of which corresponds to a possible total energy W_k.

The wave function is taken to be such that the product $\psi_k^*\psi_k$ measures the probability of finding the particles with any chosen set of coordinates. (ψ_k^* is the complex conjugate of ψ_k and is identical with ψ_k if the latter is real.) In order to fulfill this function, the wave function must be single-valued and continuous for all values of the coordinates and must vanish at the boundaries (in all cases at infinite values of the coordinates). Subject to these restrictions, the allowed values of W_k are those which permit solution of the wave equation subject to these restrictions, and these are the energy levels of the system. The states giving rise to these energy levels are often referred to as *stationary states*. The energy levels discussed in Section 16.4 are just these values of W_k.

Let the momentum of the ith particle in the x direction be defined formally by the relation

$$\mathrm{p}_{x_i}=\frac{h}{2\pi i}\frac{\partial}{\partial x_i}, \quad (16.5\text{–}2)$$

with similar equations for the y and z directions. Equation (16.5–1) then results from the application of the principle that the total energy is the sum of kinetic and potential energies, with the kinetic energy given by

$$T=\sum\frac{\mathrm{p}_{x_i}^2+\mathrm{p}_{y_i}^2+\mathrm{p}_{z_i}^2}{2\mathrm{m}_i}. \quad (16.5\text{–}3)$$

Problem 16.5-1. Deduce equation (16.5–1) from (16.5–2) and (16.5–3). (*Hint.* Multiply the total energy W_k by ψ_k, then make the substitutions indicated above.)

The formal definition of momentum given by equation (16.5–2) results from the postulate that the wave length of any of the waves whose amplitudes combine to yield ψ_k is given by

$$\lambda = \frac{h}{\mathrm{p}}. \tag{16.5–4}$$

If we consider an interval Δx over which there is any finite probability of finding the particle and the range $\Delta \mathrm{p}$, in which lie the momenta of the waves which contribute to the probability of the particle being in the interval Δx, it is a postulate of the theory that

$$\Delta \mathrm{p}\, \Delta x \sim h. \tag{16.5–5}$$

This is known as the *Heisenberg uncertainty principle.*

Since the amplitude function $\psi_k \psi_k^*$ represents a probability of finding the particles of the system simultaneously with any chosen set of coordinates, it is reasonable to look on this quantity as a product of functions due to each of the particles; thus

$$\psi_k = \psi_k(1)\psi_k(2)\psi_k(3), \text{ etc.} = \Pi \psi_k(i), \tag{16.5–6}$$

where the function $\psi_k(i)$ is a function of the coordinates x_i, y_i, z_i alone. If the particles do not interact (i.e., the potential energy of one does not depend on the coordinates of the others), substitution of this relationship into the amplitude equation (16.5–1) makes it possible to separate (16.5–1) into n equations of the form

$$-\frac{h^2}{8\pi^2 \mathrm{m}_i}\left(\frac{\partial^2 \psi_k(i)}{\partial x_i^2} + \frac{\partial^2 \psi_k(i)}{\partial y_i^2} + \frac{\partial^2 \psi_k(i)}{\partial z_i^2}\right) + V(x_i, y_i, z_i) = W_{ki}\psi_k(i). \tag{16.5–7}$$

The wave equation, as given by (16.5–1) and (16.5–7), takes account of the positions and momenta of all the particles, but not of their spins. For many purposes, this provides a sufficient description of the behavior of the system. However, it is necessary to consider the spin of the electron in order to explain the fine structure of the spectra of hydrogen and helium atoms, the effect of a magnetic field on spectra, and the behavior of an isolated electron in a magnetic field. The introduction of spin can be made only schematically. For the electron, it is accomplished by introducing two symbolic wave functions, α_i and β_i, for each particle. The wave function, including spin, for one particle is then $\psi_k \alpha$ or $\psi_k \beta$. The *spin angular momentum* associated with electron spin is

$$\sqrt{\left(\frac{1}{2}\right)\left(\frac{3}{2}\right)}\,\frac{h}{2\pi},$$

Both the orbital motion and the spin of the electron give rise to a magnetic moment. The magnetic moment associated with the orbital angular momentum is (e/2mc) times the orbit angular momentum. However, the magnetic moment associated with the spin of the electron is $\pm eh/4\pi mc$, which is (e/mc) times the component of the spin angular momentum in the direction of any arbitrary axis.

Actually the energy levels used in statistical mechanics are either the observed ones or those obtained by theoretical interpolation. However, the theory just outlined is necessary in order to understand the number and nature of levels of the same energy, as will be seen in what follows.

16.6 Energy Levels of a Free Particle

The equations given in the last section are a result of developing a phenomenological theory to fit the energy levels empirically observed for simple systems. The energy levels for a free particle cannot be measured, but they are deduced by using this phenomenological theory. For this reason it is desirable to go through the derivation of the formula for these energy levels, since it plays so large a part in the statistical mechanics of the gaseous state.

Let a single particle be confined in a box with sides of length a, b, and c in the x, y, and z directions, respectively. The potential energy inside the box is zero at all points, so that the wave equation is

$$-\frac{h^2}{8\pi^2 m}\left(\frac{\partial^2\psi_k}{\partial x^2}+\frac{\partial^2\psi_k}{\partial y^2}+\frac{\partial^2\psi_k}{\partial z^2}\right)=W_k\psi_k\,. \tag{16.6–1}$$

Upon division by ψ_k and substitution of the product $(\psi_{kx}\psi_{ky}\psi_{kz})$ for ψ_k, where ψ_{kx}, etc., are respectively functions of x, y, and z alone, the result is

$$\frac{1}{\psi_{kx}}\frac{\partial^2\psi_{kx}}{\partial x^2}+\frac{1}{\psi_{ky}}\frac{\partial^2\psi_{ky}}{\partial y^2}+\frac{1}{\psi_{kz}}\frac{\partial^2\psi_{kz}}{\partial z^2}=-\frac{8\pi^2 m}{h^2}W_k\,. \tag{16.6–2}$$

The three terms on the left are, respectively, functions of x, y, and z alone; for the sum to be constant each term must be a constant. Thus the first term on the left side may be written

$$\frac{1}{\psi_{kx}}\frac{d^2\psi_{kx}}{dx^2}=-\frac{8\pi^2 m}{h^2}W_{kx}\,, \tag{16.6–3}$$

with similar equations for the y and z directions; W_{ky}, W_{kz}, and W_{kx} are the energies in the x, y, and z directions respectively. The three equations obtained are ordinary differential equations. It is easy to see that a solution to equation 16.6–3 is

$$\psi_{kx} = A_x \sin kx, \tag{16.6–4}$$

where k is $[2\pi(2mW_{kx})^{1/2}]/h$ and A_x is a constant.

Problem 16.6-1. Verify equation 16.6–4 by substitution into (16.6–3).

If the particle is to stay within the box, the wave function must be zero everywhere outside the box and at the boundary; that is, it must be zero when $x = 0$ and when $x = a$. This is true when $a(2mW_{kx})^{1/2}/h$ is equal to $n/2$, where n is an integer (not zero); that is, when

$$W_{kx} = \frac{h^2n^2}{8\text{m}a^2}. \tag{16.6–5}$$

The same procedure holds for W_{ky} and W_{kz}, so that the total energy is

$$W = \frac{h^2}{8\text{m}}\left(\frac{n^2}{a^2} + \frac{m^2}{b^2} + \frac{l^2}{c^2}\right), \tag{16.6–6}$$

where n, m, and l are integers (not zero). Integers such as n, m, and l are called *quantum numbers*. The use of equation (16.6–6) in calculation of thermodynamic properties will be considered later.

Problem 16.6-2. By considering ψ_{kx}, show that n cannot have the value zero.

The solutions given in equations (16.6–4) and (16.6–6) are based on the assumption that the wave function is zero (i.e., the potential energy is infinite) everywhere beyond the boundaries of the box. If this is not so, the particle will have a finite probability of escaping from the box. The solution in the latter case is more complex, and will not be considered here.[1]

16.7 Classification of the Energy Levels for Hydrogen-Like Atoms and Ions

In order to classify the energy levels of the hydrogen atom and other atoms with one electron it is necessary to consider the solutions of the wave equation corresponding to each energy level. The general case is a nucleus of charge Ze of mass M, about which revolves an electron of charge $-e$ of mass m. For convenience, the original six cartesian coordinates are transformed to six consisting of the three cartesian coordinates of the center of gravity of the system and the polar coordinates

[1] See K. S. Pitzer, *Quantum Chemistry*, Prentice-Hall, Englewood Cliffs, N.J., 1953, p. 31.

of the electron relative to the nucleus at the origin. The polar coordinates are r, θ, and ϕ, illustrated in Fig. 16.7–1. The wave equation can then be separated into two equations. One represents the motion of a free particle in terms of the coordinates of the center of gravity, and the other the relative motion of the electron in polar coordinates. The first equation

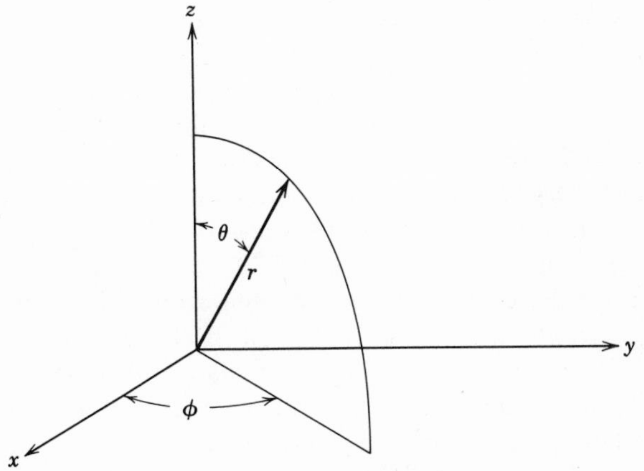

Fig. 16.7–1. Polar coordinates.

is the same as that discussed in the last section for a free particle having a mass (M + m). The second equation is

$$-\frac{h^2}{8\pi^2\mu r^2}\left[\frac{\partial}{\partial r}\left(r^2\frac{\partial\psi}{\partial r}\right)+\frac{1}{\sin\theta}\frac{\partial}{\partial\theta}\left(\sin\theta\frac{\partial\psi}{\partial\theta}\right)\right.$$
$$\left.+\frac{1}{\sin^2\theta}\frac{\partial^2\psi}{\partial\phi^2}\right]+(V(r)-W)\psi=0, \qquad (16.7\text{–}1)$$

where μ is the *reduced mass* of the nucleus and the electron, which is equal to mM/(m + M). The potential energy is the electrostatic energy of attraction for the electron by the nucleus. Acceptable values of ψ_k are obtained only for values of W_k given by

$$W_k = \frac{-2\pi^2\mu Z^2e^4}{n^2h^2}, \qquad (16.7\text{–}2)$$

where n is a quantum number with the values 1, 2, 3, 4, etc., called the *principal quantum number*. For each value of W_k, that is, for each value of n, there is a set of values of ψ_k which can be expressed by

$$\psi_k = A_{l,m}\,R_{n,l}\,. \qquad (16.7\text{–}3)$$

A table of some of the functions $A_{l,m}$ and $R_{n,l}$ is given in Appendix 6.

Only certain of the functions $A_{l,m}$ can be used with a given function $R_{n,l}$. In addition to the principal quantum number, the functions $R_{n,l}$ are characterized also by a second integer l, which is called the *angular quantum number*. For a given value of n there is a function for each value of l from zero to $n - 1$. The functions $A_{l,m}$ are characterized by the l values just mentioned and still a third integer, m. For any value of l there is a function for each positive or negative value of the integer m, starting with zero and ending with l.

States with l equal to 0, 1, 2, 3 are called *s*, *p*, *d*, and *f* states, respectively. Thus it is seen that, in general, there are several wave functions which go with each value of n and hence of W_k. Each wave function defines a definite state, but the energies of the several states with the same value of n are the same. Such states are said to be *degenerate*.

As with the empirical equation (16.7–1), equation (16.7–2) does not describe exactly the energy of the hydrogen atom. The value of l has a slight effect on the energy because of small effects due to (a) electron spin (to be discussed later) and (b) relativistic change of mass. Under high resolution the spectroscopic lines have a fine structure due to these causes; for the time being this will be neglected.

16.8 Energy Levels of Helium. Electron Spin

Helium has two electrons each attracted by a nucleus of charge $+2e$. As a first approximation the electrons are considered non-interacting. In the ground state each electron has $n = 1$, while in the excited states one electron has $n = 1$ and the other a higher value of n. However, for generality we shall consider the case when the electrons have n and n' respectively for the principal quantum number. The simplest wave function is thus

$$\psi = \psi_n(1)\psi_{n'}(2). \qquad (16.8\text{–}1)$$

This wave function is unsatisfactory since in it the electrons have been identified as (1) and (2). Such identification is not possible for electrons, because of their particle-wave nature. The simplest wave function in which the electrons have lost their identity is

$$\psi = a_1\psi_n(1)\psi_{n'}(2) + a_2\psi_{n'}(1)\psi_n(2). \qquad (16.8\text{–}2)$$

The proper values of a_1 and a_2 are those which minimize the values of W_k in the wave equation.[2] These are found to be $a_1 = 1$ and $a_2 = \pm 1$. The choice of $a_2 = +1$ leads to a wave function which does not change

[2] See, for example, L. Pauling and E. B. Wilson, *Introduction to Quantum Mechanics*, McGraw-Hill, New York, 1935, p. 180.

sign when the coordinates of the particles are interchanged and has a finite value when ψ_n and $\psi_{n'}$ become identical. Such a function is called a symmetric function. On the other hand, if $a_2 = -1$, the wave function changes sign when the coordinates are interchanged and gives a value of zero when ψ_n and $\psi_{n'}$ become identical. Such a function is called antisymmetric.

When there are two or more electrons, the effect of electron spin must be included, even for consideration of the ordinary observed spectra. Only solutions which correspond to antisymmetric total wave functions can be chosen. When this is done, it turns out that a_2 must be $+1$ if the spin momenta have opposite signs and an antisymmetric wave function, but -1 if the spin momenta have the same sign or have opposite sign but with their spin wave function symmetric. The quantum numbers, m_s, associated with the spin wave functions α and β are $+1/2$ and $-1/2$ respectively.

The total wave function in which the spins have opposite sign and an antisymmetric spin wave function is

$$[\psi_n(1)\psi_{n'}(2) + \psi_{n'}(1)\psi_n(2)][\alpha(1)\beta(2) - \beta(1)\alpha(2)]. \qquad (16.8\text{–}3)$$

It is noticed that the final product is antisymmetric because the function changes sign if the labels (1) and (2) are interchanged. For spins of the same sign the allowed functions are

$$[\psi_n(1)\psi_{n'}(2) - \psi_{n'}(1)\psi_n(2)]\alpha(1)\alpha(2) \qquad (16.8\text{–}4)$$

and

$$[\psi_n(1)\psi_{n'}(2) - \psi_{n'}(1)\psi_n(2)]\beta(1)\beta(2). \qquad (16.8\text{–}4a)$$

For the symmetric spin wave function with spins of opposite sign the function is

$$[\psi_n(1)\psi_{n'}(2) - \psi_{n'}(1)\psi_n(2)][\alpha(1)\beta(2) + \beta(1)\alpha(2)]. \qquad (16.8\text{–}4b)$$

In (16.8–4), (16.8–4a), and (16.8–4b), the total function is antisymmetric owing to the negative sign in the first bracket. In helium the energy levels corresponding to the wave function of equation (16.8–3) form one system, called the *singlet system*, and those corresponding to (16.8–4), (16.8–4a), and (16.8–4b) form another, called the *triplet system*. Figure 16.8–1[3] shows the two sets of levels. The scale of energies in volts is to the extreme left. The singlet system is to the left, and the triplet to the right. The columns represent the values of l for the excited electron, and the values opposite each line are the quantum numbers n' of the excited electron; in all cases the unexcited electron has $n = 1$, $l = 0$. If both n and n' are unity, the wave functions like (16.8–4a) are all zero, so

[3] G. Herzberg, *Atomic Spectra and Atomic Structure*, 2nd ed., Dover, New York, 1944.

that the ground state has no triplet level. Transitions can occur only between the levels of each set (i.e., singlet to singlet, triplet to triplet). Transitions from a level of one set to a level of another set (i.e., singlet to triplet) are not allowed. For any pair of wave functions ψ_n and $\psi_{n'}$ the

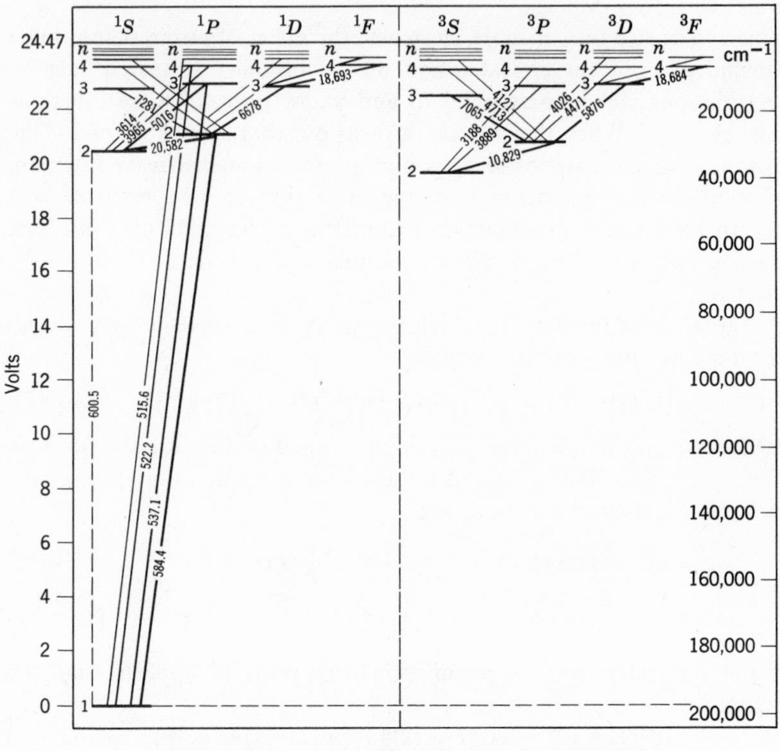

Fig. 16.8–1. Energy level diagram for helium.[3]

The running numbers and true principal quantum numbers of the emission electron are identical. The series in the visible and near ultraviolet regions correspond to the indicated transitions between terms with $n \geq 2$.

(From *Atomic Spectra and Atomic Structure*, by G. Herzberg; reproduced by permission of Dover Publications, Inc., New York ($1.95).)

wave functions represented by equations (16.8–4), (16.8–4a), and (16.8–4b) correspond to slightly different energies. Thus the spectroscopic lines corresponding to transitions from one triplet level to another are resolvable under high resolution into three components.

The wave functions in (16.8–4, 4a, 4b) are such that *if* ψ_n and $\psi_{n'}$ are identical the wave function vanishes. This is not the case for equation

(16.8–3), but if in addition the spin functions were either both α or both β the total wave function would vanish. Thus it is seen that, *if two electrons have the same orbital wave functions and the same spin wave functions at the same time, the wave function becomes zero.* The principle that no two elementary particles in a given atom can have simultaneously the same orbital and spin quantum numbers is known as the *Pauli exclusion principle.* This says that a wave function with the spin included cannot be occupied by more than one particle.

The spin wave functions possessed by the electrons of an atom have an effect on the energy not only because they change the total angular momentum but also because they change the character of the nuclear wave functions, as just discussed for helium.

With hydrogen and the alkalies there is only one electron to be considered. The electron spin can be oriented in two ways with respect to the orbital angular moment, as shown in Fig. 16.8–2a for quantities proportional to the angular momentum, with the exception noted in the legend. The orbital angular momentum vector associated with l is $\sqrt{l(l+1)}(h/2\pi)$, and its maximum component in the direction of the z axis is $lh/2\pi$. The angular momentum associated with the spin of a single electron is $\sqrt{s(s+1)}h/2\pi$ with $s = {}^1/_2$, but its component along the z axis is $m_s h/2\pi$ with $m_s = {}^1/_2$ or $m_s = -{}^1/_2$. The component of the resultant angular momentum in the z direction is thus $Jh/2\pi$, with J equal to $(l + {}^1/_2)$ or $(l - {}^1/_2)$, and the total resultant angular momentum is $\sqrt{J(J+1)}h/2\pi$. Only positive values of J need be considered, since negative ones simply mean an orientation change of π with respect to an arbitrary field. The two positive values of J correspond to different energies. It is this difference between the two energy levels which both result from the same value of l which causes the alkali doublets (e.g., the double yellow line of sodium).

The levels are given symbols, called *term symbols, S, P, D, F,* etc., which refer respectively to values of l of 0, 1, 2, 3, etc.

The number of states which can be produced by the different possible ways of combining spin and orbital angular momenta is indicated by placing this number as a superscript to the left of the term symbol, whether the states have the same or different energies. Thus the states giving rise to the alkali doublets are denoted by ${}^2P_{1/2}$, ${}^2P_{3/2}$, ${}^2D_{1/2}$, ${}^2D_{3/2}$, etc. The subscript denotes the value of J, the first pair of levels listed in the previous sentence being those discussed above. The single S level is denoted by ${}^2S_{1/2}$, since one can consider that there are the two ways of combining $l = 0$ and $s = {}^1/_2$, namely $l = 0$, $s = {}^1/_2$ and $l = 0$, $s = -{}^1/_2$, which have the same energy.

When there are two or more electrons in the outer shell as in helium and the alkaline earths, it is necessary to reconsider the coupling of orbital and spin angular momenta. In the simplest type of coupling it is

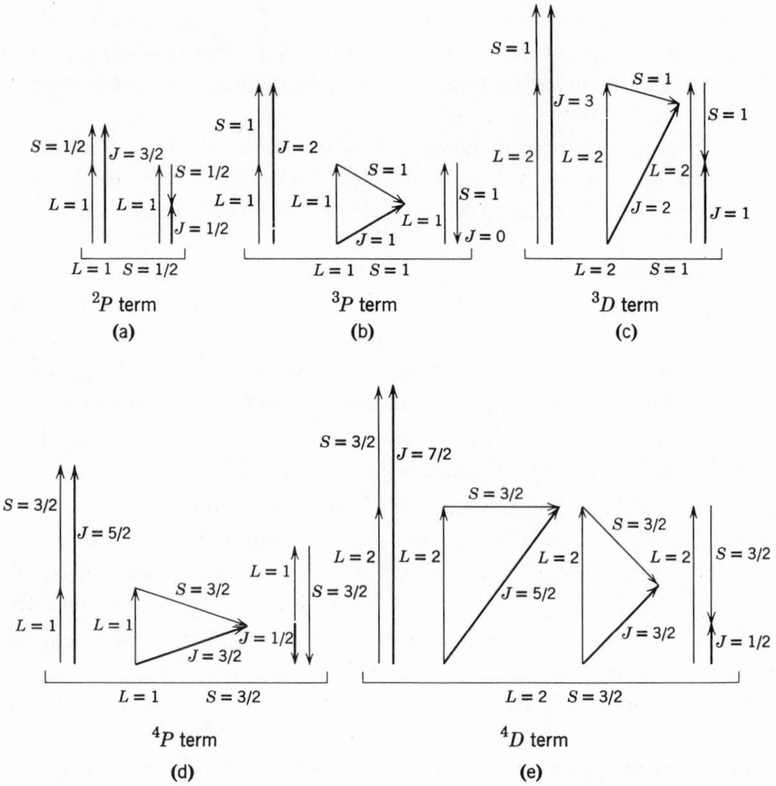

Fig. 16.8-2. Vector addition of *L* and *S* to give a resultant *J* for different examples.[3]

For a given combination of L and S, all the possible orientations of L and S with respect to one another and the corresponding total angular momenta are illustrated. The vector J is indicated by a heavy line. Its direction is fixed in space. The magnitude of the vector J (and, correspondingly, of L and S) is taken as $J\mathrm{h}/2\pi$ and not $\sqrt{J(J+1)}h/2\pi$, as it should be, strictly speaking.

(From *Atomic Spectra and Atomic Structure*, by G. Herzberg; reproduced by permission of Dover Publications, Inc., New York ($1.95.)

assumed that the orbital angular momenta couple to yield one resultant, L, while the spin angular momenta couple to yield another resultant, S. The two resultants combine to produce the final resultant. This is called

Russel-Saunders coupling. However, the way in which the individual orbital angular momenta are oriented is limited by the fact that each is limited in the direction of its orientation with respect to an arbitrary magnetic field (say in the z direction). The allowed orientations are those possible with $m_1 = l_1$ for one electron along some arbitrary z axis and $m_2 = 0, \pm 1, \pm 2, \cdots, \pm l$ for the other electron along the same axis. Thus for two electrons with values of l_1 and l_2, as in the case of helium and the alkaline earths, the resultant angular momentum can have the values $\sqrt{L(L+1)}h/2\pi$, with L given by

$$L = (l_1 + l_2), (l_1 + l_2 - 1), (l_1 + l_2 - 2), \cdots, (l_1 - l_2). \quad (16.8\text{–}5)$$

The possible L values are obtained by adding all values of m_2 possible for the second electron to the l_1 value of the first. However, the maximum angular momentum in the direction of an arbitrary field is $Lh/2\pi$. The levels with $L = 0, 1, 2, 3$, etc., are labeled respectively S, P, D, F, G, H, etc.

The orientation of the spins is likewise limited, since each electron with spin quantum number $^1/_2$ can only be oriented so that its angular momentum has the values $\pm h/4\pi$ in the direction of some arbitrary field. This is formalized by assigning to the spin angular momentum for each electron in the direction of some arbitrary field the value

$$\mathrm{p}_{sz} = \frac{m_s h}{2\pi}, \quad (16.8\text{–}6)$$

with m_s having the values $+^1/_2$ and $-^1/_2$. Thus the resultant spin angular momentum for the two electrons has the values $\sqrt{S(S+1)}h/2\pi$, with S given by

$$S = 1, 0, \text{ and } -1. \quad (16.8\text{–}7)$$

The maximum spin angular momentum in the direction of an arbitrary field is $Sh/2\pi$. The spin angular momentum p_s is now oriented so that the component of the angular momentum in the direction of the resultant orbital angular momentum p_l has values given by

$$\frac{2\pi \mathrm{p}_s}{h} = S, S-1, S-2, \cdots, -(S-2), -(S-1), -S. \quad (16.8\text{–}8)$$

There are thus $(2S + 1)$ possible orientations of p_s with respect to p_l. When p_l and p_s couple to give a resultant angular momentum in the arbitrary direction of L, the final resultant can take only values of $Jh/2\pi$ with $J = L + S, L + S - 1, \cdots, L, \cdots, L - (S - 1), L - S$. (The vector sum of L and S has been given the symbol J.) The resultant value of J can result from $2J + 1$ values of M_J, the component of J along an axis chosen at random. This means that J can have $2J + 1$ orientations of the same energy with respect to some arbitrary direction. The total angular momentum is then

$$\mathrm{p}_J = \frac{\sqrt{J(J+1)}\, h}{2\pi}. \tag{16.8–9}$$

This is illustrated in Fig. 16.8–2.

For the ground state of a helium atom, both n and n' are unity, l and l' are zero, and the electrons have values of m_s of $+{}^1/_2$ and $-{}^1/_2$. Thus L, S, and J are all zero. If n is unity and n' is 2, l is zero but l' may be zero or unity; that is, L is either zero or unity. In either case there are two possibilities for spin orientation; the one is $m_s = {}^1/_2$ and $m_s' = {}^1/_2$ $(S = 1)$; the other is $m_s = {}^1/_2$ and $m_s' = -{}^1/_2$ $(S = 0)$. Then, for $L = 0$ and $S = 1$, J can only have the value of unity; for $L = 0$ and $S = 0$, J can only have the value zero; for $L = 1$ and $S = 0$, J can only have the value 1; while for $L = 1$ and $S = 1$, J can have the values 2, 1, and 0.

In helium or the alkaline earth metals, electrons with symmetric and antisymmetric orbital functions react with the inner shells in completely different ways, which involve greatly different amounts of energy. Thus the spectrum of helium is split into a singlet system due to the single symmetric orbital function (16.8–3), and into a triplet system due to the three antisymmetric orbital wave functions (16.8–4, 16.8–4a, 16.8–4b).

The individual energies corresponding to the three terms of the triplet are also different for the same reason. However, the triplet has at most only two energy values, one for $J = 0$ and the other for $J = \pm 1$, since the latter differ only in orientation and are coincident, except in a magnetic field. Thus it is usually said that the triplet S levels correspond to one energy. It is customary to define the multiplicity as $2S + 1$ for each term and place the value of $2S + 1$ as a superscript to the left of the term.

As an example of the general case, consider a two-electron system with a resultant L of 3; that is, the resultant levels are F levels. When the spin wave function is the same for each electron $(S = 1)$, the system is a triplet $(2S + 1 = 3)$. The resulting J values are $J = 4$, 3, and 2, so that the three terms are ${}^3F_4$, ${}^3F_3$, and ${}^3F_2$, respectively. Each term has $2J + 1$ states, which may be separated by application of a magnetic field.

16.9 Energy Levels of Ions or Atoms with Incompleted Inner Shells

The wave function characterized by the values of n, l, m_l, and m_s for any electron in an atom is referred to as an *atomic orbital*. From the principle that no two electrons in an atom can have the same set of quantum numbers, it follows that the maximum number of electrons with any value of the quantum number n will be reached when there is a pair of electrons with opposite spin having each of the possible m_l values for all the possible values of l. A "completed shell" contains the maximum number of electrons for a given value of n. Each electron in this shell is in its own distinct quantum state.

The system of labeling the states of elements will be illustrated for the ground state of iron. The m_l and m_s values of a completed subshell always add up to zero, since the set of electrons within the subshell has as many negative as positive values of both m_l and m_s; consequently, the contribution of such a subshell to L, S, and J is equal to zero. The iron atom has the $n = 1$ and $n = 2$ shells completely full; for $n = 3$, the $l = 0$ and $l = 1$ subshells are also completely full. These shells and subshells contribute nothing to L, S, and J. The $l = 2$ subshell with $n = 3$ has 6 electrons. Electrons tend to distribute themselves, if possible, so that each has a different m_l value and a spin of $+^1/_2$. Since there are five m_l values for $l = 2$, there is one electron left over after filling all m_l values; this goes in $m_l = 2$ with m_s equal to $-^1/_2$. Thus the contribution to L (Σm_l) is 2 and the contribution to S (Σm_s) is also 2. There are two electrons in shell $n = 4$ with $l = 0$. This is a completed subshell, and it contributes zero to L, S, and J. The total S value is $^4/_2$, so that the multiplicity is 5, that is, $2 \times {}^4/_2 + 1$. The total value of L is 2, so that the term is a D term. In the ground state the total J value, $(L + S)$, is 4; the term is thus written $^5D_4$ for the ground state.

In ferric ion the two electrons in the 4S shell have been lost, as well as one electron from the 3d shell. Thus the value of L becomes zero, the value of S becomes $^5/_2$ (multiplicity 6), so that the value of J is $^5/_2$. The spectroscopic term for the ferric ion is thus $^6S_{5/2}$.

16.10 Energy Levels for Molecules. Introduction

In a molecule there is more than one nucleus; the procedure for determination of energy levels must be modified accordingly. In Section 16.7 the wave function for a system composed of a nucleus and an electron was regarded as the product of a wave function in the coordinates of the center of gravity and another in the coordinates of the electron relative to the nucleus. Similarly, in a system of nuclei and electrons the wave function can be written as a product of a wave function involving the coordinates of the center of gravity and a wave function in all other coordinates. The approximation thus involved is absolutely negligible.

The wave function due to coordinates other than those of the center of gravity cannot be further factored without considerable approximation. Nevertheless it is convenient to do this and to correct later the energies of the levels for the approximation. The factoring is done in terms of a wave function, ψ_r, due to rotation of the molecule as a whole assuming no other relative motion of the nuclei, a wave function ψ_v, due to relative motion of the nuclei (vibration), and a wave function ψ_e, due to motions of the electrons in the field of the nuclei in fixed equilibrium positions.

It is the wave function ψ_e due to the electronic motions which is responsible for energy levels comparable with the atomic energy levels discussed in previous sections.

Denoting the energies due to rotation, vibration, and electronic motions respectively by W_r, W_v, and W_e, a molecule with a wave function $\psi_r \cdot \psi_v \cdot \psi_e$ has energies (to a first approximation)

$$W = W_r + W_v + W_e. \tag{16.10–1}$$

16.11 Electronic States and Electronic Energy Levels of Diatomic Molecules

The exact specification of the wave equation and the calculation of exact energy levels is not generally possible for molecules, except for the very simple ones, such as H_2. The nature of the possible states is described in much the same fashion as for atoms. The orbital angular momenta of the electrons add to give a total resultant which is denoted by the symbol Λ. Similarly, the spins add together to give a resultant S. The nomenclature of the states involved follows the pattern used for atoms. States with Λ equal to 0, 1, 2, etc., are known as Σ, Π, Δ, etc., states. The component of the spin quantum number in the direction of the axis of symmetry is denoted by the symbol S, and the corresponding *multiplicity* $(2S + 1)$ is indicated by a superscript to the left of the Greek letter, as for the atomic levels. Whereas in the case of atoms the symmetry of the wave function involves only electronic coordinates, in the case of even the simplest molecule, it also involves the nuclear coordinates. Therefore an additional subscript to the right of the symbol indicates the symmetry of the total wave function (including spin) of the molecule with respect to interchange of the two atoms. Subscript g is used if the total wave function is unaltered by exchange of atoms, and subscript u if the wave function changes sign upon exchange. Finally, it is necessary, for Σ states, to indicate the behavior of the wave function with respect to reflection in a plane through the nuclei; a superscript $+$ or $-$ to the right of the Greek letter is used to indicate symmetry or lack of symmetry with respect to this operation.

Although it is not generally possible to make an *a priori* calculation of the energies of molecular states, it is usually possible to obtain the energies of the various states and to assign them term symbols by interpretation of the electronic spectra of the molecules. The separation between successive electronic states is large with molecules, as with atoms. Consequently, in most thermodynamic calculations only a few of the possible states need be considered, and frequently only one.

As an example of the nomenclature described above, the ground state of oxygen is a $^3\Sigma_g^-$. That is, the resultant orbital angular momentum is zero, and the total spin quantum number is unity; the wave function does not change sign on interchange of the atoms, but it does change sign on reflection in a plane containing the nuclei.

Problem 16.11-1. The first excited state of oxygen is $^1\Delta_g$.
(a) What is the resultant spin angular momentum?
(b) What is the resulting electronic angular momentum?

16.12 Rotational and Vibrational Energy Levels of Diatomic Molecules

A graph of the electronic energy for hydrogen against internuclear distance is shown in Fig. 16.12–1.[4] The energy zero is taken at the equilibrium distance. The full curve is experimental; the dotted curve is that calculated from the equation

$$V(r - r_e) = D_e(1 - e^{-\beta(r-r_e)})^2, \qquad (16.12\text{–}1)$$

where D_e is the dissociation energy referred to the minimum in the potential curve (shown in Fig. 16.12–1 as a vertical line drawn from the abscissa to the region of continuous energy levels), and β is a constant; r is the internuclear distance, and r_e the equilibrium distance. It should be noted that D_e is *not* the observed dissociation energy, for reasons to be discussed below. Equation (16.12–1) was first proposed by Morse;[5] it has therefore been called a Morse function. It has great value as an expression for the potential energy, since its use permits exact solution of the wave equation. Equation (16.12–1) can be approximated by

$$V(r - r_e) = f(r - r_e)^2 - g(r - r_e)^3. \qquad (16.12\text{–}1a)$$

The calculations leading to the curve in Fig. 16.12–1 were made on the basis that the nuclei were stationary. Actually, the nuclei are not stationary but are vibrating with respect to each other, while in addition the entire molecule is rotating. The assumption that the nuclei were stationary caused no error in calculation of the electronic energy because electronic motions are very rapid compared to those of the nuclei. For

[4] G. Herzberg, *Spectra of Diatomic Molecules*, Van Nostrand, Princeton, N.J., 1950.
[5] P. M. Morse, *Phys. Rev.*, **34**, 57 (1929).

the same reason the electronic energy (as a function of the internuclear distance) may be used as the potential energy for the nuclei in a wave equation involving the six coordinates of the nuclei.

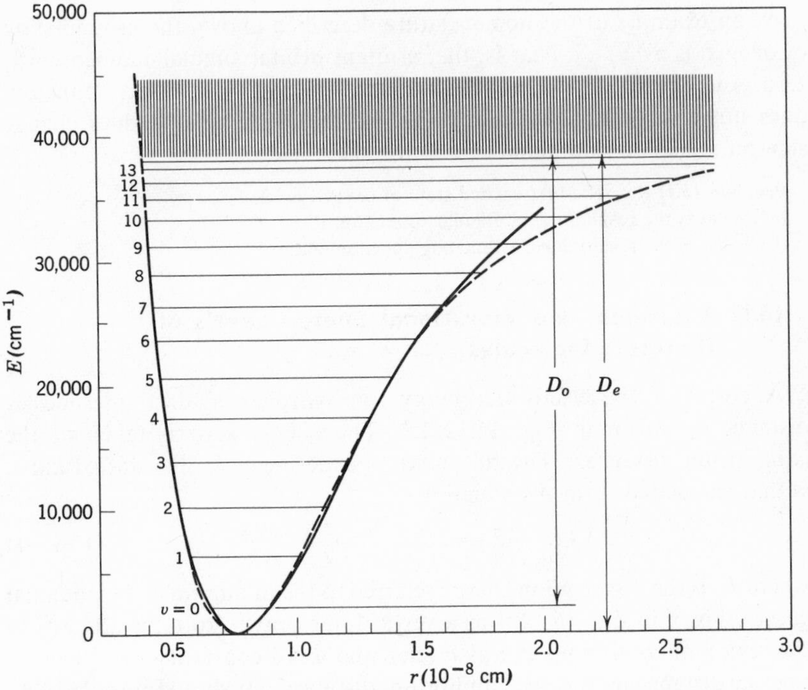

Fig. 16.12–1. Potential curve of the H_2 ground state with vibrational levels and continuous term spectrum.[4]

The full curve is drawn according to Rydberg's data. The broken curve is a Morse curve. The continuous term spectrum, above $v = 14$, is indicated by vertical hatching. The vibrational levels are drawn up to the potential curve; that is, their end points correspond to the classical turning points of the vibration. It must be remembered that in quantum theory these sharp turning points are replaced by broad maxima of the probability amplitude ψ.

(From G. Herzberg, *Molecular Spectra and Molecular Structure*, Vol. I, "Spectra of Diatomic Molecules", 2nd ed. Copyright 1950, D. Van Nostrand Company, Inc.)

It is convenient to express the energy of the rotational and vibrational levels in terms of a rotational part E_r and a vibrational part E_v. The total energy is thus

$$E = E_e + E_v + E_r, \qquad (16.12\text{–}2)$$

where E_e is the electronic energy. Expressed in terms of wave numbers, this becomes

$$T = T_e + G + F, \tag{16.12–2a}$$

where T, T_e, G, and F are the total, the electronic, the vibrational, and the rotational energies divided by hc. The vibrational energy will be considered first.

The vibrational energy is obtained by solving the wave equation for motion of the nuclei along the internuclear axis, using a function such as that of Fig. 16.12–1 for the potential energy. If (16.12–1a) is used, the vibrational part of the energy is given by

$$E_v = hc\omega_e(v + \tfrac{1}{2}) - hc\omega_e x_e(v + \tfrac{1}{2})^2 + hc\omega_e y_e(v + \tfrac{1}{2})^3 + \cdots, \tag{16.12–3}$$

where v can have only integral values, including zero; ω_e, x_e, y_e, etc., are functions of the masses of the nuclei and of the constants of the potential energy expression used in the wave equation. For example, the constant β of equation (16.12–1) is given by

$$\beta = \sqrt{\frac{2\pi c\mu}{D_e h}}\,\omega_e, \tag{16.12–4}$$

where μ is the reduced mass of the two nuclei. An expression for G is obtained by omitting the factor hc from each term of (16.12–3). The allowed values of G (vibrational energy levels in terms of wave numbers) are shown by horizontal lines in Fig. 16.12–1.

The simplest situation is where the nuclei vibrate with respect to each other as a harmonic oscillator. The corresponding energy levels are obtained when a quadratic potential energy function (with its minimum at the position of minimum energy) is used in the wave equation. If the harmonic oscillator approximation is used, the energy expression of equation (16.12–3) reduces to its first term. The expression for ω_e is then

$$\omega_e = \frac{1}{2\pi c}\sqrt{\frac{k}{\mu}}, \tag{16.12–5}$$

where μ is the reduced mass of the nuclei and k the force constant. The force constant is such that the defined force F, which causes a small displacement δ from the equilibrium position, is given by

$$\mathrm{F} = -k\delta.$$

Thus $c\omega_e$ is the *natural frequency* of vibration of a classical harmonic oscillator. If the system acted as a harmonic oscillator and underwent no changes of energy other than vibrational, an increase of v by one unit would result in absorption of light of frequency:

$$\nu = \frac{\Delta E}{h} = c\omega_e . \tag{16.12–6}$$

Therefore, for a harmonic oscillator, the frequency of light absorbed when v changes by unity is the natural frequency of the oscillator. For this reason $c\omega_e$ is spoken of as the *fundamental frequency* of the oscillator.

The lowest vibrational energy possible is obtained when $v = 0$. From equation (16.12–3) it is

$$E_0 = \frac{hc\omega_e}{2} - \frac{hc\omega_e x_e}{4} + \frac{hc\omega_e y_e}{8} + \cdots \tag{16.12–7}$$

The observed dissociation energy is the energy required to separate the atoms from a molecule originally in the lowest vibrational state. It is thus

$$D_0 = D_e - E_0 . \tag{16.12–8}$$

This value is shown as a line drawn in Fig. 16.12–1 from the horizontal line $v = 0$ to the region of continuous energy levels.

The *rotational energy levels* may be obtained approximately by solving the wave equation with the molecule considered rigid. For this *rigid rotator*, with the mass of the electrons considered, the term values which correspond to the energies are given by

$$F(J) = B_e J(J + 1) + (A - B_e)\Lambda^2, \tag{16.12–9}$$

where

$$B_e = \frac{h}{8\pi^2 c I_B} \tag{16.12–9a}$$

and

$$A = \frac{h}{8\pi^2 c I_A} . \tag{16.12–9b}$$

In the equations above I_B $(=\mu r_e^2)$ is the moment of inertia about an axis perpendicular to the line joining the nuclei; the distance r_e is the equilibrium internuclear distance. I_A is the moment of inertia of the electrons about the internuclear axis. It is naturally very small compared with I_B, so that A is much larger than B_e. Λ is the orbital quantum number discussed in Section 16.11, and it has integral values. J is the quantum number representing the total angular momentum; it takes values Λ, $\Lambda + 1$, $\Lambda + 2, \cdots$, etc. Λ usually takes on only small values, since large values correspond to very high energies. If Λ is kept constant the inclusion of the second term merely increases the energy $(A - B_e)\Lambda^2$.

The energy given by equation (16.12–9) must be corrected for two mechanical effects. First, the moment of inertia I_B will be different in various vibrational states owing to changes in the average internuclear distance. Second, the molecule is stretched by rotation due to centrifugal force. These two effects are frequently described as *vibrational* and *rotational stretching*. Upon correction for these two effects, the equation becomes

$$F_v(J) = B_vJ(J+1) + (A - B_v)\Lambda^2 - D_vJ^2(J+1)^2 + \cdots, \quad (16.12\text{–}10)$$

where B_v and D_v are given by

$$B_v = B_e - \alpha_e(v + \tfrac{1}{2}) - \cdots, \quad (16.12\text{–}11)$$

$$D_v = D_e - \beta_e(v + \tfrac{1}{2}) - \cdots, \quad (16.12\text{–}12)$$

and

$$D_e = \frac{4B_e^{\,2}}{\omega_e^{\,2}} \quad (16.12\text{–}13)$$

α_e and β_e are constants; B_e is the same as in equation (16.12–9). (The constant D_e whose value is given by equation (16.12–13) has nothing to do with the dissociation energy.)

The corrected constant B_v allows for the fact that the moment of inertia averaged over the period of any particular vibration is slightly different from that in the equilibrium position. The third term on the right side of equation (16.12–10) corrects the moment of inertia for centrifugal stretching. Its coefficient, D_v, is corrected for the effect of vibration in the same manner as B_v; the average value for a given vibrational level is given by equation (16.12–12).

The constants in the formulas are derived empirically from experimental observation of spectra and interpreted in the light of the wave equation. The actual energies of the levels are obtained directly from the spectroscopic data and are to be regarded as experimental values.

The electronic orbital angular momentum, represented by Λ, has already been discussed. When there is no nuclear spin, the total angular momentum, represented by J, is a resultant of the orbital angular momentum (Λ), the electron spin angular momentum (S, component along the figure axis Σ), and the angular momentum due to rotation of the two nuclei (represented by the quantum number N). This "coupling" of momenta may take place in two distinct ways, known as Hund's case (a) and Hund's case (b). The sets of energy states which result from the two types of coupling are quite different in character; their structure permits elucidation of the type of coupling. The types of coupling and the resulting energy level patterns are discussed briefly in Appendix 6. A more complete discussion is given by Herzberg.[6]

In any case, specification of Λ, S, N, and J specifies the energy of the state. However, there is ordinarily more than one rotational state with this energy. The total angular momentum vector $\sqrt{J(J+1)}h/2$ can be oriented with respect to any arbitrary axis in a variety of ways so that the component of the angular momentum along this axis has the value $M_J h/2\pi$, where $M_J = 0, \pm 1, \pm 2, \pm 3, \cdots, \pm J$. Each of these $2J + 1$ rotational *states* has the same energy; the energy level is thus said to be *degenerate*. The following problem can be answered by reference to Appendix 6.

Problem 16.12-1. (a) The ground state of ZrO is a $^3\Pi$. List the possible values of Ω, which is the sum of Λ and Σ, and state what values of J are possible for each.

(b) Give the values of J corresponding to $K = 1$, 3, and 5 for the $^3\Sigma_g{}^-$ ground state of oxygen. (Note that symmetry requirements to be discussed later prohibit $K =$ 0, 2, 4, etc.)

16.13 Band Spectra

The effect of the rotational and vibrational energy is to produce bands in the absorption or emission spectra of the molecule, as previously described in Sections 16.4 and 16.12. In this section the nomenclature and origin of band spectra will be discussed. A corresponding effect observed in light scattered by molecules is known as the Raman effect. The spectra due to this effect (Raman spectra) will be discussed later.

Figure 16.13–1[6] shows an emission band spectrum for the molecule PN due to the $^1\Pi \rightarrow {}^1\Sigma$ electronic transition. Each band has a *head* on the right side of which intensity falls sharply while on the other side the intensity falls slowly. The origin of such bands is discussed later. The *band heads* are marked below the bands by vertical lines so distributed as to indicate certain relations between the bands. The lines in the first horizontal row mark bands in which the vibrational quantum number v of equation (16.12–3) changes from $v' = 0$ to $v'' = 2$, 1, and 0 respectively. Bands are observed rather than lines because the changes in vibrational energy are accompanied by changes in rotational energy which produce an unresolved fine structure. This fine structure is discussed later in this section.

[6] G. Herzberg, *Spectra of Diatomic Molecules*, 1950, pp. 218 ff.

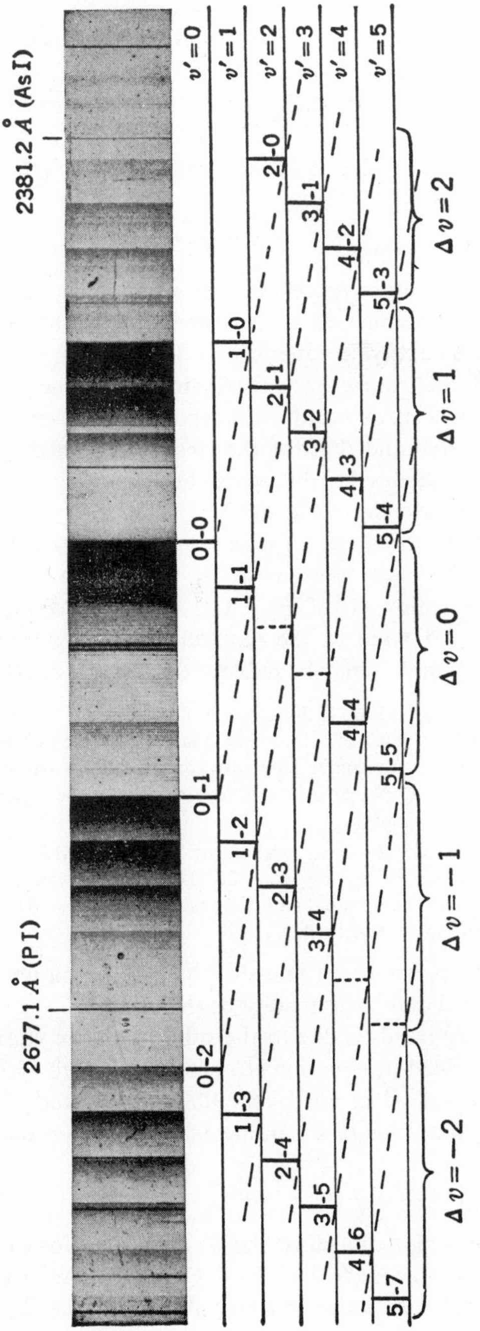

Fig. 16.13–1. Emission band spectrum of the PN Molecule.[6]

The broken leading lines refer to unobserved bands. Since the spectrogram is taken with a grating, the dispersion, in angstroms per millimeter, is approximately constant, while the wave number dispersion increases to the left.

(From G. Herzberg, *Molecular Spectra and Molecular Structure*, Vol. I, "Spectra of Diatomic Molecules," 2nd ed. Copyright 1950, D. Van Nostrand Company, Inc.)

The sets of bands marked by the rows of vertical lines constitute "*progressions.*" The bands of each row are said to form a v'' progression, since they correspond to a series of possible values of v''. The bands marked by vertical lines connected by dashed lines are said to form a v' progression for analogous reasons.

The wave numbers of all band heads in Fig. 16.13–1 can be represented by the empirical formula

$$\tilde{\nu} = 39{,}699.0 + (1094.80v' - 7.25v'^2) - (1329.38v'' - 6.98v''^2) \quad (16.13\text{–}1)$$

The totality of bands which can be represented by such a formula is called a *band system.* The wave number of any of the bands of the system is obtained approximately by applying equation (16.13–1) to the vibrational energy of the initial and final states. The wave number for the transition with no change in vibrational quantum number is 39,699.0 cm^{-1}. The difference between this value and that for the electronic transition itself, 39,805.7 cm^{-1}, is approximately the difference between the zero point vibrational energies of the two electronic states.

The energy of each vibrational level, for the lowest rotational state, is obtained by adding to the electronic energy of the state a vibrational contribution given by equation (16.12–3). The energy associated with any transition from the $^1\Pi$ state to the $^1\Sigma^+$ state is then obtained by difference; the resulting equation may be reduced to the form of (16.13–1).

Problem 16.13-1. By use of equation (16.2–3), obtain an expression for the energy associated with transition from a level of vibrational quantum number v' in the $^1\Pi$ state to a level v'' in the $^1\Sigma^+$ state. By comparison with equation (16.13–1), obtain the constants ω_e and x_e for each state; then evaluate approximately the difference in electronic energy between the two states.

Problem 16.13-2. From the constants ω_e and x_e of Problem 16.13–1 and the observed difference in electronic energy between the $^1\Pi$ and $^1\Sigma^+$ states, evaluate approximately the energy (in cm^{-1}) associated with a transition from $v' = 0$ to $v'' = 0$. Explain why this differs from the observed value.

The discussion above applies to an emission band; the nature of the corresponding absorption bands may readily be deduced.

The fine structure of the bands is due to the splitting of the vibrational levels by rotation as described by equation (16.12–10). Figure 16.13–2[6] is a diagram of the lines observed in one of the absorption bands of AlH. The lines are labeled by the value of a parameter m, given approximately by the formula

$$\tilde{\nu} = c + dm + em^2. \quad (16.13\text{–}2)$$

The absolute value of m is plotted against the wave number for each line. The curve consists of three branches called the P, Q, and R branches. The major part of the energy change is due to a transition from the $^1\Sigma^+$ to the

$^1\Pi$ electronic state, with no change in the vibrational quantum number, which is zero in both the initial and the final state. Each line on the R branch corresponds to a change in the rotational quantum number J of $+1$ in absorption (-1 in emission). Each line in the Q branch corresponds to the difference in energy between corresponding rotational levels in the initial and final states; the line shifts to lower wave numbers as the value of J increases. Each line on the P branch corresponds to a change in J of -1 in absorption ($+1$ in emission).

The value of m is positive for all levels of the Q and R branches and negative for the P branch. For the P and Q branches, the magnitude of m is equal to the value of the rotational quantum number J in the initial

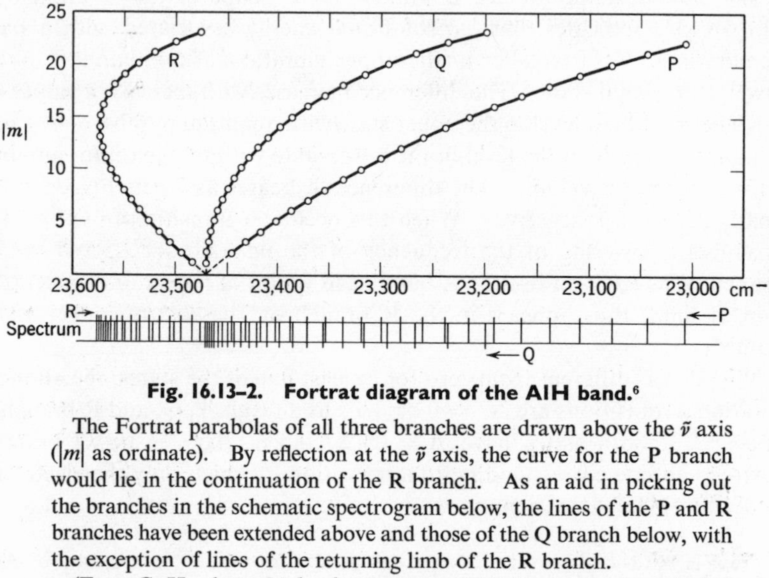

Fig. 16.13–2. Fortrat diagram of the AlH band.[6]

The Fortrat parabolas of all three branches are drawn above the $\tilde{\nu}$ axis ($|m|$ as ordinate). By reflection at the $\tilde{\nu}$ axis, the curve for the P branch would lie in the continuation of the R branch. As an aid in picking out the branches in the schematic spectrogram below, the lines of the P and R branches have been extended above and those of the Q branch below, with the exception of lines of the returning limb of the R branch.

(From G. Herzberg, *Molecular Spectra and Molecular Structure*, Vol. I, "Spectra of Diatomic Molecules," 2nd ed. Copyright 1950, D. Van Nostrand Company, Inc.)

state. For the R branch, m is one unit greater than the J value of the initial state. The constants c, d, and e are the same for the P and R branches. For the Q branch, the constant d is different, but c and e are the same. A set of curves such as Fig. 16.13–2 is called a *Fortrat diagram*. Equation (16.13–2) is typical of the equations used to represent the P, Q, and R branches.

Problem 16.13-3. The energy of a given state for AlH is given approximately by the equation $T = T_{e,v} + B_vJ(J + 1)$, where $T_{e,v}$ is the sum of the electronic and vibrational energy, and B_v is a constant for a given electronic and vibrational state.

(a) Using this type of expression for the energy levels in the $^1\Sigma$ and $^1\Pi$ states, obtain expressions for the change in energy associated with transitions in each of the P, Q, and R branches.

(b) By writing the results of part (a) in the form of equation (16.13–2), obtain expressions for the constants c, d, and e for each branch in terms of the constants $T_{e,v}$ and B_v for each state. For uniformity denote the initial state by a prime (′) and the final state by a double prime (″). *Ans.* For all branches, $c = T''_{e,v} - T'_{e,v}$; $e = B_v'' - B_v'$. For P and R, $d = B_v' + B_v''$; for Q, $d = B_v'' - B_v'$.

(c) Verify the statements above concerning relationships between the constants c, d, and e required for the several branches.

The interesting features in the Fortrat diagram are the shape of the three branches, particularly the parabolic nature of the R branch and a rather similar shape for the Q branch. The shape of the Q branch in Fig. 16.13–2 indicates that the rotational energy associated with a particular value of J is smaller in the upper vibrational state than it is in the lower vibrational state. The difference increases with increasing values of J. The rotational level in the upper state with quantum number $J + 1$ has a higher energy than the level in the lower state with the quantum number J for the lower J values. The difference decreases as J gets bigger, until finally it becomes negative. When this occurs, a transition of $\Delta J = +1$ produces a lowering of the frequency of the light absorbed, and the R branch turns back on itself. A band head (point of maximum concentration of lines) thus appears in the R branch on the side of higher wave number.

Where Λ is different from zero for at least one of the states, the allowed rotational transitions are $\Delta J = 0$ or ± 1; as a result, P, Q, and R branches appear. If both states have $\Lambda = 0$ (Σ states), there is no Q branch. There is no line corresponding to a transition in which only the electronic and vibrational states change.

Problem 16.13-4. The value of B_v is 6.296 cm^{-1} for the $^1\Sigma^+$, $v = 0$ state of AlH and is 6.024 cm^{-1} for the $^1\Pi$, $v = 0$ state.

(a) Verify the qualitative statements above about the shape of the Q and R branches.

(b) Using the results of Problem 16.13–3, calculate the value of $m\,(= J + 1)$ at which the lines of the R branch turn toward lower wave number.

If the electronic state is the same before and after the transition, the band is a *rotation-vibration* band; the final state must have a higher vibrational quantum number than the initial state. If both the electronic and vibrational states are the same before and after transition, the absorption of light is due only to rotation; this *pure rotational* spectrum contains only an R branch. Such bands are in the far infrared and in the microwave (0.1 to 10 cm).

16.14 Allowed Energy Levels and Selection Rules for Diatomic Molecules. Nuclear Spin and Symmetry of Levels

The manner in which molecular energy levels arise has been discussed above, along with examples of some of the transitions between these and the spectra which accompany such transitions. The details of the allowed levels depend on the *symmetry* of the molecule. The allowed transitions producing spectra depend on the *selection rules* governing the transitions.

In order to understand the effect of molecular symmetry on allowed levels and possible transitions, it is necessary to consider the effect of *nuclear spin.* If the nuclei of a diatomic molecule are identical, only those states are allowed whose total wave function is either *symmetric* or *antisymmetric* in the nuclei. If the nuclei have an even mass number, only symmetric levels are allowed; if they have an odd mass number, only antisymmetric levels.

Consider a gas made up of diatomic molecules containing equivalent nuclei with i units of spin angular momentum. Each nucleus has $n = 2i + 1$ spin wave functions of essentially equal energy. Let these be labeled $\chi_1, \chi_2, \chi_3, \cdots, \chi_n$ for one nucleus and $\phi_1, \phi_2, \phi_3, \cdots, \phi_n$ for the other, where χ_1 is identical with ϕ_1, etc. The allowed spin wave functions for the molecule are made up of linear combinations of the products of these, as follows. First, there are n spin wave functions $\phi_1\chi_1$, $\phi_2\chi_2$, $\phi_3\chi_3, \cdots, \phi_n\chi_n$ which are totally symmetric, since interchanging nuclei between the identical wave functions does not change the sign of the function. Second, there are $n(n - 1)/2$ spin wave functions of the type $\phi_1\chi_2 + \phi_2\chi_1$ (or, in general, $\phi_i\chi_j + \phi_j\chi_i$) which also do not change sign when nuclei are interchanged; these are also totally symmetric. Thus the number of totally symmetric wave functions of both kinds is $n(n + 1)/2$. Finally, there are the spin wave functions of the type $\phi_i\chi_j - \phi_j\chi_i$ whose sign changes when the nuclei are exchanged. These are antisymmetric and there are $n(n - 1)/2$ of them. The total number of nuclear spin wave functions is evidently $n^2 = (2i + 1)^2$.

States with nuclear spin wave functions of the symmetric type are called *ortho* states, and the antisymmetric ones are called *para* states. For identical nuclei of even mass number, ortho states will be found only where the remainder of the wave function is also symmetric, and para states occur only where the remainder of the wave function is antisymmetric, since the total wave function must be symmetric. If the nuclei have odd mass number, the remainder of the wave function must be antisymmetric for ortho states and symmetric for para states.

The symmetry with respect to the nuclei of the remainder of the wave function depends on the electronic wave function, the vibrational wave function, and the rotational wave function. Since the vibrational wave function depends only on the distance between the nuclei, it is always symmetric. The electronic and rotational wave functions are symmetric or antisymmetric depending on their nature.

Since transitions between Σ states are by far the most common, the allowed levels for such states will be discussed in detail. The symmetry, in the nuclei, of the rotational levels of Σ states depends on whether they are Σ^+ or Σ^- states as well as on whether they are g or u. For Σ states the coupling is a limiting example of Hund's case (b), the quantum number K is the one associated with the total nuclear rotational angular momentum. The quantum number K characterizes the nature of the rotational wave functions and determines the symmetry of the rotational levels. The total angular quantum number J is given by $K + S$, $K + S - 1, \cdots, K - S$ (see Appendix 6). The energy of the levels when Σ is zero is given by equation (16.12–10), with J replaced by K. The effect of a non-zero value of Σ is to change the value slightly.

For $\Sigma_g{}^+$ states of homonuclear molecules the rotational levels with even K values are symmetric and those with odd K values are antisymmetric; for $\Sigma_g{}^-$ states the reverse is true. The corresponding u states are exactly opposite. The Σ^+ states of molecules with unlike nuclei have their rotational states $+$ for even K values and $-$ for odd K values ($+$ and $-$ denote that the rotational wave function retains or changes its sign on inversion), while for the Σ^- states the opposite is true. For the $^1\Sigma$ states, of course, $K \equiv J$.

For Π and Δ states there are two levels for each value of Λ, one $+$ and the other $-$. The former behave like Σ^+ states; the latter like Σ^- states. This fact gives rise to the phenomenon known as Λ *doubling* when there is an energy difference for the states with $\pm\Lambda$.

For homonuclear diatomic molecules *without nuclear spin*, only symmetric levels are possible. (To obtain a resultant spin of zero, the numbers of particles in the nucleus must obviously be even.) For example, in $\Sigma_g{}^+$ states for such molecules, only those rotational levels with even K values can exist. Homonuclear molecules *with nuclear spin* exist in *ortho* and *para* varieties, with very slow transitions between them. Thus for transitions associated with radiation, symmetric states go over to (combine with) other symmetric states only, and not to antisymmetric states; antisymmetric states combine only with other antisymmetric states. The rules may be abbreviated $s \leftrightarrow s$, $a \leftrightarrow a$, $s \not\leftrightarrow a$, where the symbol $\leftrightarrow$ means "goes over to" and $\not\leftrightarrow$ means "does not go over to."

In general, the nature of the allowed transitions associated with radiation will depend on the mechanism of the process. For ordinary dipole radiation, a molecule will emit light during a transition only if it suffers a change of electric moment. Homonuclear diatomic molecules change electric moment only when they change their electronic states; for this reason homonuclear diatomic show only electronic spectra.

Heteronuclear diatomic molecules can suffer a change in dipole moment during vibration and rotation; as a result they display vibration-rotation and pure rotational spectra in addition to electronic spectra. Heteronuclear diatomic molecules can absorb or emit ordinary dipole radiation only for transitions between + and − states. For spectra due to other types of radiation, other rules are followed.

By considerations such as those above it is possible to deduce the *selection rules* which state what changes in the various quantum numbers may accompany the absorption or emission of radiation. As an example of the procedure, for a $^1\Sigma^+$ state of a heteronuclear diatomic molecule the rotational levels with even values of J are +, while those with odd values of J are −. For ordinary dipole radiation, the restrictions given above require that $+ \leftrightarrow -$, so that the value of J must change by a unit for transitions within this electronic state; that is, $\Delta J = \pm 1$. On the other hand, for a $^1\Pi$ state, each rotational state has + and − states; in this case, no change in J is necessary; $\Delta J = 0, \pm 1$. The reader is referred to Herzberg[7] for details of the calculations leading to selection rules. The remaining selection rules which are useful for our purposes will be stated without detailed justification.

We may now state the *selection rules.* The most common band spectra are those for which $\Delta\Lambda = 0$. In this case, for dipole radiation,

$$\Delta J = 0, \pm 1 \quad \text{for} \quad \Lambda \neq 0,$$

$$\Delta J = \pm 1 \quad \text{for} \quad \Lambda = 0.$$

For the Raman spectra, the initial and final states must have the same symmetry. In this case,

$$\Delta J = 0, \pm 2 \qquad \text{for} \quad \Lambda = 0,$$

$$\Delta J = 0, \pm 1, \pm 2 \quad \text{for} \quad \Lambda \neq 0,$$

$$J = 0 \not\leftrightarrow J = 0.$$

For dipole radiation there are additional rules depending on the type

[7] G. Herzberg, *Spectra of Diatomic Molecules, op. cit.*, Chapters III and IV.

of coupling. For electronic transitions where the coupling is Hund's case (a) or (b), the selection rules hold:

$$\Delta\Lambda = 0, \pm 1,$$
$$\Delta S = 0.$$

In Hund's case (a) there are the following additional rules:

$$\Delta\Sigma = 0,$$
$$\Delta\Omega = 0, \pm 1,$$

and

$$\Delta J = 0 \quad \text{for} \quad \Omega = 0 \rightarrow \Omega = 0.$$

For Hund's case (b) the additional selection rule is

$$\Delta K = 0, \pm 1,$$

except that

$$\Delta K \neq 0 \text{ for } \Sigma \rightarrow \Sigma \text{ transitions.}$$

16.15 Examples of Band Spectra (Hydrogen Chloride and Oxygen)

16.15.1 Hydrogen Chloride

The electronic ground state of hydrogen chloride is $^1\Sigma^+$; thus $\Lambda = 0$. Since the molecule has an electric moment, it absorbs light in the far infrared (around 40 μ) accompanied by excitation from a rotational state of quantum number J to the next higher rotational state $(J + 1)$. In these transitions, the molecule does not change its electronic or vibrational states from the ground level ($v = 0$; $\Lambda = 0$). The line of longest wave length observed[8] corresponds to a transition from $J = 3$ to $J = 4$. Since transitions from states of lower J are not observed, and because the accuracy is limited, this band is not suited for obtaining the rotational energy levels of the ground state. Instead, the rotation vibration bands are used for this purpose. Three rotation vibration bands have been studied rather thoroughly.[9–11] The band for the transition $v = 0$ to $v = 1$ (the fundamental one) is typical of the entire set ($0 \rightarrow 1$, $0 \rightarrow 2$, $0 \rightarrow 3$). It consists of pairs of lines. The weaker of each pair, which is on the longer wave length side, is due to the chlorine isotope of mass 37; the stronger is due to the more abundant isotope of mass 35. Only the lines due to the more abundant isotope will be discussed. The data of

[8] M. Czerny, *Z. Physik*, **34**, 227 (1925).
[9] C. F. Meyer and A. A. Levin, *Phys. Rev.*, **34**, 44 (1929).
[10] G. Herzberg and J. W. T. Spinks, *Z. Physik*, **89**, 474 (1934).
[11] E. Lindholm, *Naturwiss.*, **27**, 470 (1939).

Meyer and Levin[9] for this band can be represented accurately by the equation

$$\tilde{\nu} = 2885.90 + 20.577m - 0.3034m^2 - 0.00222m^3, \quad (16.15\text{–}1)$$

which represents both the P branch ($m < 0$) and the R branch ($m > 0$). In the R branch, m represents the J value for the upper vibrational state; in the P branch, $-m$ represents the J value for the lower vibrational state. (Compare with equation 16.13–2.)

Table 16.15–1 represents the data of Meyer and Levin;[9] the last column

Table 16.15–1

Wave Numbers† for the $v = 0 \to v = 1$ Transition of HCl^{35}

m	$\tilde{\nu}_{obs.}(m)$ cm^{-1}	$\Delta\tilde{\nu}(m)$	$\Delta^2\tilde{\nu}(m)$	Deviation: $\tilde{\nu}_{obs.} - \tilde{\nu}_{calc.}$ (quadratic eq.)	Deviation: $\tilde{\nu}_{obs.} - \tilde{\nu}_{calc.}$ (eq. 16.15–1)
12	3085.62			−3.52	+0.31
		12.86			
11	72.76		−0.83	−2.78	+0.17
		13.69			
10	59.07		−0.50	−2.26	−0.04
		14.19			
9	44.88		−0.73	−1.64	−0.02
		14.92			
8	29.96		−0.75	−1.14	0
		15.67			
7	14.29		−0.84	−0.78	−0.02
		16.51			
6	2997.78		−0.37	−0.66	−0.18
		16.88			
5	80.90		−0.78	−0.36	−0.08
		17.66			
4	63.24		−0.77	−0.11	−0.03
		18.43			
3	44.89		−0.60	−0.09	−0.03
		19.03			
2	25.78		−0.50	−0.06	−0.04
		19.53			
1	06.25			+0.08	+0.08
0					
−1	2865.09			+0.07	+0.07
		21.53			
−2	43.56		−0.54	+0.03	+0.01
		22.07			
−3	21.49		−0.64	+0.05	−0.01
		22.71			
−4	2798.78		−0.28	+0.04	−0.10
		22.99			
−5	75.79		−0.77	+0.36	+0.08
		23.76			
−6	52.03		−0.52	+0.49	+0.03
		24.28			
−7	27.75		−0.41	+0.75	−0.01
		24.69			
−8	03.06		−0.64	+1.17	+0.03
		25.33			
−9	2677.73		−0.43	+1.60	−0.02
		25.76			
−10	51.97		−0.47	+2.18	−0.04
		26.23			
−11	25.74		−0.51	+2.90	−0.05
		26.74			
−12	2599.00			+3.71	−1.12

† From G. Herzberg, *Molecular Spectra and Molecular Structure, Vol. I*, "Spectra of Diatomic Molecules," 2nd ed. Copyright 1950, D. Van Nostrand Company, Inc., Princeton, N.J.

of the table shows the deviation of the observed values of the wave number from those calculated from equation (16.15–1); the next to last column gives the deviations from an equation quadratic in m. This band is shown schematically in the lower half of Fig. 16.15–1; the upper half of this figure shows the rotational energy levels for $v = 0$ and $v = 1$. Above each line is shown the transition which produces it. A line in the R branch corresponds to an increase of unity in J, while one in the P branch represents a decrease of unity; in both cases v increases from zero

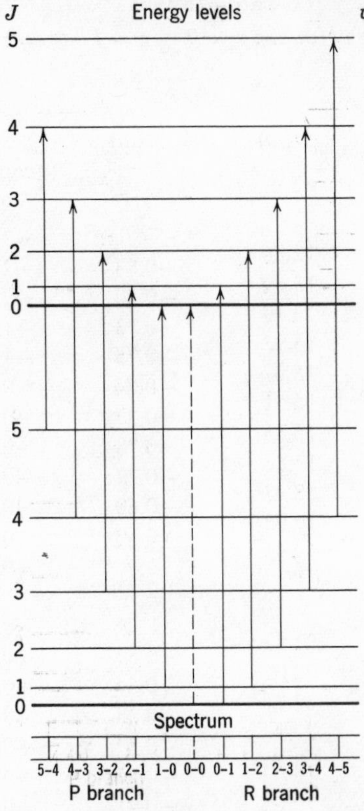

Fig. 16.15–1. Energy levels of hydrogen chloride (schematic).

to unity. Thus one can always find a pair of lines, one in the P branch and one in the R branch, both of whose transitions end in the same level. The first line R_1 of the R branch ($\tilde{\nu} = 2906.25\ \text{cm}^{-1}$) corresponds to a change in J from zero to unity. The second line of the P branch, P_2, ($\tilde{\nu} = 2843.56\ \text{cm}^{-1}$) begins with $J = 2$ and ends with $J = 1$. The difference between these lines, 62.69 cm^{-1}, gives the energy of the level $v = 0$, $J = 2$ with respect to the level $v = 0$, $J = 0$. The selection rules do not admit the transition $v = 0, J = 0$ to $v = 1, J = 0$; a value for the missing line ($\tilde{\nu} = 2885.90$ cm^{-1}) can be obtained by extrapolating the R branch by use of an equation like (16.15–1). By subtracting from this the first line of the P branch, $P_1(J = 1$ to $J = 0)(\tilde{\nu} = 2865.09$ $cm^{-1})$, an energy of 20.81 cm^{-1} is found for the level $v = 0$, $J = 1$. By such procedures the rest of the rotational levels for $v = 0$ can be obtained. The rotational levels for $v = 1$ can be derived in a similar manner. Pairs of transitions in the P and R branches *beginning* in a common level are used to obtain differences between the rotational levels for $v = 1$. These differences are combined with the energy of the $v = 0, J = 0$ to $v = 1, J = 0$ transition to give the energies of the rotational levels.

Problem 16.15-1. From the data of Table 16.15–1 calculate the energy of the first 10 rotational levels of HCl for $v = 0$ and of the first two for $v = 1$.

The energies of the rotational levels for the state $v = 0$ can be obtained somewhat more accurately from measurements of the *third harmonic* ($v = 0 \rightarrow v = 3$), which were made by Herzberg and Spinks.[10] A broken line tracing of the band is shown in Fig 16.15–2.

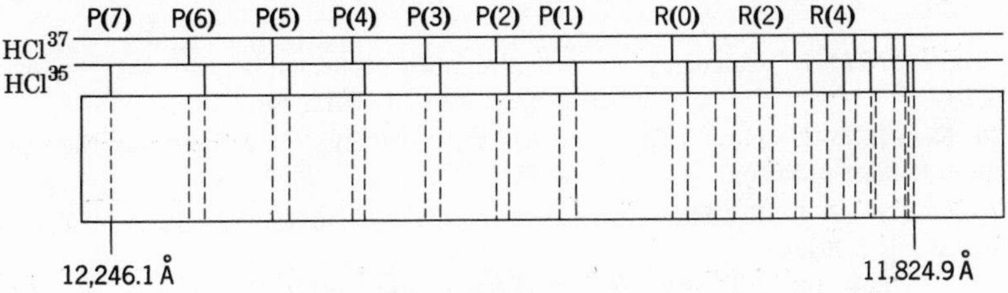

Fig. 16.15-2. Fine structure of the 3–0 band of HCl.

The numbers following the P's and R's are the J values of the lower state. The isotope effect is clearly shown.

(From G. Herzberg, *Molecular Spectra and Molecular Structure*, Vol. I, "Spectra of Diatomic Molecules," 2nd ed. Copyright 1950, D. Van Nostrand Company, Inc.)

Table 16.15–2 contains the "rotation-vibration" constants of HCl^{35} as deduced from the spectroscopic observations; the energy of a given level is obtained by using these constants in equations (16.12–3), (16.12–10), (16.12–11), and (16.12–12).

Figure 16.15–2 also shows a set of lines due to the $v = 0 \rightarrow v = 3$ transition for HCl^{37}. These are displaced about 5.8 cm^{-1} toward smaller wave numbers, owing to the larger mass of Cl^{37}. The main effect of mass is on the vibrational energy. To a first approximation the vibrational energy varies as $\mu^{-1/2}$, as with a harmonic oscillator (cf. equation 16.12–5). The exact expression for the vibrational energy (equation 16.12–3) may be corrected for changes of mass by replacing $(v + {}^1/_2)$ by $\rho(v + {}^1/_2)$ in each term. The correction factor ρ is $(\mu/\mu')^{1/2}$, where μ is the reduced mass of the isotopic species for which the constants of equation (16.12–3) are given, and μ' the reduced mass of another isotopic species. The rotational constant B varies as μ^{-1} (see equation 16.12–9a), so that the rotational energy levels are altered by a factor ρ^2.

Table 16.15–2

Rotation-Vibration Constants for HCl^{35}

B_0	10.439960 cm^{-1}	$\nu_0(3–0)$	8347.20
B_1	10.1295	B_e	10.59090
B_2	9.8441	r_e	1.2717 Å
B_3	9.53432	α_e	0.30188
D_o	0.000530	D_e	0.000532
D_3	0.000518	β_e	0.000004
$\nu_0(1–0)$	2885.88	ω_e	2989.00
$\nu_0(2–0)$	5667.96	$\omega_e x_e$	52.05

The subscripts 0, 1, 2, 3 refer to constants for the states with $v = 0, 1, 2, 3$.

Problem 16.15-2. Calculate the wave number corresponding to the transition $v = 0, J = 9 \rightarrow v = 3, J = 10$ in the ground state of HCl^{35}, for which $\Lambda = 0$.

Problem 16.15-3. How many levels are there with the same energy as the upper state in the last problem?

Problem 16.15-4. (a) Show that for the pair of molecules HCl^{35}–HCl^{37}, the value of ρ is 0.99924.

(b) Calculate the difference in vibrational energy (in cm^{-1}) between HCl^{35} and HCl^{37} in the $v = 0$ and $v = 3$ states, and from this obtain the difference in ν_0 (3–0).

(c) Calculate B_3 and B_0 for HCl^{37}; from these calculate the change in rotational energy which accompanies the transition $v = 0, J = 9 \rightarrow v = 3, J = 10$ for HCl^{37}. Assume D_e and β to be the same as for HCl^{35}. Compare with the value obtained for HCl^{35} in Problem 16.15–2.

16.15.2 Oxygen

In Section 16.11 the electronic configuration of the ground state of oxygen was stated to be ${}^3\Sigma_g^-$; the orbital quantum number Λ is zero, and spin quantum number S is unity. The angular momentum due to the electron spin and that due to the nuclei (quantum number K) may be compounded in three ways. S may be at right angles to K, so that the component of S in the direction of the nuclear angular momentum is zero; the two may be parallel, in which case K and S are additive; or they may be antiparallel, in which case S subtracts unity from K. The quantum number J is the vector sum of K and S, and it determines the total angular momentum. In this way three distinct energy levels are produced for a given value of K. These levels have J values of $K + 1$, K, and $K - 1$. This vector specified by J has $2J + 1$ orientations with respect to an arbitrary field, so that $2J + 1$ levels of the same energy correspond to each value of J. The set of energy levels with $J = K + 1$ are called the F_1 levels, and those with $J = K$ and $K - 1$ are called the

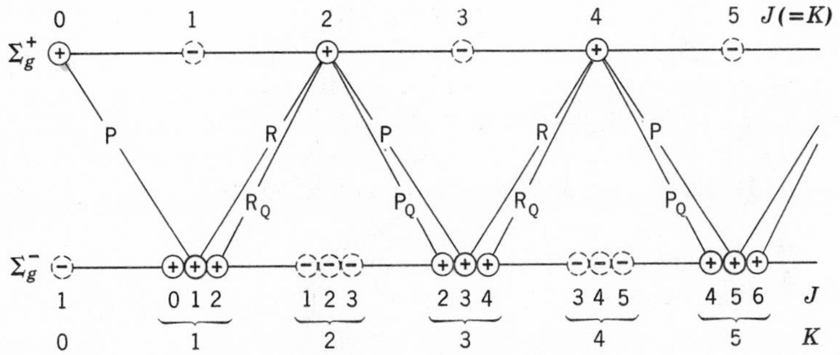

Fig. 16.15-3. Branches of band $^3\Sigma_g^- - {}^1\Sigma_g^+$.[7]

For the sake of clarity, transitions between antisymmetric levels (broken circles) have been omitted. They are absent in the only known examples of each of these (O_2) because of zero nuclear spin. Note that the lines $J = 0 \rightarrow J = 0$ are missing on account of the selection rule's restriction.

(From G. Herzberg, *Molecular Spectra and Molecular Structure*, Vol. I, "Spectra of Diatomic Molecules," 2nd ed. Copyright 1950, D. Van Nostrand Company, Inc.)

F_2 and F_3 levels respectively. The energy of these levels is determined primarily by the value of K. The F_1 and F_3 levels lie close together on the low energy side of the F_2 levels. From the considerations of Section 16.14, the allowed levels and the symmetry are simply deduced. Because the oxygen isotope of mass 16 has even mass number, the total wave function must be symmetric in the nuclei. Since the oxygen atom has no nuclear spin, the symmetry is determined entirely by the rotational states of the nuclei; for $^3\Sigma_g^-$ states, the rotational states with odd values of K are symmetric. Thus only the levels with odd K values are allowed. In the lower line of Fig. 16.15-3[7] the rotational levels of a $^3\Sigma_g^-$ state are denoted by circles and arranged in order of their J values (given on the first row). The J values are bracketed to relate them to the value of K from which they arise (given on the second row). The dotted circles denote levels excluded because of symmetry.

The rotational energy of the F_2 levels[12] can be represented by a formula of the type of equation (16.12–10). The equation for the rotational energy of the zero vibrational level ($v = 0$) of the $^3\Sigma_g^-$ state of the O^{16} isotope, in cm^{-1}, is

$$F(J) = 1.438J(J + 1) - 6.31 \times 10^{-6}J^2(J + 1)^2. \qquad (16.15\text{–}2)$$

The experimental values of the energies on which this equation is based were derived from observations of the "atmospheric bands" of oxygen, which are due to a $^3\Sigma_g^- - {}^1\Sigma_g^+$ electronic transition; the particular band used was for the $v = 0 \rightarrow v = 0$ transition. The rotational levels of the upper electronic state are shown in the upper line of Fig. 16.15–3. The equation for the rotational energy of the $^1\Sigma_g^+$ levels (for $v = 0$), in cm^{-1}, is

$$F(J) = F(0) + 1.392J(J + 1) - 5.75 \times 10^{-6}J^2(J + 1)^2. \quad (16.15\text{–}3)$$

Some of the (magnetic dipole) transitions between these two levels are shown by lines marked P, P_Q, R, and R_Q. The lines marked P and P_Q

Table 16.15–3

Energy Differences for Oxygen $^3\Sigma_g^-$ State

$J(= K)$ for F_2 level	$F_2(J) - F_3(J - 1)$	$F_2(J) - F_1(J + 1)$
1	—	1.88
3	2.09	1.94
5	2.01	1.99
7	1.94	2.01
9	1.92	2.07
11	1.90	2.09
13	1.88	2.15
15	1.86	2.31
17	1.87	2.29
19	1.86	2.13
21	1.82	2.13
23	1.81	2.19
25	1.80	2.19
27	1.77	2.21

form two closely spaced P branches, and the lines marked R and R_Q form two closely spaced R branches. This nomenclature is due to

[12] G. H. Deeke and H. D. Babcock, *Proc. Natl. Acad. Sci., U.S.*, **13**, 670 (1927).

Mulliken.[13] If J represents the quantum numbers of the $^1\Sigma_g^+$ state, then it is evident from Fig. 16.15–3 that

$$R_Q(J) - R(J) = F_2(J-1) - F_1(J) \tag{16.15–4}$$

and

$$P(J) - P_Q(J) = F_3(J) - F_2(J+1). \tag{16.15–5}$$

The differences between the F_2 level and the others can be obtained from these relationships. These are tabulated in Table 16.15–3.

Problem 16.15-5. Calculate the wave numbers of the following lines for the $v = 0$ to $v = 0$ transition of $O^{16}-O^{16}$:

$$R(2),\ R_Q(2),\ P_Q(2),\ P(2),\ R(4),\ R_Q(4),$$

where the number in parentheses represents the value of J for the $^1\Sigma_g^+$ level. The wave number estimated for the P(0) line is 13,118.04 cm^{-1}.

Problem 16.15-6. Calculate the wave numbers of the lines as in Problem 16.15-5 for the $O^{18}O^{18}$ molecule. The value of ω for the $O^{16}O^{16}$ molecules is 1580 cm^{-1} in the $^3\Sigma_g^-$ state and 1433 in the $^1\Sigma_g^+$ state. (*Hint:* calculate B_0 and ω for each state for $O^{18}O^{18}$. Assume that other constants are the same in both of the isotopic molecules.)

16.16 Raman Spectra

The Raman spectrum is useful with transitions which produce no light absorption or emission. When light is scattered by the molecule, the quantum of scattered light may retain its original energy, or have its energy change by an amount ΔE. The change in energy corresponds to energy lost or gained by the molecule in transitions such as those which give rise to the absorption or emission of light. If ν_i is the frequency of the incident light, and the energy lost or gained due to molecular transitions is $h\nu$, the energy of the scattered light of frequency ν_s, is given by

$$h\nu_s = h\nu_i \pm h\nu, \tag{16.16–1}$$

so that

$$\nu_s = \nu_i \pm \nu. \tag{16.16–1a}$$

The scattered light of frequency ν_s forms a spectrum known as the *Raman spectrum.* If the frequency ν_s is higher than that of the incident light, the lines or the band is referred to as *anti-stokes*; if lower, they are referred to as *stokes.* The bands are, of course, similar in structure to the absorption or emission bands.

When the light beam interacts with the molecule, the oscillating electric vector of the light beam induces in the molecule an electric moment proportional to the light intensity.

$$P_F = \alpha_F F, \tag{16.16–2}$$

[13] R. S. Mulliken, *Phys. Rev.*, **32**, 880 (1928).

where P_F is the induced moment in the direction of the electric intensity F and α_F is the polarizability of the molecule in the direction of the field. The polarizability depends on the direction of the field and on the phase of the molecular vibration with which the light interacts. Light scattered at right angles without change of frequency is completely polarized. Light scattered with frequency $\nu_i \pm \nu$ ordinarily has a different degree of polarization, the extent of which depends on the particular vibration. Thus the polarization is an important clue to the nature of the vibration causing the displacement in frequency.

For a displacement in the frequency of the scattered light (i.e., for a Raman line to be observed), the polarizability α_F must change during the vibration of the molecule. This is in contrast to the requirement for vibrational absorption or emission spectrum whereby the electric moment must change during vibration. Often the first condition is fulfilled when the second is not; as a result the Raman spectra yield values of the molecular energy levels in the cases where the necessary absorption spectra are lacking. (Note that the selection rules are different for the Raman spectra; see Section 16.14).

16.17 Approximate Calculation of Rotational and Vibrational Energies for a Diatomic Molecule

If a diatomic molecule AB is considered only in its ground electronic state, and if in addition the interaction between rotation and vibration is neglected, the equations for the energy levels can be greatly simplified. All terms except the first term of equation (16.12–3) can be discarded; the quadratic and higher terms of equation (16.12–10) can also be neglected. Thus the energy E and the term value $\mathbf{T}$ can be written

$$E = hc\omega(v + \tfrac{1}{2}) + hcBJ(J + 1) + hc(\mathrm{A} - \mathrm{B})\Lambda^2 \qquad (16.17\text{–}1)$$

and

$$\mathbf{T} = \omega(v + \tfrac{1}{2}) + BJ(J + 1) + (\mathrm{A} - \mathrm{B})\Lambda^2, \qquad (16.17\text{–}2)$$

with

$$\omega = \frac{1}{2\pi c}\sqrt{\frac{\mathrm{k}}{\mu}}, \qquad (16.17\text{–}3)$$

$$B = \frac{h}{8\pi^2 cI}, \qquad (16.17\text{–}4)$$

and

$$I = \mu r^2. \qquad (16.17\text{–}5)$$

μ is the reduced mass (equal to $\mathrm{m_A m_B}/(\mathrm{m_A} + \mathrm{m_B})$) of A and B, r is the equilibrium distance between A and B, and k is the force constant when

AB forms a harmonic oscillator of frequency ωc. The last term in equations (16.17–1) and (16.17–2) is retained even though electronic energies are neglected, for reasons which will develop later; however, in most cases it may be omitted for diatomic molecules. If k and r are known, an approximate calculation of the energy levels may be made.

Problem 16.17-1. The values of k and r for hydrogen chloride are 4.81×10^5 dyne cm^{-1} and 1.29×10^{-8} cm, respectively. (a) Calculate the energy of the level $J = 2$ and $v = 1$, in cm^{-1}. (b) Calculate the energy in cm^{-1} for the transition $J = 1$, $v = 0$ to $J = 2$, $v = 1$, and compare with the frequency of the absorption given for the transition in Table 16.15–1.

Problem 16.17-2. For CO, k is 1.90×10^6 dyne cm^{-1}, and r is 1.128 Å. Calculate the wave numbers of the first five lines in the infrared spectrum on either side of the $J = 0$, $J = 0$ transition for the vibrational transition $v = 0$ to $v = 3$. What lines will appear in the Raman spectrum? Will the $J = 0$ to $J = 0$ transition appear in either?

Problem 16.17-3. The values of r and k for hydrogen are 0.741 Å and 5.79×10^5 dyne cm^{-1}. Calculate the energies for the first five rotational levels of hydrogen in the vibrational state with $v = 3$, and discuss the possibility of obtaining a Raman spectrum for transitions to each of these levels from the level $J = 0$, $v = 0$.

16.18 Spectra of Carbon Dioxide

A relatively simple example of the spectra of polyatomic molecules is provided by carbon dioxide, whose spectrum will be used as a starting point for the discussion of the energy levels of polyatomic molecules. First of all, carbon dioxide has a spectrum in the ultraviolet due to its electronic levels. These electronic levels are exceedingly complicated; they will not be considered here, since under the conditions ordinarily encountered in chemical equilibria the contributions of higher electronic states are negligible.

The absorption of light due to changes in rotational and vibrational energy will be discussed below. Such absorption occurs in the infrared and produces two main bands with lines closely spaced. Whereas for the diatomic molecule there is one mode of vibration, namely, that between the pair of atoms, in this case there are three modes of vibration. The absorption bands are due to two of them. Interpretation of the bands according to theory discussed later leads to the conclusion that carbon dioxide is a symmetrical linear molecule with the carbon lying equidistant (at 1.16 Å) from the two oxygens on a line joining them. As such, the molecule has only two truly rotational degrees of freedom. The total energies (including the vibrational energy) are given approximately by (16.17–1); certain values of J are excluded owing to absence of nuclear spin for oxygen and the symmetry requirements. Instead of a single vibrational term in (16.17–1), there is one such term for each of the three vibrational modes.

Because the moment of inertia is large the value of B is small, so the spacing of the rotational levels is only 3.15 cm^{-1}.

Figure 16.18–1[14] shows the trace of infrared light intensities for the 2350-cm^{-1} (4.3-μ) band of gaseous carbon dioxide under high resolution. This band is known as a *parallel* band, for reasons given later. Figure 16.18–2 is a similar trace for the 668-cm^{-1}(15.0-μ) band, which is known

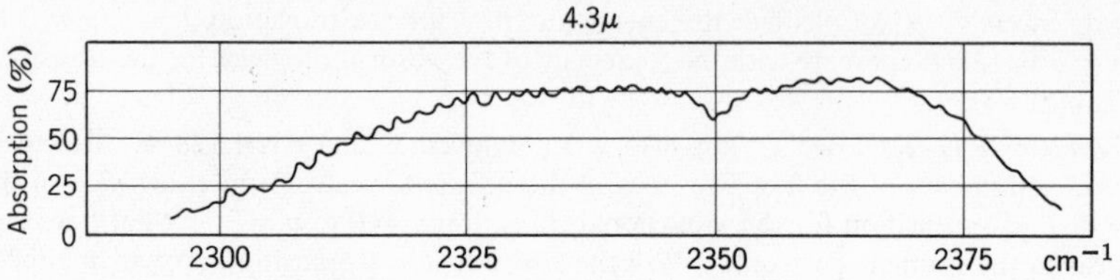

Fig. 16.18–1. 4.3-μ band of CO_2.[14]

(From G. Herzberg, *Molecular Spectra and Molecular Structure*, Vol. II, "Infrared and Raman Spectra of Polyatomic Molecules," 2nd ed. Copyright 1950, D. Van Nostrand Company, Inc.)

as a *perpendicular* band. The latter band has P, Q, and R branches; the former lacks a Q branch and consequently has a simpler and better-defined rotational structure. The value of B required for equation (16.17–1) turns out to be essentially the same for each band. Both bands

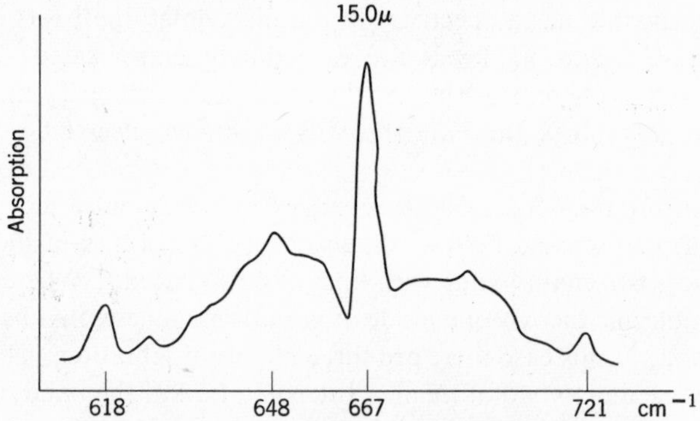

Fig. 16.18–2. 15.0-μ band of CO_2.[14]

(G. Herzberg, *Molecular Spectra and Molecular Structure*, Vol. II, "Infrared and Raman Spectra of Polyatomic Molecules," 2nd ed. Copyright 1950, D. Van Nostrand Company, Inc.)

are for $v = 0 \rightarrow v = 1$ vibrational transitions; for the parallel band ω

[14] G. Herzberg, *Infra-Red and Raman Spectra of Polyatomic Molecules*, 2nd ed., Van Nostrand, Princeton, N.J., 1950.

in equation (16.17–1) is 2350 cm^{-1}, and for the perpendicular band ω is 668 cm^{-1}.

The modes of motion of the atoms responsible for the vibrational energy of the parallel and perpendicular bands are shown in Fig. 16.18–3. Carbon dioxide has three atoms and hence nine degrees of freedom (three for each atom). Three degrees of freedom are due to translation, and two to rotation, leaving four for vibration. There are thus four modes of vibration as shown in Fig. 16.18–3. ν_3 denotes one of the modes and is the symbol used for its *fundamental* frequency. This mode is responsible for the 2350-cm^{-1} band. The modes responsible for the 668-cm^{-1} band are labeled ν_{2a} and ν_{2b} in Fig. 16.18–3. This mode is produced by two

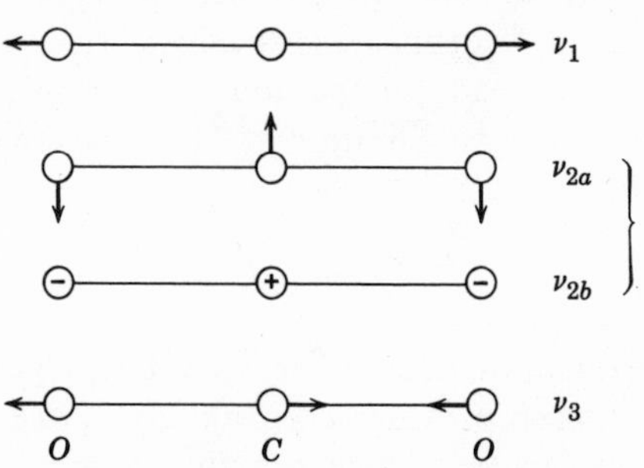

Fig. 16.18–3. Normal modes of vibration of CO_2.

degrees of freedom, one in the plane of the paper and the other at right angles. The fourth vibrational degree of freedom of carbon dioxide is labeled ν_1 in Fig. 16.18–3; it is not active in the infrared, in accord with selection rules to be discussed later. The ν_1 mode gives a band in the Raman spectrum; this is associated with a $v = 0 \rightarrow v = 1$ transition, with ω equal to 1351 cm^{-1}. In the *parallel* band associated with ν_3, $\Delta J = 0$ is forbidden, so that the Q branch is absent. Moreover, only even values of J are allowed in the lower level, while only odd values are allowed in the upper level; thus alternate lines are missing. For the *perpendicular* band associated with ν_{2a} and ν_{2b}, $\Delta J = 0$ is allowed and a Q branch is present. It is the Q branch which gives the high central peak in the trace shown as Figure 16.18–2. The appearance of a Q branch rather than a single line is due to the variation of B with the vibrational quantum number v (cf. Section 16.13 and equation 16.12–10).

The linear symmetrical structure of carbon dioxide was established by analysis of the rotational structure of the parallel and perpendicular bands, taking into account the fact that there is no infrared band due to the mode ν_1. A fuller understanding of the rotational structure of these bands requires further discussion of the origin and nature of the vibrational modes.

16.19 Vibrational Modes of Carbon Dioxide. General Theory of Vibration of a Polyatomic Molecule

The vibration frequencies of carbon dioxide can be calculated by solution of the equations of motion for the three atoms. In making the calculation it is necessary to specify the forces against which the atoms move. The details of such a calculation are given in Appendix 6. For simplicity, the motions are assumed to be harmonic; that is, the restoring forces are directly proportional to the displacements. The calculation of the fundamental vibration frequencies is a classical problem. Application of quantum mechanics leads to the additional result that only specific energies are allowed for each vibration in the harmonic oscillator approximation. For each:

$$E_i = (v_i + \tfrac{1}{2})h\nu_i\,. \qquad (16.19\text{–}1)$$

For carbon dioxide, solution of the mechanical problem yields three distinct frequencies, each of which corresponds to one or more modes of vibration of the molecule. These are the *normal modes of vibration* described in the previous section and portrayed in Fig. 16.18–3. The symmetrical "stretching" vibration ν_1 and the asymmetric "stretching" vibration ν_3 have distinctly different frequencies. The "bending" modes ν_{2a} and ν_{2b}, perpendicular to each other, have the same frequency; this frequency is said to be *doubly degenerate.*

In a normal mode of vibration, each of the atoms oscillates about its equilibrium position with the frequency of the normal mode. The amplitudes of the oscillations of the various atoms will depend on the value of v, but they must bear definite ratios to each other, characteristic of the mode of vibration. The *normal coordinate* ξ for a mode gives the simultaneous change in the coordinates of each atom for the particular mode.

Similar calculations can be made for other molecules, provided that the necessary molecular dimensions and force constants are known. The results for benzene are shown in Appendix 6. The calculations for complex molecules are quite involved, and frequently the necessary data are not available. Fortunately the frequencies may also be deduced from observed spectra, just as for diatomic molecules. The symmetry properties of the vibrations and of the allowed transitions are essential to the treatment; these are discussed in the next section.

16.20 Symmetry of Normal Vibrations

From a generalization of the results of Section 16.14 it follows that the allowed total wave functions of a molecule must be *symmetric* or *antisymmetric* with respect to exchange of like nuclei, depending on whether the mass number of the nuclei exchanged is even or odd. They may be *degenerate*, as is the case when two or more wave functions correspond to the same energy, e.g., for ν_{2a} and ν_{2b} of carbon dioxide.

The symmetry of the total wave functions depends on the electronic, vibrational, rotational, and nuclear spin wave functions. Thus, for a given electronic state, the allowed rotational levels depend on the symmetry of the vibrational wave function with respect to identical nuclei. In the diatomic molecule, the vibrational wave function is always symmetric, as shown in Section 16.14, but this is not true for polyatomic molecules. Thus the symmetry of the vibrational modes, as related to the symmetry of the molecule, is important in determining the allowed rotational levels. Moreover, since the selection rules depend on the symmetry of the entire wave function, these rules will depend, for polyatomic molecules, on the symmetry of the vibrational levels. If the electronic ground state is symmetric, the symmetry of the vibrational wave functions alone will determine the allowed rotational levels and the selection rules.

The vibrational levels of carbon dioxide just discussed constitute an example. For a diatomic molecule the vibrational wave function depended only on the absolute value of the distance between the nuclei and thus had to be symmetric for exchange of identical nuclei. For polyatomic molecules the symmetry of the vibrational wave function for a particular mode depends on the relative positions of all the atoms. If, in an operation whose only result is to exchange identical particles, the relative displacements of all the particles change sign (i.e., if the normal coordinate changes sign), the mode is said to be *antisymmetric* to the operation. If there is no such change of sign, the mode is said to be *symmetric*. In order to determine the change in sign of the vibrational wave function caused by interchange of identical particles, it is necessary to know how the vibrational wave function of a harmonic oscillator, involving the normal coordinate, changes sign with the normal coordinate ξ (i.e., how it changes sign with the relative displacements of the atoms). For even values of v in equation (16.19–1), the wave function ψ is an even function of ξ; for odd values of v it is an odd function. It thus follows that *for symmetric modes the vibrational wave function is symmetric for both even and odd values of* v, since the normal coordinate never changes sign on exchange of identical particles. For *antisymmetric* modes the levels with *odd* values of v are *antisymmetric*, and those with *even* values are *symmetric*, because for these modes the normal coordinate changes sign when identical nuclei are exchanged. Where the mode is *degenerate*, the situation is more complicated.

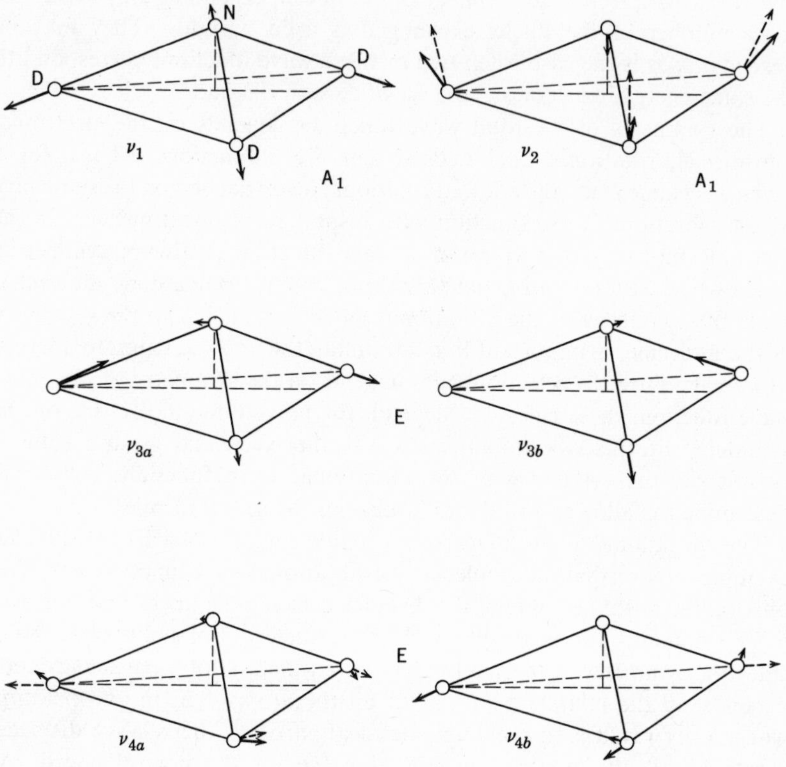

Fig. 16.20–1. Normal vibrations of the ND_3 molecule.[14]

The vibrations are drawn to scale for ND_3 in oblique projection. (For NH_3 the large mass ratio of N to H would not have allowed the displacement vectors of N to be drawn to the same scale as those of H.) Both components of the degenerate vibrations are shown. The broken-line arrows in ν_2 and ν_4 give the symmetry coordinates. In ν_{3b} there is a very small displacement (too small to show in the scale of the diagram) of the left D nucleus parallel to the line connecting the other two D nuclei. It should be noted that ν_{3a} and ν_{4a} are symmetric, ν_{3b} and ν_{4b} antisymmetric, with respect to the plane of symmetry through the left D nucleus, that is, the plane of the paper.

(From G. Herzberg, *Molecular Spectra and Molecular Structure*, Vol. II, "Infrared and Raman Spectra of Polyatomic Molecules," 2nd ed. Copyright 1950, D. Van Nostrand Company, Inc.)

Polyatomic molecules can be arranged into groups called *point groups* according to their symmetry. For example, ammonia has one threefold axis of symmetry (C_3); rotation about this axis by an angle of $2\pi/3$ produces interchange of the hydrogen atoms, a, b, and c; c for a, a for b, b for c. Such a rotation is called an *operation*. There are also three planes of symmetry (σ_v) containing this axis of symmetry and one of the hydrogen atoms; these planes make angles of $2\pi/3$ with respect to one another. Reflection in these planes interchanges two hydrogen atoms. In this case the *operation* is reflection. The axis and the planes are called *symmetry elements*. The point groups are defined in Appendix 6. Ammonia is said to belong to the point group C_{3v}. The subscript 3 denotes the threefold symmetry, and v denotes the vertical planes of symmetry containing the threefold axis.

The vibrations of the molecules of any point group can be arranged in *species* according to the symmetry of the corresponding normal coordinate with respect to the symmetry elements of the point group. For example, a molecule belonging to the point group C_{3v} has three species of vibration, namely, A_1, A_2, and E. The symbol E always indicates degenerate vibrations. Species A_1 is symmetric with respect to all elements of symmetry, and species A_2 is antisymmetric with respect to the planes, σ. The species A_1 and E are illustrated for ND_3 in Fig. 16.20–1.

The labeling of the frequencies as ν_1, ν_2, ν_{3a}, ν_{3b}, ν_{4a}, and ν_{4b} is quite arbitrary but standard. The first two belong to species A_1, and the two pairs ν_{3a}, ν_{3b} and ν_{4a}, ν_{4b} are each doubly degenerate and belong to species E. Appendix 6 contains tables (due to Kohlrausch) of the symmetry of species possible among the modes of vibration of each point group. These are also the symmetries of the vibrational levels with $v = 1$. On this basis a vibrational level is often assigned a symmetry species. The vibrational level with $v = 0$ for all modes has the same symmetry as the symmetric mode. The number of vibrational modes of each species depends on the number of groups of atoms which lie on each of the symmetry elements. Formulas for calculating the number of these vibrations are given in the tables of Appendix 6. The use of the tables is explained at the beginning of the Appendix 6; it will be discussed in connection with spectra below.

16.21 Splitting of Vibrational Levels due to Resonance

The foregoing discussion of vibrational energy levels has neglected entirely any effect due to force laws different from that giving harmonic oscillations (anharmonicity); such effects arise from a potential which contains, besides the single quadratic term in ξ, terms with higher powers of ξ and in the ξ's corresponding to other modes. It has therefore neglected the effect of a vibration in one normal mode on the vibrations with respect to another mode. We shall now give two important effects which result from interactions due to anharmonicity.

(a) *Multiple Minima Splitting.* A pyramidal molecule such as ammonia can become planar by motion of the central atom; if the central atom continues in the same direction, the molecule will turn inside out and finally become its mirror image. If the hydrogens have been replaced by different groups as in NHDF, the mirror image will be the optical isomer of the original. In this process the nitrogen atom passes through a position of maximum energy, namely, the position in the plane of the other atoms, and comes to rest in another position of minimum energy. In the position of maximum energy the force acting is zero. Thus the force cannot be proportional to the displacement from either one of the two equilibrium positions lying on either side of the plane. One can then consider two sets of modes of bending vibration, one with fundamental frequencies $\nu_1{}^{0a}$, $\nu_{2a}{}^{0a}$, $\nu_{2b}{}^{0a}$, and $\nu_3{}^{0a}$, the other with $\nu_1{}^{0b}$, $\nu_{2a}{}^{0b}$, and $\nu_3{}^{0b}$, where the superscripts a and b refer to the location of the nitrogen on either side of the plane. (*Note.* This nomenclature is entirely unrelated to that of Fig. 16.20–1.) The corresponding levels of each set would be identical if there were not wave mechanical resonance between the two sets. This resonance produces two sets of levels of slightly different energy; one set gives rise to frequencies $\nu_1{}^a$, $\nu_{2a}{}^a$, etc., and the other to frequencies $\nu_1{}^b$, $\nu_{2a}{}^b$, etc.; that is, the frequencies ν^0 have been split into frequencies ν^a and ν^b because of the two potential minima. The same argument follows for the stretching modes. If there are n potential minima, the frequencies are split into n slightly different frequencies. The smaller the energy difference between the maximum and minimum, the larger the splitting is. An example of such splitting is found in ammonia, where the levels are all double.

(b) *Fermi Resonance.* When two different vibrational levels of the same species have nearly the same energy and have the same symmetry, they perturb each other and produce two levels of energy different from the original pair. This is the general case of which the splitting discussed above is a special case. Each one of the new pair is a combination of the original two. For example, for carbon dioxide the first excited state of ν_1 has almost the same energy as the second excited state of ν_{2a}, ν_{2b}, and they both are of the species $\Sigma_g{}^+$. Thus the first excited level of ν_1 becomes split into two levels. The observed Raman line at 1285.5 cm^{-1} is not that due to a transition $v = 0 \rightarrow v = 1$ for the mode designated ν_1, but is one of a pair of lines due to transitions from $v = 0$ in the ground state to a pair of states; each of the upper states is a composite of the first excited level of ν_1 and the second excited level of ν_{2a} and ν_{2b}. The other line of the pair is at 1388.3 cm^{-1}.

16.22 Rotational Energy Levels of Polyatomic Molecules

In treating the rotational energy levels of a diatomic molecule (see Section 16.12) it was necessary to take into account an angular momentum, $\Lambda h/2\pi$, about the figure axis due to the component of electronic angular momentum in this direction.

In polyatomic molecules in the ground electronic states this angular momentum is almost always zero. Thus it would appear that the energy of a linear polyatomic molecule such as carbon dioxide can be given by an equation like (16.12–9) without inclusion of the term in Λ. This is the case for the modes of vibration ν_1 and ν_3. However, Λ must be *included* for the degenerate modes ν_{2a} and ν_{2b}, because of the resultant rotation of the molecule about the symmetry axis when there is simultaneous vibration in the modes ν_{2a} and ν_{2b}, in which the motions in the two modes are 90 degrees out of phase (see Section 16.18).

Non-linear polyatomic molecules can be divided into two well-defined types according to the nature of their moments of inertia. For one of these there are only two principal moments of inertia, and equation (16.12–9) can be used for the energy. Molecules of this type are called *symmetric top* molecules. (A special case arises if A is equal to B in equation (16.12–9). In this case the molecules are termed *spherical top* molecules.) The other type of molecule has three distinct moments of inertia and is referred to as the *asymmetric top* type; the formula (16.12–9) cannot be used for this type.

In general, a molecule has three *moments of inertia* and three *products of inertia*, which may be defined for any arbitrary set of perpendicular axes through the center of gravity. These are defined as follows:

$$I_{xx} = \Sigma \mathrm{m}_i(y_i^2 + z_i^2), \tag{16.22–1a}$$

$$I_{yy} = \Sigma \mathrm{m}_i(z_i^2 + x_i^2), \tag{16.22–1b}$$

$$I_{zz} = \Sigma \mathrm{m}_i(x_i^2 + y_i^2), \tag{16.22–1c}$$

$$I_{xy} = \Sigma \mathrm{m}_i x_i y_i = I_{yx}, \tag{16.22–1d}$$

$$I_{yz} = \Sigma \mathrm{m}_i y_i x_i = I_{zy}, \tag{16.22–1e}$$

$$I_{zx} = \Sigma \mathrm{m}_i z_i x_i = I_{xz}. \tag{16.22–1f}$$

In any molecule there is always a set of axes, corresponding to coordinates x_i', y_i', z_i', for which $I_{x'y'} = I_{y'z'} = I_{z'x'} = 0$. These are called the *principal axes of moment of inertia.* The moments of inertia $I_{x'x'}$, $I_{y'y'}$,

$I_{z'z'}$ are called the *principal moments* and usually designated I_A, I_B, and I_C (or simply A, B, and C). The product of these three is given by

$$\mathrm{ABC} = \begin{vmatrix} I_{xx} & -I_{xy} & -I_{xz} \\ -I_{yx} & I_{yy} & -I_{yz} \\ -I_{zx} & -I_{zy} & I_{zz} \end{vmatrix}. \tag{16.22–2}$$

The individual moments may be found by solving the equation

$$\begin{vmatrix} I_{xx} - \lambda & -I_{xy} & -I_{xz} \\ -I_{yx} & I_{yy} - \lambda & -I_{yz} \\ -I_{zx} & -I_{zy} & I_{zz} - \lambda \end{vmatrix} = 0, \tag{16.22–3}$$

whose three roots are respectively equal to A, B, and C.

The direction cosines α_A, β_A, and γ_A of the principal axis about which A is taken are obtained by simultaneous solution of the relations

$$\alpha_A(I_{xx} - \eta) - \beta_A I_{xy} - \gamma_A I_{xz} = 0, \tag{16.22–4a}$$

$$-\alpha_A I_{xy} + \beta_A(I_{yy} - \eta) - \gamma_A I_{yz} = 0, \tag{16.22–4b}$$

$$-\alpha_A I_{xz} - \beta_A I_{yz} + \gamma_A(I_{zz} - \eta) = 0, \tag{16.22–4c}$$

after substituting for η one of the values of λ from above. Thus the principal moments and the direction cosines of the principal axes are found simultaneously.

Problem 16.22-1. In the water molecule, the equilibrium O–H distance is 0.957 Å and the bond angle is 105°.

(a) Take a set of cartesian axes through the center of gravity, with the z axis the bisector of the H–O–H angle and the x axis in the plane of the molecule. Calculate the moments and products of inertia of the molecule with respect to these axes, and the product ABC.

(b) Show that the axes chosen were actually the principal axes of the molecule.

Problem 16.22-2. (a) Using the same bond distances and angles as in Problem 16.22–1, calculate the moments and products of inertia for HDO. Take the z axis parallel to the bisector of the H–O–D angle.

(b) Calculate the individual principal moments of HDO and the direction cosine of the angles they make with the axes originally chosen.

16.22.1 The Symmetric Top

If A and B are equal, any axis in the plane of the axis of A and B is a principal axis, and the moment about it is A. A molecule for which this is true is called a *symmetric top*. Oxygen and carbon dioxide are examples.

The constants B_e and A of (16.12–9) are given, in terms of these new symbols, by

$$B_e = \frac{h}{8\pi^2 c\mathrm{A}} \qquad (16.22\text{–}5a)$$

and

$$A = \frac{h}{8\pi^2 c\mathrm{C}}\,. \qquad (16.22\text{–}6b)$$

With this nomenclature, the energy levels of symmetric top molecules are

$$E_{J,K} = \frac{h^2}{8\pi^2}\left[\frac{J(J+1)}{\mathrm{A}} + K^2\left(\frac{1}{\mathrm{C}} - \frac{1}{\mathrm{A}}\right)\right]. \qquad (16.22\text{–}7)$$

Here K can have the values 0, ± 1, ± 2, ± 3. It has replaced Λ in equation (16.12–9). *K is not to be confused with the K used in the discussion of the spectrum of oxygen. There it was used for the rotational quantum number that combined with S to yield J (equal to $K + S$).* In equation (16.22–7), J cannot be less than $|K|$ and therefore can have the values $|K|$, $|K+1|$, $|K+2|$, etc. The total angular momentum is $J(J+1)(h/2\pi)$, while that about the figure axis is $K(h/2\pi)$. C is the moment of inertia about the figure axis, and A is that perpendicular to it. Ammonia is an example of a symmetric top.

Problem 16.22-3. (a) Taking the NH distance as 1.014 Å and the HNH angle as 106°47′ for ammonia, show that the products of inertia are all zero and that two of the moments are equal if the symmetry axis is taken as one of the axes for the moments of inertia.

(b) Calculate A and C.

(c) Calculate the energies of the rotational level with $J = 1$, $K = 0$, and that with $J = 2$, $K = 1$.

It is best to retain equation (16.12–10) (which applies to diatomic molecules) for the energy levels of linear polyatomic molecules. When applied to linear polyatomic molecules, the value of A in equation (16.12–10) is not, as a rule, due to electronic angular momentum; neither is it due to a moment of inertia such as C above; instead it is due to a moment characteristic of the vibrational mode, as was seen in Section 16.19.

The symmetric top has three rotational degrees of freedom. Only two of these, involving axes at right angles, contribute to the rotational energy, namely, one involving the moment C and the other the moment A. The third degree of freedom determines the orientation of these mutually perpendicular axes in space. They can be oriented with respect to an arbitrary direction in such a way that the total angular momentum in the chosen arbitrary direction has the values $\pm Jh/2\pi$, $\pm(J-1)h/2\pi \pm (J-2)h/2\pi \pm \cdots \pm 2h/2\pi$, $+h/2\pi$, and zero. There are thus $2J + 1$

possible orientations of the vector $\sqrt{J(J+1)}h/2\pi$), each of which is a distinct energy level but all have the same value of the energy.

16.22.2 The Spherical Top

If A, B, and C are all equal, the last term in equation (16.22–7) becomes zero. Thus the energy depends only on the quantum number J. A given value of J can occur with several values of K, since J has values of K, $K+1$, $K+2$, etc.; moreover, as with Λ-type doubling of electronic states (see Section 16.14), there are two states for each non-zero value of K. A given value of J can occur for all values of K from zero up to the value of J itself. There are thus $2J+1$ states of equal energy corresponding to the different possible values of K. This is true for *each* of the $2J+1$ orientations of the spherical top which had the same energy. Thus there are $(2J+1)^2$ energy levels all with the same energy. If variation of moment with rotation and vibration is neglected, this energy is given by

$$E = J(J+1)\frac{h^2}{8\pi^2 A}\cdot \tag{16.22–8}$$

Problem 16.22-4. Methane is an example of a spherical top. The C–H distance is 1.09 Å, and the H–C–H angles are all 109° 28′. Calculate the moment of inertia of methane.

16.22.3 The Asymmetric Top

For the asymmetric top A, B, and C are different. When variation of these moments of inertia with rotation and vibration is neglected, the energy levels of the asymmetric top are given by

$$E = \frac{h^2}{8\pi^2}\left[\left(\frac{1}{2A}+\frac{1}{2B}\right)J(J+1)+\left(\frac{1}{C}-\frac{1}{2A}-\frac{1}{2B}\right)W_\tau\right], \tag{16.22–9}$$

where W_τ is a complicated function of A, B, and C with $2J+1$ values. Formulas for W_τ are given by Herzberg,[15] in terms of a slightly different labeling of the moments of inertia. All orientations of the top have different energies. Thus the $2J+1$ levels of equal energy for the symmetric top become distinct.

Problem 16.22-5. (a) Show that equation (16.22–9) reduces to the equation for the symmetric top when the two equal moments are A and B.

(b) Deduce zeroth-order approximate values of W_τ for the case where A is approximately equal to B.

[15] G. Herzberg, *Infra-Red and Raman Spectra, op. cit.*, p. 46.

(c) How many almost equal values of W_τ are possible for any chosen A and B? What happens to these values of W_τ as A → B?

Problem 16.22-6. The water molecule, considered in Problem 16.22–1, is an example of a planar asymmetric top. Ethanol is also an asymmetric top. The bond distances for ethanol are: C–H, 1.09 Å; C–C, 1.54 Å; C–O, 1.42 Å; O–H, 0.95 Å. Assume all H–C–H and H–C–C angles to be 109° 28′ and that the C–O–H angle is 110°. Calculate the product (ABC) of the principal moments of inertia for the configuration of ethanol in which the carbons, the oxygen, and two hydrogens are in the same plane and the hydroxyl hydrogen is as far as possible from the methyl group. (*Hint.* Take the plane as the xz plane, with the x axis parallel to the bisector of the C–C–O angle.)

16.23 Allowed Rotational Levels

The restrictions on allowed values of J are important because of the effect they have on thermodynamic properties (to be discussed later). The construction of general rules for choice of allowed values is extremely difficult, but the discussion of two examples will illustrate a rule which allows the number of excluded rotational levels to be calculated for a molecule of any given symmetry class. In carbon dioxide, only the oxygen atoms are affected by rotation. As was seen in connection with the oxygen molecule (Section 16.15), the oxygen atom has an even number of particles in the nucleus and a nuclear spin of zero, so that the total wave function must be symmetric in the nuclei. Even-numbered rotational levels are symmetric, and odd-numbered levels are antisymmetric; thus totally symmetric vibrational levels will require even rotational levels, and antisymmetric vibrational levels will require odd rotational levels. The normal coordinate of the mode, ν_3, (see Fig. 16.18–3) is antisymmetric, but the wave function does not change sign on reflection in any of the planes through the symmetry (figure) axis. Its even vibrational states are analog us to the Σ_u^+ electronic states of oxygen, while the odd vibrational states are analogous to the Σ_u^- electronic states. Thus the former contain only odd rotational levels, while the latter contain only even rotational levels. The mode ν_1 is symmetric and also does not change sign on reflection in one of the planes through the symmetry axis. Thus the even vibrational levels are analogous to Σ_g^+ electronic states, while the odd vibrational levels are analogous to Σ_g^- electronic states. The former allow only the even rotational levels, and the latter only the odd rotational levels. The mode ν_{2a} and ν_{2b} has vibrational levels analogous to the Π, Δ, etc., levels of oxygen. For these l (analogous to Λ for oxygen) has respectively the values ± 1, ± 2, etc. It is thus seen that, in any vibrational level, half the rotational states are excluded.

The allowed rotational levels of ammonia are also determined by the symmetry class of the vibrational level. There are the species A and the doubly degenerate species E. The sets of rotational levels allowed are those which, together with the vibrational wave function, produce a wave function of the proper symmetry in the nuclei. Therefore the species of rotational level must be such that the total wave function has the symmetry A. Thus it turns out that one third of the rotational levels are allowed for any given vibrational symmetry species.

Problem 16.23-1. Why must the total wave function of ammonia have the symmetry A in the protons?

The detailed sorting of the allowed levels is complicated and is unnecessary for our purposes, as will be seen in Section 20–3. Fortunately it can be shown that the allowed levels constitute a fraction $1/\sigma$ of the total, where σ is the number of distinct exchanges of numbered identical atoms which can be brought about by rotation with respect to the symmetry axes.

Problem 16.23-2. Determine the value of σ for methane and for benzene.

16.24 Assignment of Spectroscopic Lines

Infrared and Raman Spectra ordinarily contain not only the lines (bands) corresponding to fundamental vibration frequencies but also lines (bands) due to combinations or to harmonics of these fundamental frequencies. The selection rules given in Appendix 6 make possible the assignment of the observed lines to modes of vibration. The

Table 16.24-1

Infrared and Raman Spectra of *Trans*-Dichloroethylene

Infrared (gas) (cm^{-1})	Raman (liquid) (cm^{-1})
620 (m.)	349 p (s.)
820 (s.)	758 p (m.)
917 (s.)	844 p (s.)
1200 (s.)	1270 p (s.)
3089 (s.)	1576 p (s.)
	1626 p (v.w.)
	1692 p (w.)
	3071 p (s.)
	3142 dp? (w.)

(s.) = strong; (m.) = medium; (w.) = weak; (v.w.) = very weak; p = polarized; dp = depolarized.

fundamental frequencies required for thermodynamic calculations may then be evaluated from the spectroscopic observations. The spectra of *trans*-dichloroethylene ($C_2H_2Cl_2$) will be considered as an example.

The observed frequencies are given in Table 16.24–1. The symbols used are explained below the table.

trans-Dichloroethylene belongs to point group C_{2h}. By use of Table A6.8–5 of Appendix 6 it is seen that there are five fundamental frequencies of species A_g, two of species A_u, one of species B_g, and four of species B_u. Only the vibrations of species A_g and B_g are Raman active, with the former polarized and the latter depolarized. Similarly, only A_u and B_u are infrared active; the former give rise to parallel bands, and the latter to perpendicular bands. In the absence of information about band structure, it can be assumed that the perpendicular bands will be more intense.

The five strong polarized Raman lines at 3071, 1576, 1270, 844, and 349 cm^{-1} may be assigned immediately as fundamental modes of species A_g; they are designated ν_1, ν_2, ν_3, ν_4, and ν_5 respectively. The four strong infrared lines at 3089, 1200, 917, and 820 may be assigned to species B_u; they are designated ν_9, ν_{10}, ν_{11}, and ν_{12}. The remaining infrared band at 620 cm^{-1} is then one of the A_u fundamentals (ν_6). The Raman line of moderate intensity at 758 cm^{-1} is probably the fundamental mode of species B_g (ν_8), even though it appears to be polarized. The second fundamental of species A_u is missing; it probably lies below 600 cm^{-1}.

In order to explain the Raman lines at 1626, 1692, and 3142, it is necessary to consider the symmetry of combination frequencies and harmonics. The first harmonics of all species (see Appendix 6) will have the symmetry of A_g and will produce polarized lines in the Raman spectra, as will combination of any two members of a given species; no combinations between vibrations of different species will have A_g symmetry. Frequencies near 1600 cm^{-1} will be provided by $2\nu_4$ (1688), $2\nu_{12}$ (1640), $\nu_3 + \nu_5$ (1619); the actual assignment is $2\nu_{12}$ for the line at 1626 cm^{-1}, and $\nu_3 + \nu_5$ for the line at 1692 cm^{-1}. The weak line at 3142 cm^{-1} is probably $2\nu_2$. The frequency ν_7 cannot be obtained with any certainty from these data.

For complex molecules it is seldom feasible to solve the mathematical problem involved in getting the actual normal vibrations associated with the fundamental frequencies. Frequently an approximate set of vibrations may be deduced by analogy with simpler molecules with due regard to the symmetry requirements. A set of possible normal coordinates for *trans*-dichloroethylene is given by Herzberg.[16]

In most cases it is possible to ascribe some of the frequencies to specific types of motion of the molecule. For example, the two frequencies near 3000 cm^{-1} (ν_1 and ν_9) involve primarily stretching of the C—H bond; they are known as "C—H stretching frequencies." The frequency at 1576 cm^{-1} (ν_2) is a "C=C stretching frequency"; ν_4 and ν_{12} (near

[16] G. Herzberg, *Infra-Red and Raman Spectra*, *op. cit.*, p. 331.

900 cm^{-1}) are "C—Cl stretching frequencies." The frequencies near 1200 cm^{-1} (ν_3 and ν_{10}) involve mainly bending of the H—C—Cl bonds. The remaining frequencies involve more complicated motions, such as bending of the entire molecule. The simple frequencies vary little from molecule to molecule and are thus an aid to the assignment. For example, in CH_3Cl the C—H stretching frequencies are 2966 and 3042 cm^{-1} (two-fold); and the C—Cl stretching frequency is 732 cm^{-1}.

The assignment of overtone and combination frequencies for degenerate modes is complicated. The necessary methods are summarized by Herzberg.[17] The similarities of the frequencies for various molecules is often an aid in the assignment; in addition, the study of isotopic molecules frequently provides keys to the type of vibrations.

Problem 16.24-1. The infrared spectrum of water vapor contains the following bands below 9000 cm^{-1}: 1595.0 (v.s.), 3151 (m.), 3652 (s.), 3756 (v.s.), 5332 (m.), 6874 (w.), 7552 (m.), 8807 (s.). The first three of these appear to be "parallel" bands, and the remainder to be "perpendicular" bands. There is a strong Raman line at 3654 cm^{-1}.

(a) Assign the water molecule to a point group, and obtain the number of fundamental modes of each species.

(b) Determine which are the fundamental frequencies, in the set above, and assign the others as combination frequencies or overtones. Note that, owing to anharmonicity, a combination frequency will frequently be somewhat smaller than the sum of the two (or more) fundamentals from which it arises.

Problem 16.24-2. The infrared spectrum of gaseous *cis*-dichloroethylene contains strong bands at 570, 694, 857, 1303, 1591, and 3086 cm^{-1}. The Raman spectrum of the liquid contains the following lines: 173 (p,s.), 406 (dp,s.), 563 (dp,m.) 711 (p,s.), 807 (v.w.), 876 (dp,w.), 1179 (p,s.), 1587 (p,s.), 1689 (dp?,w.), 3077 (p,v.s.), 3160 (dp) cm^{-1}. Obtain the fundamental frequencies in each of the possible species, and explain the sources of the additional lines. Note that the Raman lines occur a few cm^{-1} below the corresponding infrared lines. (*Hint.* The vibration of species B corresponds to an out-of-plane motion, and it should occur at a lower frequency than the other modes of species B; also, the Raman line at 1689 cm^{-1} should appear polarized.)

Problem 16.24-3. Discuss the frequency ν_7 of *trans*-dichlorethylene and the possibility of getting it from the infra-red line at 620 cm^{-1}.

16.25 Energy Levels of Internal Rotational Modes

Consider, as a simple example, the hindered rotation of one of the methyl groups relative to the other in ethane,[18–20] and suppose that the hindrance to rotation is caused by a repulsive force between hydrogen atoms, although this supposition is not essential to the argument. As one group performs a single complete revolution with respect to the other,

[17] G. Herzberg, *Infra-Red and Raman Spectra*, *op. cit.*, Chapter II.

[18] E. Teller and B. Topley, *J. Chem. Soc.*, **885** (1935).

[19] L. Pauling, *Phys. Rev.*, **36**, 430 (1930).

[20] H. Nielsen, *Phys. Rev.*, **40**, 445 (1932).

there will be three equally spaced maxima in the potential energy and three equally spaced minima, one midway between each pair of maxima. A potential function fulfilling these conditions is

$$V = \tfrac{1}{2}V_0(1 - \cos 3\phi). \tag{16.25–1}$$

This function is sinusoidal with minima at $\phi = 0$, $0 = 2\pi/3$, $\phi = 4\pi/3$ and maxima at $\phi = \pi/3$, $\phi = \pi$, $\phi = 5\pi/3$. Because of the simplicity of this type of function and lack of any further specific knowledge, we choose it for further calculation. In the general case of n equal minima this function becomes

$$V = \tfrac{1}{2}V_0(1 - \cos n\phi). \tag{16.25–2}$$

The wave equation for a rotor with such a potential function will yield the necessary energy levels for the hindered rotor; this equation is

$$\frac{\partial^2\psi(\phi)}{\partial\phi^2} + \frac{8\pi^2 I_{\text{red}}}{h^2}[E_r - \tfrac{1}{2}V_0(1 - \cos n\phi)]\,\psi = 0, \tag{16.25–3}$$

where I_{red} is the "reduced moment of inertia" of the two groups, discussed below. Substituting $2x/n$ for ϕ, placing $M(x) = \psi(\phi)$ and $\theta = 8\pi^2 I_{\text{red}} V_0/n^2h^2$ with

$$a_r = \frac{32\pi^2 I_{\text{red}}}{n^2h^2}(E_r - \tfrac{1}{2}V_0), \tag{16.25–4}$$

we obtain

$$\frac{\partial^2 M(x)}{\partial x^2} + (a_r + 2\theta \cos 2x)M(x) = 0, \tag{16.25–5}$$

which is Mathieu's differential equation. This equation has physically significant values of M for certain characteristic (integral) values of a_r only, namely a_1, a_2, a_3, etc. From these values of a_r we calculate the corresponding values of E_r, using equation (16.25–4). These values, E_1, E_2, E_3, etc., are the energy levels of the system.

Provided that all n minima are equivalent, values of E_r corresponding to wave functions of the proper symmetry are obtained by choosing only the even values of a_r. Wilson[21] has tabulated the even values of a_r up to seven levels for rounded values of θ from 0 to 40.

It is instructive to consider the levels where E_r is much less than V_0. In these levels the "rotating" group does not rotate at all, but oscillates about its position of minimum energy. In keeping with this, the values of E_r and the eigenfunctions $M_r = \psi_r(\phi)$ for low values of r are those of a harmonic oscillator. Consider the potential function of equation (16.25–2),

$$V = \tfrac{1}{2}V_0(1 - \cos n\phi). \tag{16.25–2}$$

[21] E. B. Wilson, Jr., *Chem. Revs.*, **27**, 17 (1940).

The force torque (F_ϕ) acting on the rotor at the angle ϕ from its equilibrium position is

$$F_\phi = -\frac{\partial V}{\partial \phi} = -\frac{nV_0 \sin n\phi}{2}. \tag{16.25–6}$$

For small displacements from the equilibrium position,

$$\sin n\phi \simeq n\phi$$

and

$$F_\phi = -\frac{n^2 V_0 \phi}{2}. \tag{16.25–7}$$

For a pair of bodies executing simple angular harmonic oscillations about an axis about which their moments are respectively I_1 and I_2,

$$F_\phi = -k_\phi \phi, \tag{16.25–8}$$

and the frequency is

$$\nu_0 = \frac{1}{2\pi}\sqrt{\frac{k_\phi}{I_{red}}}, \tag{16.25–9}$$

where

$$\frac{1}{I_{red}} = \frac{1}{I_1} + \frac{1}{I_2}. \tag{16.25–10}$$

Hence equation (16.25–7) represents a circular simple harmonic oscillation with

$$k_\phi = \frac{n^2 V_0}{2} \tag{16.25–11}$$

and

$$\nu_0 = \frac{1}{2\pi}\sqrt{\frac{n^2 V_0}{2I_{red}}} = \frac{n}{2\pi}\sqrt{\frac{V_0}{2I_{red}}}. \tag{16.25–12}$$

The corresponding energy levels are

$$\epsilon_v = (v + \tfrac{1}{2})h\nu_0. \tag{16.25–13}$$

At high energies the term in cos $2x$ can be omitted from equation (16.25–5), which then becomes

$$\frac{\partial^2 M(x)}{dx^2} = -a_r M(x), \tag{16.25–14}$$

which is satisfied by

$$M(x) = e^{i(\sqrt{a_r})x} = e^{i(\sqrt{a_r})n\phi/2} \tag{16.25–15}$$

This is the wave function for a free rotor, without any potential barrier. Considering ethane with the spins of the hydrogen all $+{}^1/_2$ or all $-{}^1/_2$ on each methyl group, the function $M(x)$ must come back to its original value for a change of $n\phi$ by 2π, therefore $\sqrt{a_r}/2$ can only have the integral values $m = 0, \pm 1, \pm 2, \pm 3$, etc.

Thus, referring to equation (16.25–4),

$$\frac{32\pi^2 I_{\text{red}}}{4n^2h^2}(E_r - \tfrac{1}{2}V_0) = m^2 \qquad (16.25\text{–}16)$$

and

$$E_r = \tfrac{1}{2}V_0 + \frac{n^2m^2h^2}{8\pi^2 I_{\text{red}}}. \qquad (16.25\text{–}17)$$

If nm is denoted by K', K' can have the values $0, \pm n, \pm 2n, \pm 3n$, etc. In ethane, in which $n = 3$, K' of course has the values $0, \pm 3, \pm 6$, etc.

Figure 16.25–1[1] shows the energy levels for a restricted rotor B and the

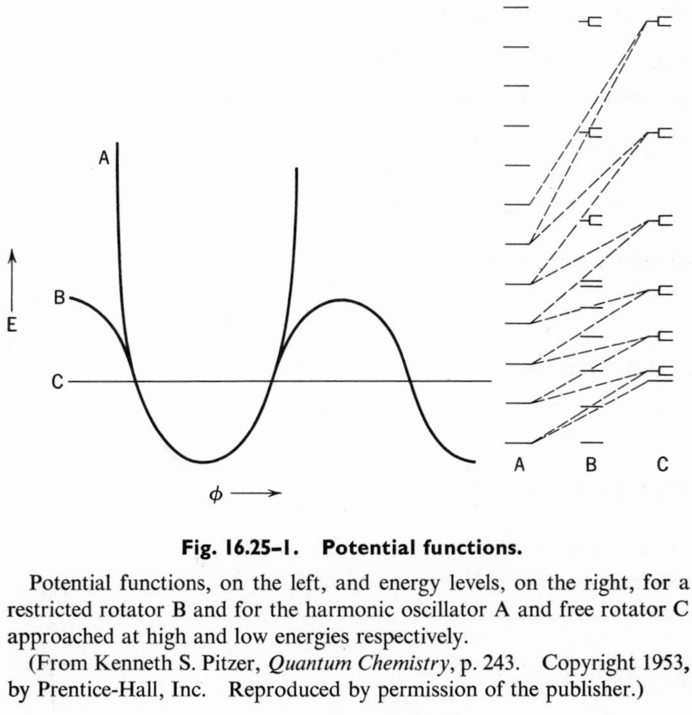

Fig. 16.25–1. Potential functions.

Potential functions, on the left, and energy levels, on the right, for a restricted rotator B and for the harmonic oscillator A and free rotator C approached at high and low energies respectively.

(From Kenneth S. Pitzer, *Quantum Chemistry*, p. 243. Copyright 1953, by Prentice-Hall, Inc. Reproduced by permission of the publisher.)

energy levels for the harmonic oscillator which is approached by B in its lower levels. The figure also shows the energy levels for the free rotor ($K = 0, \pm 1, \pm 2$, etc.) which B approaches at high energies. The range of the graph is from 0 to 2, where $m = 3$. The corresponding pure vibrational and free rotational levels are connected by broken lines.

Because all values of m can have a positive and negative sign, all the rotational levels are doubly degenerate.

The situation just discussed (which corresponds to rotational levels of species A), is true only if all nuclear spins are $+\frac{1}{2}$ or all $-\frac{1}{2}$ (i.e., if the nuclear spin function is of species A). The other possible spin combinations are of species E. It can be shown that they require values of K' of ± 1, ± 4, etc., and ± 2, ± 5, ± 8, etc., respectively which belong to species E. Thus each nuclear spin variety can have only one third of the possible rotational levels of the hindered rotor. In general, if there are n equivalent positions of the rotating group, only $1/n$ of the levels are allowed in each.

The case of ethane just considered is typical of any problem involving internal rotation, for the highest and lowest levels. However, if the molecule in which the methyl group is substituted is an asymmetric top, the intermediate levels are modified somewhat. If there are no equivalent positions of the rotating group (i.e., $n = 1$), that is, if a deuterium atom is substituted for one of the hydrogen groups on the methyl group of methyl alcohol, then all the levels corresponding to values of K' of 0, ± 1, ± 2, ± 3, etc., are allowed.

Introduction to Statistical Mechanics. The Distribution Laws

CHAPTER 17

17.1 Introduction

Statistical mechanics attempts to calculate the most probable behavior of a system. In statistical mechanics *the individual quantum states of an elementary particle, an atom, or a molecule are assumed to have equal probability*. To justify this assumption it is first necessary to consider a collection of fundamental particles, atoms, and/or molecules that are distributed as the assumption requires, and to prove by application of the laws of quantum mechanics that such a distribution would not change with time. It must also be demonstrated that the collection of particles is capable of assuming a set of quantum states which are representative of the entire system of states which the molecules may occupy.

This is, in fact, the important use of mechanics in statistical mechanics. This was the problem considered, with great generality, for classical states by Gibbs,[1] using classical mechanics. Quantum mechanics must be used to justify the assumptions concerning probability and accessibility of quantum states as well as to assign energies to them. The latter problem was dealt with briefly in the preceding chapter. The more general problem, in which the method of Gibbs is applied to quantized systems, will be postponed to Chapter 23, and the assumption of equal probability will be taken for granted at this point.

[1] J. Willard Gibbs, "Elementary Principles of Statistical Mechanics," in *Collected Works*, Vol. II, Longmans, Green, New York, 1928.

A partial justification of the assumptions is that they predict all *observed* facts.

There are two ways of using statistical mechanics to calculate the most probable behavior of a system. One of these is to calculate the most probable distribution of the energy among the constituent elementary particles, atoms, and molecules, and to prove that other distributions, differing appreciably, can occur only a small fraction of the time. The properties of the most probable state are then calculated. A more elegant way is to calculate the properties of all distributions and obtain the average value over all distributions weighted according to their probability. The former procedure is used in this book; the latter procedure has been used by Fowler[2] and will be discussed briefly in Chapter 23.

17.2 Definitions

A container of any sort, with matter within, is said to enclose a *system*. This definition of a system is in accord with the one used in thermodynamics and is the one used by Gibbs and by Tolman.[3] The elementary particles, atoms, molecules, or modes of vibration (e.g., in crystals) will be spoken of as *elements*. Statistical mechanics predicts the time average behavior of such a system; it is assumed that the time average will be the same as an average taken over a large number of systems identical with the one of interest. The large number of systems considered is said to constitute an *ensemble* of systems, in keeping with the nomenclature of Gibbs and Tolman.

To describe the behavior of an element which contains a atoms requires $3a$ coordinates and the $3a$ momenta associated with them. It was seen in Chapter 16 that for any quantum state

$$\delta \mathrm{q}_i \, \delta \mathrm{p}_i \cong h, \tag{17.2–1}$$

when q_i and p_i represent respectively a coordinate and the corresponding momentum. The $6a$-dimensional space with axes for each of these coordinates and momenta is called the *μ-space* for the element.

We shall consider n elements where n is *large*. It is to be observed *carefully* (except when otherwise obvious or noted) that n hereafter denotes the *number of elements*, to be carefully distinguished from the number of moles of elements.

In considering a system of n elements, a space of $6na$ dimensions

[2] R. H. Fowler, *Statistical Mechanics*, Cambridge University Press, Cambridge, 1929.

[3] R. C. Tolman, *The Principles of Statistical Mechanics*, Oxford University Press, Oxford, 1938.

($3na$ coordinates and $3na$ momenta) is required in order that a single point in it will define completely the state of each and every element in the system. Such a coordinate space is called a *γ-space*. The motion of a point in the γ-space describes the mechanical behavior of an entire system. A single state of a system, for which each element is in a specified single quantum state, is called a *microscopic* state or a complexion. It follows at once that, if each state of an element has assigned to it the volume in the μ-space

$$\mathrm{dq}_1\,\mathrm{dq}_2 \cdots \mathrm{dq}_a\,\mathrm{dp}_1 \cdots \mathrm{dp}_a = h^{3a}, \tag{17.2–2}$$

then the volume occupied by a single microscopic state of a system in the γ-space is h^{3na}.

The volume in the γ-space occupied by a collection of states of the same energy, each possessing some feature in common with the rest, is a measure of the probability of the collection of states. Such a collection of states is referred to as a *macroscopic* state. The reader may find the utility of the μ-space and the γ-space obscure at this stage. In Section 17.4, where the distribution law is derived, the meaning and utility of these concepts will be more apparent, as will also the other concepts just defined.

17.3 Statistical Mechanics Applied to Quantized Systems. General

Consider a system of n elements (electrons, atoms, or molecules) which constitute a single phase (gas, liquid, or crystal). (In general, n will be taken for a mole.) Let the zeroth-order wave functions for an element be $\phi_1, \phi_2, \cdots$. A zeroth-order wave function for the system is

$$\psi_1 = \phi_1(1)\phi_2(2)\phi_3(3) \cdots \phi_n(n), \tag{17.3–1}$$

where $\phi_i(k)$ means that the kth element is in a quantum state characterized by the wave function ϕ_i.

The wave function ψ_1 satisfies the zeroth-order wave equation for the system. Other such wave functions can be obtained by permuting the wave functions ϕ_i among the elements; thus

$$\psi_2 = \phi_1(2)\phi_2(1)\phi_3(3) \cdots \phi_n(n)$$

represents another solution. All the wave functions ψ_i correspond to the same energy. Any linear combinations of the wave function ψ_i will satisfy the zeroth-order wave equation for the system. The allowed solutions of the zeroth-order wave function for the system are (a) a linear combination with all the coefficients $+1$ or (b) one with coefficients $+1$

for terms produced by even permutation of elements and -1 for terms produced by odd permutation. The former does not change sign when elements are exchanged in the entire linear combination; the latter reverses its sign. The former is called the *symmetric* wave function and is possessed by systems of elements composed of an even number of elementary particles (protons, neutrons, and electrons); the latter is called the *antisymmetric* wave function and is possessed by elements composed of an odd number of elementary particles. In the latter, none of the functions ϕ_i can be identical.

When the correct wave functions and energies are obtained from the zeroth-order functions by a perturbation method, it may happen that the correct wave functions closely resemble the wave functions ψ_i. If high energy barriers prevent rearrangement of the elements in space corresponding to a change of the system from ψ_i to ψ_j, the elements are then *identifiable* with (essentially) permanent locations (wave functions). Such systems are called systems of *localized* elements. Crystalline substances are in this class. Other systems of localized elements are the *internal* modes of vibration and rotation of molecules (see below).

If, as in a gas, this identification is impossible, the systems are said to be *non-localized.* Except for systems of localized elements, it is meaningless to consider elements *identifiable.* The application of statistical mechanics is somewhat simpler for localized systems than for non-localized systems, and the results of the two cases are somewhat different, as will be seen below. Localized systems will be considered first.

In crystals the elements are localized. The wave functions are the vibrational wave functions corresponding to the fundamental modes of vibration of the crystal. Each one of these can be considered as applying to a definite mode of motion of the crystal. Thus the modes of the crystal may be considered as the elements. Interchange of different vibrational eigenfunctions between modes of the same frequency is distinguishable, but merely exchanging particles between positions is not. Under any circumstance the degrees of freedom other than translation are localized because they are to be associated with the translational wave functions of the center of gravity. These wave functions are identifiable by the quantum numbers n, l, and m. Thus the internal wave functions of the elements, which are defined as the product of the rotational, vibrational, and electronic wave functions, can be considered localized. They are to be assigned to the identifiable translational wave functions of the non-identifiable centers of gravity of the elements (atoms or molecules).

In the application of statistical mechanics to quantized systems, it is necessary to assign to each quantum state (for a particular degree of freedom) the area lying between two neighboring states in a coordinate space with p plotted against the corresponding q. To the state of lowest energy we assign the area included by the corresponding state. To the next state we assign the area between this state and the next, and so on. Thus, corresponding to the specification of the degree of freedom for an element as lying in a particular range dq dp, to specify a single quantum state we say that the energy has a certain value and that the coordinates and momenta are within the range dq dp $= h$.

17.4 Distribution Law for Localized Elements

In this section the problem is to find the manner in which the total energy of a system fixed at a value, E, is distributed among its elements at thermal equilibrium. In a system of n localized elements there are n ways of giving a single element the entire kinetic energy of the system, but there is only one way of distributing the kinetic energy so that each element has the same kinetic energy. There are $n(n-1)$ ways of giving one element half the kinetic energy of the container in one degree of freedom and another the other half in another degree of freedom, but only $n(n-1)/2$ ways of giving each of two elements half of the kinetic energy in the same degree of freedom, because the $n(n-1)$ ways include all cases where a pair of elements with an identical configuration is exchanged. Interchanging the members of this pair does not give rise to a new distinguishable configuration. By similar considerations one may determine the number of ways of getting any particular distribution.

Problem 17.4-1. Find the number of distinguishable ways of arranging three a's and two b's to form a five-letter sequence (a) by permutation formulas, (b) by writing the sequences out.

Problem 17.4-2. Calculate the probability of obtaining a total of 20 with a throw of four dice.

Problem 17.4-3. For 10 tosses of a coin, calculate the probability (a) that all are heads; (b) that 5 are heads and 5 are tails; (c) that 4 are of one variety and 6 are of the other.

Problem 17.4-4. Calculate the probability of throwing each of the sums 2 to 12 with a pair of dice each weighted so that on the average the 6's appear 25% of the time and each of the other sets of spots 15% of the time. Compare the result with the normal distribution of throws. (This information is for academic use only.)

Problem 17.4-5. (a) Determine the number of ways **P** in which each of the possible number combinations of 10 dice can be secured such that the total score is 17. Also determine the total number of ways of throwing a total score of 17. (*Note.* It is convenient to label arrangements as $1_3 2_4 3_1 \cdots$, etc., to represent three 1's, four 2's, one 3, etc.) This total is $\Sigma\mathbf{P}$.

(b) Label the most probable number combination(s) (whose probability may be signified as $\mathbf{P}_{\max}$ whose total is 17.

(c) Compare $\log \mathbf{P}_{\max}$ with $\log \Sigma\mathbf{P}$.

Problem 17.4-6. Calculate the values of the function $n_i = 13.0e^{-0.8x_i}$ for $x_i = 1$, 2, 3, 4, 5, and 6. This function represents an exponential (Boltzmann) distribution. Compare the values of n_i so obtained with the number of appearances of the numbers 1, 2, $\cdots$, 6 in the *most probable* distributions obtained in the previous problem. See Problem 17.4–9. (*Note.* Distribution $\equiv$ number combination.)

Problem 17.4-7. Using the section to follow as a guide, derive an equation for the most probable combinations of Problem 17.4–5, and use it to identify the constants of the equation given in Problem 17.4–6.

The distribution of energy which can be obtained in the largest number of distinguishable ways of attaining that distribution is the *most probable distribution.* Each distinguishable way is called a *microscopic* state; there are many such states corresponding to the macroscopic state of each distribution. Since each quantum state is equally probable, it follows that each microscopic state has an equal probability.

The probability of a given macroscopic state is the number of ways in which the elements can be arranged with n_1 in quantum states 1, n_2 in state 2, n_3 in state 3, $\cdots$, to n_i in state i. Each individual arrangement is a complexion or microscopic state of equal probability. The probability of the macroscopic state is thus given by

$$\mathbf{P} = \frac{n!}{n_1!n_2!n_3!\cdots n_i!}. \tag{17.4–1}$$

(The probability $\mathbf{P}$ is proportional to the volume in the γ-space assignable to the macroscopic state.) To get the most probable distribution we must find an expression for the numbers in each state, n_i, which make $\mathbf{P}$ a maximum. However, as previously stated, the total number of molecules, n, is a constant and the total energy has been set at a value E. Thus

$$n = \sum n_i = \text{constant} \tag{17.4–2}$$

and

$$E = \sum n_i\epsilon_i = \text{constant}, \tag{17.4–3}$$

where $\epsilon_1, \epsilon_2, \cdots, \epsilon_i$ are the energies of the individual elements in the states 1, 2, 3, etc.; some of these energies may be identical.

When we find an expression which gives the values of $n_1, n_2, \cdots, n_i, \cdots$, etc., that make $\mathbf{P}$ a maximum subject to these conditions, we have found the most probable value for the number of elements in each of the states. Looked at another way, since this distribution can be obtained by the largest number of ways, each with the same probability, it has the largest possible probability. The condition that $\mathbf{P}$ be a maximum is that no change in $\mathbf{P}$ be produced by a very small change in each n_i. In mathematical notation, $\delta \mathbf{P} = 0$, and thus $\delta \ln \mathbf{P} = 0$, for a set of changes δn_i. Thus

$$\delta \ln \mathbf{P} = \delta \ln n! - (\delta \ln n_1! + \delta \ln n_2! + \cdots + \delta \ln n_i! + \cdots) = 0. \tag{17.4–4}$$

According to Stirling's approximation formula for the factorial, if a number n is large,[4]

$$\ln n! \approx n \ln n - n. \tag{17.4–5}$$

Substituting this approximation into equation (17.4–4) for the $n_i!$ and noting that $\delta \ln n! = 0$, since n is a constant,

$$\ln n_1 \, \delta n_1 + \ln n_2 \, \delta n_2 + \cdots + \ln n_i \, \delta n_i + \cdots = 0. \tag{17.4–6}$$

If the change $\delta \ln P$ were made by completely arbitrary changes in n_1, n_2, etc., $\delta n_1, \delta n_2, \cdots, \delta n_i, \cdots$, the only solution to equation (17.4–6) would be that $\ln n_1 = \ln n_2 = \cdots = \ln n_i = 0$. In this case all the n_i would be unity, so that there would be equal distribution among μ-space cells. Actually, all the δn_i cannot be arbitrary, since they are subject to the conditions given by equations (17.4–2) and (17.4–3). The relations between the δn_i are

$$\delta n_1 + \delta n_2 + \cdots + \delta n_i + \cdots = 0 \tag{17.4–7}$$

and

$$\epsilon_1 \, \delta n_1 + \epsilon_2 \, \delta n_2 + \cdots + \epsilon_i \, \delta n_i + \cdots = 0. \tag{17.4–8}$$

These two relations (17.4–7 and 17.4–8) limit the arbitrariness of the δn_i. They may be looked on as showing how δn_1 and δn_2 depend on the remaining $(n - 2)$ quantities δn_i. Multiplying (17.4–7) and (17.4–8) by α and by β respectively and adding both to (17.4–6) gives

$$\sum_{i=1}^{i=\infty} (\ln n_i + \alpha + \beta \epsilon_i) \, \delta n_i = 0. \tag{17.4–9}$$

By choosing α and β to make

$$\ln n_1 + \alpha + \beta \epsilon_1 = 0 \quad \text{and} \quad \ln n_2 + \alpha + \beta \epsilon_2 = 0, \tag{17.4–10}$$

[4] For systems of localized elements there is nothing to prevent n_i from being large. It is always possible to choose n (and therefore E) so large that this will be the case. The time average extensive properties of systems where n, and therefore E, are quite small may then be obtained by proportion. With non-localized systems the situation is similar. In all cases the validity of the reasoning up to the point of applying the Stirling approximation is not affected by the apparent necessity of the approximation. The approximation can be and has been avoided (see Fowler, *op. cit.*, p. 22) by a method in which the factorials need not be expanded.

we thus eliminate the first two terms in the sum on the left-hand side of equation (17.4–9), so that

$$\sum_{i=3}^{i=\infty} (\ln n_i + \alpha + \beta\epsilon_i)\,\delta n_i = 0. \tag{17.4–11}$$

Equation (17.4–11) now only contains $\delta n_3, \delta n_4, \cdots, \delta n_i, \cdots, \delta n_\infty$, which are independent as a result of the artifice; hence the only solution of (17.4–11) is that all $(n - 2)$ quantities in parentheses are zero. Thus, in general,

$$\ln n_i + \alpha + \beta\epsilon_i = 0. \tag{17.4–12}$$

Upon rearrangement, equation (17.4–12) becomes

$$n_i = e^{-(\alpha+\beta\epsilon_i)} \tag{17.4–13}$$

or

$$n_i = C''e^{-\beta\epsilon_i}, \tag{17.4–14}$$

where $C'' = e^{-\alpha}$ is a new constant. Either C'' or α is easily determined by noting that Σn_i must equal the total number of elements, n. Thus

$$n = \Sigma n_i = C''\,\Sigma e^{-\beta\epsilon_i} \tag{17.4–15}$$

and

$$C'' = \frac{n}{\Sigma e^{-\beta\epsilon_i}}. \tag{17.4–15a}$$

The constant β can be determined similarly by noting that $\Sigma n_i\epsilon_i$ is equal to the total energy E. Thus

$$\Sigma C''\epsilon_i e^{-\beta\epsilon_i} = E. \tag{17.4–16}$$

This equation is true, as will be shown later, for localized and non-localized systems. By the so-called "kinetic equation," the translational energy of a mole of a perfect gas is $3P\tilde{V}/2$. This is proved in Appendix 7 by a procedure which does not make the assumptions of the elementary derivations. It is shown in effect in Section 18.7, by use of equation (17.4–16), that the energy of one mole of a perfect gas (non-localized) is $3\mathbf{N}/2\beta$. (Actually β is carried along during the derivation as the quantity $1/kT$, which has been arbitrarily substituted for convenience.) Thus, noting that $P\tilde{V}$ per mole of gas is equal to RT, $\mathbf{N}/\beta$ is equal to RT and β is equal to $1/kT$, where k is $R/\mathbf{N}$ and is known as the Boltzmann constant. (This is, of course, the reason for the arbitrary substitution.) The correct equations for a perfect gas can also be obtained as the limiting case of localized systems. (Consider the solidification of a gas by pressure above its critical point.) It thus seems natural to take β as $1/kT$ for localized systems also. However, in Section 18.3 β is identified with $1/kT$ for localized systems in a manner which is perfectly general. Replacing β in (17.4–14) and (17.4–15a),

$$n_i = \frac{ne^{-\epsilon_i/kT}}{\Sigma e^{-\epsilon_i/kT}}. \tag{17.4–17}$$

Equation (17.4–17) is the *Boltzmann* distribution law, derived here for localized elements.

If there are p_k states of equal energy, the number of elements n_k in all p_k states is given by

$$n_k = \frac{np_k e^{-\epsilon_k/kT}}{\Sigma p_k e^{-\epsilon_k/kT}}, \tag{17.4–18}$$

where the sum is now taken over the *groups* of states with energy ϵ_k. The quantities p_k are called the *a priori probabilities* of the groups of states of energy ϵ_k; sometimes they are referred to as the *weights* of the groups of states, or the *degeneracy* of the energy level. The denominator of the right side of equations (17.4–17) and (17.4–18) is called the *partition function;* it will be denoted by Q.

$$Q = \sum_k p_k e^{-\epsilon_k/kT}. \tag{17.4–19}$$

It is easy to show that, where there are p_k states in each group of energy ϵ_k, and n_k elements in each group, equation (17.4–9) becomes

$$\sum_k (\ln n_k - \ln p_k + \alpha + \beta\epsilon_k)\, \delta n_k = 0. \tag{17.4–20}$$

Problem 17.4-8. Show that when there are p_k states of energy ϵ_k, with n_k/p_k in each, the expression for **P** is

$$\mathbf{P} = \frac{n!}{\prod_k \left(\frac{n_k}{p_k}!\right)^{p_k}}. \tag{17.4–21}$$

On the basis of this equation derive (17.4–20), and show that it leads to equation (17.4–18).

Problem 17.4-9. Regarding the expression of Problem 17.4–6, namely $n_i = 13.0e^{-0.8x_i}$, as a Boltzmann distribution, assign analogues to energy, number of molecules, and distribution with respect to energy, in terms of the respective units of that problem.

Another form of the distribution law relates the number of elements in two different states in the same container. This is

$$\frac{n_j}{n_i} = \frac{p_j}{p_i} e^{-(\epsilon_j - \epsilon_i)/kT}. \tag{17.4–22}$$

Problem 17.4-10. Show that equation (17.4–22) is an immediate consequence of (17.4–18).

It is frequently convenient to choose the lowest energy under consideration as the zero of energy in order to simplify calculations. Such a choice has no effect on equation (17.4–22). It increases the value of the partition function Q, and also the numerator of (17.4–18), by a factor $e^{\varepsilon_0/kT}$, where ϵ_0 is the actual energy of the lowest state. The justification for this choice of the energy zero will be discussed later.

The *a priori* probabilities of various types of energy states were discussed in Chapter 16. Some of the more important types are repeated here for reference purposes. We shall frequently refer to *a priori* probability as *weight.*

For atoms, the number of electronic states of the same energy is defined by the value of the quantum number J and is $2J + 1$ for each value of J. For example, a $^3P_2$ level comprises five distinct quantum states (independent wave functions) and has a weight of 5. The other components of the ^3P multiplet are $^3P_0$ and $^3P_1$ with weights of 1 and 3 respectively. Usually multiplets such as the ^3P are resolved into their several components, each with different energy. If unresolved, a ^3P level would have a total weight of $5 + 3 + 1 = 9$. For hydrogen, the energy depends almost entirely on the principal quantum number n; the number of states for a given energy is the total number of wave functions which can be assigned to an electron in the nth shell. Finally, where the nucleus has a spin i, each atomic state is accompanied by $2i + 1$ nuclear spin states.

For molecules, the weight of a given state is the product of the weights due to rotation, vibration, electronic motion, and nuclear spin. For rotation of diatomic molecules, as before, the *a priori* probability of a given state is $2J + 1$ (see Section 16.12). However, if the coupling is Hund's case (b), as in Σ states, the energy of a given state is determined mainly by the quantum number K. With each value of K are associated $2S + 1$ values of J (see Section 16.14); the energies corresponding to these several J states are usually but not always resolved. Furthermore, in Π and Δ states, there are in any event two states having the same value of J, which may or may not be resolved. This is known as Λ-type doubling (see Section 16.14).

The rotational levels of *symmetric top* molecules have additional degeneracy. In this case, the quantum number J can take values K, $K + 1$, $K + 2, \cdots$. If $K \neq 0$, each J value is doubly degenerate because of "K-type doubling" in addition to the ordinary degeneracy of $2J + 1$. If in addition the molecule is non-planar, each level (for all values of K) is twofold owing to "inversion doubling." Thus the statistical weights are either $2J + 1$ (planar, $K = 0$), $4J + 2$ (planar, $K \neq 0$, or non-planar, $K = 0$), or $8J + 4$ (non-planar $K \neq 0$). For a *spherical top* molecule, the energy is again determined only by the quantum number J, but the total weights are $(2J + 1)^2$. For the *asymmetric top*, the weights are more complicated and will not be considered here.

Non-degenerate vibrational states have a statistical weight of unity; degenerate states have the weight corresponding to the number of independent vibrations which give rise to that energy. Nuclear spin gives rise to additional weighting factors and in addition determines the over-all symmetry of the state (see Section 16.14). For an asymmetric molecule, the weight of each state is increased by a factor involving n ($= 2i + 1$), where i is the nuclear spin of any atom. For a symmetrical diatomic molecule, there will be varieties, depending on the nuclear spin, i, of the atoms in the molecule. There are two varieties with weights $n(n + 1)/2$ due to nuclear spin which can take even or odd rotational levels, but not both (see Section 16.14). For symmetrical polyatomic molecules, several nuclear spin varieties are possible (see Problem 17.4–18). Symmetrical diatomic or linear molecules without nuclear spin (all i zero) have certain rotational states excluded (see Section 16.14 and the discussion of O_2 in Section 16.15).

Problem 17.4-11. Determine the *a priori* probabilities of the electronic energy levels for the hydrogen atom for $n = 1, 2, 3, 4, 5$, and 6, (a) excluding nuclear spin; (b) taking into account the nuclear spin $i = {}^1/_2$. (Neglect small splittings.)

Problem 17.4-12. The sodium D lines, which are the lowest frequency members of the Principal series, arise from transitions between the $3p$ and $3s$ electronic shells of sodium. The upper states are ${}^2P_{1/2}$ and ${}^2P_{3/2}$.

(a) What is the total weight of each of the upper states?

(b) The ${}^2P_{1/2}$ and ${}^2P_{3/2}$ states are of almost identical energy. What weight would have to be assigned if they were considered a single ${}^2P$ state?

(c) Assuming that the energies are approximately equal and that transition probabilities are equal, the intensities of spectroscopic lines are proportional to the populations of the states in which they originate. What relationship would you expect for the intensities of the two lines making up the doublet?. (Neglect nuclear spin.)

Problem 17.4-13. Give (a) the total weight of the helium ${}^3P$ state, and (b) the weights of the individual ${}^3P_0$, ${}^3P_1$, and ${}^3P_2$ states.

Problem 17.4-14. Calculate the statistical weights of the levels $v = 0, J = 5$, and $v = 1, J = 6$, for the vibration-rotation states of HCl.

Problem 17.4-15. Calculate the statistical weights of the states $v = 0, J = 5$ and $v = 0, J = 6$ for H_2. The nuclear spin of the proton is ${}^1/_2$. The ground state of hydrogen is ${}^1\Sigma_g{}^+$: states with nuclear spin I of zero go with even J, and those with unit nuclear spin go with odd J.

Problem 17.4-16. For a ${}^3\Sigma$ state of a heteronuclear diatomic molecule with $K = 5$, calculate (a) the possible values of the quantum number J, (b) the total weight of the state. (c) What happens if the two nuclei are identical? Note that the molecule follows Hund's case (b).

Problem 17.4-17. Taking into account the Λ-type doubling, calculate the total weight of the lowest levels of the states ${}^3\Pi_0$, ${}^3\Pi_1$, and ${}^3\Pi_2$.

Problem 17.4-18. A tetrahedral molecule (e.g., CH_4) containing four identical nuclei of spin $^1/_2$ exists in three varieties. They correspond to a total nuclear spin of 0, 1, and 2; they are called the E, F, and A varieties. The singlet variety (E) has no states for $J = 0$, 1, and 3; it has two states each for $J = 2$, 4, 5, 6, 7. The triplet variety (F) has no states for $J = 0$; it has three states for $J = 2$, 3; six for $J = 4$, 5; nine for $J = 6$, 7, etc. The quintet variety (A) has no states for $J = 1$, 2, and 5; it has five states for $J = 0$, 3, 4, 7, and ten for $J = 6$. Calculate the total statistical weight for each of the states $J = 2$, 4, and 6.

The energies corresponding to various types of states have also been considered in Chapter 16, where both exact and approximate formulas were given. We repeat some of them for use in the problems below.

For the electronic energy of the hydrogen atom

$$\epsilon_n = -\frac{\mathrm{R_H}}{n^2}, \tag{16.4–2}$$

where n is the principal quantum number, and $\mathrm{R_H} = 109{,}678\ \mathrm{cm}^{-1}$ (2.2×10^{-11} erg/molecule).

Similar formulas may be written for the energy levels of the alkali metal atoms.

The vibrational and rotational energies of a diatomic molecule in a Σ state are given approximately by

$$E_{\mathrm{vib}} = hc\omega(v + \tfrac{1}{2}) \tag{17.4–23}$$

and

$$E_{\mathrm{rot}} = hcBJ(J + 1), \tag{17.4–24}$$

with

$$B = \frac{h}{8\pi^2 cI}. \tag{16.17–4}$$

(In these formulas ω is the fundamental frequency and I is the moment of inertia; for further details see Section 16.17.) The approximate equation (17.4–23) may also be used for polyatomic molecules, with the energy summed over its set of fundamental vibration frequencies ω_i. Equation (17.4–24) may also be used for linear polyatomic molecules and spherical tops such as CH_4. The more complicated expressions required for other polyatomic molecules will be considered later. In general, no simple expressions may be written for the electronic energy levels of molecules. The effect of nuclear spin on the energy is exceedingly small.

The partition function Q may be separated into a product of separate terms for the various degrees of freedom to the extent that the corresponding energies are separable. The problems below are designed to give the student practice in calculation and use of the partition function for various simple cases. It will be assumed in these problems that the approximate formulas for the energy may be used, and that the partition function may be calculated separately for each degree of freedom. It will also be assumed that the lowest attainable state in any degree of freedom may be chosen as the energy zero.

Problem 17.4-19. Calculate, in cm^{-1} and ergs, the energies of the first six electronic states of the hydrogen atom (a) with respect to zero at $n = \infty$; (b) with respect to zero at $n = 1$. (c) Calculate the ratio of the number of atoms in the lowest state to those in the $n = 2$ state at 3000°K.

Problem 17.4-20. Other things being equal, the relative intensities of related spectroscopic lines depend on the population of the states from which the corresponding transitions originate. In the Balmer series for hydrogen, the observed lines are the result of transitions to the $n = 2$ level from levels $n = 3, 4, \cdots$, etc. Estimate the relative intensities of the H_α ($n = 3 \rightarrow n = 2$) and H_β ($4 \rightarrow 2$) lines in the *emission* spectrum of monatomic hydrogen (a) at 2000°K, (b) at 3000°K.

Problem 17.4-21. The moment of inertia of HCl^{35} is 2.72×10^{-40} g cm^3. Calculate the relative populations of the $J = 5$ and $J = 6$ levels in the $v = 0$ state at (a) 200°K, (b) 2000°K.

Problem 17.4-22. Calculate the rotational contribution to the partition function of gaseous HCl^{35} at 100°K, using the moment of inertia given in Problem 17.4–21.

Problem 17.4-23. Duffendack and LaRue[5] used the CN band at 4216 Å to measure the temperature of a carbon arc. They found that the line originating with $J = 49$ was 25% less intense than that originating with $J = 44$. Estimate the temperature of the arc. You may make the same assumptions as in Problem 17.4–20 and may take the value of B in equation (17.4–24) to be 1.89 cm^{-1}.

Problem 17.4-24. The temperatures of the planetary atmospheres have been deduced from observations of the rotation-vibration absorption spectra of substances (such as CO_2) which occur within them. Such spectra show a broad maximum for that value of J (in the lower vibrational state) which is most greatly populated at thermal equilibrium. The moment of inertia of CO_2 is 72×10^{-40} g cm^2.

(a) Calculate the value of n_J/n_0 for CO_2 at 300°K for values of J between 10 and 20. (Note that only even J values are allowed by the symmetry.)

(b) Repeat the calculation of part (a) for 400°K.

(c) Assuming that a rotation-vibration spectrum for CO_2 shows a maximum for $J = 18$, estimate the temperature of the atmosphere containing the CO_2.

17.5 The Einstein-Bose Distribution Law

We shall now derive the distribution law which is applicable to a system of elements having symmetric wave functions; this is a characteristic of most neutral molecules in the gaseous or liquid state. All elements may be put in a single quantum state. It is necessary to find the number of microscopic states which correspond to conditions, first, of definite energy and, second, of definite pressure for the system. The second requirement is fulfilled by fixing the number of elements as n in a container of volume V, and the first requirement is fulfilled by a limitation on the

[5] O. S. Duffendack and J. M. LaRue, *J. Opt. Soc. Am.*, **31**, 146 (1941).

choice of the wave functions for the elements to be distributed among the n non-identified elements. Let ϵ_k be the energy of a group of p_k degenerate wave functions. Let there be n_k elements with quantum states in this group and therefore with the energy ϵ_k. The conditions on energy and number give, as before,

$$E = \sum_k n_k \epsilon_k = \text{constant} \tag{17.5–1}$$

and

$$\sum n_k = n. \tag{17.5–2}$$

We have now to find a general expression for the number of distinguishable ways, **P**, of putting n_1 elements in the first group of p_1 states with energy ϵ_1, elements n_2 in the second group of p_2 states with energy ϵ_2, etc., and n_k elements in the kth group of p_k states of energy ϵ_k, etc. This expression is to be used to find $n_1, n_2, \cdots, n_k, \cdots$ for the most probable state of the system, that is, that which makes **P** a maximum. To obtain this expression we can find the number of ways (O_k) of distributing the n_k indistinguishable elements among the p_k states for each group and multiply the numbers of ways thus obtained for all groups ($\Pi_k O_k$). Let us imagine $p_k - 1$ partitions separating the elements into p_k regions, each region representing a state. (For example, one partition is required to divide the elements into two states, two partitions for division into three states, etc.) The $p_k - 1$ partitions mark off the same p_k regions in space after any permutation of the partitions. We have to find how many ways there are of distributing n_k identical elements among the p_k regions. This is the number of distinguishable ways of distributing $p_k - 1$ partitions and n_k elements. The total number of ways is $(n_k + p_k - 1)!$ The n_k elements and the $p_k - 1$ partitions are indistinguishable, so that exchanges among them are respectively indistinguishable. The total is $(n_k!)(p_k - 1)!$ times the number of distinguishable ways. The final result is thus

$$O_k = \frac{(n_k + p_k - 1)!}{n_k!(p_k - 1)!} \tag{17.5–3}$$

and

$$\mathbf{P} = \prod_k \frac{(n_k + p_k - 1)!}{n_k!(p_k - 1)!}. \tag{17.5–4}$$

Equation (17.5–4) now replaces (17.4–1), and equations (17.5–1) and (17.5–2) are identical with equation (17.4–3) and (17.4–2). With this change[6] we may proceed as we did to derive the distribution law for localized elements. Using the approximation of equation (17.4–5) and neglecting unity compared to n_k and p_k,

$$\ln \mathbf{P} = \sum_k (n_k + p_k) \ln (n_k + p_k) - (n_k + p_k) - n_k \ln n_k + n_k - p_k \ln p_k + p_k \qquad (17.5\text{–}5)$$

or

$$\ln \mathbf{P} = \sum_k \left[n_k \ln \left(1 + \frac{p_k}{n_k}\right) + p_k \ln \left(1 + \frac{n_k}{p_k}\right)\right]. \qquad (17.5\text{–}6)$$

The condition that the number of microscopic states be a maximum is

$$\delta \ln \mathbf{P} = \delta \sum_k \left[n_k \ln \left(1 + \frac{p_k}{n_k}\right) + p_k \ln \left(1 + \frac{n_k}{p_k}\right)\right] = 0. \quad (17.5\text{–}7)$$

Remembering that p_k, the number of states in a group, is constant,

$$\sum_k \left[\ln \left(1 + \frac{p_k}{n_k}\right) \delta n_k + n_k \left(-\frac{p_k}{n_k^2}\right) \frac{n_k}{n_k + p_k} \delta n_k + p_k \left(\frac{1}{p_k}\right) \frac{p_k}{n_k + p_k} \delta n_k \right] = 0, \quad (17.5\text{–}8)$$

so that

$$\sum_k \ln \left(\frac{p_k}{n_k} + 1\right) \delta n_k = 0. \qquad (17.5\text{–}9)$$

The variations δn_k are not all independent but are subject to the restrictions given by equations (17.5–1) and (17.5–2.) In differential form these equations become

$$\sum_k \epsilon_k \, \delta n_k = 0 \qquad (17.5\text{–}10)$$

and

$$\sum_k \delta n_k = 0. \qquad (17.5\text{–}11)$$

As before, these relations limit the arbitrariness of the δn_k, so that two of

[6] In general p_k will always be large, so that the Stirling approximation is easily justified for $(p_k - 1)!$ and for $(p_k + n_k - 1)!$. It is always possible to choose a sufficiently large sample to make n_k sufficiently large for any state, so that the Stirling approximation is also valid for its factorial. Even if such a large sample does not occur in practice, in the ordinary time of observation sufficient changes have occurred in the sample available that the extensive macroscopic properties represent averages with the same result.[4]

them must be dependent. Multiplying equation (17.5–10) by β and equation (17.5–11) by α, and subtracting equation (17.5–9),

$$\sum_k \left[\beta\epsilon_k + \alpha - \ln\left(\frac{p_k}{n_k} + 1\right)\right] \delta n_k = 0. \qquad (17.5\text{–}12)$$

In deriving the distribution for localized elements (Boltzmann statistics), the three corresponding equations were added. Equation (17.5–9) is subtracted in the present case and also when we come to derive the Fermi-Dirac distribution laws. In this way the resulting expression is made to reduce to the corresponding one for localized elements for the limiting case when $p_k \gg n_k$, namely (17.4–18). The constants β and α are chosen to make the quantity inside the square brackets zero for the first two terms in the sum $\sum_k$, thus eliminating the two terms containing the dependent quantities δn_1 and δn_2, as before. By this procedure,

$$\beta\epsilon_k + \alpha - \ln\left(\frac{p_k}{n_k} + 1\right) = 0, \qquad (17.5\text{–}13)$$

so that

$$\frac{p_k}{n_k} + 1 = e^{\beta\epsilon_k + \alpha}$$

or

$$n_k = \frac{p_k}{e^{(\beta\epsilon_k + \alpha)} - 1}. \qquad (17.5\text{–}14)$$

This distribution law is called the *Einstein-Bose distribution law.*

The distribution of energy in black-body radiation affords an interesting example of the Bose-Einstein statistics. The elements are *photons*, which must have symmetric wave functions. In an isolated system of photons the total energy must be conserved, but the total number of elements need not be. Thus equations (17.5–2) and (17.5–11) do not apply. The derivation of the distribution law follows the same procedure as above, except that the constant α does not appear. The result is (for photons)

$$n_k = \frac{p_k}{e^{\beta\epsilon_k} - 1}, \qquad (17.5\text{–}15)$$

where all symbols have the same meaning as above. The constant β may, as before, be identified with $1/kT$.

Problem 17.5-1. (a) Derive equation (17.5–15) in the manner used for (17.5–14).

(b) For photons the number of states, p_k, having frequencies between ν and $\nu + d\nu$ is $(8\pi\nu^2\, d\nu/c^3)$ per unit volume, where c is the velocity of light. Obtain an expression for the number of photons per unit volume having frequencies between ν and $\nu + d\nu$.

(c) The energy density, $E(\nu)\, d\nu$, of black-body radiation is defined as the energy per unit volume provided by photons of frequency between ν and $\nu + d\nu$. Noting that $E = h\nu$ and that $\beta = 1/kT$, show that the treatment above gives, for the energy density, the Planck formula,

$$E(\nu)\, d\nu = \frac{8\pi h\nu^3}{c^3} \frac{d\nu}{e^{h\nu/kT} - 1}.$$

17.6 The Fermi-Dirac Distribution Law

In finding the distribution law applicable to elements (such as electrons) with antisymmetric wave functions, we must remember that there can be only one particle with each wave function, because of the antisymmetric nature of the total wave function. Except for this restriction, we may proceed exactly as for elements whose wave functions are symmetrical.

We must accordingly find the number of ways of assigning quantum states (wave functions), chosen from the group consisting of p_k states of energy ϵ_k, to the n_k indistinguishable elements in such a way that each state is assigned to only one element; this can be done only when

$$p_k \geqq n_k. \tag{17.6–1}$$

The number of ways, O_k, is simply the number of combinations of p_k states taken n_k at a time; that is,

$$O_k = \frac{p_k(p_k - 1)(p_k - 2) \cdots [p_k - (n_k - 1)]}{n_k!} = \frac{p_k!}{(p_k - n_k)!\,n_k!}. \tag{17.6–2}$$

The total number of ways of assigning all n elements to groups of quantum states of energy ϵ_k is equal to the product of the O_k for each group, that is, to $\Pi_k O_k$. Thus[7]

$$\mathbf{P} = \prod_k \frac{p_k!}{(p_k - n_k)!\,n_k!}. \tag{17.6–3}$$

Equation (17.6–3) is subject to the conditions stated in equation (17.5–1) and (17.5–2); thus we must satisfy simultaneously

$$\delta \ln \mathbf{P} = \sum_k \ln \left(\frac{p_k}{n_k} - 1\right) \delta n_k = 0, \tag{17.6–4}$$

$$\sum_k \epsilon_k\, \delta n_k = 0, \tag{17.6–5}$$

and

$$\sum_k \delta n_k = 0. \tag{17.6–6}$$

[7] See footnotes 4 and 6

By a method analogous to that used in the Einstein-Bose case, we obtain

$$n_k = \frac{p_k}{e^{\beta\epsilon_k+\alpha} + 1} \cdot \tag{17.6–7}$$

This distribution law is called the *Fermi–Dirac distribution law.*

Problem 17.6-1. Derive equation (17.6–7) by the method indicated in the text.

17.7 Evaluation of the Constants α and β

If the exponential terms of equations (17.5–14) and (17.6–7) are sufficiently large, these equations reduce to

$$n_k = p_k e^{-\alpha} e^{-\beta\epsilon_k}. \tag{17.7–1}$$

This is the *Boltzmann distribution law* whose constant is also equal to $e^{-\alpha}$. We see that α plays the same role in equations (17.5–14) and (17.6–7) that it does in the Boltzmann distribution law. Its value is to be determined from the total number of particles, n, through the equation

$$n = \Sigma \frac{p_k}{e^{\beta\epsilon_k+\alpha} \pm 1} \cdot \tag{17.7–2}$$

The plus sign applies to equation (17.6–7) (Fermi distribution law) and the minus sign to equation (17.5–4) (Bose distribution law). Direct evaluation of α is difficult in either case because of the extra term in the denominator of equation (17.7–2). However, the number of states, p_k, is proportional to the volume of the container; thus, for any volume V of a particular system, α will be large whenever n is small (i.e., when the density is small). It is quite evident that β must have the same value for all systems, including those where α is large. As anticipated in Section 17.4, β can be shown to be equal to $1/kT$ by calculating the energy of a perfect gas in terms of β, using the limiting distribution law for non-localized systems; this is compared with a similar calculation in terms of PV. The identification is made with greater rigor in Chapter 18 and with even more generality but greater abstraction in Chapter 23.

17.8 The Maxwell-Boltzmann Distribution Law

It has been seen in the last section that the Einstein-Bose and Fermi-Dirac distribution laws reduce to the Boltzmann distribution in the form

$$n_k = p_k \epsilon^{-\alpha} \epsilon^{-\epsilon_k/kT} \tag{17.7–1}$$

for large values of α. This will be true whenever the denominator in equations (17.5–14) and (17.6–7) is large compared with unity for any energy state present in appreciable numbers. The most unfavorable case will involve those states for which ϵ/kT approaches zero; for the law to hold for these states, e^{α} must be relatively large compared with unity.

It turns out that equation (17.7–1) is correct to a very small fraction of a per cent, even for the lowest energy states, for any but extreme conditions. For the translation of gases at room temperature, e^{α} is greater than 10^5, and the term unity may be neglected for all energy levels. (*Note.* Two important exceptions are (a) helium gas near its boiling point, $e^{\alpha} \approx 1$; and (b) the "electron gas" in a metal, for which $e^{\alpha} < 1$ at room temperature.) Thus it is possible to apply the distribution law for localized systems to the translational energies of a dilute gas composed of molecules.

According to equation (17.2–2) and Section 17.3, the number of quantum states, p_k, corresponding to ranges $\mathrm{d}x$, $\mathrm{d}y$, and $\mathrm{d}z$ in the coordinates of the centers of gravity and $\mathrm{d}(\mathrm{m}\dot{x})$, $\mathrm{d}(\mathrm{m}\dot{y})$, and $\mathrm{d}(\mathrm{m}\dot{z})$ in the translational momenta, is given by

$$p_k = \frac{\mathrm{d}x\,\mathrm{d}y\,\mathrm{d}z\,\mathrm{d}(\mathrm{m}\dot{x})\,\mathrm{d}(\mathrm{m}\dot{y})\,\mathrm{d}(\mathrm{m}\dot{z})}{h^3}. \tag{17.8–1}$$

According to (17.7–1), the number of molecules in these states is

$$\mathrm{d}n = \frac{C''\mathrm{m}^3 e^{-\epsilon_k/kT}}{h^3}\,\mathrm{d}x\,\mathrm{d}y\,\mathrm{d}z\,\mathrm{d}\dot{x}\,\mathrm{d}\dot{y}\,\mathrm{d}\dot{z}, \tag{17.8–2}$$

where C'' has been written for $e^{-\alpha}$. The value of C'' is obtained by integration of (17.8–2) over the volume of the container for x, y, and z and from $-\infty$ to $+\infty$ for $\dot{x}$, $\dot{y}$, and $\dot{z}$. The resulting integral is the total number of molecules, n. Thus

$$C'' = e^{-\alpha} = \frac{nh^3}{\mathrm{m}^3 \int_0^x \int_0^y \int_0^z \int_{-\infty}^{\infty} \int_{-\infty}^{\infty} \int_{-\infty}^{\infty} e^{-\mathrm{m}(\dot{x}^2+\dot{y}^2+\dot{z}^2)/2kT}\,\mathrm{d}\dot{x}\,\mathrm{d}\dot{y}\,\mathrm{d}\dot{z}\,\mathrm{d}x\,\mathrm{d}y\,\mathrm{d}z}$$

$$= \frac{nh^3}{V(2\pi\mathrm{m}kT)^{3/2}}, \tag{17.8–3}$$

in which V is the result of the integration over the volume of the container, and the rest of the denominator results from the other three integrals. The necessary integral is found in Appendix 5. Thus

$$\mathrm{d}n = \frac{n\mathrm{m}^3}{V(2\pi\mathrm{m}kT)^{3/2}}\,e^{-\mathrm{m}(\dot{x}^2+\dot{y}^2+\dot{z}^2)/2kT}\,\mathrm{d}x\,\mathrm{d}y\,\mathrm{d}z\,\mathrm{d}\dot{x}\,\mathrm{d}\dot{y}\,\mathrm{d}\dot{z}. \tag{17.8–4}$$

If (17.8–4) is integrated only over the volume of the container, the number of molecules $\mathrm{d}n'$ in the velocity range $\mathrm{d}\dot{x}\,\mathrm{d}\dot{y}\,\mathrm{d}\dot{z}$ is

$$\mathrm{d}n' = n\left(\frac{\mathrm{m}}{2\pi kT}\right)^{3/2} e^{-\mathrm{m}(\dot{x}^2+\dot{y}^2+\dot{z}^2)/2kT}\,\mathrm{d}\dot{x}\,\mathrm{d}\dot{y}\,\mathrm{d}\dot{z}. \tag{17.8–5}$$

This equation is known as the *Maxwell-Boltzmann distribution law of velocities.* It gives the number of molecules with translational velocities of the center of gravity whose components lie in the range between $\dot{x}$, $\dot{y}$, $\dot{z}$ and $\dot{x} + d\dot{x}$, $\dot{y} + d\dot{y}$, and $\dot{z} + d\dot{z}$.

Problem 17.8-1. The average (translational) kinetic energy of a gas molecule is given by kinetic theory (justified by experiment) as $(E_t)_{\text{ave}} = {}^3/_2 kT$. Show that this is the average kinetic energy $(m\dot{x}^2 + m\dot{y}^2 + m\dot{z}^2)/2$ of an element in a system whose energies are distributed among all values of velocity in accord with equation (17.8–5). This result is another justification for equating β to $1/kT$. (*Hint.* If the number of elements of a system in a group of states is given by $dn = f(\lambda)\,d\lambda$, the *average* value of a property x is defined by

$$\bar{x} = \frac{\int x(f\lambda)\,d\lambda}{\int f(\lambda)\,d\lambda}. \tag{17.8–6}$$

The symbol λ indicates the coordinates (e.g., $\dot{x}$, $\dot{y}$, etc.) used to define the region in which dn_i is evaluated. The necessary integrals may be evaluated most readily by transposition into spherical coordinates $c^2 = \dot{x}^2 + \dot{y}^2 + \dot{z}^2$, and $d\lambda = c^2 \sin\theta\,dc\,d\theta\,d\phi$.

Problem 17.8-2. In terms of spherical coordinates p, θ, and ϕ, the number of photons having momenta in a range between p and p + dp in directions between θ and $\theta + d\theta$, ϕ and $\phi + d\phi$ is $2p^2 \sin\theta\,d\theta\,d\phi\,dp$. Obtain the number of photons having frequencies between ν and $\nu + d\nu$ (given in Problem 17.5–1) by the following procedure. (a) Noting that for a photon $p = h\nu/c$, rewrite the number of photons in terms of the frequency ν. (b) As in the section above, multiply by $dx\,dy\,dz$, divide by h^3, and integrate over all variables except ν.

Problem 17.8-3. By applying the gas law to photons show that in equilibrium the pressure of light is given by $P = {}^2/_3(E/V)$.

Thermodynamic Functions for Systems of Localized Elements and "Dilute" Gases

CHAPTER 18

18.1 Relation of Entropy to Probability

When an isolated system undergoes a spontaneous change, the entropy increases and the system passes toward a more probable state; thus there is evidently a connection between entropy and probability.[1] When we say that a system in a given state has a probability W, we mean that a system withdrawn from a large number of similar systems has a fractional chance W of being the chosen state (compared to a chance of unity that it will in some one of all the possible states). Let us take two systems, in states whose probabilities are W_1 and W_2 and whose entropies are S_1 and S_2, from the ensemble and combine them. The combined probability of the systems is $W_1 W_2$, since probabilities are multiplicative. On the other hand, the entropies of the systems are additive. The only type of functional relation that will satisfy these considerations is that

$$S = K \ln W + \text{constant}, \tag{18.1–1}$$

where the additive constant gives the value of the entropy corresponding to $W = 1$.

For application of equation (18.1–1) it is necessary to find the value of

[1] L. Boltzmann, *Vorlesungen über Gastheorie*, Barth, Leipzig, 1912.

K. This can be done readily by considering the expansion of one mole of a perfect gas from a pressure P_1 to a pressure P_2; this is accomplished by allowing the gas to expand from one container of volume V_1 into another of volume V_2 such that

$$\frac{V_1}{V_1 + V_2} = \frac{P_2}{P_1}. \tag{18.1–2}$$

With the containers connected the chance w_1 that a single molecule will be in the container of volume V_1 rather than in the total volume $V_1 + V_2$ is

$$w_1 = \frac{V_1}{V_1 + V_2}. \tag{18.1–3}$$

The corresponding chance W_1 that all **N** molecules (where **N** is the Avogadro number) will lie in the volume V_1 is

$$W_1 = \left(\frac{V_1}{V_1 + V_2}\right)^{\mathbf{N}}. \tag{18.1–4}$$

The chance W_2 of finding the molecules in the volume $V_1 + V_2$ is, of course, unity.

Let the entropy be S_1 before expansion and S_2 after expansion. Applying equation (18.1–1),

$$S_2 - S_1 = K \ln\left(\frac{W_2}{W_1}\right) = K \ln\left(\frac{V_1}{V_1 + V_2}\right)^{-\mathbf{N}} = K \ln\left(\frac{V_1 + V_2}{V_1}\right)^{\mathbf{N}}. \tag{18.1–5}$$

However, according to Section 6.14 the entropy increase on expansion from V_1 to $V_1 + V_2$ is

$$S_2 - S_1 = R \ln\left(\frac{V_1 + V_2}{V_1}\right) = k \ln\left(\frac{V_1 + V_2}{V_1}\right)^{\mathbf{N}}, \tag{18.1–6}$$

where $k = R/\mathbf{N}$ is the Boltzmann gas constant. Comparing equations (18.1–5) and (18.1–6), we see that $K = k$. Thus equation (18.1–1) becomes

$$S = k \ln W + \text{constant}. \tag{18.1–7}$$

This is the Boltzmann relation between entropy and probability.

If only entropy differences are involved, it is not necessary to inquire into the value that is to be assigned to the additive constant. Thus we shall use equation (18.1–7) in the form

$$S_2 - S_1 = k \ln \frac{W_2}{W_1} \tag{18.1–8}$$

and consider only ratios of probabilities. As in Chapter 17, the probability of finding a system in a given macroscopic state is proportional to the number of microscopic states which correspond to it, each of which has the same probability.

It is the convention to assign zero entropy to perfect crystals at the absolute zero; this is permissible since we shall show that all such crystals have the same entropy. At the absolute zero every element in a perfect crystal is in its lowest quantum state; in addition, the system is one with fixed unit cells. For example, if a crystal of an element had one atom of a radioactive isotope at a particular point in the lattice, it would be found that the radioactive atom would stay at that point. Evidently the state of a particular perfect crystal at the absolute zero is represented by *one* and *only one* microscopic state; thus it is clear why each has the same entropy. It is true that reconstruction of the crystal from its particles would give a different arrangement of particles. However, we would not regard the new arrangement as giving rise to a different region in the γ-space (different microscopic state) because, apart from the positions which they occupy, the particles have no identity and the new crystal is not distinguishable from the old one in any way. If it were physically possible to have a very mobile crystal at the absolute zero so that the particles could change places rapidly, such a crystal would still correspond only to one microscopic state because of the indistinguishability of the particles; it would thus have the same entropy as the perfect crystal of fixed particles, its modes of vibrations being localized.

It is thus natural to assign zero entropy to a system defined by a single microscopic state. The entropy of a system is then given by

$$S = k \ln \mathbf{P}, \tag{18.1–9}$$

where $\mathbf{P}$ is the number of microscopic states, each of which represents (i.e., corresponds to) the state of the system. By this choice the constant is eliminated from equation (18.1–7). In addition, the number of microscopic states $\mathbf{P}$, defined as in Chapter 17, is used as a measure of the probability W.

The calculation of the number of microscopic states may readily be made for the perfect crystal at absolute zero. The crystal is a localized system, and each element is in its lowest quantum state. Thus the probability is, according to equation (17.4–1),

$$\mathbf{P} = \frac{n!}{n!} = 1, \tag{18.1–10}$$

and

$$S = k \ln \mathbf{P} = 0, \tag{18.1–11}$$

in agreement with the convention of assigning zero entropy to a crystal at the absolute zero.

The summary of these considerations has come to be known as the *third law of thermodynamics*. This law has already been briefly stated in a limited way and used in Section 12.10. It does not seem to many, including the authors, that it is proper to call this summary a law. For systems with a degenerate lowest level, the entropy will not be zero for equilibrium at 0°K. Where there is no equilibrium, as in glasses, a formal calculation of the entropy at 0°K has no meaning, as has been pointed out in Section 12.10, even though a positive value is obtained. That perfect crystals at the absolute zero, with a non-degenerate lowest state, have the lowest possible entropy follows from the previous considerations based on quantum mechanics. To give this the value zero is merely a convention. It could have been given any other value by introducing the proper constant in all thermodynamic equations. Thus it is incorrect to state as a law that the entropy is zero at the absolute zero for all systems at equilibrium. To itemize the conditions where it is correct, in the form of a law, is thus quite nugatory.

18.2 Total Energy and Heat Capacity for Localized Elements

Evidently the total energy of n elements of a localized system is obtained by multiplying the number n_i in each quantum state by the energy of the state and summing over all states. Thus

$$E = \sum_i n_i \epsilon_i. \tag{18.2–1}$$

If n_k is the number of elements in p_k states each with energy ϵ_k, an equivalent expression for the energy is

$$E = \sum_k p_k n_k \epsilon_k, \tag{18.2–1a}$$

where the sum is now taken over all groups of states.

For a system of localized particles, the number of particles, n_k, of each energy is given by equation (17.4–18):

$$n_k = \frac{n p_k e^{-\epsilon_k/kT}}{\Sigma p_k e^{-\epsilon_k/kT}}. \tag{17.4–18}$$

When this is substituted into (18.2–1a), the result is

$$E = \frac{n \Sigma p_k \epsilon_k e^{-\epsilon_k/kT}}{\Sigma p_k e^{-\epsilon_k/kT}}. \tag{18.2–2}$$

Problem 18.2-1. Calculate, in calories, the energy due to rotation and vibration of a mole of HCl^{35} at 298.15°K. For evaluation of the energies, use equations (16.12–3) and (16.12–10) together with the data of Table 16.15–2. The weighting factors p_k are given in Section 17.4. Note that $\Lambda = 0$. For convenience, take the energy zero at $v = 0, J = 0$.

The denominator of equation (18.2–2) is, of course, the partition function Q, as defined in Section 17.4,

$$Q = \Sigma p_k e^{-\epsilon_k/kT}. \tag{17.4–19}$$

When Q is differentiated, term by term, with respect to $1/T$, the result is

$$\frac{\partial Q}{\partial(1/T)} = -\frac{1}{k}\Sigma p_k \epsilon_k e^{-\epsilon_k/kT}, \tag{18.2–3}$$

and, since $d(1/T) = -dT/T^2$,

$$kT^2\frac{\partial Q}{\partial T} = \Sigma p_k \epsilon_k e^{-\epsilon_k/kT}. \tag{18.2–4}$$

Upon substitution of this result into (18.2–2), the expression becomes

$$E = \frac{nkT^2}{Q}\frac{\partial Q}{\partial T}. \tag{18.2–5}$$

We have used the partial notation rather than the total because the latter can be regarded as a special case of the former when any other possible variables are regarded as constant. Actually, for energy levels to have a real meaning, the boundary conditions must be fixed, and this means constant volume. Thus the variables are T and V. The partial derivatives are therefore to be regarded as at constant volume.

If we deal with a mole of elements, n becomes the Avogadro number, N, and nk becomes equal to R; on a molal basis, alternative expressions for $\tilde{E}$ as a function of Q are

$$\tilde{E} = RT^2\frac{\partial \ln Q}{\partial T} \tag{18.2–6}$$

or

$$\tilde{E} = -\frac{R}{Q}\left[\frac{\partial Q}{\partial(1/T)}\right] = -R\frac{\partial \ln Q}{\partial(1/T)}. \tag{18.2–7}$$

Problem 18.2-2. Carry out in detail the derivations of equations (18.2–3) through (18.2–7).

The heat capacity at constant volume is defined as

$$C = \frac{\partial E}{\partial T} = -\frac{1}{T^2}\frac{\partial E}{\partial(1/T)}, \tag{18.2–8}$$

where the partial derivative is retained as a reminder that the mechanical conditions establishing the energy levels of the elements must be retained. If equations (18.2–6) and (18.2–7) are differentiated with respect to T, the results are

$$\tilde{C} = 2RT\frac{\partial \ln Q}{\mathrm{d}T} + RT^2\frac{\partial^2 \ln Q}{\partial T^2} \tag{18.2–9}$$

and

$$\tilde{C} = -R\frac{\partial^2 \ln Q}{\partial(1/T)\,\partial T} = \frac{R}{T^2}\frac{\partial^2 \ln Q}{\partial^2(1/T)}. \tag{18.2–10}$$

An alternative set of expressions for $\tilde{E}$ and $\tilde{C}$ is obtained if one denotes $[\partial Q/\partial(1/T)]$ by Q' and $[\partial^2 Q/\partial(1/T)^2]$ by Q''. Then, from equation (18.2–7),

$$\tilde{E} = -R\frac{Q'}{Q}, \tag{18.2–11}$$

and, from (18.2–8),

$$\tilde{C} = \frac{\partial \tilde{E}}{\partial T} = -\frac{1}{T^2}\frac{\partial \tilde{E}}{\partial(1/T)} = \frac{R}{T^2}\left[\frac{Q''}{Q} - \left(\frac{Q'}{Q}\right)^2\right]. \tag{18.2–12}$$

The value of Q'' is obtained by further differentiation of equation (18.2–3):

$$Q'' = \frac{\partial^2 Q}{\partial(1/T)^2} = \frac{1}{k^2}\Sigma p_k \epsilon_k^2 e^{-\epsilon_k/kT}. \tag{18.2–13}$$

Using (17.4–19), (18.2–3), and (18.2–13) in equation (18.2–12),

$$\tilde{C} = \frac{\mathrm{N}}{kT^2}\left[\frac{\Sigma p_k \epsilon_k^2 e^{-\epsilon_k/kT}}{\Sigma p_k e^{-\epsilon_k/kT}} - \left(\frac{\Sigma p_k \epsilon_k e^{-\epsilon_k/kT}}{\Sigma p_k e^{-\epsilon_k/kT}}\right)^2\right]. \tag{18.2–14}$$

Problem 18.2-3. (a) Obtain equation (18.2–14) by substituting for Q in equation (18.2–9) and performing the differentiations indicated. Note that $\mathrm{d}\ln x = \mathrm{d}x/x$. (b) Show that equation (18.2–14) can be rearranged into the form

$$\tilde{C} = R\left[\frac{\Sigma p_k(\epsilon_k/kT)^2 e^{-\epsilon_k/kT}}{\Sigma p_k e^{-\epsilon_k/kT}} - \left(\frac{\Sigma p_k(\epsilon_k/kT) e^{-\epsilon_k/kT}}{\Sigma p_k e^{-\epsilon_k/kT}}\right)^2\right]. \tag{18.2–15}$$

Note that each term of (18.2–15) depends on the dimensionless parameter ϵ_k/kT.

18.3 Entropy of a System of Localized Elements

The entropy change in a system of localized elements, like that of any substance at constant volume, is

$$\mathrm{d}S = \frac{\mathrm{d}E}{T}. \tag{18.3–1}$$

The value of $\mathrm{d}E$ is obtained by taking the differential of equation (18.2–6). When this is substituted into (18.3–1),

$$\mathrm{d}\tilde{S} = R\left[2\left(\frac{\partial \ln Q}{\partial T}\right)\mathrm{d}T + T\,\mathrm{d}\left(\frac{\partial \ln Q}{\partial T}\right)\right] \tag{18.3–2}$$

or

$$\mathrm{d}\tilde{S} = R\left[\left(\frac{\partial \ln Q}{\partial T}\right)\mathrm{d}T + \mathrm{d}\left(T\frac{\partial \ln Q}{\partial T}\right)\right]. \tag{18.3–3}$$

Problem 18.3-1. (a) Prove equation (18.3–2).
(b) Show that (18.3–3) and (18.3–2) are equivalent.

Integrating with respect to T, the entropy is

$$\tilde{S} = R\left[\ln Q + T\frac{\partial \ln Q}{\partial T}\right] + \text{constant}. \tag{18.3–4}$$

Upon replacement of the second term by use of equation (18.2–6), this expression becomes

$$\tilde{S} = \frac{\tilde{E}}{T} + R\ln Q + \text{constant}. \tag{18.3–5}$$

In order to evaluate the constant of integration it is necessary to use equation (18.1–9),

$$S = k\ln \mathbf{P}. \tag{18.1–9}$$

The number of states $\mathbf{P}$ is given by equation (17.4–1). For a mole of elements,

$$\mathbf{P} = \frac{\mathbf{N}!}{\Pi n_i!}, \tag{18.3–6}$$

where $\mathbf{N}$ is the Avogadro number. Upon replacement of $\mathbf{P}$ and use of Stirling's approximation as before, equation (18.1–9) becomes

$$\begin{aligned}\tilde{S} &= k\ln\frac{\mathbf{N}!}{n_1!n_2!\cdots n_k!} = k(\mathbf{N}\ln\mathbf{N} - \mathbf{N} - \sum_i n_i\ln n_i + \sum_i n_i)\\ &= k(\mathbf{N}\ln\mathbf{N} - \sum_i n_i\ln n_i).\end{aligned} \tag{18.3–7}$$

(Note that $\sum_i n_i = \mathbf{N}$.) Equation (18.3–7) may be rewritten

$$\tilde{S} = k\,(\sum_i n_i\ln\mathbf{N} - \sum_i n_i\ln n_i) \tag{18.3–8}$$

$$= -k\sum_i n_i\ln\frac{n_i}{\mathbf{N}} \tag{18.3–9}$$

$$= -R\sum_i\frac{n_i}{\mathbf{N}}\ln\frac{n_i}{\mathbf{N}}. \tag{18.3–10}$$

The quantity n_i/N is obtained by use of equation (17.4–17); for a mole of elements it is

$$\frac{n_i}{\mathrm{N}} = \frac{e^{-\epsilon_i/kT}}{\sum_i e^{-\epsilon_i/kT}} = \frac{e^{-\epsilon_i/kT}}{Q}. \tag{18.3–11}$$

The denominator is the same Q as in equation (17.4–19), since it is immaterial whether states are summed individually or in groups of p_k. The entropy is thus

$$\tilde{S} = -R\sum_i \frac{e^{-\epsilon_i/kT}}{Q} \ln \frac{e^{-\epsilon_i/kT}}{Q}$$

$$= R\sum_i \frac{e^{-\epsilon_i/kT}}{Q} (\ln Q) + \sum_i \frac{\epsilon_i}{kTQ} e^{-\epsilon_i/kT}. \tag{18.3–12}$$

In equation (18.3–12) the summation is made over all states. If the number of states, p_k, of a given energy E_k is introduced, the summation may be made over the energies, as before. When this is done and constant factors are removed from the summations,

$$\tilde{S} = R\left(\frac{\ln Q}{Q}\sum_k p_k e^{-\epsilon_k/kT} + \frac{1}{kTQ}\sum_k p_k \epsilon_k e^{-\epsilon_k/kT}\right), \tag{18.3–13}$$

where k stands for the quantum numbers which determine the energy, and p_k is the number of states of energy ϵ_k. Replacing the summations by use of equations (17.4–19) and (18.2–4), the entropy is

$$\tilde{S} = R\left[\ln Q + T\frac{\partial \ln Q}{\partial T}\right]. \tag{18.3–14}$$

Since equation (18.3–14) duplicates (18.3–4) except for the constant, it is evident that the constant of integration in equations (18.3–4) and (18.3–5) must be zero. Thus the final result for the entropy is

$$\tilde{S} = \frac{\tilde{E}}{T} + R \ln Q. \tag{18.3–15}$$

It is at this point that the identification of β with $1/kT$ is justified. Had β been other than equal to $1/kT$ in the distribution laws, equation (18.3–4) could not possibly have resulted frcm the use of equation (18.2–2) for the energy. It is because β is equal to $1/kT$ that equation (18.2–2) differentiates as it does.

If the Boltzmann relation between entropy and probability (18.1–9) is accepted, then equation (18.3–13) may be derived in terms of β. Equation

(18.3–5) could not be written as it stands in terms of β because its functional form is determined by the fact that β was equated to $1/kT$. This is done with perfect generality in Chapter 23. It is done quite generally for all cases in the classical limit at the end of this chapter, by a method which is a mathematical formalization of the remarks just made concerning the role of β during the operation of differentiation.

In the same terms as equations (18.2–11) and (18.2–12), the entropy becomes

$$\tilde{S} = R\left(\ln Q - \frac{Q'}{QT}\right). \tag{18.3–16}$$

Problem 18.3-2. Prove equation (18.3–16).

18.4 Entropy of a System of Non-localized Elements in the Classical Limit

It has already been seen, in Section 17.7, that at high temperatures and low densities the Fermi-Dirac and Einstein-Bose distribution laws reduce to the distribution law for localized elements. The expressions for **P** in the two cases were

$$\mathbf{P} = \prod_k \frac{p_k!}{(p_k - n_k)!n_k!} \tag{17.6–3}$$

and

$$\mathbf{P} = \prod_k \frac{(p_k + n_k - 1)!}{(p_k - 1)!(n_k!)}. \tag{17.5–4}$$

In both cases, if $p_k \gg n_k$, these expressions may be replaced, for the purposes of thermodynamic calculations, by

$$\mathbf{P} = \prod_k \frac{p_k^{\,n_k}}{n_k!}. \tag{18.4–1}$$

The proof of (18.4–1) for the Fermi-Dirac case is as follows. Rewriting (17.6–3),

$$\mathbf{P} = \prod_k \frac{(p_k)(p_k - 1)(p_k - 2)\cdots(p_k - n_k + 1)}{n_k!}. \tag{18.4–2}$$

If $p_k \gg n_k$, the fractional error in **P** introduced by writing p_k for each of the terms in the numerator is negligibly small. Since thermodynamic calculations involve only the logarithm of **P**, the fractional (not the absolute) error is all that matters, and the substitution is justified. When this has been done, the equation reduces to (18.4–1). The proof for the Bose-Einstein case follows the same lines.

Problem 18.4-1. Derive the expression

$$\mathbf{P} = \prod_k \frac{p_k^{n_k}}{n_k!}$$

corresponding to the Einstein-Bose distribution law in the classical limit. Compare with Problem 17.4–8.

Where these approximations cannot be made, the following derivation of an expression for the entropy of a non-localized system will not be valid, nor will the expressions based upon it for the thermodynamic functions. At the end of the chapter (Section 18.12) expressions are derived for the thermodynamic functions which do not make any approximation. Since the method is somewhat abstract, it is postponed until more concrete cases have been considered.

Equation (18.4–1) must be used in place of (18.3–6) for the probability of a non-localized system in the classical limit. The corresponding expression for the entropy is

$$S = k \ln \mathbf{P} = k \sum (\ln p_k^{n_k} - \ln n_k!). \tag{18.4–3}$$

Substituting $n_k \ln n_k - n_k$ for $\ln n_k!$ and rearranging,

$$S = k \sum (n_k \ln p_k - n_k \ln n_k + n_k)$$
$$= k \sum n_k \left(\ln \frac{p_k}{n_k} + 1\right). \tag{18.4–4}$$

The classical limit of the distribution law for the Fermi-Dirac or Bose-Einstein distribution law is

$$n_k = p_k e^{-\alpha} e^{-\beta\epsilon_k}. \tag{17.7–1}$$

For one mole of gas this becomes, after substitution for α and β,

$$n_k = \frac{\mathbf{N} p_k e^{-\epsilon_k/kT}}{\Sigma p_k e^{-\epsilon_k/kT}}, \tag{17.4–18}$$

where $\mathbf{N}$ is the Avogadro number, so that

$$\frac{n_k}{p_k} = \frac{\mathbf{N} e^{-\epsilon_k/kT}}{Q}. \tag{18.4–5}$$

When (18.4–5) is inserted into (18.4–4), the result is

$$\tilde{S} = k \sum_k n_k \left(\ln Q - \ln \mathbf{N} + \frac{\epsilon_k}{kT} + 1\right)$$
$$= k\left(\ln \frac{Q}{\mathbf{N}} + 1\right) \sum_k n_k + \frac{1}{T} \sum_k n_k \epsilon_k. \tag{18.4–6}$$

However,

$$\sum_k n_k = \mathbf{N} \quad \text{and} \quad \sum_k n_k \epsilon_k = \tilde{E},$$

so that

$$\tilde{S} = \mathbf{N}k\left(\ln\frac{Q}{\mathbf{N}} + 1\right) + \frac{\tilde{E}}{T}$$

$$= R\ln\frac{Q}{\mathbf{N}} + R + \frac{\tilde{E}}{T}, \qquad (18.4\text{–}7)$$

or

$$\tilde{S} = R\left[\ln\frac{Q}{\mathbf{N}} + T\frac{\partial \ln Q}{\partial T} + 1\right]. \qquad (18.4\text{–}7a)$$

It will be observed that equations (18.4–7) and (18.4–7a) are the same as equations (18.3–5) and (18.3–4) except for substitution of the term $-R\ln\mathbf{N} + R$ for the constant. It is this term which takes account of non-localization of the elements. The differentiations with respect to T must be made with the other variables held such that the energy of each state is fixed, that is, that the wave mechanical boundary conditions are not changed. In practice, this means that the volume must be held constant. It is clear that equation (18.4–7) must be used to calculate the entropy of any gas composed of molecules (in the classical limit) from a partition function

$$Q = \Sigma p_k e^{-\epsilon_k/kT}. \qquad (17.4\text{–}19)$$

Strictly speaking, up to this point β should replace $1/kT$. The general identification of β with $1/kT$ can be made as in Section 18.3. This is done with perfect generality in Chapter 23. The energy ϵ_k is made up of contributions from translation, rotation, vibrations, nuclear spin, electron spin, and electronic angular momentum. The corresponding state of the molecule is thus described by a set of quantum numbers, namely, l, m, and n for translation; J, K, etc., for rotation; v_i for vibration; i for nuclear spin; s for electron spin; Λ for electronic angular momentum. The subscript k denotes such a particular set of values of the various quantum numbers.

If the energy ϵ_k can be separated approximately into independent contributions from the various degrees of freedom, it may be written as a sum of these contributions, each denoted by its own quantum numbers:

$$\epsilon_k = \epsilon_{l,m,n} + \epsilon_{J,K} + \sum_i \epsilon_{v_i} + \epsilon_i + \epsilon_s + \epsilon_\Lambda. \qquad (18.4\text{–}8)$$

The corresponding *a priori* probabilities $p_{l,m,n}$, etc., are multiplicative, and thus the partition function may be written in expanded form as

$$Q = \sum_{l,m,n} p_{l,m,n}e^{-\epsilon_{l,m,n}/kT} \sum_{J,K} p_{JK}e^{-\epsilon_{JK}/kT} \prod_i \sum_{v_i} p_{v_i}e^{-\epsilon_{v_i}/kT}$$

$$\sum_i p_i e^{-\epsilon_i/kT} \sum_s p_s e^{-\epsilon_s/kT} \sum_\Lambda p_\Lambda e^{-\epsilon_\Lambda/kT}. \qquad (18.4\text{–}9)$$

In equation (18.4–9) the terms $p_{l,m,n}$, $p_{J,K}$, etc., are the weighting factors for the translational, rotational, and other degrees of freedom. In general, there is more than one vibrational degree of freedom, and the separate sums over each of these (denoted by its quantum number v_i) must be multiplied together; this is indicated by the large Π in front of the vibrational term. The equation may be written in condensed form as

$$Q = Q_t Q_r \prod_i Q_{v_i} Q_{ns} Q_{es} Q_e, \qquad (18.4\text{–}10)$$

where each Q represents one of the summations of equation (18.4–9).

Problem 18.4-2. Using the values of B_e and ω_e for HCl in Table 16.15–2, calculate ϵ_J and ϵ_v for $J = 10$ and $v = 4$. (*Note.* Use the second and first terms in the right side of equation (16.7–1).) Calculate the correct energy of this level and the error made by treating the rotational and vibrational energies as independent, as in equation (16.17–1).

Thus the partition function can be represented, using equation (18.4–10), as a product of partition functions due to translation (t), rotation (r), individual modes of vibration (v_i), nuclear spin (ns), electron spin (es), and electronic energies (e). The nuclear spin energies are practically equal for all values of the quantum numbers, as are also the electron spin energies to a first approximation. On this account the partition functions reduce to a number equal to the number of states p_{ns} and p_{es} respectively. For all systems except hydrogen and deuterium, p_{ns} can be separated out and is the product of the partition functions $(p_{ns})_k$ for each nucleus. On this account nuclear spin effects cancel in calculating thermodynamic properties for chemical reactions involving elements other than hydrogen and deuterium. In Section 19.5 nuclear spin effects are considered in detail, but for the time being we shall neglect them. The electronic spin function p_{es} is seldom other than unity. Oxygen, however, is an example of a case where p_{es} is equal to 3; it will be discussed in Section 19.2. Because excited electronic states are rarely present, p_e is usually unity. For the present only states where p_{es} and p_e are unity will be considered. Thus equation (18.4–10) takes on a very simple form, involving only sums for translation, rotation, and vibration.

Problem 18.4-3. Calculate Q_r and Q_v for HCl^{35} at 298.15°K by evaluating the energies of the levels approximately as in Problem 18.4–2, using equation (16.17–1).

Problem 18.4-4. Calculate the partition function Q_{int}, for HCl^{35} at 298.15°K by summing directly over the rotational and vibrational energy levels as given by equations (16.12–3) and (16.12–10). Compare this with the product $Q_r \cdot Q_v$ of the quantities calculated in the previous problem.

When the separation described by equation (18.4–10) cannot be made, it is always possible to make the separation of the energies into (a) the energy due to translation and (b) the energy due to rotation and vibration coupled with the electronic energy. Usually the molecule is in its electronic ground state, so that only the energy levels due to rotation and vibration are involved. (Oxygen is an example of an exception.) Thus the energy may usually be written

$$\epsilon_k = \epsilon_{l,m,n,} + \epsilon_{J,K,v_i}, \tag{18.4–11}$$

where the last term is a rotation-vibration energy level. The partition function is then written

$$Q = Q_t Q_{\text{int}}, \tag{18.4–12}$$

where Q_{int} is the *internal partition function.* When all except rotation and vibration can be neglected, this is

$$Q_{\text{int}} = \Sigma p_{J,K,v_i} e^{-\epsilon_{J,K,v_i}}. \tag{18.4–13}$$

When the partition function (18.4–12) has been substituted into equation (18.4–7a) the resulting expression for the entropy of a polyatomic gas is

$$\tilde{S} = R\left[\ln \frac{Q_t}{\mathbf{N}} + T\frac{\partial \ln Q_t}{\partial T} + 1\right] + R\left[\ln Q_{\text{int}} + T\frac{\partial \ln Q_{\text{int}}}{\partial T}\right]. \tag{18.4–14}$$

The right side of this equation separates into two parts:

$$\tilde{S}_t = R\left[\ln \frac{Q_t}{\mathbf{N}} + T\frac{\partial \ln Q_t}{\partial T} + 1\right], \tag{18.4–15}$$

and

$$\tilde{S}_{\text{int}} = R\left[\ln Q_{\text{int}} + T\frac{\partial \ln Q_{\text{int}}}{\partial T}\right]. \tag{18.4–16}$$

The latter of these two equations is, of course, the same as the expression for the entropy of localized elements (18.3–14). The elements are here the wave functions of the centers of gravity of the molecules identified by the translational quantum number n, l, and m, among which the rotation-vibrational energy levels are distributed. The first equation is the expression for non-localized elements which are the indistinguishable centers of gravity of the molecules among which the rotational-vibration wave function are distributed.

Problem 18.4-5. Calculate the entropy due to rotation and vibration of hydrogen chloride (HCl^{35}) at 298.15°K, assuming that the partition function can be separated as in equation (18.4–9). (See also Problems 18.4–2 and 18.4–4.)

Problem 18.4-6. Calculate the entropy due to rotation and vibration of HCl^{35} at 298.15°K, using equations (16.12–3) and (16.12–10) to evaluate the energies. Compare the result with that of the last problem.

18.5 Partition Function for Translation

The translational energy of a molecule of mass m in a container with sides of length a, b, and c is given by

$$\epsilon_{l,m,n} = \frac{h^2}{8m}\left(\frac{l^2}{a^2} + \frac{m^2}{b^2} + \frac{n^2}{c^2}\right). \tag{18.5–1}$$

Thus the partition function is

$$Q_t = \sum_l \sum_m \sum_n e^{-\epsilon_{l,m,n}/kT} \tag{18.5–2}$$

(note that the weight of a state with given l, m, n is unity), or

$$Q_t = \sum_{l=1}^{\infty} e^{-h^2l^2/8\text{m}a^2kT} \sum_{m=1}^{\infty} e^{-h^2m^2/8\text{m}b^2kT} \sum_{n=1}^{\infty} e^{-h^2n^2/8\text{m}c^2kT}. \tag{18.5–3}$$

To a first approximation, when a, b, and c are large,

$$\sum_{l=1}^{\infty} e^{-h^2l^2/8\text{m}a^2kT} = \int_0^{\infty} e^{-h^2l^2/8\text{m}a^2kT}\, dl = \frac{(2\pi\text{m}kT)^{1/2}a}{h}, \tag{18.5–4}$$

and similarly for the other two summations. (See Appendix 5 for a table of integrals.) Thus

$$Q_t = \frac{(2\pi\text{m}kT)^{3/2}abc}{h^3} \tag{18.5–5}$$

$$= \frac{(2\pi\text{m}kT)^{3/2}V}{h^3} \tag{18.5–6}$$

As will be shown later, this partition function leads to the perfect gas law

$$PV = nkT.$$

Consequently, the partition function may also be written

$$Q_t = \frac{(2\pi\text{m})^{3/2}(kT)^{5/2}n}{Ph^3}. \tag{18.5–7}$$

Problem 18.5-1. (a) For a helium atom in a cubical box whose side is 5 cm, calculate the first twenty translational *energy levels*.

(b) For each energy obtained in part (a), list the possible combinations of l, m, and n which give this energy, and thus obtain the number of *states* for each energy.

(c) By use of equation (18.5–2), obtain the contribution of these energy levels at 300°K to the partition function Q_t. Note that for $x \ll 1$, $e^{-x} \approx 1 - x$.

Problem 18.5-2. Calculate the translational partition function of helium gas in a volume of 125 cm³ at 300°K. From the result estimate roughly the number of states which contribute appreciably to the partition function (see Problem 18.5–1).

Problem 18.5-3. As a rough approximation, an electron trapped in a crystal may be considered a particle in a box. Calculate the first three translational energy levels of a particle with the mass of an electron trapped in a cubical box 4 Å on a side. Compare the energies so obtained with the value of kT at 300°K.

If the boundary conditions, and thus the energy of each state, are to be maintained constant, each of the lengths a, b, and c must be held constant. That is, the volume must be kept constant. However, equation (18.5–7) shows how the partition function changes with pressure. The effect of pressure is entirely due to the changing boundary conditions so long as n is left fixed; for example, at the number of molecules, **N**, in one gram mole.

The expressions (18.5–6) and (18.5–7) can also be deduced from the results of Section 17.8. The term $e^{-\alpha}$ (denoted also by C'') in equation (17.7–1) is given by equation (17.8–3) as

$$e^{-\alpha} = C'' = \frac{nh^3}{V(2\pi \mathrm{m}kT)^{3/2}} . \tag{17.8–3}$$

However, according to equation (17.4–15a), this term is given in general by

$$e^{-\alpha} = \frac{n}{\sum_i e^{-\beta\epsilon_i}} = \frac{n}{Q} . \tag{18.5–8}$$

Upon comparison of (17.8–3) and (18.5–8), if translation alone is considered, the partition function Q_t must be given as in equation (18.5–6).

18.6 Translational Entropy of a Gas. The Sackur-Tetrode Equation

The translational entropy of a gas is obtained by substitution of Q_t, as given by equation (18.5–6), into equation 18.4–15. To be sure that the same set of energy levels is retained, the volume V must be held constant during the differentiation. Then, for n molecules,

$$S_t = nk\left[\ln \frac{(2\pi \mathrm{m}kT)^{3/2}V}{h^3 n} + T\frac{\mathrm{d} \ln T^{3/2}}{\mathrm{d}T} + 1\right]$$

$$= nk\left[\ln \frac{(2\pi \mathrm{m}kT)^{3/2}V}{h^3 n} + \frac{5}{2}\right] . \tag{18.6–1}$$

V may now be replaced by nkT/P, so that

$$S_t = nk\left[\ln \frac{(2\pi \mathrm{m})^{3/2}(kT)^{5/2}}{h^3 P} + \frac{5}{2}\right] . \tag{18.6–2}$$

For a mole of gas,

$$\tilde{S}_t = R\left[\frac{5}{2}\ln T - \ln P + \ln\frac{(2\pi \mathrm{m})^{3/2}k^{5/2}}{h^3} + \frac{5}{2}\right]. \qquad (18.6\text{–}3)$$

This equation is known as the Sackur-Tetrode equation.[2–4]

Problem 18.6-1. Show that if the mass m is expressed in terms of the gram molecular weight, $\tilde{M}$, and if numerical values are substituted for the universal constants, equation (18.6–3) becomes (for P in atmospheres)

$$\tilde{S}_t = R(\tfrac{5}{2}\ln T - \ln P + \tfrac{3}{2}\ln \tilde{M} - 1.164). \qquad (18.6\text{–}4)$$

The necessary values for k and h are found in Appendix 1.

Problem 18.6-2. Calculate the molal entropy of gaseous argon at its normal boiling point, 87.3°K; compare with the measured value of 30.85 cal mole^{-1} deg^{-1}.

Problem 18.6-3. Calculate the translational entropy (a) of HCl^{35}, and (b) of oxygen, at 298.15°K, 1 atm.

Problem 18.6-4. Calculate the total entropy of HCl^{35} at 298.15°K, 1 atm.

Equation (18.6–2) (or its equivalent, equation 18.6–1) may also be obtained, in a formal manner, by using the relationship

$$\tilde{S}_t = R\left[\ln\left(\frac{Q_t}{\mathbf{N}}\right) + T\left(\frac{\partial \ln Q_t}{\partial T}\right)_P\right], \qquad (18.6\text{–}5)$$

with Q_t given by equation (18.5–7).

Problem 18.6-5. Prove the last statement.

18.7 Expressions for the Thermodynamic Functions

Whether a system is localized or not, its energy under classical conditions must be given by the same expression, since under these conditions all distribution laws become identical. The expression is

$$\tilde{E} = RT^2\frac{\partial \ln Q}{\partial T}. \qquad (18.2\text{–}6)$$

In dealing with the translational partition function of a gas, the volume V must be held constant to keep the boundary conditions on the wave equation fixed. Thus, for the translational energy of one mole of perfect gas,

$$\tilde{E}_t = RT^2\left(\frac{\partial \ln Q_t}{\partial T}\right)_V, \qquad (18.7\text{–}1)$$

[2] O. Sackur, *Ann. Physik*, **36**, 958 (1911).

[3] H. Tetrode, *Ann. Physik*, **38**, 434 (1912); *Verslag. Akad. Wetenschappen*, **23,** 1110 (1915).

[4] P. Ehrenfest and V. Trkal, *Proc. Acad. Sci.*, Amsterdam, **23,** 162 (1920).

where Q_t is given by equation (18.5–6). Wherever the translational partition function is involved, it can be expressed as a function of T and V or of T and P. It is usually desirable to indicate this in the partial derivative notation. It then follows immediately that

$$\tilde{E}_t = \frac{3RT}{2}. \tag{18.7–2}$$

Problem 18.7-1. Prove equation (18.7–2) by substituting (18.5–6) into (18.7–1) and carrying out the differentiation.

The translational enthalpy of a perfect gas is then given by

$$\tilde{H}_t = \tilde{E}_t + P\tilde{V} = \frac{5RT}{2}. \tag{18.7–3}$$

Alternatively, the translational contribution to the enthalpy is

$$\tilde{H}_t = RT^2\left(\frac{\partial \ln Q_t}{\partial T}\right)_P, \tag{18.7–4}$$

where Q_t is given by equation (18.5–7).

Problem 18.7-2. Show by appropriate substitution and differentiation that equation (18.7–4) yields the result $\tilde{H}_t = 5RT/2$.

The contribution of translation to the Gibbs free energy is, of course,

$$\tilde{F}_t = \tilde{H}_t - T\tilde{S}_t. \tag{18.7–5}$$

When equations (18.6–5) and (18.7–4) are used for the entropy and enthalpy respectively, the Gibbs free energy due to translation is, for one mole of gas,

$$\tilde{F}_t = -RT \ln \frac{Q_t}{\mathrm{N}}. \tag{18.7–6}$$

Making use of equations (18.6–3) and (18.7–3),

$$\tilde{F}_t = -RT\left[\frac{5}{2}\ln T - \ln P + \frac{\ln\,(2\pi \mathrm{m})^{3/2}k^{5/2}}{h^3}\right]. \tag{18.7–7}$$

When the mass m is expressed in atomic weight units

$$\tilde{F}_t = -RT\left[\frac{5}{2}\ln T - \ln P + \frac{3}{2}\ln \tilde{M} - 3.664\right]. \tag{18.7–8}$$

Problem 18.7-3. Calculate the free energy of argon at 298.15°K, 1 atm.

The contribution of translation to the heat capacity at constant volume is

$$(\tilde{C}_V)_t = \left(\frac{\partial \tilde{E}_t}{\partial T}\right)_V = \left(\frac{\partial}{\partial T}\right)_V \left[RT^2\left(\frac{\partial \ln Q_t}{\partial T}\right)_V\right] = \frac{3R}{2}, \quad (18.7\text{–}9)$$

where Q_t is to be expressed by equation (18.5–6). Similarly, for the contribution of translation to the heat capacity at constant pressure,

$$(\tilde{C}_P)_t = \left(\frac{\partial \tilde{H}_t}{\partial T}\right)_P = \left(\frac{\partial}{\partial T}\right)\left[RT^2\left(\frac{\partial \ln Q}{\partial T}\right)_P\right] = \frac{5R}{2}, \quad (18.7\text{–}10)$$

where Q_t is to be expressed by equation (18.5–7).

Problem 18.7-4. Derive equations (18.7–9) and (18.7–10) in detail.

In considering the contribution of internal degrees of freedom to the free energy of a gas, it must be noted that the $P\tilde{V}$ term is taken care of in the translational degrees of freedom, so that other degrees of freedom may be treated as if localized. Then $H_{\text{int}} = E_{\text{int}}$, and

$$F_{\text{int}} = E_{\text{int}} - TS_{\text{int}}. \quad (18.7\text{–}11)$$

The contribution of the internal degrees of freedom to the energy, $\tilde{E}_{\text{int}}$, is given by equation (18.2–6):

$$\tilde{E}_{\text{int}} = RT^2 \frac{\partial \ln Q_{\text{int}}}{\partial T}. \quad (18.7\text{–}12)$$

The contribution of the internal degrees of freedom to the entropy, $\tilde{S}_{\text{int}}$, is given by the expression for localized systems:

$$\tilde{S}_{\text{int}} = \frac{\tilde{E}_{\text{int}}}{T} + R \ln Q_{\text{int}}. \quad (18.7\text{–}13)$$

Thus

$$\tilde{F}_{\text{int}} = -RT \ln Q_{\text{int}}. \quad (18.7\text{–}14)$$

It is to be noted that Q_{int} is independent of pressure and volume, so that its temperature derivatives at constant pressure and at constant volume are equal.

It is now possible to write down all the thermodynamic functions for one mole of any gas in terms of the complete partition function Q, which is the product of Q_t and Q_{int}. These are

$$\tilde{E}^\circ - \tilde{E}_0^\circ = RT^2\left(\frac{\partial \ln Q}{\partial T}\right)_V, \tag{18.7–15}$$

$$\tilde{H}^\circ - \tilde{E}_0^\circ = RT^2\left(\frac{\partial \ln Q}{\partial T}\right)_P, \tag{18.7–16}$$

$$\tilde{C}_V^\circ = \left(\frac{\partial}{\partial T}\right)_V\left[RT^2\left(\frac{\partial \ln Q}{\partial T}\right)_V\right] = \frac{R}{T^2}\left[\frac{\partial^2 \ln Q}{\partial(1/T)^2}\right]_V, \tag{18.7–17}$$

$$\tilde{C}_P^\circ = \left(\frac{\partial}{\partial T}\right)_P\left[RT^2\left(\frac{\partial \ln Q}{\partial T}\right)_P\right] = \frac{R}{T^2}\left[\frac{\partial^2 \ln Q}{\partial(1/T)^2}\right]_P, \tag{18.7–18}$$

$$\tilde{F} - \tilde{E}_0^\circ = -RT \ln \frac{Q}{\mathbf{N}}, \tag{18.7–19}$$

and

$$\tilde{S} = \frac{\tilde{H} - \tilde{E}_0^\circ}{T} + R \ln \frac{Q}{\mathbf{N}}. \tag{18.7–20}$$

The superscript (°), as usual, denotes the standard state which is the ideal gas at 1 atm. The superscript is omitted from $\tilde{S}$, $\tilde{F}$, and $\tilde{A}$ because of their pressure dependencies. $\tilde{E}$, $\tilde{H}$, $\tilde{C}_V$, and $\tilde{C}_P$ are independent of pressure because the gases are ideal. The quantity $\tilde{E}_0^\circ$ is essentially a constant of integration. It represents the energy of the system at the absolute zero. For a monatomic gas here regarded as classical, $\tilde{E}_0^\circ$ must be taken as zero because in deriving the Sackur-Tetrode equation (18.6–3) integration was made from $l = n = m = 0$ to $l = n = m = \infty$ in deriving equation (18.5–4). For gaseous molecules $\tilde{E}_0^\circ$ usually will be their zero point vibrational energy plus the change in electronic energy during formation from the gaseous elements. In other words, it is the heat of formation of the gaseous compound at the absolute zero. Obviously $\tilde{E}_0^\circ$ will be modified if the reference state is not the constituent elements with zero energy at the absolute zero.

Since

$$S = \frac{H}{T} - \frac{F}{T},$$

the constant of integration cancels from $\tilde{S}$. For differentiation at constant volume, Q must be expressed in terms of the volume; for differentiation at constant pressure, Q must be expressed explicitly in terms of the pressure. Finally, for completeness, the expression for the Helmholtz free energy is

$$\tilde{A} - \tilde{E}_0^\circ = \tilde{F} - RT = -RT\left[\ln \frac{Q}{\mathrm{N}} + 1\right] = -kT \ln \frac{Q^{\mathrm{N}}}{\mathrm{N}!}. \quad (18.7\text{–}21)$$

Problem 18.7-5. Derive equation (18.7–21) in detail, remembering that $\ln \mathrm{N}! = \mathrm{N} \ln \mathrm{N} - \mathrm{N}$.

Problem 18.7-6. Calculate $\tilde{E}$, $\tilde{H}$, $\tilde{C}_P$, $\tilde{C}_V$, $\tilde{S}$, $\tilde{F}$, and $\tilde{A}$ for HCl^{35} at 298.15°K, 1 atm, assuming that rotational and vibrational energy can be separated as in Problems 18.4–3 and 18.4–5. Discussion of the case of the natural isotopic mixture which constitutes ordinary hydrogen chloride is reserved for Section 18.10.

Problem 18.7-7. Using the equation relating the thermodynamic functions to the partition function, derive an expression for the pressure of a gas. By considering the translational partition function, show that $P = RT/\tilde{V}$. (*Hint.* Use the expression for the Helmholtz free energy $\tilde{A}$.)

Problem 18.7-8. Derive the relations $(\partial\tilde{F}/\partial T)_P = -\tilde{S}$ and $(\partial\tilde{S}/\partial P)_T = -(\partial\tilde{V}/\partial T)_P$ for a perfect gas, using the relations of the thermodynamic functions to the partition function.

The last two problems illustrate that the thermodynamic functions defined in terms of Q, as has been done above, differentiate exactly like the thermodynamic functions as they have been defined in Chapter 6. Actually this is all that is required of the definition. For practical purposes, it would have been sufficient to write down the relations and show that they differentiate properly, without the detailed considerations outlined in this chapter.

18.8 Contributions of Electronic States to Thermodynamic Properties

The contributions of higher (excited) electronic states to the thermodynamic properties of a monatomic gas may be treated quite simply, since there are no rotational or vibrational modes to interact with the electronic motion. The electronic states may thus be treated as another internal degree of freedom and handled as a localized system. The formulas given in Sections 18.2 and 18.3 for the energy, heat capacity, and entropy then apply, and the other thermodynamic properties may be derived from them as in Section 18.7. The required partition function is

$$Q_e = \sum p_e e^{-\epsilon_e/kT}, \quad (18.8\text{–}1)$$

with the summation taken over all electronic levels. The assignment of appropriate weighting factors to the electronic levels has been discussed in Section 17.4. Usually only a small number of levels need be considered; the partition function and the thermodynamic properties are obtained from direct summations, as in equations (18.2–2), etc.

The electronic states of a diatomic or polyatomic gas, if they need to be considered, interact strongly with the rotational and vibrational modes. This will be seen in the examples of the next chapter, where special techniques are described for particular cases. The contribution of electronic states in molecules will not be considered further here for this reason. The electronic states of solids and liquids are frequently properties of the substance as a whole, rather than of a particular atom (as, for example, in conducting metals). For this reason they are generally beyond the scope of this book. In some cases, however, the electron spin and electron orbital contributions may be considered for independent atoms or molecules; then they are treated the same as in the monatomic gases.

Problem 18.8-1. The ground state of the oxygen atom is a $^3P_2$. The lowest excited levels are a $^3P_1$ at 158.5 cm^{-1} a $^3P_0$ at 226.5 cm^{-1}, and a $^1D_2$ at 15,870 cm^{-1}.

(a) Calculate the electronic contribution to the energy, entropy, and heat capacity of atomic oxygen at 150°K.

(b) Calculate the total energy, entropy, and heat capacity at 150°K, 1 atm of atomic oxygen.

(c) Calculate the fraction of oxygen atoms in the $^1D_2$ state at 5000°K. (Levels higher than the $^1D_2$ do not contribute appreciably to this calculation.)

Problem 18.8-2. The ground state of atomic bromine is $^2P_{3/2}$. There is a $^2P_{1/2}$ level 3685 cm^{-1} above the ground state, and the next level is a $^4P_{5/2}$ at 63,430 cm^{-1}. Calculate the electronic energy, entropy, and heat capacity of atomic bromine at (a) 2000°K, (b) 4000°K.

Problem 18.8-3. The ground state of cobalt is a $^4F_{9/2}$. Succeeding levels, up to 18,000 cm^{-1}, are given below (all units cm^{-1}). Calculate the electronic entropy of gaseous cobalt at the boiling point, 2900°C.

$^4F_{7/2}$	816	$^4F_{5/2}$	4,690	$^4P_{3/2}$	14,036	$^2G_{9/2}$	16,468
$^4F_{5/2}$	1,406.8	$^4F_{3/2}$	5,076	$^4P_{1/2}$	14,399	$^2G_{7/2}$	17,234
$^4F_{3/2}$	1,809.3	$^2F_{7/2}$	7,442	$^4P_{5/2}$	15,184	$^2D_{3/2}$	16,471
$^4F_{9/2}$	3,483	$^2F_{5/2}$	8,461	$^4P_{3/2}$	15,774	$^2D_{5/2}$	16,778
$^4F_{7/2}$	4,125	$^4P_{5/2}$	13,796	$^4P_{1/2}$	16,196	$^2P_{3/2}$	18,390

Problem 18.8-4. The ionization potentials of atomic oxygen, in order, are 13.6, 35.1, 55.1, 77.3, 113.7, 138.1, 739, and 871 v. (Note that the second ionization potential is the potential required to remove an electron from O^+, etc.) Estimate the temperature range at which an appreciable fraction of elementary oxygen would exist as the nucleus without any electrons. As a very crude approximation it may be assumed that the total number of electronic excited states for each ionic species is roughly the same.

Problem 18.8-5. The ground state of the nickel ion in $NiSO_4 \cdot 7H_2O$ is a triplet, corresponding to the three possible orientations of the unit electron spin of the ion. The crystalline environment produces differences in energy between the three orientations. Stout and Giauque[5] interpret their observed low temperature heat capacity data in terms of a model in which the three levels are distinct, with a separation of 2.6 cm^{-1} between each pair. Using this spacing for the energy levels, calculate the "magnetic" heat capacity associated with transitions between them at 1°, 2°, 5°, and 10°K.

[5] J. W. Stout and W. F. Giauque, *J. Am. Chem. Soc.*, **63,** 714 (1941).

Problem 18.8-6. The ground state of Nd in $Nd_2(SO_4)_3 \cdot 8H_2O$ is a $^4I_{9/2}$. According to theory, the tenfold degeneracy of the state is split by the crystalline environment into a doublet (lowest) and two quartets. The spectroscopic results of Spedding, Hamlin, and Nutting[6] place the upper states at 77 cm^{-1} and 260 cm^{-1} respectively.

(a) Calculate the electronic contribution to the molar heat capacity at 30°K (the total heat capacity is about 6.6 cal mole^{-1} deg^{-1} at this temperature).

(b) Estimate the temperature at which the state at 260 cm^{-1} would contribute heavily to the heat capacity.

18.9 Relation of Thermodynamic Functions from Statistical Mechanics to the Equilibrium Constant

It is clear that the ΔH of a chemical reaction

$$\text{aA} + \text{bB} = \text{lL} + \text{mM} \tag{18.9–1}$$

is given by

$$\Delta H = \Delta E_0^\circ + \text{l}(\tilde{H} - \tilde{H}_0^\circ)_\text{L} + \text{m}(\tilde{H} - \tilde{H}_0^\circ)_\text{M} - \text{a}(\tilde{H} - \tilde{H}_0^\circ)_\text{A} - \text{b}(\tilde{H} - \tilde{H}_0^\circ)_\text{B}, \tag{18.9–2}$$

where $(\tilde{H} - \tilde{H}_0^\circ)_\text{A}$, etc., are the molal enthalpies relative to those at 0°K. ΔH at some given temperature being known, ΔE_0° can be calculated through evaluation of $(\tilde{H} - \tilde{H}_0^\circ)_\text{A}$, etc., at this same temperature. If the compounds in equation (18.9–1) are all ideal gases or gases at zero pressure, the equations of this chapter suffice to calculate $(\tilde{H}^\circ - \tilde{H}_0^\circ)_\text{A}$, etc. Other cases will be taken up in later chapters. In this special case ΔH is then ΔH°, and equation (18.9–2) is written

$$\Delta H^\circ = \Delta E_0^\circ + \text{l}(\tilde{H}^\circ - \tilde{H}_0^\circ)_\text{L} + \text{m}(\tilde{H}^\circ - \tilde{H}_0^\circ)_\text{M} - \text{a}(\tilde{H}^\circ - \tilde{H}_0^\circ)_\text{A} - \text{b}(\tilde{H}^\circ - \tilde{H}_0^\circ)_\text{B}. \tag{18.9–3}$$

ΔE_0° having been found, ΔF° and the equilibrium constant K can at once be calculated from the equation

$$\Delta F^\circ = -RT \ln K = \Delta \tilde{E}_0^\circ + \text{l}(\tilde{F}^\circ - \tilde{E}_0^\circ)_\text{L} + \text{m}(\tilde{F}^\circ - \tilde{E}_0^\circ)_\text{M} - \text{a}(\tilde{F}^\circ - \tilde{E}_0^\circ)_\text{A} - \text{b}(\tilde{F}^\circ - \tilde{E}_0^\circ)_\text{B} \tag{18.9–4}$$

where $(\tilde{F}^\circ - \tilde{E}_0^\circ)_\text{A}$, etc., are to be calculated from equation (18.7–19) at a pressure of 1 atm.

Problem 18.9-1. Calculate the equilibrium constant for the reaction $H_2 + Cl_2 = 2HCl$ from the following values of $\tilde{H}^\circ - \tilde{E}_0^\circ$ and $\tilde{F}^\circ - E_0^\circ$ at 298.15°K. At 298.15°K, ΔH° for this reaction is −44,126 cal.

	$\tilde{H}^\circ - \tilde{E}_0^\circ$	$\tilde{F}^\circ - \tilde{E}_0^\circ$
H_2	2023.8	−7,282
Cl_2	2064.4	−11,251
HCl	2149.2	−13,701

[6] F. H. Spedding, H. F. Hamlin, and G. C. Nutting, *J. Chem. Phys.*, **5**, 191 (1937).

18.10 An Alternative Method of Relating Thermodynamic Functions to the Partition Function for Localized Degrees of Freedom

Giauque[7] has used an interesting method of deriving the expressions of the previous section for localized degrees of freedom only, which is valid where they accompany translational degrees of freedom, as in hydrogen, hydrogen chloride, etc. He starts with the assumption that all quantum states have equal probability and treats each quantum state as a chemical compound. The relation of entropy to probability then assigns to each of these states equal entropy. In the transition of one state (A) to another state (B), on the basis of one mole of elements in each of the states, it follows that $\Delta\tilde{S}^\circ = 0$ and

$$\Delta F^\circ = \tilde{F}_B{}^\circ - \tilde{F}_A{}^\circ = \tilde{E}_B{}^\circ - \tilde{E}_A{}^\circ \tag{18.10–1}$$

since the $P\tilde{V}$ products are the same for each state. That isolated rotational and vibrational states accompanying all possible states of translation can be treated thermodynamically is obvious on considering the case of *o*-hydrogen at about 9°K, where the only state present has $v = 0$, $J = 1$. It is easier to follow the contributions of groups of translational states in a single rotational and vibrational state to the thermodynamic properties than to follow the extreme abstractions of Gibbs outlined in Chapter 23. All such states make exactly the same contribution to the pressure for a given amount.

Moreover,

$$\Delta F^\circ = -RT \ln K = \frac{n_B}{n_A}, \tag{18.10–2}$$

where n_B and n_A are the number of elements in each state. The volume accessible to each state is the same, thus making concentrations proportional to the number of elements. Thus

$$\frac{n_B}{n_A} = \frac{e^{-\tilde{E}_B{}^\circ/RT}}{e^{-\tilde{E}_A{}^\circ/RT}}. \tag{18.10–3}$$

Writing ϵ_A and ϵ_B for $\tilde{E}_A{}^\circ/N$ and $\tilde{E}_B{}^\circ/N$ respectively, we have

$$\frac{n_B}{n_A} = \frac{e^{-\epsilon_B/kT}}{e^{-\epsilon_A/kT}}. \tag{18.10–4}$$

From this the distribution law for localized elements follows at once.

[7] W. F. Giauque, *J. Am. Chem. Soc.*, **52**, 4808 (1930). The author of this paper once explained to the senior author that it was written in an effort to make chemists and physicists of the time understand how to treat the case of *o*- and *p*-hydrogen to obtain the measured values.

Problem 18.10-1. Derive equation (17.4–18),

$$n_k = \frac{np_k e^{-\epsilon_k/kT}}{\Sigma p_k e^{-\epsilon_k/kT}}; \qquad (17.4\text{–}18)$$

for the number of molecules in a group of p_k states of energy ϵ_k from equation (18.10–4).

Giauque then considers that the entropy due to the localized elements is due to entropy of mixing. The mole fraction in each individual quantum state for one mole of elements is $n_i/\mathbf{N}$ and thus, using equation (11.2–3),

$$\tilde{S} = -\Sigma \frac{n_i}{\mathbf{N}} R \ln \frac{n_i}{\mathbf{N}}. \qquad (18.10\text{–}5)$$

From this the equation,

$$\tilde{S} = \frac{\tilde{E}}{T} + R \ln Q \qquad (18.3\text{–}15)$$

results at once after substituting for n_i (using the Boltzmann distribution law).

Problem 18.10-2. Derive equation (18.3–15) starting with equation (18.10–5) and using the Boltzmann distribution law in the appropriate form.

Problem 18.10-3. Explain why the methods of this section cannot be applied to translational degrees of freedom.

18.11 Effect of Isotopic Composition

In calculating the entropy through equation (18.4–14), the quantities used should be those for only one of the isotopic species. The quantity obtained by calculating the entropy of the gas due to each isotope and adding these together is

$$\tilde{S}' = \sum_i \tilde{N}_i \tilde{S}_i, \qquad (18.11\text{–}1)$$

where $\tilde{N}_i$ and $\tilde{S}_i$ are respectively the mole fraction and entropy of each isotopic species. If the *true* entropy of the mixture is desired, we must add to the total $\tilde{S}'$ the entropy of mixing:

$$\Delta\tilde{S}_m = -R\,\Sigma \tilde{N}_i \ln \tilde{N}_i. \qquad (18.11\text{–}2)$$

Since the isotopic composition of compounds is normally constant, the entropy of mixing as given by equation (18.11–2) is constant and is manifest only in processes involving the separation of isotopes. In the crystal the isotopic constituents form a perfect solution. It is therefore evident that the entropy of mixing may be neglected except in processes involving the separation of isotopes, and the entropy may therefore be computed for each isotopic species as described above and averaged using equation (18.11–1). Moreover, the sum in the rotational-vibrational partition function of equation (18.4–13) can be taken over energy levels which are averages of the levels of the isotopes, weighted according to composition. This function, when substituted into equation (18.3–14), gives an average value of the practical rotational and vibrational entropy of the isotopes. When this average value is combined with a translational entropy, calculated from equation (18.6–3) by using the average molecular weight, the result differs only minutely from that calculated by using equation (18.11–1). The average over the energy levels can be obtained directly from averages taken over the spectroscopic multiplets weighted according to intensity. The other thermodynamic quantities can be calculated similarly, with the entropy of mixing excluded from the free energy.

Problem 18.11-1. Calculate the entropy of ordinary HCl gas at 298.15°K, 1 atm, assuming that the isotopic composition is Cl^{35}, 75.4 mole per cent, Cl^{37}, 24.6 mole per cent, assuming that the energy is given by equation (16.4–9). Use the data of Problem 16.15–4.

18.12 Thermodynamic Functions Corresponding to Einstein-Bose and Fermi-Dirac Systems at High Densities

In Section 18.4 we derived expressions for the thermodynamic functions for non-localized systems that were applicable to Einstein-Bose and Fermi-Dirac systems in the classical limit which is reached at relatively high temperatures or low densities. We shall now proceed to derive expressions which do not have these limitations.[8] In deriving the distribution laws the expression (17.5–12), which led to the Einstein distribution law, could have been deduced directly from the expression

$$\sum_k \left(\beta\epsilon_k + \alpha - \frac{\partial \ln \mathbf{P}}{\partial n_k}\right)\delta n_k = 0, \qquad (18.12\text{–}1)$$

with $\mathbf{P}$ given by (17.5–4). Exactly the same expression, but with $\mathbf{P}$ given by equation (17.6–3), leads to the Fermi-Dirac distribution law. The Stirling approximation has, of course, not yet been made in equation (18.12–1).

Problem 18.12-1. Deduce the Einstein-Bose and Fermi-Dirac distribution laws from equation (18.12–1) after making the proper substitutions.

Equation (18.12–1) may now be integrated, with the temperature held

[8] The following is essentially the method used by A. Sommerfeld, *Z. Physik*, **47,** 1 (1928).

constant (i.e., β constant). However, it must be remembered that α is dependent on n. The result, after substituting E for $\Sigma n_k \epsilon_k$ is

$$\beta E + \Sigma \int \alpha \, dn_k - \ln \mathbf{P} = 0. \tag{18.12–2}$$

We may now equate $k \ln \mathbf{P}$ to the entropy S and β to $(kT)^{-1}$ and rewrite (18.2–2):

$$E - TS = -kT \, \Sigma \int \alpha \, dn_k \tag{18.12–3}$$

or

$$A = -kT \, \Sigma \int \alpha \, dn_k. \tag{18.12–4}$$

Now, according to equation (9.1–18), the partial molecular free energy is given by

$$\tilde{\mu} = \frac{\mu}{\mathbf{N}} = \left(\frac{\partial A}{\partial n}\right)_{V,T} \tag{18.12–5}$$

Thus

$$\frac{\mu}{\mathbf{N}} = -kT \frac{\partial}{\partial n} \Sigma \int \alpha \, dn_k \tag{18.12–6}$$

or

$$\frac{\mu}{\mathbf{N}} = -kT \frac{\partial}{\partial n} \Sigma \int \alpha \frac{dn_k}{dn} \, dn, \tag{18.12–7}$$

$$\frac{\mu}{\mathbf{N}} = -kT \, \Sigma \alpha \frac{dn_k}{dn}, \tag{18.12–8}$$

or, since $\Sigma \, dn_k = dn$,

$$\frac{\mu}{\mathbf{N}} = -kT\alpha. \tag{18.12–9}$$

In the classical limit, it was shown in Section 18.5 that

$$e^{-\alpha} = \frac{n}{Q}, \tag{18.5–8}$$

where Q was the complete partition function (molecular) for non-interacting atoms or molecules in a gas.

In the classical limit, therefore, equation (18.12–9) reduces to

$$\frac{\mu}{\mathbf{N}} = -kT \ln \frac{Q}{\mathbf{N}}. \tag{18.12–10}$$

After correcting for the energy zero and noting that the Gibbs (or Lewis) free energy for one mole of gas is identical with the partial molal free energy μ, we see that this equation is identical with (18.7–19):

$$\tilde{F} - \tilde{E}_0^\circ = -RT \ln \frac{Q}{\mathbf{N}}. \qquad (18.7\text{–}19)$$

Equation (18.12–9) can be rewritten, after substituting for μ the expression in terms of the absolute activity given in Chapter 6,

$$\mu = RT \ln \lambda, \qquad (6.22\text{–}1)$$

where λ is the absolute activity. We thus obtain

$$kT \ln \lambda = -kT\alpha; \qquad (18.12\text{–}11)$$

that is,

$$\lambda = e^{-\alpha}. \qquad (18.12\text{–}12)$$

This is an absolute expression for the absolute activity.

Actually equation (18.12–2) can be used to identify β and α independently of any previous argument. Taking the differential of equation (18.12–2) and remembering that V is constant,

$$\beta \, \mathrm{d}E + \Sigma\alpha \, \mathrm{d}n_k - \mathrm{d} \ln \mathbf{P} = 0. \qquad (18.12\text{–}13)$$

Now $k \, \mathrm{d} \ln \mathbf{P}$ can be replaced by $\mathrm{d}S$ and the equation rearranged to yield (for constant volume)

$$\mathrm{d}E = -\frac{1}{\beta} \Sigma\alpha \, \mathrm{d}n_k + \frac{1}{k\beta} \mathrm{d}S. \qquad (18.12\text{–}14)$$

Since α is a constant and $\Sigma \, \mathrm{d}n_k$ is equal to $\mathrm{d}n$, equation (18.12–14) can be written

$$\mathrm{d}E = -\frac{\alpha}{\beta} \mathrm{d}n + \frac{1}{k\beta} \mathrm{d}S. \qquad (18.12\text{–}15)$$

Since the volume is constant, the remaining variables are n and S. Therefore

$$\left(\frac{\partial E}{\partial n}\right)_{V,S} = -\frac{\alpha}{\beta} \qquad (18.12\text{–}16)$$

and

$$\left(\frac{\partial E}{\partial S}\right)_{V,n} = \frac{1}{k\beta}. \qquad (18.12\text{–}17)$$

According to equation (9.1–24) the left side of the last of these equations is equal to T, and thus β is equal to $(kT)^{-1}$. According to equation (9.1–26) the left side of (18.12–16) is equal to $\mu/\mathbf{N}$ (where the division by the Avogadro number is made because n is the number of molecules, not moles). Thus, after substituting $(kT)^{-1}$ for β, equation (18.12–9) results:

$$\frac{\mu}{\mathbf{N}} = -kT\alpha. \qquad (18.12\text{–}9)$$

Calculation of the Thermodynamic Properties of Diatomic Gases

CHAPTER 19

19.1 Introduction

In the last chapter all equations for calculation of the thermodynamic properties of gases were derived from statistical thermodynamics. Although limited in the case of translation to the classical approximation, the equations are valid for all gases at temperatures where the substance has an appreciable vapor pressure, with the single exception of helium below its boiling point.

The contribution of rotation and vibration to the thermodynamic properties of simple diatomic gases, such as hydrogen chloride, which are in a $^1\Sigma$ ground state, can be calculated in a simple way, as was illustrated in Problem 18.7–6. The necessary calculations involve only a simple summation of $p_J e^{-\epsilon_{J,v}/kT}$ and of $p_J \epsilon_J e^{-\epsilon_{J,v}/kT}$ over the rotational and vibrational quantum numbers; however, at high temperatures the labor of direct summation is excessive. Fortunately it is possible to replace the sums by integrals without loss of accuracy. The method for doing so is considered in Section 19.3. In most cases still further approximation can be made, as shown in Sections 19.5 and 19.6. This leads to simple methods of calculating thermodynamic functions for ideal gases composed of polyatomic molecules. For the non-specialized student it may be desirable to pass directly to these sections and return to portions of Sections 19.2, 19.3, and 19.4 only when reference to them may seem necessary. On second reading, such students will certainly benefit by studying the omitted material, which seems to us the best approach to the approximate methods.

The case of oxygen whose ground state is a $^3\Sigma_g^-$ is sufficiently more complicated to merit detailed consideration. This is provided in the next section.

19.2 The Thermodynamic Properties of Oxygen by Direct Summation

The oxygen molecule has one unit of electron spin, and the orientation of the spin has a small but appreciable effect on the electronic energy of the ground state. The energy levels obtained were discussed in Section 16.15. The differences between the F_1, F_2, and F_3 levels of the $^3\Sigma_g^-$ state (in any vibrational state) were given for some of the states in Table 16.15–3. They are expressed by the equations

$$F_1(K+1) - F_2(K) = (2K+3)B - \lambda - [(2K+3)^2B^2 + \lambda^2 - 2\lambda B]^{1/2} + \mu(K+1) \quad (19.2\text{–}1)$$

and

$$F_3(K-1) - F_2(K) = -(2K-1)B - \lambda + [(2K-1)^2B^2 + \lambda^2 - 2\lambda B]^{1/2} - \mu K. \quad (19.2\text{–}2)$$

The values of the constants for both equations are $B = 1.438\ \text{cm}^{-1}$, $\lambda = 1.985$, and $\mu = -0.008\ \text{cm}^{-1}$. In both equations K is the value of J for the F_2 levels, whence of course the J value of the F_1 level is $K+1$ and that of the F_3 level is $K-1$.[1]

Problem 19.2-1. Using equations (19.2–1) and (19.2–2), check the entries in Table 16.15–3 for $K = 1, 3, 5$, and 7.

The vibrational energy for the F_2 levels of oxygen can be represented by a formula like (16.12–3), and the rotational energy of these levels can be represented by a formula like (16.12–10). Thus the rotation-vibrational energy of each F_2 level, defined by a particular v and K, can be represented by the formula

$$\epsilon_{v,K}/hc = \sum_j \sum_k Y_{jk}(v+\tfrac{1}{2})^j K^k(K+1)^k. \quad (19.2\text{–}3)$$

The units are determined by those of the coefficients Y_{jk} and are chosen to be wave numbers. The ground state is taken as the $^3\Sigma_g^-$ electronic state F_3 level ($J = 0$), with the zero point vibrational energy included. It is evident that Y_{10} is identical with the ω_e of equation (16.12–3), Y_{20} with $-\omega_e x_e$, and Y_{30} with $\omega_e y_e$, etc.; Y_{01}, Y_{02}, etc., are to be identified with the coefficients B_e, $-D_e$, etc., of equation (16.12–10). The quantities Y_{11}, Y_{12}, etc., are to be identified with $-\alpha_e$ of equation (16.12–11) and

[1] H. W. Wooley, *J. Research Natl. Bur. Standards,* **40,** 163 (1948).

β_e of equation (16.12–12), while the quantities Y_{21}, Y_{22}, etc., are to be identified with coefficients of the next higher terms of these equations.

Problem 19.2-2. Obtain Y_{01} and Y_{02} from the data on the atmospheric bands of oxygen, given in Section 16.15. Explain why values of Y_{10}, Y_{11}, etc., cannot be deduced from these data.

The accepted values for the coefficients (in cm^{-1}) for the $^3\Sigma_g^-$ state are

$$Y_{00} = -786.08, \quad Y_{10} = 1580.36, \quad Y_{20} = -12.073,$$

$$Y_{30} = 0.0546, \quad Y_{40} = -0.00143, \quad Y_{01} = 1.4456,$$

$$Y_{11} = -0.0158, \quad Y_{02} = -4.838 \times 10^{-6}, \quad Y_{12} = -4.96 \times 10^{-9},$$

$$Y_{03} = 0.1387 \times 10^{-12}, \quad Y_{04} = -32.2 \times 10^{-18}.$$

An equation similar to (19.2–3) can be used to express the energies of the rotational and vibrational levels of the $^1\Delta_g$ and $^1\Sigma_g^+$ electronic states. For the $^1\Delta_g$ state the values of the constants are

$$Y_{00} = 7132.1, \quad Y_{10} = 1509.3, \quad Y_{20} = -12.9,$$

$$Y_{01} = 1.4264, \quad Y_{11} = -0.0171, \quad Y_{02} = -4.86 \times 10^{-6}\ \text{cm}^{-1}.$$

For the $^1\Sigma_g^+$ state the values of the constants are

$$Y_{00} = 12409.2, \quad Y_{10} = 1432.615, \quad Y_{20} = -13.925,$$

$$Y_{01} = 1.4014, \quad Y_{11} = -0.0188. \quad Y_{02} = -5.36 \times 10^{-6},$$

In either case, the value of Y_{00} is equal to the amount by which the electronic energy (with no zero point energy) is above the electronic energy of the F_3 level with $v = 0$, $J = 0 (K = 1)$, that is, above the electronic energy of the $^3\Sigma_g^-$ *state with its zero point energy* and in an F_3 level with $K = 1$.

Problem 19.2-3. Show that the energy absorbed in a transition from a $^1\Delta_g$ level with K equal to zero and v equal to zero to a $^1\Sigma_g^+$ level with K equal to zero and v equal to zero is equivalent to 5238.51 cm^{-1}.

Problem 19.2-4. Calculate the energy of a $^3\Sigma_g^- F_2$ level with $K = 3$ and $v = 2$, and from it deduce the energy of the corresponding F_1 and F_3 levels.

Having established the energy levels, it is a matter of arithmetic to calculate the partition function Q; the weighting factor $p_{J,v}$ is equal to $2J + 1$. The corresponding sums

$$\sum_J \sum_v p_{J,v} \epsilon_{J,v} e^{-\epsilon_{J,v}/kT} \quad \text{and} \quad \sum_J \sum_v p \epsilon^2 e^{-\epsilon/kT}$$

are also needed for calculation of the thermodynamic properties. The values of $(\tilde{E} - \tilde{E}_0^\circ)$, $-(\tilde{F} - \tilde{E}_0^\circ)/T$, $\tilde{S}$, and $\tilde{C}$ for rotation and vibration can readily be calculated by use of equations (18.2–2), (18.7–14), (18.7–13), and (18.2–14). With the proper substitutions these equations become

$$\tilde{E} - \tilde{E}_0^\circ = \frac{\mathrm{N} \sum_J \sum_v (2J+1)\epsilon_{J,v} e^{-\epsilon_{J,v}/kT}}{\sum_J \sum_v \epsilon_{J,v} e^{-\epsilon_{J,v}/kT}}, \tag{19.2–4}$$

$$-(\tilde{F} - \tilde{E}_0^\circ)/T = R \ln \sum_J \sum_v (2J+1) e^{-\epsilon_{J,v}/kT}, \tag{19.2–5}$$

$$\tilde{S} = \frac{(\tilde{E} - \tilde{E}_0^\circ)}{T} - \frac{\tilde{F} - \tilde{E}_0^\circ}{T}, \tag{19.2–6}$$

$$\tilde{C} = \frac{d\tilde{E}}{dT} = \frac{\mathrm{N}}{kT^2}\left[\frac{\sum_J \sum_v (\epsilon_{J,v})^2 (2J+1) e^{-\epsilon_{J,v}/kT}}{\sum_J \sum_v (2J+1) e^{-\epsilon_{J,v}/kT}} - \left(\frac{\sum_J \sum_v \epsilon_{J,v}(2J+1) e^{-\epsilon_{J,v}/kT}}{\sum_J \sum_v (2J+1) e^{-\epsilon_{J,v}/kT}}\right)^2\right]. \tag{19.2–7}$$

For the $^3\Sigma_g{}^-$ electronic state the sums are taken over the F_1, F_2, and F_3 levels. For the F_2 levels $J = K$, for the F_1 and F_3 levels $J = K + 1$ and $J = K - 1$ respectively. Table 19.2–1 gives the contributions at 298.16°K, to the sums

$$\sum_J \sum_v (2J+1) e^{-\epsilon_{J,v}/kT} \quad \text{and} \quad \sum_J \sum_v \epsilon_{J,v}(2J+1) e^{-\epsilon_{J,v}/kT}$$

of the F_1, F_2, and F_3 levels of the $^3\Sigma_g{}^-$, for the vibrational states $v = 0$, $v = 1$, and $v = 2$ as given by Giauque. The table is taken from the early work of Giauque and Johnston.[2] The values are given in terms of earlier

Table 19.2–1

Sums in the Entropy Equation[2] for Oxygen at 298.16°K

	$\Sigma p e^{-\epsilon/kT}$	$\frac{1}{kT} \Sigma p \epsilon e^{-\epsilon/kT}$
F_1, $v = 0$	83.831	77.959
F_2, $v = 0$	72.882	72.628
F_3, $v = 0$	63.155	67.363
	219.868	217.950
$(F_1 + F_2 + F_3)$, $v = 1$	0.125	1.005
$(F_1 + F_2 + F_3)$, $v = 2$	0.000	0.000
	219.993	218.955

[2] W. F. Giauque and H. L. Johnston, *J. Am. Chem. Soc.*, **51**, 2300 (1929

constants. They serve for illustration and provide a rough check on the arithmetic of the problems below.

Problem 19.2-5. (a) Calculate

$$\sum pe^{-\epsilon/kT} \quad \text{and} \quad \sum p\epsilon e^{-\epsilon/kT}$$

for O_2^{16} at 298.16°K.

(b) Calculate the translational entropy of oxygen at 298.16°K.

(c) Calculate the total entropy for oxygen at 298.16°K.

Problem 19.2-6. Calculate $\Sigma pe^{-\epsilon/kT}$ for rotation and vibration of oxygen at 2000°K: (a) for the $^3\Sigma_g^-$ levels; (b) for the $^1\Delta_g$ levels; (c) for the $^1\Sigma_g^+$ levels.

Problem 19.2-7. Calculate $\tilde{F}^\circ - \tilde{E}_0^\circ/T$ for gaseous oxygen at 5000°K and 1 atm, including the translational contribution; the summations, $\Sigma pe^{-\epsilon/kT}$ for the electronic states $^3\Sigma_g^-$, $^1\Delta_g$, and $^1\Sigma_g^+$ are 10,690, 785, and 94 respectively.

Problem 19.2-8. Calculate the relative populations of the $^3\Sigma_g^-$, $^1\Delta_g$, $^1\Sigma_g^+$ levels of oxygen at 5000°K.

Problem 19.2-9. The dissociation energy D_0 of oxygen in the $^3\Sigma^-$ state is 117,040 cal mole^{-1}, referred to that of the atoms in their ground state. Using this and the proper partition function, calculate the equilibrium constant for the dissociation of oxygen into atoms at 5000°K. Assume that no higher electronic states of atomic oxygen are excited.

19.3 Approximate Methods for Evaluating the Partition Function and Its Derivatives. Introduction

Expressions have already been given for the energy, heat capacity, and entropy in terms of the energy levels of rotational, vibrational, and electronic degrees of freedom. In terms of the partition function and its derivatives, these are

$$\tilde{E} = -R\frac{Q'}{Q}, \tag{18.2–11}$$

$$\tilde{C} = \frac{R}{T^2}\left[\frac{Q''}{Q} - \left(\frac{Q'}{Q}\right)^2\right], \tag{18.2–12}$$

and

$$\tilde{S} = R\left(\ln Q - \frac{Q'}{QT}\right), \tag{18.3–16}$$

where Q' and Q'' denote the first and second derivatives of the partition functions with respect to $1/T$.

It is desirable to set up a simple expression for Q in which the cumbersome sum of exponentials has been eliminated. It is also desirable to have the expression an explicit function of $1/T$ (or T), so that Q' and Q'' can be obtained by straightforward differentiation. All approximate methods of obtaining thermodynamic functions directly from the energy levels have this as their object. The first step in this direction was made by Mulholland,[3] who gave an expression for Q_r (for the rotational energy levels of a diatomic molecule) in which the exponentials had been eliminated.

The rotational energy of a rigid diatomic molecule can be expressed in the form

$$\epsilon = J(J + 1)Bhc,$$

where $B = h/8\pi^2 Ic$, and J can have the values 0, 1, 2, 3, 4, etc. Thus Q_r can be written

$$Q_r = \sum_{J=0}^{J=\infty} (2J + 1)e^{-BhcJ(J+1)/kT}. \tag{19.3–1}$$

This expression can be rearranged to give

$$Q_r = e^{Bhc/4kT} \sum_{J=0}^{J=\infty} 2(J + \tfrac{1}{2})e^{-Bhc(J+1/2)^2/kT}, \tag{19.3–2}$$

and, writing m for $(J + {}^1/_2)$, one obtains

$$Q_r e^{-Bhc/4kT} = \sum_{m=1/2}^{m=\infty} 2me^{-Bhcm^2/kT}. \tag{19.3–3}$$

Equation (19.3–3) can be rewritten in the form

$$Q_r e^{-Bhc/4kT} = \sum_{m=1/2}^{m=\infty} 2me^{-Bhcm^2/kT} - \sum_{m=1}^{m=\infty} 2me^{-Bhcm^2/kT}, \tag{19.3–4}$$

where in the first sum m takes on all the values 1/2, 1, 3/2, 2, 5/2, · · · , $n/2$, $(n + 1)/2$, · · · , ∞, and in the second sum the values 1, 2, 3, · · · , $2n/2$, · · · , ∞.

We now make use of the Euler-Maclaurin expansion formula in the form

$$\int_a^{a+r\omega} F(x)\,dx = \omega\{\tfrac{1}{2}F(a) + F(a + \omega) + F(a + 2\omega) + \cdots + \tfrac{1}{2}F(a + r\omega)\}$$
$$+ \sum_{m-1}^{n-1} \frac{(-)^m B_m \omega^{2m}}{(2m)!} \{F^{(2m-1)}(a + r\omega) - F^{(2m-1)}(a)\} + R_n, \tag{19.3–5}$$

where $F^{(2m-1)}$ indicates the $(2m - 1)$th derivative of F. R_n is of the order of ω^n and may be dropped from the equations. The quantities B_m are the Bernoulli numbers, $B_1 = {}^1/_6$, $B_2 = {}^1/_{30}$, $B_3 = {}^1/_{42}$, $B_4 = {}^1/_{30}$, $B_5 = {}^5/_{66}$, etc.[4] It is easily seen that both of the sums in (19.3–4) can be treated

[3] H. P. Mulholland, *Proc. Cambridge Phil. Soc.*, **24**, 280 (1928).

[4] See E. T. Whittaker and G. H. Watson, *A Course of Modern Analysis*, 4th ed., Cambridge University Press, 1935, p. 128.

alike; in the first $\omega = {}^1/_2$ and in the second $\omega = 1$. For both sums,

$$F(a + r\omega) = 2me^{-Bhcm^2/kT}, \tag{19.3–6}$$

and

$$a = 0; \qquad F(0) = F(\infty) = 0; \tag{19.3–7}$$

thus equation (19.3–4) may be replaced by

$$\begin{aligned} Q_r e^{-Bhc/4kT} &= \frac{2}{2}\left\{\tfrac{1}{2}F(0) + F\left(\frac{1}{2}\right) + F\left(\frac{1}{2} + \frac{1}{2}\right) + F\left(\frac{1}{2} + \frac{2}{2}\right)\right. \\ &\quad \left. + F\left(\frac{1}{2} + \frac{3}{2}\right) + \cdots + F\left(\frac{1}{2} + \frac{2\mu}{2}\right) + \cdots + \tfrac{1}{2}F\left(\frac{1}{2} + \frac{\infty}{2}\right)\right\} \\ &\quad - \{\tfrac{1}{2}F(0) + F(1) + F(1 + 1) + F(1 + 2) + F(1 + 3) \\ &\quad + \cdots + F(1 + \mu) + \cdots + \tfrac{1}{2}F(1 + \infty)\} - 2R'_{k+1} + R''_{k+1}, \end{aligned} \tag{19.3–8}$$

where μ is a typical integer. Applying equation (19.3–5) to each of the sums in equation (19.3–8) with $\omega = {}^1/_2$ in the first of them and $\omega = 1$ in the second, the expression becomes

$$\begin{aligned} Q_r e^{-Bhc/4kT} &= 2\int_0^\infty 2xe^{-Bhcx^2/kT}\,dx - \int_0^\infty 2xe^{-Bhcx^2/kT}\,dx \\ &\quad - 2\sum_{n=0}^{k} \frac{(-)^{n+1}B_{n+1}(\frac{1}{2})^{2(n+1)}}{[2(n+1)]!}\{F^{(2n+1)}(\infty) - F^{(2n+1)}(0)\} \\ &\quad + \sum_{n=0}^{k} \frac{(-)^{n+1}B_{n+1}}{[2(n+1)]!}\{F^{(2n+1)}(\infty) - F^{(2n+1)}(0)\} + R_{k+1}. \end{aligned} \tag{19.3–9}$$

When the integrations in equation (19.3–9) have been carried out, the result is

$$\begin{aligned} Q_r e^{-Bhc/4kT} &= \frac{kT}{Bhc} + \sum_{n=0}^{k} \frac{(-)^{n+1}B_{n+1}}{2(n+1)!}(1 - 2^{-2n-1})\{F^{(2n+1)}(\infty) \\ &\quad - F^{(2n+1)}(0)\}. \end{aligned} \tag{19.3–10}$$

Because of the negative exponent, $F^{(2n+1)}(\infty)$ always vanishes. Some other terms are: $F(0) = 0$, $F^{\text{I}}(0) = +2$, $F^{\text{II}}(0) = F^{\text{IV}}(0) = F^{\text{VI}}(0) = 0$, $F^{\text{III}}(0) =$

$-4 \times 3(Bhc/kT), F^{\mathrm{V}}(0) = +6 \times 5 \times 4(Bhc/kT)^2, F^{\mathrm{VII}} = -8 \times 7 \times 6 \times 5(Bhc/kT)^3$. In general,

$$-\frac{(-)^{n+1}F^{(2n+1)}(0)}{[2(n+1)]!} = +\frac{(Bhc/kT)^n}{(n+1)!},$$

and

$$Q_r e^{-Bhc/4kT} = \frac{kT}{Bhc} + \sum_{n=0}^{k} \frac{B_{n+1}(Bhc/kT)^n}{(n+1)!}(1 - 2^{-2n-1}) + R_{k+1}, \quad (19.3\text{–}11)$$

or

$$Q_r e^{-Bhc/4kT} = kT/Bhc + \frac{1}{12} + \frac{7}{480}\frac{Bhc}{kT} + \cdots. \quad (19.3\text{–}12)$$

This is Mulholland's result.[5] For homonuclear molecules the rotational partition function Q_r thus obtained must be divided by 2, because symmetry requirements for the wave functions allow only even or odd values of J. This requirement also applies to the results obtained in succeeding sections.

Equation (19.3–12) was restricted to a rigid rotor. This restriction will now be removed. The energy of a $^1\Sigma$ diatomic molecule can be expressed in general by the equation

$$\begin{aligned}\epsilon = {} & B_{v,e}J(J+1) + D_{v,e}J^2(J+1)^2 + F_{v,e}J^3(J+1)^3 \\ & + (v+\tfrac{1}{2})\omega_e + (v+\tfrac{1}{2})^2 x_e\omega_e + (v+\tfrac{1}{2})^3 y_e\omega_e + \epsilon_e, \end{aligned} \quad (19.3\text{–}13)$$

where J takes on the values 0, 1, 2, 3, etc., and v the values 0, 1, 2, 3, etc.; the quantity ϵ_e is the electronic energy. In this case the general expression for the partition function, due to the internal degrees of freedom (including rotational) is

$$Q_{\text{int}} = \sum_e \sum_v \sum_J (2J+1)e^{-\epsilon hc/kT}. \quad (19.3\text{–}14)$$

This expression can be written

$$Q_{\text{int}} = \sum_e \sum_v (Q_r)_{v,e} e^{-\epsilon_{ve}hc/kT}, \quad (19.3\text{–}15)$$

where

$$(Q_r)_{v,e} = \sum_J (2J+1)e^{-\epsilon_{Jv}hc/kT}. \quad (19.3\text{–}16)$$

[5] Essentially the same development has been made by Mayer and Mayer (J. E. Mayer and M. G. Mayer, *Statistical Mechanics*, Wiley, New York, 1940, Chapter VII), who also use the Euler-Maclaurin formula in a slightly different procedure. They expand the exponential term and combine it with the right side of the equation, giving (in our notation)

$$Q_r = \frac{kT}{Bhc} + \frac{1}{3} + \frac{1}{15}\frac{Bhc}{kT} + \cdots. \quad (19.3\text{–}12a)$$

The student may perform the expansion and show that the two expressions are equivalent, if he wishes.

The energies are given by

$$\epsilon_{ve} = (v + \tfrac{1}{2})\omega_e + (v + \tfrac{1}{2})^2 x_e\omega_e + (v + \tfrac{1}{2})^3 y_e\omega_e + \cdots + \epsilon_e \qquad (19.3\text{–}17)$$

and

$$\epsilon_{Jv} = B_{ve}J(J + 1) + D_{ve}J^2(J + 1)^2 + F_{ve}J^3(J + 1)^3 + \cdots. \qquad (19.3\text{–}18)$$

It is to be noted that the energies of electronic levels as obtained directly from experiments are

$$\epsilon_{0e} = \tfrac{1}{2}\omega_e + (\tfrac{1}{2})^2 x_e\omega_e + (\tfrac{1}{2})^3 y_e\omega_e + \epsilon_e.$$

That is, they include the zero point vibrational energy obtained by putting $v = 0$ in the expression for the vibrational energy. However, ϵ_e, as usually defined, is the *electronic energy*. Evidently the replacement of $(Q_r)_{v,e}$ by an expression such as (19.3–12) will save tremendous labor in the evaluation of Q. If the molecule were completely rigid, the expression given in (19.3–12) would suffice. Giauque and Overstreet[6] solved this problem for the non-rigid case.

In the following discussion the subscripts v and e are dropped for convenience, and ϵ_0' is written for $(\tfrac{1}{4})B + (\tfrac{1}{4})^2 D + (\tfrac{1}{4})^3 F$.[7] For a molecule with a $^1\Sigma$ ground state,

$$\begin{aligned} Q_r &= e^{hc\epsilon_0'/kT}\, \Sigma 2m e^{[-hc(Bm^2 + Dm^4 + Fm^6 + \cdots]/kT} \\ &= e^{hc\epsilon_0'/kT}\, \Sigma 2m e^{-Bhcm^2/kT}\, e^{-Dhcm^4/kT}\, e^{-Fhcm^6/kT} + \cdots, \end{aligned} \qquad (19.3\text{–}19)$$

where m has been written for $(J + \tfrac{1}{2})$. Expanding the second and third exponential factors,

$$\begin{aligned} Q_r = e^{hc\epsilon_0'/kT}\, \Sigma 2m e^{-Bhcm^2/kT} &\left[1 - \frac{Dhcm^4}{kT} + \frac{1}{2!}\left(\frac{Dhcm^4}{kT}\right)^2 + \cdots\right] \\ \times &\left[1 - \frac{Fhcm^6}{kT} + \frac{1}{2!}\left(\frac{Fhcm^6}{kT}\right)^2 + \cdots\right] \end{aligned} \qquad (19.3\text{–}20)$$

$$\begin{aligned} = e^{hc\epsilon_0'/kT}\, \Sigma 2m e^{-Bhcm^2/kT} &\left[1 - \frac{Dhcm^4}{kT} - \frac{Fhcm^6}{kT} + \frac{1}{2!}\left(\frac{Dhcm^4}{kT}\right)^2 \right. \\ &\left. + \frac{Dhcm^4}{kT}\frac{Fhcm^6}{kT} + \frac{1}{2!}\left(\frac{Fhcm^6}{kT}\right)^2 + \cdots\right]. \end{aligned} \qquad (19.3\text{–}21)$$

Multiplying each term in the square brackets by the factor outside and considering the term by term sums, one notes that the first sum is simply

[6] W. F. Giauque and R. Overstreet, *J. Am. Chem. Soc.*, **54**, 1731 (1932).

[7] Giauque and Overstreet use ϵ_0 for this quantity, Since the symbol ϵ_0 is used later in another connection we have used ϵ_0' instead. Note also that we follow their convention in making the quantities D_v and $x_e\omega_e$ negative, rather than the more recent convention used in Section 16.12.

that whose value is given by (19.3–12). The remainder of the sums can be replaced by integrals of the form

$$I = \text{constant}\left(\frac{hc}{kT}\right)^r \int_0^\infty 2m^{2k+1}e^{-Bhcm^2/kT}\,dm$$
$$= \text{constant}\left(\frac{hc}{kT}\right)^r \frac{k!}{B^{k+1}}\left(\frac{kT}{hc}\right)^{k+1} \qquad (19.3\text{–}22)$$

without loss of accuracy. For example,

$$\Sigma 2m^5e^{-Bhcm^2/kT} = \int_0^\infty 2m^5e^{-Bhcm^2/kT}\,dm + \frac{31}{4032} = \frac{2!}{B^3}\left(\frac{kT}{hc}\right)^3 + \frac{31}{4032}. \qquad (19.3\text{–}23)$$

When the sums have been replaced by integrals, the partition function becomes

$$Q_r = e^{hc\epsilon_0'/kT}\frac{kT}{Bhc}\left[1 + \frac{B}{12}\cdot\frac{hc}{kT} - 2!\frac{D}{B^2}\left(\frac{kT}{hc}\right) - 3!\frac{F}{B^3}\left(\frac{kT}{hc}\right)^2 + \frac{4!}{2!}\cdot\frac{D^2}{B^4}\left(\frac{kT}{hc}\right)^2 + 5!\frac{DF}{B^5}\left(\frac{kT}{hc}\right)^3 + \cdots\right]. \qquad (19.3\text{–}24)$$

This expression is in a form suitable for evaluation of its first and second temperature derivatives.[8]

An example of the results obtained is given in Table 19.3–1, which shows the computation of Q_r for the lowest vibrational and electronic state of hydrogen chloride at 1000°K and 2000°K. The last column gives the value obtained by direct summation, and the preceding one that obtained using equation (19.3–21).

Table 19.3–1
Comparison of Q_r Values for HCl^{35} by Summation and Approximation Methods

T (°K)	$e^{hc\epsilon_0'/kT} \times \frac{kT}{Bhc} \times \left(1 + \frac{Bhc}{12kT} - 2!\frac{D}{B^2}\cdot\frac{kT}{hc} - \cdots\right)$	Q Approx. ($n = 1/2$)	Q Summation ($n = 1/2$)
1000	1.00374 × 66.825 × (1 + 0.00125 + 0.00684)	67.618	67.618
2000	1.00184 × 133.651 × (1 + 0.00062 + 0.01386)	135.84	135.85

[8] As for equation (19.3–12), the exponential term may be expanded and combined with the remainder, as done by Mayer and Mayer (*op. cit*). The result is

$$Q_r = \frac{kT}{Bhc}\left[1 + \frac{B}{3}\frac{hc}{kT} - 2!\frac{D}{B^2}\left(\frac{kT}{hc}\right) + \cdots\right]. \qquad (19.3\text{–}24a)$$

Since another exponential term enters the expression when Q_r is summed over all vibrational levels, the choice between expanded and unexpanded versions for Q_r makes very little difference in the convenience of the formula. (It should be noted that Mayer and Mayer carry their development only through the constant D and neglect the terms in F.)

The term $Bhc/12kT$ in the second column shows the effect of replacing the most important sum by an integral without correction. It is 0.125% in Q_r at 1000°K and, incidentally, about 0.4% in Q_r at 300°K. This would affect the free energy by 2.4 cal/mole at 300°K. The next term in this column shows that neglect of stretching at 1000°K would cause about five times the error produced by replacing the important sum by an integral, or about 6.8 cal/mole in the free energy at 1000°K.

The quantities Q_r can be evaluated by the methods above for particular vibrational states; they must then be summed over all vibrational states. Johnston and Davis[9] found that at any temperature the partition functions for successive vibrational states bore a constant ratio, so that exact evaluation of the partition function and its derivatives was required only for the first few vibrational states. Gordon and Barnes[10] provided a more exact way of handling the upper vibrational states. Kassel[11] obtained $(Q_r)_v$ in the same manner as Giauque and Overstreet,[6] but he included all correction terms in the replacement of sums by integrals (e.g., see equation 19.3–23); in addition he provided a method for treating the upper vibrational states which is more accurate but more complicated than that of Gordon and Barnes.

For molecules which are not in $^1\Sigma$ states it is necessary to sum over the low-lying electronic states with due regard to multiplicities. The molecule NO, which is a $^2\Pi$ state, is an example. The lowest level of the $^2\Pi_{3/2}$ state is about 120 cm^{-1} above the lowest level of the $^2\Pi_{1/2}$ state, and the fundamental vibration frequencies (about 1900 cm^{-1}) are slightly different for the two states. In this case, the partition function must be summed over the rotational and vibrational energy levels of both states. (Note that the J values for the $^2\Pi_{3/2}$ state are $^3/_2$, $^5/_2$, $^7/_2$, etc., and those for the $^2\Pi_{1/2}$ state are $^1/_2$, $^3/_2$, $^5/_2$, etc.) Johnston and Chapman[12] evaluated the thermodynamic properties of NO by direct summation.

General methods for treating molecules in states other than $^1\Sigma$ have been discussed by Kassel.[11]

Problem 19.3-1. The molecule $C^{12}O^{16}$ has a $^1\Sigma$ ground state and no other low-lying electronic states. For the $^1\Sigma$ state the vibrational energy is given approximately by the equation

$$\epsilon_v = 2167.4(v + \tfrac{1}{2}) - 12.70(v + \tfrac{1}{2})^2,$$

and the rotational energy by

$$\epsilon_J = B_v J(J + 1) - D_v J^2(J + 1)^2,$$

where $B_v = 1.931 - 0.0175(v + \tfrac{1}{2})$; $D_v = [6.43 - 0.04(v + \tfrac{1}{2})] \times 10^{-6}$.

[9] H. L. Johnston and C. O. Davis, *J. Am. Chem. Soc.*, **56**, 271 (1934).
[10] A. R. Gordon and C. Barnes, *J. Chem. Phys.*, **1**, 297 (1933).
[11] L. S. Kassel, *J. Chem. Phys.*, **1**, 576 (1933); *Chem. Revs.*, **18**, 277 (1936).
[12] H. L. Johnston and A. T. Chapman, *J. Am. Chem. Soc.*, **55**, 153 (1933).

(a) Calculate the partition function of CO (excluding translation) at 1000°K.

(b) Calculate the total contribution of rotation and vibration to the entropy and heat capacity of CO at 1000°K.

(c) Calculate the total entropy and heat capacity of CO at 1 atm, 1000°K, assuming the gas to be ideal.

Problem 19.3-2. For $N^{14}O^{16}$ the electronic energy (excluding vibration and rotation) of the $^2\Pi_{3/2}$ state is 121.1 cm^{-1} greater than that of the $^2\Pi_{1/2}$ state. To a first approximation the constants for both electronic states may be taken as $\omega_e = 1903.8$, $\omega_e x_e = 13.97$, $\omega_e y_e = 0.0012$; $B_e = 1.705$, $\alpha_e = 0.018$, $D_v = 5 \times 10^{-6}$. There are no other low-lying electronic states.

(a) Calculate the fraction of NO molecules in the $^2\Pi_{3/2}$ state at the normal boiling point, 122°K, and 1 atm.

(b) Calculate the heat capacity and entropy of NO gas at 122°K, 1 atm, assuming perfect gas behavior. (*Note.* Johnston and Chapman[12] used a different set of equations for rotational and vibrational energy, with separate sets of constants for each electronic state.)

19.4 The Thermodynamic Functions for Hydrogen and Deuterium

As pointed out in Section 16.14, a homonuclear diatomic molecule in which each atom has i units of nuclear spin has $n(n + 1)/2$ symmetric and $n(n - 1)/2$ antisymmetric nuclear wave functions, where n is equal to $2i + 1$. In all, there are n^2 nuclear wave functions each of which may be looked on as defining a distinct species. They are distinct in the sense that in a mixture each has its own entropy. The total entropy is the sum of that due to each individual species, plus an entropy of mixing calculated on the basis of perfect solution. The entropy of each species is calculated from a partition function including only the allowed rotational and vibrational states for that species. The entropy of mixing is calculated on the basis of the mole fractions of the species, as discussed in Section 18.10, where the thermodynamic functions were derived on the basis of the entropy of mixing of quantum states. The spin species may be, but *need not necessarily be, in equilibrium.*

For hydrogen the nuclear spin i is $^1/_2$; n is therefore equal to 2. There are thus four species. One of them is antisymmetric in the nuclear spin and called *para,* while three are symmetric in the nuclear spin and are called *ortho.* Under ordinary circumstances the para species cannot change into any of the ortho species. The para species can only have the rotational levels with $J = 0, 2, 4, 6$, etc., while each of the three ortho species can have only rotational levels with $J = 1, 3, 5, 7, 9$, etc.

Problem 19.4-1. Deuterium gas has $i = 1$ for each atom in the diatomic molecule. The species with the antisymmetric nuclear spin wave function is called para, and the species with the symmetric wave function is called ortho.

(a) How many kinds of para- and of ortho-deuterium are there, and how are they differentiated?

(b) What J values are allowed for the para and the ortho species, and why?

(c) Counting all allowed nuclear spin species, what is p for J equal to 0? What is p for J equal to 1?

By considerations such as those of the last section, it can be shown that near room temperature the values of $\Sigma p_J e^{-\epsilon_J/kT}$ for the para and the ortho species approach a common limit; thus at equilibrium the amounts of the para species and of *each* of the three ortho species are equal. Such a mixture is called *normal* hydrogen. Hydrogen gas under equilibrium conditions at room temperatures thus contains three times as much ortho- as para-hydrogen.

Problem 19.4-2. Calculate the value of Q for para hydrogen by summing over even rotational levels and for ortho hydrogen by summing over odd levels at 300°K. The moment of inertia of hydrogen is 0.46×16^{-40} gm cm²/molecule. Assume that the vibrational energy may be neglected and the rotational energy is given by $J(J+1)h^2/8\pi^2 I$.

For convenience the energy will be considered first. For all mixtures of ortho and para hydrogen at low pressure the translational energy is $3RT/2$. When the two species of hydrogen cannot change into each other, the rotational and vibrational energy of each species is first calculated by using equation (18.2–2). The energy of a mole of the mixture is then simply the sum of the energy due to the mole fraction of the para molecules and the energy due to the mole fraction of the ortho molecules.

Problem 19.4-3. Calculate the total energy of one mole of gaseous normal hydrogen (a) at 20.4°K, (b) at 100°K. Neglect vibrational energy, and consider that the energy of the rotational levels is $J(J+1)h^2/8\pi^2 I$.

If the two species of hydrogen are in equilibrium, the energy is to be calculated from a partition function for rotation and vibration which is

$$Q_{\text{int}} = \sum_{\text{even}} p_J e^{-\epsilon_J/kT} + 3\sum_{\text{odd}} p_J e^{-\epsilon_J/kT}\,. \tag{19.4–1}$$

The factor 3 multiplying the odd levels is due to the fact that there are three times as many ortho as para states. For each individual species p is equal to $p_J = 2J+1$. If the ortho states are grouped, $p = 3p_J$ (see Problem 19.4–1).

Problem 19.4-4. Calculate the total energy of 1 mole of an equilibrium mixture of gaseous ortho and para hydrogen (a) at 20°K; (b) at 100°K. Calculate the energy released in calories at 20°K and 100°K when 1 mole of normal hydrogen is brought to equilibrium.

It is simple to calculate the heat capacity due to rotation and vibration when the para species cannot change into the ortho species. The rotational and vibrational heat capacity of the ortho and para species is calculated in each case by using equation (18.2–14). For the ortho species the sums are taken over even J values only, while for the para they are taken over odd J values only.

The rotational-vibrational heat capacity per mole of the room temperature equilibrium mixture is then the sum of the values for one quarter of a mole of the para and three-quarters of a mole of the ortho species. The heat capacity contributions due to translation at constant volume and at constant pressure are $3R/2$ and $5R/2$ respectively, when the gas is perfect. Figure 19.4–1[13] shows the rotational heat capacity of ortho, para, normal,

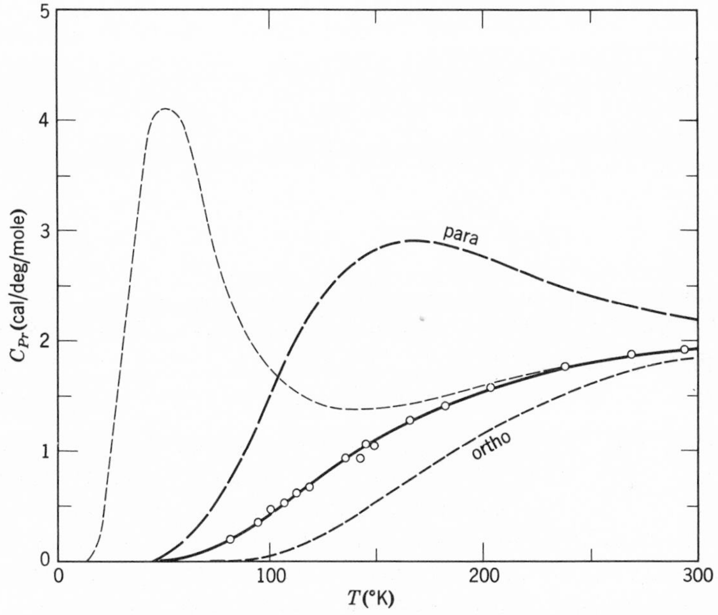

Fig. 19.4–1. Rotational heat capacity of hydrogen as a function of temperature.[13]

The broken lines represent the theoretical rotational heat capacities of ortho-, para- and equilibrium-hydrogen, the full line that of the 3:1 room temperature mixture (normal). The circles represent the observed heat capacities after subtraction of the translational contribution $5R/2$.

(From G. Herzberg, *Molecular Spectra and Molecular Structure*, Vol. 1, "Spectra of Diatomic Molecules," 2nd ed. Copyright 1950, D. Van Nostrand Company, Inc.)

and equilibrium hydrogen calculated in this way, along with the experimental values for normal hydrogen.

Problem 19.4-5. Calculate the total molal heat capacity at constant volume of para hydrogen and of normal hydrogen at 100°K, and compare with the experimental values

[13] G. Herzberg, *Spectra of Diatomic Molecules*, Van Nostrand, Princeton, N. J., 1950.

in Fig. 19.4–1. Neglect vibration, and assume that the energy of the rotational levels is given by $J(J+1)h^2/8\pi^2 I$.

In the presence of a catalyst which would bring the ortho species into rapid equilibrium with the para species, the rotational-vibrational heat capacity of the mixture must be calculated from the partition function given by equation (19.4–1).

Problem 19.4-6. (a) Calculate the total heat capacity of an equilibrium mixture of ortho and para hydrogen at 100°K.

(b) If $\Delta\tilde{C}_p$ is the difference in heat capacity between the equilibrium mixture and normal hydrogen, what is the value of

$$\int_{20^\circ\mathrm{K}}^{100^\circ\mathrm{K}} \Delta\tilde{C}_p \, dT?$$

(See Problem 19.4–4.)

The entropy of normal hydrogen is simply the sum of that due to each species plus the entropy of mixing, which is

$$\Delta\tilde{S}_{\mathrm{mix}} = -R \sum_{i=1}^{i=4} \tilde{N}_i \ln \tilde{N}_i \,. \tag{19.4–2}$$

Since each species has a mole fraction of $^1/_4$, the entropy of mixing is $R \ln 4$.

Let the molal entropies of the gases be $\tilde{S}_1$, $\tilde{S}_2$, $\tilde{S}_3$, and $\tilde{S}_4$; the total entropy of a mole of mixture will then be[14]

$$\tilde{S} = \tfrac{1}{4}(\tilde{S}_1 + \tilde{S}_2 + \tilde{S}_3 + \tilde{S}_4) + R \ln 4. \tag{19.4–3}$$

Let $\tilde{S}_1$ be the molal entropy of the molecules with the antisymmetric nuclear wave function. The translational entropy is given by equation (18.6–4), and the rotational and vibrational entropy by equation (18.3–15), with the necessary sums taken only over even rotational states. The entropies $\tilde{S}_2$, $\tilde{S}_3$, and $\tilde{S}_4$ are respectively the molal entropies of the molecules with the three kinds of symmetric wave functions respectively. The translational entropy of each is again given by equation (18.6–4), but the rotational and vibrational entropies are now given by equation (18.3–15), with the sums carried out over the odd rotational levels. The entropy of hydrogen in the ideal gas state is therefore given by

$$\begin{aligned} \tilde{S} = \tilde{S}_t &+ \tfrac{1}{4}R\left[\frac{\Sigma p \dfrac{\epsilon}{kT} e^{-\epsilon/kT}}{\Sigma p e^{-\epsilon/kT}} - \ln \Sigma p e^{-\epsilon/kT}\right]_{\mathrm{even}} \\ &+ \tfrac{3}{4}R\left[\frac{\Sigma p \dfrac{\epsilon}{kT} e^{-\epsilon/kT}}{\Sigma p e^{-\epsilon/kT}} - \ln \Sigma p e^{-\epsilon/kT}\right]_{\mathrm{odd}} + R \ln 4, \end{aligned} \tag{19.4–4}$$

[14] W. F. Giauque, *J. Am. Chem. Soc.*, **52**, 4816 (1930).

where the second and third terms of the right side are the rotational entropies due to the para and ortho rotational states, respectively, and the last term is the entropy of mixing. Only at temperatures where the distribution may be regarded as classical do the two bracketed quantities in equation (19.4–4) become equal; such temperatures are reached at about 300°K. (See Problem 19.4–2.)

In this way the entropy of hydrogen at 298.16°K in the ideal gas state at 1 atm is found to be 33.98 cal/deg/mole, the entropy due to nuclear spin being included.

Problem 19.4-7. Calculate the total entropy of normal hydrogen at 100°K, 1 atm, assuming that the rotational energy levels are given by $J(J+1)h^2/8\pi^2 I$. Neglect vibrational energy.

Problem 19.4-8. Repeat the calculation of the last problem if the two varieties are in equilibrium, in which case the partition function given by equation (19.4–1) must be used.

To calculate the equilibrium ratio of the ortho to para species, it is merely necessary to use the partition functions for the para and for the ortho in the free energy expressions. For para-hydrogen,

$$Q_{\text{para}} = \sum_{\text{even}} (2J+1)e^{-\epsilon_J/kT}, \tag{19.4–5}$$

and, for ortho-hydrogen,

$$Q_{\text{ortho}} = 3\sum_{\text{odd}} (2J+1)e^{-\epsilon_J/kT}. \tag{19.4–6}$$

Thus the ratio of ortho to para is given by

$$K = \frac{Q_{\text{ortho}}}{Q_{\text{para}}}.$$

Problem 19.4-9. (a) Calculate the composition of the high temperature equilibrium variety of deuterium (normal deuterium).

(b) Calculate the ratio of ortho- to para-hydrogen at 100°K.

(c) Calculate the ratio of ortho- to para-deuterium at 100°K.

The moment of inertia of deuterium is 0.92×10^{-4} g cm². The nuclear spin of deuterium is 1.

Problem 19.4-10. Calculate the entropy of normal deuterium at 100°K, 1 atm, using the data of the previous problem.

It is interesting to consider crystalline normal hydrogen at the absolute zero, where there is no possibility of change of ortho into para hydrogen. It will be assumed that the ortho and para varieties form a solid solution. At first sight this would mean that at the absolute zero there could still be the entropy of mixing of the four varieties, which are present in equal amounts. The entropy of mixing would then be $R \ln 4$ or 2.75 cal deg^{-1} mole^{-1}.

However, it appears that ortho-hydrogen rotates in the crystal at low temperatures (10°K) and is in the rotational level with $J = 1$. Thus there are $2J + 1 = 3$ rotational states of ortho-hydrogen of approximately the same energy but differing in their orientation in space. Each of the three varieties of ortho-hydrogen, distinguished by their nuclear spin wave functions, may have any one of these three rotational levels; thus nine kinds of molecules are possible, all with the same probability. In other words, nine wave functions correspond to ortho-hydrogen. These constitute three quarters (i.e., nine twelfths) of the total, so that each kind forms one twelfth of the total. The para-hydrogen is in the lowest rotational state; it therefore has only one rotational wave function, namely, that corresponding to no rotation at all. Because there is only one nuclear spin wave function, the antisymmetric, only one wave function corresponds to the para-hydrogen which forms one quarter (i.e., three twelfths) of the total. The entropy of mixing of the different kinds of hydrogen is then

$$\begin{aligned}\tilde{S} &= -R[\tfrac{3}{12}\ln\tfrac{3}{12} + 9(\tfrac{1}{12}\ln\tfrac{1}{12})] \\ &= -R(\tfrac{1}{4}\ln\tfrac{1}{4} + \tfrac{3}{4}\ln\tfrac{1}{12}) = 4.39 \text{ cal/deg/mole.} \qquad (19.4\text{–}7)\end{aligned}$$

Since any one of the kinds of hydrogen would be assigned zero entropy at the absolute zero, this is the entropy of the crystal instead of the $R \ln 4$ (2.76 cal/deg/mole) which would be present if the ortho-hydrogen was limited to one kind of rotational level. Thus the entropy measured by using the *third law* and the calorimetric data from 12°K to 298.15°K should be $33.98 - 4.39 = 29.59$ cal/deg/mole at 298.15°K. The value actually found is 29.74 cal/deg/mole.

Problem 19.4-11. Calculate the entropy of the crystal of normal deuterium corresponding to extrapolation from 10°K and the discrepancy between the spectroscopic and calorimetric entropy to be expected on this basis.

19.5 Entropy Due to Nuclear Spin

For hydrogen and deuterium, whether there is equilibrium or not, the individual partition functions of the four spin varieties are equal above 300°K. They are thus present in equal amounts, and each constitutes one fourth of the total. The entropy of mixing of the varieties is $R \ln 4$, which can be looked on as the nuclear spin entropy.

In general, for homonuclear diatomic gases where each nucleus has i units of nuclear spin there are $(2i + 1)^2$ varieties whose partition functions will all approach equality as the temperature is raised. Each will constitute a fraction $(2i + 1)^{-2}$ of the total. The nuclear spin entropy will thus be $2R \ln (2i + 1)$, or $R \ln (2i + 1)$ for each nucleus.

In all gases except hydrogen and deuterium the partition functions of the various nuclear spin varieties become equal at temperatures considerably below the normal boiling points of the gases. Also, hydrogen and deuterium alone have rotation in the crystal at very low temperatures. In any case, the crystal will consist of a solid solution containing equal mole fractions of all varieties, if the amounts stay equal to those in the high temperature equilibrium mixture. As a rule, lack of equilibrium will prevent change from the high temperature proportions.

For heteronuclear molecules such as hydrogen chloride, all levels are allowed for each spin variety. If one nucleus has i' units of nuclear spin, it will have $2i' + 1$ orientations. If the second nucleus has i'' units of nulcear spin, it will have $(2i'' + 1)$ orientations. Thus the total number of orientations of the nuclear spin with respect to the symmetry axis of the molecule is $(2i' + 1)(2i'' + 1)$, which is the number of nuclear spin species. Under all circumstances the partition functions of all species are equal, since all levels are allowed for each. The entropy of mixing of the varieties is thus always $R \ln [(2i' + 1)(2i'' + 1)]$, which is equal to $[R \ln (2i' + 1) + R \ln (2i'' + 1)]$. The nuclear spin is thus equal to $R \ln (2i + 1)$ for each nucleus, as for the homonuclear molecule.

Because the nuclear spin entropy can be assigned to the individual atoms, the effect of nuclear spin cancels in all reactions. It can therefore be left out of consideration in all cases but those of molecular hydrogen and molecular deuterium.[15] Entropies are usually calculated without regard to nuclear spin, with the partition function evaluated by the integration methods of Section 19.3. In the case of homonuclear molecules, since the sum is made over only one half of the levels, the integrals are divided by 2. The contribution due to nuclear spin is omitted. Heteronuclear molecules containing hydrogen, such as hydrogen chloride, may be treated in the same way. In molecular hydrogen and molecular deuterium the entropy must be calculated as described above. However, when it is used with entropies of other molecules where nuclear spin has been neglected, an amount $R \ln 4$ must be subtracted from the molecular hydrogen values and an amount $R \ln 9$ from the molecular deuterium values. This is equivalent to subtracting off the $R \ln (2i + 1)$ for each nucleus which has been neglected in the case of the other gases.

Problem 19.5-1. Nitrogen has a nuclear spin of one unit.

(a) Calculate the entropy of NO including nuclear spin at 122°K from the results of Problem 19.3–2.

(b) Calculate the entropy due to nuclear spin for gaseous N_2, and show that neglect of nuclear spin produces no errors in calculating the entropy of the reaction $N_2 + O_2 = 2NO$.

[15] G. E. Gibson and W. Heitler, *Z. Physik*, **49**, 465 (1928).

Problem 19.5-2. The constants in the energy equations for nitrogen are: $B_e = 2.003$, $D_e = 5.8 \times 10^{-6}$; $\alpha = 0.023$, $\beta = 8.6 \times 10^{-8}$; $\omega_e = 2359.6$, $\omega_e x_e = 14.44$. Calculate the entropy of nitrogen at 300°K, 1 atm, (a) excluding nuclear spin, (b) including nuclear spin. (Assume the ideal gas state, use equation (19.3–24), and neglect all terms contributing less than 0.01 cal mole^{-1} deg^{-1}.)

19.6 "Semiclassical" Expressions for Partition Functions

Situations may arise for which it is not important to evaluate all the terms of equation (19.3–24) or its derivatives, either because less accuracy is needed or because the necessary data are not available. If all correction terms are neglected, the rotational partition function for a heteronuclear diatomic molecule reduces to

$$Q_r = \frac{kT}{Bhc} \cdot \qquad (19.6\text{–}1)^{**}$$

The size of the error made by this simplification may be seen by examining the correction terms of equation (19.3–24). These are given explicitly in Table 19.3–1 for the ground vibrational state of HCl^{35}; the error in the partition function is about 1.2% at 1000°K and 1.6% at 2000°K. The error is smaller for molecules with larger moments of inertia (smaller values of B). For the ground vibrational state of CO, the corresponding errors are 0.29% at 500°K, 0.30% at 1000°K, and 0.48% at 2000°K.

To about the same order of approximation, the variation of B with vibrational quantum number may be neglected, provided that the contributions from the higher vibrational states are small. The variation in Q_r between successive vibrational states may be relatively large, but its effect on the total partition function is greatly reduced by the rapid diminution of the exponential factor containing the vibrational energy. For HCl, B_1 is 3% lower than B_0, but the error introduced by neglecting this difference is less than 0.1% at 1000°K, and about 0.4% at 2000°K. For CO, the corresponding errors are 0.04% at 1000°K and 0.2% at 2000°K.

The maximum degree of simplification is obtained if the molecule is considered as a rigid rotator and harmonic oscillator. Then all interaction between rotation and vibration is neglected, as well as the anharmonicity of vibration, so that B_e alone is used to calculate the rotational energy, and ω_e alone for the vibrational energy. If this approximation is used, the partition function may be separated into the product of terms for rotation and vibration; that is,

$$Q_{r,v} = Q_r Q_v , \qquad (19.6\text{–}2)^{**}$$

with Q_r of the same form as in equation (19.6–1). The discussion thus far has concerned only heteronuclear diatomic molecules. For homonuclear molecules (e.g., N_2), where a given species has only even or odd rotational states, it is necessary to sum only half of the available rotational levels for each species. To this order of approximation, it may be assumed that the sums over even and odd states are equal (compare Problem 19.4–2). The rotational partition function for a homonuclear molecule is thus half that for a heteronuclear molecule with the same constants, and, in general,

$$Q_r = \frac{kT}{\sigma B_e hc}, \qquad (19.6\text{–}3)^{**}$$

where σ is the symmetry number (2 for a homonuclear molecule, 1 for a heteronuclear molecule).

The corresponding vibrational partition function (taking the lowest vibrational level as the energy zero) is

$$Q_v = \sum_v e^{-vhc\omega_e/kT} = \sum_v e^{-vh\nu_0/kT}. \qquad (19.6\text{–}4)^{**}$$

This sum is readily obtained by means of the binomial theorem; it is

$$Q_v = (1 - e^{-x})^{-1}, \qquad (19.6\text{–}5)^{**}$$

where $x = h\nu_0/kT = hc\omega_e/kT$.

The thermodynamic properties corresponding to the approximate partition functions can be derived readily by using the equations of Section 18.7. The rotational energy (enthalpy) and heat capacity give the "classical" values of RT and R, respectively. This is as it should be, since the use of integrations without correction is tantamount to the assumption of a continuous spectrum of energy levels. The rotational partition function can be written in an alternative form, in which B_e is replaced by its value $(h/8\pi^2 Ic)$. In this case,

$$Q_r = \frac{8\pi^2 IkT}{\sigma h^2}. \qquad (19.6\text{–}6)^{**}$$

The latter form is useful if the moment of inertia, I, is known or may be estimated from molecular data.

The problems below provide examples of the use of these approximate methods. Table 19.6–1 summarizes the results of various approximations for HCl and CO. The results given in the table are to be interpreted as examples of the approximations involved for two fairly "stiff" diatomic molecules in $^1\Sigma$ states. The student may observe for himself the effect of these approximations on the several thermodynamic properties considered.

Table 19.6–1
Contribution of Rotation and Vibration to the Thermodynamic Properties of Hydrogen Chloride and Carbon Monoxide

Substance	Temperature (°K)	Method	Q	$\frac{\tilde{E}^\circ - \tilde{E}_0^\circ}{R}$	$\tilde{C}/R$	$\tilde{S}/\tilde{R}$	$\frac{-\tilde{F}^\circ - E_0^\circ}{\tilde{R}}$
HCl	1000	(19.3)	68.474	1070.3	1.297	5.397	4226.5
		(19.6)	66.52	1057.6	1.244	5.255	4197.7
	2000	(19.3)	155.74	2655.0	1.440	6.376	10096.0
		(19.6)	148.52	2448.0	1.432	6.244	9996.0
CO	500	(19.3)	181.67	506.5	1.088	6.215	2601.1
		(19.6)	179.95	506.1	1.077	6.197	2592.4
	1000	(19.3)	378.68	1142.9	1.479	7.090	5947.0
		(19.6)	376.50	1131.5	1.392	7.063	5930.7

The rows labeled (19.3) resulted from calculations using equation (19.3–24) for the partition function. The fundamental constants used are the recent ones given in Appendix 1; for this reason the results for the partition function differ slightly from those given in Table 19.3–1. The rows labeled 19.6 result from the use of equations (19.6–3)* and (19.6–5)*.

The situation alters considerably if molecules with low vibration frequencies or a multiplicity of electronic states are considered, as may be seen from the problems.

Problem 19.6-1. The ground state of hydrogen deuteride (HD) is a $^1\Sigma_g{}^+$ with $\omega_e = 3817.09$ and $B_e = 45.655$.

(a) Using the approximate methods described above, estimate the contributions of rotation and vibration to Q, $\tilde{E}$, $\tilde{S}$, $\tilde{C}$, and $\tilde{F}$ at 2000°K.

(b) Calculate the translational contribution to $\tilde{E}$, $\tilde{S}$, $\tilde{C}_P$, and $\tilde{F}$ at 2000°K, 1 atm.

(c) Estimate the total values of $\tilde{E}$, $\tilde{S}$, $\tilde{C}_P$, and $\tilde{F}$ for HD at 2000°K, 1 atm (nuclear spin excluded).

Problem 19.6-2. The dissociation energy of HD from the state $v = 0$, $J = 0$, ($D_0{}^\circ$) is 4.511 electron volts. Using the results of Problem 19.6–1, estimate the equilibrium constant for the dissociation of HD into H and D atoms at 2000°K.

Problem 19.6-3. The molecular species $Br^{79}Br^{81}$, which makes up about 50% of natural Br_2, is in a $^1\Sigma^+$ ground state, with no low-lying electronic states; ω_e is 323.2 cm^{-1}, and B_e 0.03091 cm^{-1}. Estimate the contributions of rotation and vibration to Q, $\tilde{E}$, $\tilde{S}$, and $\tilde{C}$ of this substance at 500°K.

Problem 19.6-4. The $^1\Sigma^+$ ground state of $Cl_2{}^{35}$ has $\omega_e = 564.9$, $B_e = 0.2438$. Estimate the total heat capacity at constant pressure of $Cl_2{}^{35}$ at 300°, 500°, 1000°, and 1500°K, using the methods of the present section.

Problem 19.6-5. Using the constants given in Problem 19.5–2, calculate the entropy of nitrogen at 1 atm, 1500°K, excluding nuclear spin, using the methods of this section.

Problem 19.6-6. At sufficiently high temperature, the differences in energy of the F_1, F_2, and F_3 levels of O_2 may be neglected. The energies of the $^3\Sigma_g{}^-$ state may then be obtained approximately by taking $\omega_e = 1580.4$, $B_e = 1.4456$; the $^1\Delta_g$ state, 7918.1 cm^{-1} above, has $\omega_e = 1509$, $B_e = 1.426$; the $^1\Sigma_g{}^+$ state, 13,195 cm^{-1} above, has

$\omega_e = 1433$, $B_e = 1.400$. Use these data to obtain the contribution of the rotational and vibrational levels of each state to the partition function of O_2 at 5000°K, taking proper count of electronic degeneracies. Compare with the data of Problem 19.2–7.

Problem 19.6-7. The ${}^1\Sigma_g{}^+$ ground state of $K_2{}^{39}$ has $\omega_e = 92.64$ cm^{-1}, $B_e = 0.05622$. The dissociation energy D_0 is 0.514 electron volts to the ground state of atomic potassium.

(a) Calculate $\tilde{F}° - \tilde{E}_0°$ for $K_2{}^{39}$ at 1000°K.

(b) Estimate the dissociation constant, of $K_2{}^{39}$ at 1000°K (approximately the boiling point of potassium).

Problem 19.6-8. The ground state of the OH radical is a ${}^2\Pi$, with a spacing of about 140 cm^{-1} in the electronic energy of the two components of the doublet; $\omega_e =$ 3735 cm^{-1}. Calculate approximately the energy and heat capacity of the OH radical at 500°K.

19.7 Tables of Thermodynamic Functions for Diatomic Gases

By the methods of this chapter, values of the thermodynamic functions have been calculated for a large number of diatomic gases. Some of these values are given in Appendix 7.

Calculation of the Partition Functions and Thermodynamic Properties of Polyatomic Gases

CHAPTER 20

20.1 Rotational Contribution of Linear Molecules

It was seen in Section 16.23 that the energy levels of linear polyatomic molecules can be treated similarly to those of diatomic molecules, except that the linear molecule has more than one fundamental vibration frequency. Detailed analysis of the infrared and Raman spectra to obtain rotational and vibrational energy levels is frequently prohibitively complicated, and it is almost impossible to obtain exact formulas for all the energy levels. It is therefore necessary to consider the rotational energy as given by the formula

$$\epsilon_r = \frac{J(J+1)h^2}{8^2\pi I}. \qquad (20.1\text{–}1)$$

Similarly, the vibrational energy is taken as

$$\epsilon_v = (v + \tfrac{1}{2})h\nu \qquad (20.1\text{–}2)$$

for each vibrational degree of freedom.

This division of the energy into rotational and vibrational contributions corresponds to the "semiclassical" approximation of Section 19.6, and the internal partition function is given by

$$Q_{\text{int}} = Q_r Q_v. \qquad (20.1\text{–}3)$$

The rotational partition function Q_r is easily evaluated by using equation (19.3–12). Thus, if all J values are allowed,

$$Q_r e^{-Bhc/4kT} = kT/Bhc + \tfrac{1}{12}, \tag{20.1–4}$$

where B denotes $h/8\pi^2 Ic$. In molecules such as CO_2 and HCN, kT/Bhc is sufficiently large that the exponent on the left side of equation (20.1–4) is essentially zero, and the quantity $^1/_{12}$ on the right side may be neglected. When this may be done,

$$Q_r = \frac{8\pi^2 IkT}{\sigma h^2}, \tag{20.1–5}$$

where σ is unity if all J values are allowed, but 2 if symmetry requirements exclude half the J values.

In the case of linear molecules such as carbon dioxide which have a center of symmetry, either odd or even J values are excluded since the rotational wave functions must be either symmetric or antisymmetric in the nuclei. This is automatically allowed for by making σ equal to 2 when there is a center of symmetry.

Problem 20.1-1. Which rotational levels are excluded for carbon dioxide. Why?

Problem 20.1-2. Calculate kT/Bhc for (a) HCN, (b) CO_2 at 200°K from the following bond distances. For HCN, the C—H distance is 1.059 Å, and the C≡N distance is 1.157 Å. For CO_2, the C=O distance is 1.162 Å. Estimate the error in each case caused by: (a) equating the exponential to unity in the left of equation (20.1–4), and (b) neglect of the quantity $^1/_{12}$ in equation (20.1–4).

Substitution of the partition function into equations (18.7–12), (18.2–8), (18.7–14), and (18.7–13) yields the following expressions for the thermodynamic quantities due to rotational degrees of freedom.

$$\tilde{E}_r = RT, \tag{20.1–6}$$

$$\tilde{C}_r = R, \tag{20.1–7}$$

$$\tilde{F}_r/T = -R\left[\ln IT - \ln\sigma + \ln\frac{8\pi^2 k}{h^2}\right], \tag{20.1–8}$$

and

$$\tilde{S}_r = R\left[1 + \ln IT - \ln\sigma + \ln\frac{8\pi^2 k}{h^2}\right]. \tag{20.1–9}$$

Upon substitution of the proper constants, equations (20.1–8) and (20.1–9) become

$$\frac{\tilde{F}_r}{T} = -R[\ln IT - \ln\sigma + 88.408] \tag{20.1–10}$$

and

$$\tilde{S}_r = R[\ln IT - \ln\sigma + 89.408]. \tag{20.1–11}$$

Problem 20.1-3. Derive equations (20.1–6) to (20.1–11) inclusive in the manner indicated in the text.

Problem 20.1-4. Calculate $\tilde{C}_r$, $\tilde{E}$, $\tilde{H}$, $\tilde{S}$, and $\tilde{F}/T$ due to rotation for HCN at 300°K from the following bond distances: C—H, 1.059 Å; C≡N, 1.157 Å.

Problem 20.1-5. Calculate the value of $\tilde{F}/T$, due to rotation only, for carbon dioxide at 298.16°K from the following bond distance: C═O, 1.162 Å.

The vibrational partition function and the corresponding vibrational thermodynamic properties are discussed in Section 20.3.

20.2 Rotational Contribution of Non-linear Polyatomic Molecules

The rotational partition function of non-linear polyatomic molecules may be obtained by procedures like those used for linear molecules. From this the thermodynamic functions due to rotation may be obtained. The thermodynamic functions due to vibration are considered in Section 20.3. The rotational partition function is obtained, in general, by considering the energy levels of an asymmetric rotator, as given by equation (16.22–9). The partition function is

$$Q = \Sigma e^{-\epsilon/kT}, \tag{20.2–1}$$

with ϵ given by equation (16.22–9). The *a priori* probability p is unity, since there is only one state for each energy. If the molecule lacks an axis of symmetry, all values of the quantum numbers are allowed for each nuclear spin species. In principle, the sum may be replaced by a multiple integral. The mathematics involved in doing so is too complicated to be profitably considered here, but Problem 16.22–5 gives some idea of the situation. The final result of the integration is

$$Q_r = \frac{8\pi^2}{h^3}(8\pi^3\text{ABC})^{1/2}(kT)^{3/2}. \tag{20.2–2}$$

The mathematical complexity involved in replacing these sums by appropriate integrals can be avoided, because the value of Q_r may be obtained directly by use of the classical expression for the energy of an asymmetric top with principal moments A, B, and C. The energy may be expressed in terms of the Eulerian angles θ, ϕ, and ψ by[1]

$$\epsilon = \frac{1}{2}\left(\frac{\sin^2\psi}{\text{A}} + \frac{\cos^2\psi}{\text{B}}\right)$$
$$\left\{p_\theta + \left(\frac{1}{\text{B}} - \frac{1}{\text{A}}\right)\frac{\sin\psi\cos\psi}{\sin\theta\left(\dfrac{\sin^2\psi}{\text{A}} + \dfrac{\cos^2\psi}{\text{B}}\right)}(\text{p}_\phi - \text{p}_\psi\cos\theta)\right\}^2$$
$$+ \frac{1}{2\text{AB}\sin^2\theta}\frac{1}{\dfrac{\sin^2\psi}{\text{A}} + \dfrac{\cos^2\psi}{\text{B}}}(\text{p}_\phi - \text{p}_\psi\cos\theta)^2 + \frac{1}{2\text{C}}\text{p}_\psi{}^2. \tag{20.2–3}$$

[1] See R. Fowler and E. A. Guggenheim, *Statistical Thermodynamics*, Cambridge University Press, 1949, p. 106.

The expression for the number of states in the range $dp_\theta\, dp_\phi\, dp_\psi\, d\theta\, d\phi\, d\psi$ is

$$p = \frac{dp_\theta\, dp_\phi\, dp_\psi\, d\theta\, d\phi\, d\psi}{h^3}. \tag{20.2–4}$$

The partition function is thus

$$Q_r = \frac{1}{h^3} \int\!\!\int\!\!\int\!\!\int\!\!\int\!\!\int e^{-\epsilon/kT}\, dp_\theta\, dp_\phi\, dp_\psi\, d\theta\, d\phi\, d\psi. \tag{20.2–5}$$

Equation (20.2–2) is then obtained by substitution for ϵ (from equation 20.2–3) and subsequent integration from left to right over all values of the coordinates and momenta as illustrated in the problem below.

Problem 20.2-1. Derive equation (20.2–2) by integration of equation (20.2–5). (This problem is no more than an exercise in algebra which may be omitted if the student is willing to accept the final result on faith.)

If the molecule has an n-fold axis of symmetry, only $1/n$ of the possible rotational wave functions satisfy the symmetry requirements for any particular combination of nuclear spin wave functions of the constituent atoms. As a result it is necessary to divide Q_r by n if there is an n-fold axis of symmetry.[2] In general, if σ is the number of equivalent positions of the molecule which can be produced by rotation of the molecule about axes of symmetry, the rotational partition function of an asymmetric top is

$$Q_r = \frac{8\pi^2}{\sigma h^3}(8\pi^3 \mathrm{ABC})^{1/2}(kT)^{3/2}. \tag{20.2–6}$$

If σ is other than unity, the molecule usually becomes a *symmetric top.* This, however, merely means that two of the three principal moments A, B, and C become equal. For molecules of tetrahedral symmetry σ is 12 and A = B = C; in this case the molecule is a *spherical top.*

Substituting equation (20.2–6) into (18.7–12), (18.2–8), (18.7–14), and (18.7–13) yields the molal thermodynamic quantities due to the rotational degrees of freedom. The expressions obtained are

$$\tilde{E}_r = \frac{3RT}{2}, \tag{20.2–7}$$

$$\tilde{C}_r = \frac{3R}{2}, \tag{20.2–8}$$

$$\tilde{F}/T = -R[\tfrac{3}{2}\ln T + \tfrac{1}{2}\ln \mathrm{ABC} - \ln\sigma + \ln 8\pi^2(8\pi^3k^3)^{1/2}h^{-3}], \tag{20.2–9}$$

and

$$\tilde{S}_r = R[\tfrac{3}{2} + \tfrac{3}{2}\ln T + \tfrac{1}{2}\ln \mathrm{ABC} - \ln\sigma + \ln 8\pi^2(8\pi^3k^3)^{1/2}h^{-3}]. \tag{20.2–10}$$

[2] J. E. Mayer, S. Brunauer, and M. G. Mayer, *J. Am. Chem. Soc.*, **55**, 37 (1933).

By substitution of numerical constants into equations (20.2–9) and (20.2–10),

$$-\left(\frac{\tilde{F}}{T}\right)_r = R(\tfrac{3}{2}\ln T + \tfrac{1}{2}\ln \text{ABC} - \ln\sigma + 133.186), \qquad (20.2\text{–}11)$$

and

$$\tilde{S}_r = R(\tfrac{3}{2}\ln T + \tfrac{1}{2}\ln \text{ABC} - \ln\sigma + 134.686). \qquad (20.2\text{–}12)$$

The principal moments of inertia required for these equations are obtained by the methods of Section 16.22.

Problem 20.2-2. Derive equations (20.2–7) to (20.2–12) inclusive in the way indicated in the text.

Problem 20.2-3. Calculate Q_r, $\tilde{F}_r/T$, $\tilde{S}_r$ for sulfur dioxide from the following bond distances and angles at 298.16°K: S=O = 1.46 ± 0.02 Å, < OSO = 122 ± 5°.

20.3 The Vibrational Contribution for Polyatomic Molecules

In general, the vibrational energy of a molecule lies in several modes of vibration each of which constitutes a single degree of freedom; some of the modes may be degenerate in energy. Such modes of vibration are often called Einstein modes.[3] The energy for a particular quantum state is approximately that of a harmonic oscillator,

$$\epsilon_v = (v + \tfrac{1}{2})h\nu_0, \qquad (20.3\text{–}1)$$

where $v = 1, 2, 3, 4$, etc. The procedure for obtaining the vibrational partition function under such circumstances has been given in Section 19.6 for the diatomic molecule, but is repeated here in detail for convenience.

The partition function is

$$Q_v = e^{-h\nu_0/2kT}\sum e^{-vh\nu_0/kT}, \qquad (20.3\text{–}2)$$

which can be rewritten

$$Q_v = e^{-h\nu_0/2kT}\sum e^{-vx}, \qquad (20.3\text{–}3)$$

where $x = h\nu_0/kT$.

By the binomial theorem, since $e^{-vx} < 1$,

$$\sum e^{-vx} = \frac{1}{1 - e^{-x}}, \qquad (20.3\text{–}4)$$

so that

$$Q_v = \frac{e^{-h\nu_0/2kT}}{1 - e^{-x}}. \qquad (20.3\text{–}5)$$

The factor $e^{-h\nu_0/2kT}$ introduces an additive term $(-h\nu_0/2kT)$ into the ln of the partition function, which leads to the addition of a term $(\mathbf{N}h\nu_0/2)$

[3] Albert Einstein, *Ann. Physik*, **22**, 180 (1907).

in the molar energy, free energy, etc. It is convenient to absorb this contribution into the constant term $\tilde{E}_0^\circ$ and to take the vibrational partition function as

$$Q_v = \frac{1}{1 - e^{-x}} = \frac{1}{1 - e^{-h\nu_0/kT}} \cdot \qquad (20.3\text{–}6)$$

This procedure corresponds to taking the zero of energy as the energy of the level for which $v = 0$.

The energy per mole associated with a single vibrational mode is obtained by substituting equation (20.3–6) for the vibrational partition function into equation (18.2–6). It is

$$\tilde{E}_v - \tilde{E}_0 = \frac{RTx}{e^x - 1}, \qquad (20.3\text{–}7)$$

the energy level for $v = 0$ being taken as zero. The vibrational heat capacity is obtained by substitution into (18.2–8); it is

$$\tilde{C}_v = \frac{Rx^2e^x}{(e^x - 1)^2} \cdot \qquad (20.3\text{–}8)$$

In both (20.3–7) and (20.3–8), $x = h\nu_0/kT$. The subscript v denotes vibration. The quantity $\tilde{C}_v$ is not to be confused with the heat capacity at constant volume.

Tables for $(\tilde{E} - \tilde{E}_0)/T$, as obtained from (20.3–7), and $\tilde{C}$ (from 20.3–8) are given in Appendix 4. These are called Einstein functions. This treatment is valid whenever the rotational and vibrational partition functions are separable and the vibration is harmonic.

It is of interest to evaluate $\tilde{C}$ at high temperatures. When T is large, x is small and e^x can be replaced by the first two terms of its power expansion, namely, $(1 + x)$; thus

$$\tilde{C} = \frac{Rx^2(1 + x)}{x^2} = R(1 + x). \qquad (20.3\text{–}9)$$

However, since x is small, it can be neglected compared with unity, so that $\tilde{C}$ approaches the value R. This is the "classical" value obtained from the *principle of equipartition*.[4]

The calculation of the vibrational contribution to the energy and heat capacity will be illustrated for the methane molecule. Methane has

[4] This theorem was developed from classical statistical mechanics by Maxwell and Boltzmann. It states that (in the classical limit) the kinetic energy and the potential energy residing in any degree of freedom will each be $\frac{1}{2}RT$. For vibration this means a total energy of RT and a heat capacity of R per vibrational degree of freedom. Since translation or rotation involve no potential energy, they contribute $\frac{1}{2}RT$ to the energy and $R/2$ to the heat capacity for each degree of freedom.

five atoms corresponding to fifteen degrees of freedom, of which translation and rotation of the molecule account for six; nine degrees of freedom are left, all of which are vibrational in character. The nine degrees of freedom, in this case, give rise to only four fundamental frequencies or modes of vibration. One of these (ν_1) corresponds to one of the degrees of freedom, a second ($\nu_{2,3}$) corresponds to two of the degrees of freedom, while the remaining two ($\nu_{4,5,6}$ and $\nu_{7,8,9}$) each correspond to three degrees of freedom. The frequencies have the values $\nu_1 = 2915$, $\nu_{2,3} = 1520$, $\nu_{4,5,6} = 1304$, $\nu_{7,8,9} = 3022$ cm^{-1}.[5] The vibrational contributions to the energy and heat capacity are obtained by applying equations (20.3–7) and (20.3–8) to *each* vibrational degree of freedom; the resulting values are added to obtain the total vibrational contribution (in this particular case, a term involving $\nu_{4,5,6}$ is added three times, etc.). This method applies if it is permissible to neglect (a) the interaction between rotation and vibration and (b) any anharmonicity in vibration. Corrections for these effects are discussed below.

Problem 20.3-1. Calculate the heat capacity of methane at constant pressure in the ideal gas state at 400°K, 1 atm. Consider translation, rotation, and vibration, assuming that the interaction between rotation and vibration and the anharmonicity of vibration can be neglected. The experimental value is 10.1 cal deg^{-1} mole^{-1}.

Values of $-\tilde{F}_v/T$ are obtained by substitution of equation (20.3–6) into equation (18.7–14) for each vibrational degree of freedom. These are also tabulated in Appendix 4. The entropy can be obtained from

$$\tilde{S}_v = \frac{E_v}{T} - \frac{F_v}{T}. \qquad (20.3\text{–}10)$$

Problem 20.3-2. (a) Calculate the total $(\tilde{F}^\circ - \tilde{E}^\circ)/T$ and total entropy of methane (less nuclear spin) in the ideal gas state at the normal boiling point of 112°K and 1 atm. The measured value of the entropy (corrected to the ideal gas state) is 30.5 cal deg^{-1} mole^{-1}. Use the data of Problem 20.3–1. The C—H distance is 1.0934 Å and the angles are tetrahedral.

(b) Repeat the calculation at 400°K. The value calculated for the entropy at 400°K, taking anharmonicity into account, is 47.17.

20.4 Correction for Anharmonicity and Centrifugal Stretching in the Thermodynamic Functions of Polyatomic Molecules

The effects of anharmonicity and of centrifugal stretching were taken into account for diatomic molecules by the inclusion of appropriate terms in the expression for the energy levels. In the energy expression given as equation (19.3–13), the quadratic and cubic terms in $(v + {}^1/_2)$ accounted

[5] For discussion see L. S. Kassel, *J. Am. Chem. Soc.*, **55**, 1357 (1933).

for the anharmonicity of vibration; the effect of rotational stretching was given by the quadratic and cubic terms in $J(J+1)$; the interaction of vibration and rotation was reflected in the dependence of each of the rotational constants B_v, D_v, etc., upon the vibrational quantum number. The evaluation of the partition function for this type of energy expression was described in Section 19.3.

The situation for a linear polyatomic molecule is only slightly more complex. HCN, for example, has three fundamental frequencies, one of which (ν_2) is doubly degenerate. The vibrational energy is given by

$$\begin{aligned}\frac{\epsilon_v}{hc} &= \omega_1(v_1+\tfrac{1}{2}) + \omega_2(v_2+1) + \omega_3(v_3+\tfrac{1}{2}) \\ &\quad + x_{11}(v_1+\tfrac{1}{2})^2 + x_{22}(v_2+1)^2 + x_{33}(v_3+\tfrac{1}{2})^2 \\ &\quad + g_{22}l_2^{\,2} + x_{12}(v_1+\tfrac{1}{2})(v_2+1) \\ &\quad + x_{13}(v_1+\tfrac{1}{2})(v_3+\tfrac{1}{2}) + x_{23}(v_2+1)(v_3+\tfrac{1}{2}) \\ &\quad + y_{333}(v_3+\tfrac{1}{2})^3. \end{aligned} \tag{20.4–1}$$

The rotational energy is given by the formula

$$\frac{\epsilon_r}{hc} = B_v J(J+1) - D_v J^2(J+1)^2. \tag{20.4–2}$$

The constants for HCN are given in Table 20.4–1.

Table 20.4–1

Rotational-Vibrational Constants for Hydrogen Cyanide

$\omega_1 = 2000.6$	$x_{11} = +52.0$	$x_{12} = -4.2$	$x_{13} = -14.4$
$\omega_2 = 729.3$	$x_{22} = -2.8$	$x_{23} = -19.53$	$g_{22} = +3.25$
$\omega_3 = 3451.5$	$x_{33} = -55.48$	$y_{333} = +0.768$	

$$B_v = 1.4878 - 0.0093(v_1+\tfrac{1}{2}) + 0.0007(v_2+1) - 0.0108(v_3+\tfrac{1}{2})$$

$$D = 3.3 \times 10^{-6} \text{ (all values of } v_i)$$

The partition function of a linear polyatomic molecule may then be evaluated in the same manner as described for a diatomic molecule in Section 19.3. Q_r is evaluated for each set of values v_1, v_2, v_3, and l_2, and then summed over all values with appropriate exponential and weighting factors. In doing so it should be noted that the quantum number l_2 can take values $v_2, v_2 - 2, \cdots$ to 1 or 0, and that all resulting levels for $l_2 \neq 0$ are doubly degenerate. For convenience, the energy of the state in which all v are zero may be taken as the energy zero. The derivatives of the partition function may be obtained as before.

Problem 20.4-1. Evaluate the partition function for HCN at 1000°K by extension of the methods of Section 19.3.

The above type of treatment is not practical for polyatomic molecules in general. Instead, it is necessary to use the approximations of Sections 20.1 to 20.3, with subsequent corrections for anharmonicity and centrifugal stretching. The partition function may be put in the form

$$Q = Q_r Q_{rc} \Pi Q_{\text{HO}} Q_c , \tag{20.4–3}$$

where Q_r is the partition function for a rigid rotor, given in general by equation (20.2–6). ΠQ_{HO} is the product of the harmonic oscillator partition functions of equation (20.3–5); Q_{rc} is the correction to the rotational partition function for centrifugal stretching, and Q_c contains the correction for anharmonicity and rotation-vibration interaction.

The term Q_{rc} corrects for rotational stretching; it is of the form $(1 + \rho T + \cdots)$, as shown by Wilson.[6] The constant ρ is significant only for light molecules. It has the values 2.04×10^{-5} for water, 1.62×10^{-5} for H_2S, and 1.45×10^{-5} for ammonia. Inclusion of the term $(1 + \rho T)$ in the partition function leads to an additive term $2\rho RT$ in both the heat capacity and the entropy.

Problem 20.4-2. Verify the statement in the last sentence for small values of ρT.

Because of the interaction of vibration with rotation, in any complete expression of the rotational energy of a polyatomic molecule, each of the "constants" must be given as a function of the several vibrational quantum numbers. The terms which give this dependence are analogous to the α's and β's used in calculating rotational constants for a given vibrational level of a diatomic molecule. They are expressed in the form of power series in the v_i including cross products. The corrections to vibrational energy levels for anharmonicity are expressed in a similar power series, as in equation (20.4–1). The correction term Q_c is the combined contribution to the partition function of these two sets of correction terms. The calculation of Q_c for the general case has been given by Wooley.[7] The final expression for Q_c is a set of power series of functions like equation (20.3–5).

The correction terms necessary for application of the various formulas can, in principle, be obtained from spectroscopic observations, as were the constants given above for HCN. Unfortunately, this has been done only for a very few non-linear polyatomic molecules, such as water and ammonia,[8] and then only in most cases to terms linear in $v_i v_j$. For this reason the equations are not included here.

[6] E. B. Wilson, Jr., *J. Chem. Phys.*, **4,** 526 (1936).
[7] H. W. Wooley, *J. Research Natl. Bur. Standards*, **56,** 105 (1956).
[8] D. M. Dennison, *Revs. Mod. Phys.*, **12,** 175 (1940).

An interesting empirical approach has been used by McCullough,[9] who set up simple empirical expressions, in appropriate form, for the contribution of anharmonicity to the heat capacity, enthalpy, and entropy. These expressions contain a temperature-independent constant Z and a function $(hc\tilde{\nu}^*/kT)$. The parameters Z and $\tilde{\nu}^*$ can then be evaluated from the observed anharmonicity contribution. This is evaluated by comparison of experimental heat capacity data with values calculated neglecting anharmonicity. The parameters Z and $\tilde{\nu}^*$ may then be used to calculate the correction at other temperatures. As an example, the correction to the heat capacity is

$$\tilde{C}^\circ(\text{anh}) = Z\left(\frac{\tilde{C}^\circ}{R}\right)\left[\left(\frac{3\tilde{C}^\circ}{Ru}\right) - \left(1 + \frac{2}{u}\right)\left(\frac{\tilde{H}^\circ - \tilde{H}_0^\circ}{RT}\right)\right], \qquad (20.4\text{–}4)$$

where $u = hc\tilde{\nu}^*/kT$. For thiocyclohexane,[9] the correction to the heat capacity for anharmonicity is 1.2% at 400°K and 2.2% at 483°K.

20.5 Partition Function and Thermodynamic Properties for Internal Rotation

It is simplest to consider first of all a molecule in which one or more groups of atoms can rotate only to a very limited degree because of the existence of high sinusoidal potential barriers, n in number. In this case, the number of molecules in any energy level corresponding to passage of the rotating groups over (or through) the barrier is negligibly small, providing that the temperature is not unreasonably high. For such a situation, the angular force constant associated with a hindered internal rotation has been shown (in Section 16.25) to be

$$k_\phi = \frac{n^2 V_0}{2}, \qquad (16.25\text{–}11)$$

where V_0 is the height of the sinusoidal barrier, and n the number of minima. It is then possible to make a normal coordinate analysis in which the internal rotations are treated simply as vibrations. If it is assumed that solutions of the secular equation yields modes corresponding essentially to torsional vibrations about each of the bonds, the frequency of such a vibration is given by

$$\nu_0 = \frac{n}{2\pi}\sqrt{\frac{V_0}{2I_{\text{red}}}}, \qquad (16.25\text{–}12)$$

where I_{red} is the reduced moment of the two rotating groups, to be discussed below. If ν_0 can be obtained from the infrared or Raman spectrum,

[9] J. P. McCullough et al., *J. Am. Chem. Soc.*, **76**, 2661 (1954).

the thermodynamic functions may be obtained by the methods of the last section, using the Einstein tables of Appendix 4. Obviously, the height of the barrier, V_0, can be obtained from equation (16.25–12).

Problem 20.5-1. Table 20.5–1 lists the frequency assignment for trimethylamine as obtained from infrared and Raman spectra.[10] The frequencies labeled Γ_1 and $\Gamma_{2,3}$ are due to the restricted rotation of the methyl groups.

(a) Calculate the entropy at 200°K due to the hindered rotation of the three methyl groups treated as harmonic oscillators.

(b) Calculate the entropy due to translation and rotation of the rigid molecule at 200°K and 1 atm, using the following bond lengths and angles: CN, 1.47 Å; CH, 1.09 Å; CNC angle, 108°; HCH angle, 109° 28′ ($\sigma = 3$). (*Hint.* Choose the orientation of maximum symmetry.)

(c) Calculate the total entropy at 200°K, 1 atm. The measured value for the entropy of the ideal gas is 61.60 ± 0.14. Suggest a cause for the discrepancy.

(d) Calculate V_0 in the equation giving the potential V as a function of angle

$$V = \tfrac{1}{2}V_0(1 - \cos 3\theta). \qquad (16.25\text{–}1)$$

The reduced moment of inertia required may be taken as

$$I_{\text{red}} = \frac{I_{\text{CH}_3} I_{(\text{CH}_3)_2\text{N}}}{I_{\text{CH}_3} + I_{(\text{CH}_3)_2\text{N}}},$$

where the individual moments are taken about the C—N bond.

Table 20.5–1

The Frequency Assignment of Trimethylamine,[10] Point Group C_{3v}

	Type		
	A_1	A_2	E
Description	Frequencies†		
Skeleton	ω_1, 368	$\omega_{3,4}$, 424	
	ω_2, 827	$\omega_{5,6}$, 1050	
Hydrogen (internal)	ν_1, 2766	$\delta_{4,5}$, 1466	$\nu_{4,5}$, 2970
	ν_2, 2943	$\delta_{6,7}$, 1441	$\nu_{6,7}$, 2970
	ν_3, 3000	$\delta_{8,9}$, 1441	$\nu_{8,9}$, 2970
	δ_1, 1441		
	δ_2, 1466		
	δ_3, 1400		
Hydrogen (rocking)	γ_1, 1179	γ_2, 1040	$\gamma_{3,4}$, 1276
			$\gamma_{5,6}$, 1040
Internal rotation		Γ_1, 272	$\Gamma_{2,3}$, 272

† The symbols ω, ν, δ, γ, and Γ distinguish skeletal, stretching, bending, rocking, and internal rotational modes of methyl groups, respectively.

[10] *J. Am. Chem. Soc.*, **66**, 1177 (1944).

When the temperature is relatively high, this procedure is not possible, and another method must be used to calculate the thermodynamic functions.

Ideally the wave equations should be solved for the entire molecule, the energy levels derived, and a partition function Q_{int} (as defined by equation 18.4–13) obtained, where Q_{int} cannot be separated into components for internal and external rotation. This procedure is obviously too laborious to be practical. The actual procedure is first to set up the classical partition function for the total rotational energy of a molecule including that due to the m internally rotating groups which may be different but are considered completely free. The effect of potential barriers hindering internal rotation is treated as a correction. For details the reader is referred to the original literature.[11–13]

If proper reduced moments are assigned to the internally rotating groups, the free rotational partition function can be factored with good approximation into a part due to external rotation and a part due to internal rotation. Thus the equation

$$Q_r = Q_{r\,\text{ext}} \prod_m r_m \tag{20.5–1}$$

is obtained, where $Q_{r\,\text{ext}}$ is given by equation (20.2–2) in terms of the principal moments A, B, and C of the molecule (regarded as rigid); the quantity r_m is the partition function for the mth internally rotating group. These partition functions are given by the relation

$$r_m = \frac{(8\pi^3 I_m kT)^{1/2}}{nh}. \tag{20.5–2}$$

In this equation I_m is the reduced moment of the mth rotating group, and n usually represents the number of exchanges of identical atoms which can be brought about by internal rotation. Strictly speaking, the necessity for introduction of the factor n arises in the same way that σ enters equation (20.2–6). However, when restricted rotation is considered it may have a somewhat different meaning and may arise from another cause (see below). After substitution of values for the constants, with I_m in gram cm^2 per molecule, this equation becomes

$$r_m = \frac{2.7935(10^{38} I_m T)^{1/2}}{n}. \tag{20.5–3}$$

[11] *J. Chem. Phys.*, **3**, 379 (1935).
[12] L. S. Kassel, *J. Chem. Phys.*, **4**, 276 (1936).
[13] K. S. Pitzer, *J. Chem. Phys.*, **14**, 239 (1946).

The "reduced" moment I_m to be used in equations (20.5–2) and (20.5–3) can usually be taken as

$$I_m = \frac{A_m A_r}{A_m + A_r}, \tag{20.5–4}$$

where A_m and A_r are respectively moments of inertia of the groups m and of the rest of the molecule about the axis of rotation.

If a rotating group m has a non-zero product of inertia about its axis of rotation, it is said to be asymmetrical with respect to the axis. In such a case the principal moments of inertia of the rigid molecule depend on the relative positions of the rotating groups. Usually the changes in the moments produced by rotation of the groups are small enough that it is sufficient to calculate the value of the moment for any convenient position of the rotating groups. If the change is large, the principal moments must be averaged with respect to the angular coordinates ω_m of all asymmetric internal rotors.

The strictly correct value of I_m must be defined[14,15] in terms of the following quantities:

I_1, I_2, I_3, and M are the principal moments of inertia and mass of the molecule in cgs units.

$A_m = \sum_i \mathrm{m}_i(x_i^2 + y_i^2)$ is the moment of inertia of the mth top (rotating group) about its z axis, which is chosen as the axis of rotation.

$B_m = \sum_i \mathrm{m}_i x_i z_i$ is the corresponding xz product of inertia.

$C_m = \sum_i \mathrm{m}_i y_i z_i$ is the corresponding yz product of inertia.

$U_m = \sum_i \mathrm{m}_i x_i$ for the mth top is called the "off balance factor."

In the mth top, the matrix

$$\begin{pmatrix} \alpha_m^{1x} & \alpha_m^{2x} & \alpha_m^{3x} \\ \alpha_m^{1y} & \alpha_m^{2y} & \alpha_m^{3y} \\ \alpha_m^{1z} & \alpha_m^{2z} & \alpha_m^{3z} \end{pmatrix}$$

gives the direction cosines between the axes (x, y, z) of the mth top and the principal axes of the whole molecule (1, 2, 3). (Both sets of axes must be uniformly left- or right-handed; that is, the determinant of the α's must be equal to $+1$.)

[14] K. S. Pitzer and W. D. Gwinn, *J. Chem. Phys.*, **10**, 428 (1942).
[15] K. S. Pitzer, *J. Chem. Phys.*, **14**, 238 (1946).

The vector from the center of gravity of the whole molecule to the origin of coordinates of the top is r_m with components $r_m{}^1$, $r_m{}^2$, $r_m{}^3$ on the principal axes.

A quantity characteristic of the interaction between two tops, m and m', is defined:

$$\Lambda_{mm'} = \sum_i \left\{ \frac{\alpha_m{}^{iy}\alpha_{m'}{}^{iy}U_m U_{m'}}{M} + \frac{\beta_m{}^i\beta_{m'}{}^i}{I_i} \right\}, \tag{20.5–5}$$

where

$$\beta_m{}^i = \alpha_m{}^{iz}A_m - \alpha_m{}^{ix}B_m - \alpha_m{}^{iy}C_m + U_m(\alpha_m^{i-1,y}\, r_m^{i+1} - \alpha_m^{i+1,y}\, r_m^{i-1}), \tag{20.5–6}$$

$(i - 1)$ and $(i + 1)$ referring to cyclic shifts of axes (i.e., if $i = 1, i - 1 = 3$; and, if $i = 3, i + 1 = 1$).

In terms of these quantities, the reduced moment of inertia of the mth group is given by

$$I_m = I_m{}^\circ - \frac{1}{2} \sum_{m' \neq m}{}' \frac{\Lambda^2_{mm'}}{I_{m'}{}^\circ}, \tag{20.5–7}$$

with

$$I_m{}^\circ = A_m\left(1 - \sum_i \frac{A_m\alpha^2_{z,i}}{I_i}\right).$$

To a first approximation, this reduces to the expression

$$I_m = A_m - \Lambda_{mm}. \tag{20.5–8}$$

Problem 20.5-2. Show that I_m for the internal rotation of ethane is just one quarter of the moment of the whole molecule about the axis joining the methyl groups.

Problem 20.5-3. (a) Show that, for one rotating group only,

$$I_m \equiv I_m{}^\circ.$$

(b) Show that, if the rotating groups are symmetrical about the axis of rotation, then

$$\Lambda_{mm'} = A_m A_{m'} \sum_i \frac{\alpha_m{}^{iz}\alpha_{m'}{}^{iz}}{I_i}. \tag{20.5–9}$$

Problem 20.5-4. For m-chloroethylbenzene the bond distances are C—C in C_6H_5, 1.39 Å; C—Cl, 1.69 Å; C—C_2H_5, 1.50 Å; C—C in C_2H_5, 1.53 Å; CH in C_2H_5, 1.09 Å; angles in C_2H_5 tetrahedral; all other angles 120°.

(a) Calculate I_1, I_2, I_3, $I_m{}^\circ$, and I_m.

(b) What is the percentage difference between I_m as given approximately by equation (20.5–4) and the exact equation (20.5–7)?

(c) What is the percentage difference between I_m as given by equation (20.5–8) and by equation (20.5–7)?

It is to be seen from the last problem that equation (20.5–4) is an adequate approximation for I_m to within the usually required accuracy, as is verified by Problem 20.5–6.

If the tops themselves are not rigid, complications arise in obtaining exact values for the reduced moments.[16] Usually it is sufficient to treat any rotating group, R, as rigid, with any rotating groups, R_i', which are part of it, at rest in their equilibrium positions. This rigid group has the moment A_m in equation (20.5–4); the rest of the molecule has moment A_r. The rotating groups, R_i', in the group R are then treated as single rotators of moment A_m, rotating with respect to the rest of the molecule of moment A_r, including all parts of R but R_i'. The reduced moment, in either case, is calculated by using equation (20.5–4).

The thermodynamic functions for a freely rotating group are obtained from the partition function r_m of equation (20.5–1) with the use of equations (18.7–12), (18.7–13), and (18.7–14). They are, after substitutions of the constants,

$$\tilde{C}_f = \tilde{C}_V \text{ (or } \tilde{C}_P) = \frac{R}{2}, \qquad (20.5\text{–}10)$$

$$\tilde{E}_f \text{ (or } \tilde{H}_f) = \frac{RT}{2}, \qquad (20.5\text{–}11)$$

$$-\frac{\tilde{F}_f}{T} = R[\tfrac{1}{2} \ln T - \ln n + \tfrac{1}{2} \ln I_m \times 10^{40} - 1.275], \qquad (20.5\text{–}12)$$

and

$$\tilde{S}_f = R[\tfrac{1}{2} \ln T - \ln n + \tfrac{1}{2} \ln I_m \times 10^{40} - 0.775]. \qquad (20.5\text{–}13)$$

Problem 20.5-5. Derive equations (20.5–10) to (20.5–13) inclusive.

Problem 20.5-6. Calculate the percentage error in using equation (20.5–4) to calculate the entropy of free rotation at 400°K due to both rotating groups in *m*-chloroethylbenzene see Problem (20.5–4).

Problem 20.5-7. The mutual internal rotation of the methyl groups in dimethylacetylene is free.

(a) Calculate the entropy at 298.15°K due to free rotation of a methyl group in dimethylacetylene.

(b) Calculate the entropy due to rotation of the rigid molecule.

(c) Calculate the vibrational entropy of dimethylacetylene.

(d) Calculate the total entropy at 291°K and 1 atm. The measured value is 67.5 ± 0.3. (*Note.* Since the group CH_3—C≡C— is linear, only one methyl group is considered to be freely rotating. The symmetry number σ for the rigid rotator is 6, while for the free rotation the corresponding quantity n is 3.) The lengths and angles are: CH_3—C, 1.47 Å; C≡C, 1.20 Å; CH, 1.09 Å; CH_3 angles tetrahedral. Dimethylacetylene has D_{3d} symmetry. Its fundamental frequencies are given in Table 20.5–2. Note that the frequencies marked E are doubly degenerate.)

[16] J. E. Kilpatrick and K. S. Pitzer, *J. Chem. Phys.*, **17**, 1064 (1949).

The calculation of thermodynamic functions for cases where the rotation is not free, but is hindered by a potential given by

$$V = \frac{V_0(1 - \cos n\theta)}{2}, \qquad (16.25\text{–}2)$$

are most conveniently approached by first considering the ethane molecule. In this case the problem can be treated exactly, since the energy levels corresponding to the hindered rotation can be obtained exactly if interaction between rotation and vibration is neglected. These energy levels have been discussed in Section 16.25; they depend on the height of the

Table 20.5–2
Designation, Character, Species, and Values of the Normal Vibrations of CH_3—C≡C—CH_3, Symmetry D_{3d}

Description	A_{1g}	A_{1u}	A_{2u}	E_u	E_g
C—H stretching	ν_1, 2920	—	ν_6, 2975	ν_9, 2975	ν_{13}, 2961
C≡C stretching	ν_2, 2312.7	—	—	—	—
CH_3 deformation	ν_3, 1379	—	ν_7, 1380	ν_{10}, 1468	ν_{14}, 1447
CH_3 rocking	—	—	—	ν_{11}, 1050	ν_{15}, 1029
C—C stretching	ν_4, 697.4	—	ν_8, 1126	—	—
C—C≡C—C bending	—	—	—	ν_{12}, 213	ν_{16}, 374
CH_3 twisting (torsion)	—	ν_5, ?†	—	—	—

† ν_5 is infrared and Raman inactive.

barrier, V_0, the number of minima, n, and the reduced moment of inertia. The thermodynamic functions must be calculated from a partition function evaluated by direct summation, by using equation (18.4–13).

It is possible to apply the results obtained for ethane to each rotating group in any molecule for which the potential energy of rotation is

$$V = \frac{V_0(1 - \cos n\theta)}{2}, \qquad (16.25\text{–}2)$$

and to tabulate the results in terms of convenient parameters involving the potential maximum V_0, the reduced moment I_m, the number of minima n, and the temperature. The parameters used are V_0/RT and $1/r_m$, where r_m is the partition function for free internal rotation as given by equation (20.5–2). The values of $-\tilde{F}/T$ and $\tilde{E}/T$ are given in Tables A4–3 and A4–4 (of Appendix 4). When there are several internally rotating groups, the proper reduced moments I_m must be calculated by using equation (20.5–7) or suitable approximations.

Problem 20.5-8. Calculate the entropy of trimethylamine at 298.15°K and 1 atm as exactly as possible, using Tables A4-3 and A4-4 (Appendix 4) and the data of Problem 20.5-2. Calculate the errors resulting from using equations (20.5-4) and (20.5-8) respectively to calculate the reduced moment I_m. The potential barrier, V_m, is 4270 cal mole^{-1}.

Problem 20.5-9. Calculate the entropy of ethane at 181°K and 1 atm from the following data. The principal moments are 42.23, 42.23, and 10.81 × 10^{-40} g cm^2 per molecule, the latter being about the line joining the carbon atoms. The vibrational frequencies are given in Table 20.5-3. The barrier hindering internal rotation is 2750 cal mole^{-1}. Compare with the calorimetric value of 54.85 cal deg^{-1} mole^{-1}.

Problem 20.5-10. Calculate the error made in the calculated entropy at 300°K of *m*-chloroethylbenzene by use of (a) (20.5-8), (b) (20.5-4) for calculation of I_m. The rotation of the methyl group may be assumed to be free.

Table 20.5-3
Vibrational Frequencies of Ethane†
(for D_{3d} Symmetry)

Description	A_{1g}	A_{2u}	E_u	E_g
C—H stretching	ν_1, 2955	ν_5, 2954	ν_7, 2996	ν_{10}, 2963
C—C stretching	ν_3, 993			
CH_3 deformation	ν_2, 1375	ν_6, 1375	ν_8, 1472	ν_{11}, 1460
Bending			ν_9, 821.5	ν_{12}, 1190

† From L. G. Smith, *J. Chem. Phys.*, **17**, 139 (1949).

When the rotating groups are not symmetrical, it is often not possible to represent the potential as a simple sinusoidal function of *n* minima; however, a sinusoidal potential function can often be fitted over fractions of a revolution. Usually, when the group passes from one position of minimum energy to another, there is a change in the potential energy at the minimum, and the compound may be considered as changing from one form (rotational isomer) to another. Thus the potential is represented by a different (but still sinusoidal) function for each form, and the forms have different energies when at their potential minima.

An example of a calculation in which the potential minima are not equivalent is that for 1,3-butadiene, which consists of a mixture of *s-cis* and *s-trans* forms. The potential energy function of the *s-trans* form which best fits the third law entropy and gaseous heat capacities is[17]

$$V_{trans} = 2500\left(1 - \cos\frac{\theta}{0.406}\right) \text{ cal mole}^{-1}, \tag{20.5-14}$$

while that for the *s-cis* form is

$$V_{cis} = 2425 + 1288\left[1 - \cos\frac{(\theta - \pi)}{0.594}\right] \text{ cal mole}^{-1}. \tag{20.5-15}$$

[17] *J. Chem. Phys.*, **14**, 67 (1946).

As can be seen from these equations, the minima of the *s-cis* and *s-trans* forms are separated by 180°, but the maxima are so located that the *s-cis* form exists up to 0.594 of a complete revolution and the *s-trans* form beyond this for the rest of the revolution. The constant term in the expression for the *s-cis* form indicates that its energy zero is 2.425 kcal higher than that of the *s-trans* form.

In each case, equation (20.5–7) is used to calculate the reduced moments. In calculating the internal rotational (or torsional) entropy of each isomer (of the two forms), the barrier hindering the rotation is taken as 1288 cal mole^{-1} for the *s-cis* isomer and 2500 cal mole^{-1} for the *s-trans* isomer, with the potential functions of equations (20.5–14) and (20.5–15). The number n in equations (20.5–2), (20.5–12), and (20.5–13) is taken as 1/0.594 for the *s-cis* form and 1/0.406 for the *trans* form (if each isomer occupied half a revolution, n would be 2 for both isomers). By this means the partition function is reduced to 0.594 and 0.406 of its value for the *cis* and *trans* forms respectively to allow for the fact that the rotational angle covers only these fractions of a revolution.

The following treatment reduces to the method originally given by Pitzer[18] if appropriate approximations are made. The total entropy is obtained by adding, to the entropy of translation, rotation, vibration, and internal rotation due to both isomers, the entropy of mixing of these isomers as given by equation (11.2–3). In order to do this, one must know the mole fractions of each isomer. These can be calculated by combining the total free energy functions *for each isomer* with the value of $\Delta\tilde{E}_0{}^\circ$, the difference between the energy zeros of the two isomers, to obtain the free energy difference between the isomers, and hence the equilibrium constant for their interconversion. Thus for the conversion of isomer i into isomer j,

$$-\frac{\Delta\tilde{F}^\circ}{T} = -\frac{(\tilde{F}_j{}^\circ - \tilde{F}_i{}^\circ)}{T} = R\ln\frac{X_j}{X_i}$$

$$= -\frac{(\tilde{F}_j{}^\circ - \tilde{E}_0{}^\circ)}{T} + \frac{(\tilde{F}_i{}^\circ - \tilde{E}_0{}^\circ)}{T}, \qquad (20.5\text{–}16)$$

where X_i and X_j are the mole fractions of the isomers i and j. It must be emphasized that $\tilde{F}_j{}^\circ$ and $\tilde{F}_i{}^\circ$ include translational, external rotational, and vibrational contributions as well as those due to restricted internal rotation, and have been brought to a common energy zero by adding $\Delta\tilde{E}_0{}^\circ$ to the formally calculated value of $(\tilde{F}^\circ - \tilde{E}_0{}^\circ)$ for the isomer of higher energy. The total heat content is given by

$$(\tilde{H}^\circ - \tilde{E}_0{}^\circ) = \Sigma X_i(\tilde{H}_i{}^\circ - \tilde{E}_0{}^\circ), \qquad (20.5\text{–}17)$$

[18] K. S. Pitzer, *J. Chem. Phys.*, **8**, 711 (1940).

where the sum is to be taken over all isomers and $\tilde{H}_i^\circ - \tilde{E}_0^\circ$ is the total heat content of each isomer expressed with respect to a common energy zero (i.e., $3RT$ is included for translation and external rotation; the vibrational contributions have been included, as well as that for the restricted rotation and $\Delta\tilde{E}_0^\circ$ has been added to the formally calculated value of $(\tilde{H}^\circ - \tilde{E}_0^\circ)$ for the isomer of higher energy. The total heat capacity is given by

$$\tilde{C}_P^\circ = \frac{\mathrm{d}(\tilde{H}^\circ - \tilde{E}_0^\circ)}{\mathrm{d}T}$$

$$= \Sigma X_i \frac{\mathrm{d}(\tilde{H}_i^\circ - \tilde{E}_0^\circ)}{\mathrm{d}T} + \Sigma(\tilde{H}_i^\circ - \tilde{E}_0^\circ)\frac{\mathrm{d}X_i}{\mathrm{d}T}, \tag{20.5–18}$$

or

$$\tilde{C}_P^\circ = \Sigma X_i \tilde{C}_{P_i}^\circ + \Sigma(\tilde{H}_i^\circ - \tilde{E}_0^\circ)\frac{\mathrm{d}X_i}{\mathrm{d}T}. \tag{20.5–19}$$

The first term on the right side is the sum of the contributions of the individual isomers to the heat capacity, and the second term can be obtained from the individual heat contents with respect to the common energy zero and the change in mole fraction of the isomers with temperature.

The case of butane is similar. For minimum potential energy there are three positions of the ethyl groups with respect to each other, obtained by rotations of 0, $2\pi/3$, $4\pi/3$ from the equilibrium position. The position of zero rotation (*trans*) corresponds to all the carbon atoms arranged in one plane, while the other two positions (*gauche*) are obtained by rotation of 120° and 240°, respectively, about the carbon–carbon bond. The two *gauche* forms represent optical isomers of identical normal vibrations, which differ from the normal vibrations of the *trans* form. Pitzer has shown that, if (a) a potential barrier of 3000 cal is assumed to hinder rotation about the carbon–carbon bond between the ethyl groups as well as the internal rotation of the methyl groups, and if (b) the energy of the *trans* form is assumed to be 800 cal lower than that of the *gauche* form, the entropies and heat capacities calculated in the manner described above give an excellent fit with the experimental data.[18,19]

[19] B. P. Dailey and W. A. Felsing, *J. Am. Chem. Soc.*, **65**, 44 (1943).

Calculation of the Thermodynamic Properties of Crystals

CHAPTER 21

21.1 Thermodynamic Properties of a Mode of Vibration

A crystal is one example of a localized system in which a partition function cannot be assigned to the individual atoms or molecules. The thermal energy of a crystal lies in its elastic modes of vibration characteristic of the crystal as a whole. Similarly, in the inside of a container with walls completely opaque to all radiation and containing no matter (*in German: Hohlraum*), there is an amount of energy, due to radiation, characteristic of the volume and temperature. As a result, the enclosed space, empty except for trapped radiation, has thermodynamic properties.

If the crystal chosen contains 1 gram molecule, or if the enclosure of the radiation is of a reasonable size, it is assumed that either can be divided into a relatively large number of "units" which behave in an identical way. These units replace the atoms and molecules previously considered elements of the system.

For example, 1 gram atom of a crystal of a monatomic element can be divided in n identical units, each containing a atoms, where a is of the order of 10^{12} and n of the order of 10^{12}. Each unit will have (except for surface effects) the same thermodynamic properties as the larger unit.

In principle, if not in fact, the equations of motion of a unit can be set up in terms of the forces between the atoms, a secular equation can be derived, and the characteristic fundamental vibrational frequencies can be obtained. There will be $3a - 6$ of these characteristic frequencies since, of the $3a$ degrees of freedom, 6 represent linear and torsional vibration of the unit in the larger crystal. The energy associated with these is negligible, so approximately there are $3a$ characteristic modes of vibration, many of which will have the same or nearly the same frequency. For the whole crystal, there are n modes of each kind, but of course many of the sets of n modes will have the same frequency. A set of n modes of characteristic frequency ν constitutes a localized system of elements, as pointed out in Section 17.3. An enclosure containing radiation can similarly be divided; the way of doing this is a matter of individual preference.

A vibrational mode of frequency ν has a set of energy levels $\epsilon(\nu)_0$, $\epsilon(\nu)_1$, $\epsilon(\nu)_2$, $\epsilon(\nu)_3$, etc. The number of modes, $n_i'(\nu)$, with any energy $\epsilon(\nu)_i$ is obtained using equation (17.4–17):

$$n'(\nu)_i = \frac{ne^{-\epsilon(\nu)_i/kT}}{\Sigma e^{-\epsilon(\nu)_i/kT}}, \qquad (21.1\text{–}1)$$

where the sum in the denominator is taken over all quantum states characteristic of the mode. If there are $g'(\nu)$ modes of the same frequency ν, the total number of modes with energy $\epsilon(\nu)_i$ is

$$n(\nu)_i = \frac{g'(\nu)ne^{-\epsilon(\nu)_i/kT}}{\Sigma e^{-\epsilon(\nu)_i/kT}}. \qquad (21.1\text{–}2)$$

The contribution to the energy of 1 gram atm of crystal due to the modes of frequency ν is then given by

$$E(\nu) = \sum_i \epsilon(\nu)_i n(\nu)_i = \frac{g'(\nu)n \sum_i \epsilon(\nu)_i e^{-\epsilon(\nu)_i/kT}}{\sum_i e^{-\epsilon(\nu)_i/kT}}, \qquad (21.1\text{–}3)$$

where the sum is again taken over all quantum states characteristic of the modes of frequency ν_i.

The number of modes of frequency ν in 1 gram atom of crystal, $g(\nu)$, is equal to $g'(\nu)n$; upon replacement of $g'(\nu)$, equation (21.1–3) becomes

$$E(\nu) = \frac{g(\nu) \sum_i \epsilon(\nu)_i e^{-\epsilon(\nu)_i/kT}}{\sum_i e^{-\epsilon(\nu)_i/kT}}. \qquad (21.1\text{–}4)$$

This expression is exactly equivalent to equation (18.2–2), with n replaced by $g(\nu)$. All the p_k are unity because each quantum state is considered separately. Thus the thermodynamic functions for any of the modes are those given in Sections 18.2 and 18.3 for localized elements multiplied by $g(\nu)/\mathbf{N}$, provided the modes are independent. The corresponding partition function is

$$Q(\nu) = \sum_i e^{-\epsilon(\nu)_i/kT}. \qquad (21.1\text{–}5)$$

If the modes of vibration can be considered harmonic, the energy levels $\epsilon(\nu)_0$, $\epsilon(\nu)_1$, etc., are those of a harmonic oscillator; that is,

$$\epsilon(\nu)_i = (i + \tfrac{1}{2})h\nu, \qquad (21.1\text{–}6)$$

where i is identical with the quantum number v of equation (16.19–1); hence i takes the values 0, 1, 2, 3, etc. The partition function for a particular mode is thus that of a harmonic oscillator, given by equation (20.3–6):

$$Q(\nu) = \frac{1}{1 - e^{-h\nu/kT}}. \qquad (21.1\text{–}7)$$

The energy zero is, of course, that of the zero point energy of the mode $(h\nu/2)$. For modes which are harmonic oscillators, the expression for the energy given by equation (21.1–4) can be simplified by use of equation (20.3–7). Thus the energy relative to that of the lowest energy level of the mode is given by

$$E(\nu) = g(\nu)kT^2\,\frac{\partial \ln Q(\nu)}{\partial T} = \frac{g(\nu)kTx}{e^x - 1} = \frac{g(\nu)h\nu}{e^{h\nu/kT} - 1}. \qquad (21.1\text{–}8)$$

Because of interaction between the modes, the thermodynamic quantities for a crystal cannot be obtained, in general, by summing those for each mode. However, the energy is given by

$$E = \sum_{\nu} E(\nu). \qquad (21.1\text{–}9)$$

Thus substitution of the partition function

$$\kappa = \Pi\, Q(\nu)^{g(\nu)/\mathbf{N}} \qquad (21.1\text{–}10)$$

into equation (18.2–7) will give the correct energy.

Problem 21.1-1. Prove the statement made in the last sentence. It will be seen later that C_V, S, and the Helmholtz free energy can also be calculated from this partition function.

21.2 Modes of Vibration of a Real Crystal of Monatomic Elements

It is necessary to take a representative unit of the crystal, containing a sufficient number of atoms, a, to possess all the mechanical properties of the crystal as a whole. The frequencies of the normal modes must then be obtained by setting up the equations of motion for each atom, deriving the secular equation and solving it for the frequencies. The treatment is similar but much more complicated than that which is given for a molecule in Appendix 6, and which leads to the secular equation (A6.3–20).

The problem was first treated by Born and Von Kármán[1] and has been carried further by Blackman.[2] The expression for $g(\nu)$ thus obtained is extraordinarily complicated. Each mode is assumed to be a harmonic oscillator, and (21.1–10) is used to calculate the partition function. The reader is referred to the original papers for details.

21.3 Number of Modes of Vibration in a Continuous Elastic Solid

The complications of the last section can be avoided by assuming that the crystal behaves like a continuous elastic solid. The mechanical properties of a continuous elastic medium are considered in this section. It is convenient to take a rectangular slab of the continuous medium with sides of length a, b, and c along and parallel to the coordinate axes. Standing waves can exist in the direction parallel to the x axis with terminal antinodes at $x = 0$ and $x = a$, such that

$$\frac{l}{a} = \frac{2}{\lambda}, \tag{21.3–1}$$

where λ is the wave length (a distance $\lambda/2$ between nodes), and l is an integer. If this were the only type of wave which could be put in the box, there would be as many modes of wave length greater than λ_0 as there are integers less than l. By considering the boundary conditions for standing waves set up in any direction, it is found that the corresponding condition is

$$\frac{l^2}{a^2} + \frac{m^2}{b^2} + \frac{n^2}{c^2} = \left(\frac{2}{\lambda}\right)^2, \tag{21.3–2}$$

where l, m, and n are integers. The number of modes z with wave length greater than λ_0 is equal to the number of ways of choosing values of positive integers α, β, and γ, with the maximum value of each to be l, m, and n respectively. This number is the number of integers contained inside the positive octant of the ellipsoid whose envelope satisfies the equation

$$\frac{\alpha^2}{a^2} + \frac{\beta^2}{b^2} + \frac{\gamma^2}{c^2} = \left(\frac{2}{\lambda_0}\right)^2. \tag{21.3–3}$$

If the ellipsoid is sufficiently large, this number is equal to the volume of an octant of the ellipsoid; thus

$$z = \frac{4}{3}\pi\left(\frac{2}{\lambda_0}\right)^3\frac{abc}{8} = \frac{4}{3}\pi\frac{V}{\lambda_0^{\,3}}, \tag{21.3–4}$$

[1] M. Born and T. von Kármán, *Physik. Z.*, **13**, 297 (1912).
[2] M. Blackman, *Proc. Roy. Soc.* (*London*), **A159**, 416 (1937).

where V is the volume of the slab of medium. Since the frequency of the modes is given by

$$\nu = \frac{v}{\lambda}, \tag{21.3–5}$$

where v is the velocity of the standing wave, the number of modes with frequency less than ν_0 is

$$z = \frac{4}{3}\pi \frac{V\nu_0^{\,3}}{v^3}. \tag{21.3–6}$$

The number of modes with frequency between ν and $\nu + \mathrm{d}\nu$ is obtained by taking the differential of equation (21.3–6). The following equation is thus obtained:

$$\mathrm{d}z = \frac{4\pi V\nu^2\,\mathrm{d}\nu}{v^3}. \tag{21.3–7}$$

The quantity $\mathrm{d}z$ is to be used for $g(\nu)$ in equation (21.1–10) to give the distribution function for frequencies in the range ν to $\nu + \mathrm{d}\nu$.

21.4 The Debye Approximation for Monatomic Crystals

The results obtained in the last section can now be used directly to simplify the treatment of crystals outlined in Section 21.2. When the medium is in thermal motion, three sets of standing (acoustical) waves will be set up in the medium; one of these is a longitudinal mode in which the atoms move in the direction of motion *of the wave*, and two transversely at right angles. The former have the velocity c_L, and the latter c_T. The number of modes of vibration, $\mathrm{d}z$, with frequencies lying between ν and $\nu + \mathrm{d}\nu$, is obtained for each of these sets of standing waves from equation (21.3–7). When the contributions from each of the three sets are added, the result is

$$\mathrm{d}z = \frac{4\pi V\nu^2\,\mathrm{d}\nu}{c_L^{\,3}} + \frac{8\pi V\nu^2\,\mathrm{d}\nu}{c_T^{\,3}}, \tag{21.4–1}$$

where V is the volume occupied by the medium. The first term gives the number of longitudinal modes, and the second the number of transverse modes. The number of transverse waves is twice that of the longitudinal waves, since there are two sets of the latter to one of the former. The quantity $\mathrm{d}z$ is to be identified with $g(\nu)$ in equation (21.1–4). It is assumed that the vibrations in all the modes are harmonic.

It is now possible to set up the partition function, denoted by κ, for the atoms in the crystal. This is obtained by substituting into equation (21.1–10) for $g(\nu)$ the value of $\mathrm{d}z$ given by equation (21.4–1). In using

(21.1–10), $Q(\nu)$ is obtained from equation (21.1–7). The expression is most conveniently put in the logarithmic form.

The contribution to $\ln \kappa$ for the frequencies in the range between ν and $\nu + d\nu$ is then

$$d \ln \kappa = -\frac{1}{\text{N}}\left(\frac{4\pi V\nu^2}{c_L{}^3} + \frac{8\pi V\nu^2}{c_T{}^3}\right) \ln\left(1 - e^{-h\nu/kT}\right) d\nu. \quad (21.4\text{–}2)$$

The total number of modes for one gram atom of a real crystal is

$$z = 3\text{N} - 6 \approx 3\text{N}. \quad (21.4\text{–}3)$$

Thus the integration of equation (21.4–2) must be limited to a range which gives the proper value of z.

Debye adopted the ingenious practical device of assuming that the situation existing in a real crystal is that of a continuous medium with a maximum frequency ν_{D} such that

$$\int_0^{\nu_{\text{D}}} dz = 4\pi\tilde{V}\left(\frac{1}{c_L{}^3} + \frac{2}{c_T{}^3}\right)\int_0^{\nu_{\text{D}}} \nu^2\, d\nu = 3\text{N}. \quad (24.1\text{–}4)$$

Upon integration, this equation may be solved for ν_{D}; thus

$$\nu_{\text{D}} = \left[\frac{9\text{N}c_L{}^3 c_T{}^3}{4\pi\tilde{V}(c_T{}^3 + 2c_L{}^3)}\right]^{1/3}. \quad (21.4\text{–}5)$$

Upon replacement of c_T and c_L by a suitable mean velocity c, equation (21.4–5) becomes

$$\nu_{\text{D}} = \left(\frac{\text{N}}{\tilde{V}}\frac{3c^3}{4\pi}\right)^{1/3}. \quad (21.4\text{–}6)$$

For brevity it is convenient to define a quantity, θ_{D}, called the Debye characteristic temperature, by the equation

$$\theta_{\text{D}} = \frac{h\nu_{\text{D}}}{k} = \frac{hc}{k}\left(\frac{3\text{N}}{4\pi\tilde{V}}\right)^{1/3}. \quad (21.4\text{–}7)$$

In terms of θ_{D}, equation (21.4–2) can be written

$$d \ln \kappa = -\left(\frac{9T^3}{\theta_{\text{D}}{}^3}\right) x^2 \ln\left(1 - e^{-x}\right) dx, \quad (21.4\text{–}8)$$

where x is equal to $h\nu/kT$. The value of $\ln \kappa$ due to all frequencies is

$$\ln \kappa = \int_0^{\theta_{\text{D}}/T} d \ln \kappa = -\frac{9T^3}{\theta_{\text{D}}{}^3}\int_0^{\theta_{\text{D}}/T} x^2 \ln\left(1 - e^{-x}\right) dx. \quad (21.4\text{–}9)$$

As the temperature is raised at constant pressure, the elastic constants of the crystal, on which the frequencies of the modes depend, change because the density changes. The density changes because of thermal motion of the atoms, that is, because of the excitation of higher energy states of *all* the modes of vibration of the crystal. Thus, at constant pressure, any mode will change its characteristic frequency as the result of excitation of the others. The frequencies can be considered fixed by the temperature-dependent variable, atomic volume V/n. The energy zero has been taken such that the crystal with each mode in its lowest energy state is assigned zero energy. The lowest energy state of each mode is $h\nu/2$. Thus ν and the energy zero will be independent of temperature only if the atomic volume is kept constant. Therefore only at constant atomic volume can the energy at any temperature be calculated correctly with respect to an arbitrarily assumed zero point energy. Thermodynamic functions involving differentiation of the energy (or functions of it) with respect to temperature *at constant atomic volume* can therefore be related to a partition function such as that given by equation (21.4–9). However, thermodynamic functions involving differentiation at constant pressure cannot be obtained. Hitherto, for localized systems only E, S, and A (the Helmholtz free energy) have really been considered, since the volume dependence was not involved. The Helmholtz and Gibbs free energy were therefore equal. This is due to the fact that the translational degrees of freedom were considered separately. In the case of a crystal, all degrees of freedom are involved, including translation, for which A and F differ by PV. Thus F cannot be obtained from the partition function given by equation (21.4–9) unless it is referred to a temperature-independent energy zero.

It is preferable to employ a partition function which applies to a representative macroscopic sample of the crystal containing n atoms rather than to a single atom. The partition function for this sample is

$$\mathrm{K} = \kappa^n e^{-n\chi_0/kT} = e^{-n\chi_0/kT} \prod Q(\nu)^{ng(\nu)/\mathbf{N}}, \qquad (21.4\text{–}10)$$

where n is the number of atoms in the sample, and χ_0, which is temperature-dependent, is a correction to a temperature-independent energy zero. Thus each mode, when it has only the zero point vibrational energy $h\nu/2$, has an energy $\chi_0/3$ relative to the infinitely expanded crystal (i.e., the infinitely dilute gas).[3] Thus

$$\ln \mathrm{K} = -\frac{9nT^3}{\theta_\mathrm{D}^3} \int_0^{\theta_\mathrm{D}/T} x^2 \ln(1 - e^{-x})\, dx - \frac{n\chi_0}{kT}, \qquad (21.4\text{–}11)$$

where $n\chi_0$ is the energy, relative to the ideal gas state at zero pressure, of $n/\mathbf{N}$ moles of crystal at the temperature T if all the modes were assigned their respective zero point energies ($^1/_2 h\nu_i$). This partition function is not

[3] See R. Fowler and E. A. Guggenheim, *Statistical Thermodynamics*, Cambridge University Press, 1949, p. 133, which this treatment follows closely.

to be confused with the partition functions previously used, which were for the molecule. The partition function K is for the system containing n/N moles. We shall speak of such a partition function as a *system partition function* if the number of moles is not defined, and as a *molar partition function* if the system contains one mole.

It is not immediately obvious how all of the thermodynamic functions can be calculated from this quantity, but this will be shown in the next section. For the time being we shall be content to calculate the energy, heat capacity, and entropy of one mole of the crystal by the appropriate differentiations and integrations at constant volume.

When dz as given by (21.4–1) is substituted for $g(\nu)$ in equation (21.1–8), the energy, dE (relative to the infinitely dilute gas), lying in modes of frequency between ν and $\nu + \mathrm{d}\nu$ is given by equation (21.4–12), where $\tilde{V}$ is the volume of one mole, dE_0 is the difference between the energy of the modes in the infinitely dilute gas and the vibration energy $h\nu/2$ at the density, $\mathrm{N}/,\tilde{V}$ of the crystal under consideration. This is

$$\mathrm{d}E = 4\pi V\left(\frac{1}{c_L{}^3} + \frac{2}{c_T{}^3}\right)\frac{h\nu^3\,\mathrm{d}\nu}{e^{h\nu/kT} - 1} + \mathrm{d}E_0. \qquad (21.4\text{–}12)$$

The total energy per mole is

$$\tilde{E} = 4\pi\tilde{V}h\left(\frac{1}{c_L{}^3} + \frac{2}{c_T{}^3}\right)\int_0^{\nu_\mathrm{D}}\frac{\nu^3\,\mathrm{d}\nu}{e^{h\nu/kT} - 1} + \tilde{E}_0, \qquad (21.4\text{–}13)$$

or, in terms of θ and x previously defined,

$$\tilde{E} = 9\mathrm{N}kT\left(\frac{T}{\theta}\right)^3\int_0^{\theta/T}\frac{x^3}{e^x - 1}\,\mathrm{d}x + \tilde{E}_0, \qquad (21.4\text{–}13a)$$

where $\tilde{E}_0$ is equal to $\mathrm{N}\chi_0$ and is the energy of one mole of the crystal, with each mode in its lowest energy state, referred to the infinitely dilute gas.

Problem 21.4-1. Prove that the contribution of the zero point energies ($^1/_2\, h\nu$) to $\tilde{E}_0$ is $9\mathrm{N}k\theta_\mathrm{D}/8$.

It is clear that the fundamental frequencies ν of the modes and $\tilde{E}_0$ depend on the density $\mathrm{N}/\tilde{V}$. Since N is constant for differentiations or integrations at constant volume, ν and $\tilde{E}_0$ will remain constant.

The expression for the molal heat capacity at constant volume is obtained by differentiating equation (21.4–13a) with respect to temperature:

$$\tilde{C}_V = \left(\frac{\partial\tilde{E}}{\partial T}\right)_V = 9\mathrm{N}k\left[4\frac{T^3}{\theta^3}I + T\left(\frac{T}{\theta}\right)^3\frac{\partial I}{\partial T}\right], \qquad (21.4\text{–}14)$$

where I stands for the integral in equation (21.4–13a). Now

$$\frac{\partial I}{\partial T} = \frac{\partial I}{\partial(\theta/T)}\cdot\frac{\partial(\theta/T)}{\partial T} = -\frac{\partial I}{\partial(\theta/T)}\cdot\frac{\theta}{T^2}. \qquad (21.4\text{–}14a)$$

The lower limit of the integral is not a function of θ/T, so that in evaluation of $\partial I/\partial(\theta/T)$ it is necessary to differentiate only the upper limit; the result is the integrand, with θ/T replacing x; thus

$$\tilde{C}_V = 9Nk\left[4\left(\frac{T}{\theta}\right)^3 \int_0^{\theta/T} \frac{x^3}{e^x - 1}\,dx - \left(\frac{\theta}{T}\right)\frac{1}{e^{\theta/T} - 1}\right]. \tag{21.4–15}$$

Equations (21.4–13a) and (21.4–15) are not very convenient for calculation, but, by use of these equations, tables of $(\tilde{E} - \tilde{E}_0)/T$ and $\tilde{C}$ have been computed as functions of θ/T. These tables, which permit ready application of the equations, are given in A4–1 (Appendix 4).

Table 21.4–1 illustrates the agreement between theory and experiment[4]

Table 21.4–1

Comparison of the Values of θ from Specific Heat Data and Direct Calculation from the Elastic Constants[4]

Element	ρ	$K \times 10^{12}$	σ	θ_{calc}	θ_{exp}
Al	2.71	1.36	0.337	398	402
Cu	8.96	0.74	0.334	315	332
Ag	10.53	0.92	0.379	215	214
Pb	11.32	2.0	0.446	88	73

for crystals of metallic elements. Column 1 gives the element, column 2 the density, column 3 the compressibility K, column 4 Poisson's ratio σ. In terms of these elastic constants the velocities c_L and c_T are

$$c_L^2 = \frac{3(1 - \sigma)}{(1 + \sigma)K\rho} \quad \text{and} \quad c_T^2 = \frac{3(1 - 2\sigma)}{2(1 + \sigma)K\rho}. \tag{21.4–16}$$

Column 5 gives the value of θ calculated from the elastic constants, and column 6 that calculated from equation (21.4–15) so as to give the best fit with the heat capacity curves.

Figure 21.4–1 shows a graph of $\tilde{C}_V$ against T/θ for certain substances. The points represent experimental data, and the solid curve is calculated from the equation (21.4–15). In plotting the experimental points, the value of θ used for each substance was chosen to give the best fit with this curve.

At low temperatures θ/T is large; therefore the second term of equation (21.4–15) is negligible because of the exponential in its denominator. The

[4] M. Born, "Atomtheorie des festen Zustandes," *Encycl. Math. Wiss.*, Vol. V, part 3, No. 25, 27 (1923).

integral in the first term becomes $\int_0^\infty x^3/(e^x - 1)\, dx$ because θ/T is very large. This integral is

$$\int_0^\infty \frac{x^3}{e^x - 1}\, dx = \frac{\pi^4}{15}, \qquad (21.4\text{–}17)$$

so that equation (21.4–15) becomes

$$\tilde{C}_V = \frac{12\pi^4 NkT^3}{5\theta^3} = aT^3. \qquad (21.4\text{–}18)$$

Similarly it can be shown that

$$\tilde{E} - \tilde{E}_0 = \frac{3\pi^4 NkT^4}{5\theta^3} = \frac{aT^4}{4}. \qquad (21.4\text{–}19)$$

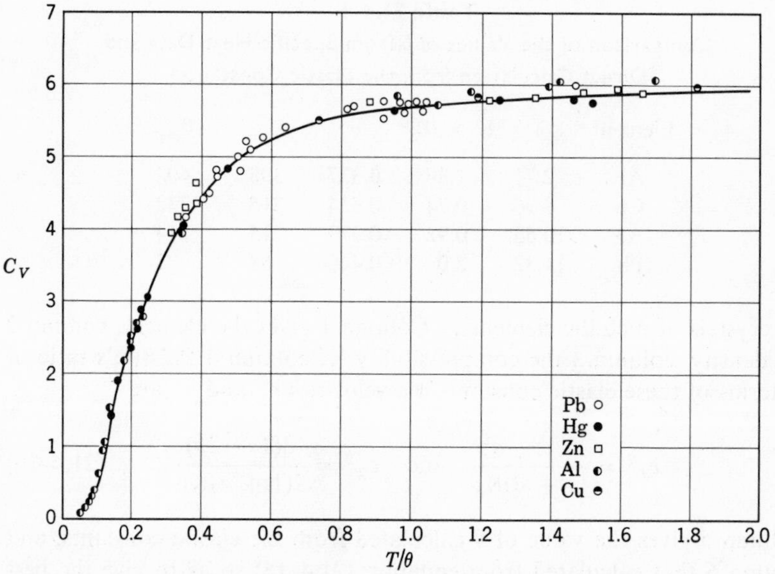

Fig. 21.4–1. The heat capacity of various solids as functions of T/θ.

We thus see that at low temperatures the heat capacity of the postulated crystal becomes proportional to the third power of the temperature, a fact which is important in the extrapolation of heat capacities to 0°K.

At high temperatures equation (21.4–15) becomes

$$\tilde{C}_V = 9Nk\left[4\left(\frac{T}{\theta}\right)^3 \int_0^{\theta/T} x^2\, dx - 1\right], \qquad (21.4\text{–}20)$$

because θ/T and x are small, so that e^x may be replaced by $(1 + x)$; thus

$$\tilde{C}_V = 9Nk[\tfrac{4}{3} - 1] = 3Nk = 3R. \qquad (21.4\text{–}21)$$

This result could have been predicted from the principle of equipartition, since at high temperatures the crystal consists of **N** atoms each with three classically excited vibrational degrees of freedom. In the same way it can be shown that at high temperatures

$$\tilde{E} - \tilde{E}_0 = 3RT. \qquad (21.4\text{–}22)$$

The entropy of a perfect crystal is given by

$$\tilde{S} = \int_0^T \tilde{C}_P \, \mathrm{d} \ln T = \int_0^T \tilde{C}_V \, \mathrm{d} \ln T + \int_0^T (\tilde{C}_P - \tilde{C}_V) \, \mathrm{d} \ln T, \qquad (21.4\text{–}23)$$

since the entropy at the absolute zero is zero. The last term of equation (21.4–23) is evaluated, approximately, by making use of the rule of Lindemann and Magnus[5] that

$$\tilde{C}_P - \tilde{C}_V = aT^{3/2}, \qquad (21.4\text{–}24)$$

whence

$$\int_0^T (\tilde{C}_P - \tilde{C}_V) \, \mathrm{d} \ln T = \int_0^T aT^{1/2} \, \mathrm{d}T = \frac{2}{3} aT^{3/2} = \frac{2}{3} (\tilde{C}_P - \tilde{C}_V). \qquad (21.4\text{–}25)$$

For a monatomic crystal the integration of the first term of (21.4–23) is made taking $\tilde{C}_V$ as given by equation (21.4–15). The values of the integral ($\tilde{S}_{\mathrm{Debye}}$) thus obtained are tabulated in Appendix 4. The calculation of $\tilde{S}$ is made in two parts, $(\tilde{E} - \tilde{E}_0)/T$ and $(\tilde{E}_0 - \tilde{A})/T$, such that

$$\frac{\tilde{A} - \tilde{E}_0}{T} = 3R \ln (1 - e^{-\theta/T}) - \frac{1}{3}\left(\frac{\tilde{E} - \tilde{E}_0}{T}\right) \qquad (21.4\text{–}26)$$

and

$$\tilde{S} = \frac{\tilde{E} - \tilde{E}_0}{T} + \frac{\tilde{E}_0 - \tilde{A}}{T}. \qquad (21.4\text{–}27)$$

Equation (21.4–26) can be obtained directly from an appropriate partition function, as will be shown in the next section.

21.5 Calculation of the Thermodynamic Functions for a Crystal

The system partition function deduced in the last section need not be limited to the Debye approximation. Before proceeding with the calculation of thermodynamic properties, it is better to write down the system partition function for a sample of crystal, containing n atoms, without any other approximation but that the modes of vibration are harmonic.

[5] F. A. Lindemann and A. Magnus, *Z. Elektrochem.*, **16**, 269 (1910).

To do this we return to equation (21.4–10). By expressing the energies relative to the infinitely dilute gas, and proceeding as we did to obtain the system partition function in equation (21.4–11) for the Debye approximation,

$$\ln \mathrm{K} = n \ln \kappa - \frac{n\chi_0}{kT} = -\int_0^\infty ng''(\nu) \ln (1 - e^{-h\nu/kT})\, \mathrm{d}\nu - \frac{n\chi_0}{kT}, \quad (21.5\text{–}1)$$

where $n\chi_0$ is, as in the last section, the energy of n atoms with their zero point vibrational energies relative to the infinitely dilute gas, while $g''(\nu)$ is defined as $g(\nu)/\mathrm{N}$. The quantity χ_0 in equation (21.5–1) depends only on V/n, the volume per atom, which will be denoted by $\tilde{\tilde{V}}$. Thus K depends on T, $\tilde{V}$, and n. The considerations of Section 21.1 make it apparent that $g''(\nu)$ also depends only on $\tilde{V}$.

The energy of the crystal relative to the ideal gas is then obtained in a fashion similar to that used in obtaining equation (21.4–13a) for the energy corresponding to the Debye approximation. Thus

$$E = \int \frac{ng''(\nu)h\nu\, \mathrm{d}\nu}{e^{h\nu/kT} - 1} + \tilde{E}_0 . \quad (21.5\text{–}2)$$

It is convenient to regard K as a function of T, V, and n. By differentiating (21.5–1), it is readily shown that

$$E = kT^2\left[\frac{\partial \ln \mathrm{K}(T,V,n)}{\partial T}\right]_{V,n}, \quad (21.5\text{–}3)$$

thus verifying the statement made in the last section.

It is now simple to show that the relation of the Helmholtz free energy to the system partition function which will lead to correct expressions for the other thermodynamic functions is

$$A = -kT \ln \mathrm{K}(T,V,n). \quad (21.5\text{–}4)$$

Dividing equation (21.5–4) by T and taking the differential,

$$\begin{aligned} \mathrm{d}\frac{A}{T} = &-k\left[\frac{\partial \ln (\mathrm{K}T,V,n)}{\partial T}\right]_{V,n} \mathrm{d}T \\ &-k\left[\frac{\partial \ln \mathrm{K}(T,V,n)}{\partial V}\right]_{T,n} \mathrm{d}V \\ &-k\left[\frac{\partial \ln \mathrm{K}(T,V,n)}{\partial n}\right]_{T,V} \mathrm{d}n. \end{aligned} \quad (21.5\text{–}5)$$

Noting that

$$\mathrm{d}\frac{A}{T} = \frac{1}{T}\mathrm{d}A - \frac{A}{T^2}\mathrm{d}T, \quad (21.5\text{–}6)$$

and that, according to equation (9.1–15),

$$\mathrm{d}A = -P\,\mathrm{d}V - S\,\mathrm{d}T + \tilde{\mu}\,\mathrm{d}n,$$

then

$$\mathrm{d}\frac{A}{T} = -\left(\frac{S}{T} + \frac{A}{T^2}\right)\mathrm{d}T - \frac{P}{T}\mathrm{d}V + \frac{\tilde{\mu}}{T}\mathrm{d}n$$

$$= -\frac{E}{T^2}\,\mathrm{d}T - \frac{P}{T}\mathrm{d}V + \frac{\tilde{\mu}}{T}\mathrm{d}n, \tag{21.5–7}$$

where $\tilde{\mu}$ is now the partial molecular free energy, μ/N. By comparison with equation (21.5–5),

$$\frac{E}{T^2} = k\left[\frac{\partial \ln \mathrm{K}(T,V,n)}{\partial T}\right]_{V,n}, \tag{21.5–8}$$

$$\frac{P}{T} = k\left[\frac{\partial \ln \mathrm{K}(T,V,n)}{\partial V}\right]_{T,n}, \tag{21.5–9}$$

$$-\frac{\tilde{\mu}}{T} = k\left[\frac{\partial \ln \mathrm{K}(T,V,n)}{\partial n}\right]_{T,V}. \tag{21.5–10}$$

Equation (21.5–8) is the same as equation (21.5–3), as is to be expected. Equation (21.5–10) can be put into the alternative form

$$k\left[\frac{\partial \ln K(T,V,n)}{\partial \ln n}\right]_{T,V} = -\frac{n\tilde{\mu}}{T}. \tag{21.5–11}$$

If a partition function, κ', is defined

$$\kappa'(T,\approx{V}) = \mathrm{K}(T,V,n)^{1/n}, \tag{21.5–12}$$

κ' is a function of T and $\overset{\approx}{V}$ only, because the properties of a crystal depend only on the atomic volume, $\overset{\approx}{V}$, and the temperature. In terms of κ', equation (21.5–10) becomes (since κ' depends on n through $\overset{\approx}{V}$)

$$-\frac{\tilde{\mu}}{T} = k\ln\kappa' + kn\left[\frac{\partial \ln \kappa'(T,\overset{\approx}{V})}{\partial n}\right]_{T,V}, \tag{21.5–13}$$

while equation (21.5–9) becomes

$$kn\left[\frac{\partial \ln \kappa'(T,\overset{\approx}{V})}{\partial V}\right]_{T,n} = \frac{P}{T}. \tag{21.5–14}$$

Since, when n is constant, $\mathrm{d}V$ is equal to $n\,\mathrm{d}\tilde{\tilde{V}}$, this equation can be rewritten

$$\frac{P\tilde{\tilde{V}}}{T} = k\tilde{\tilde{V}}\left[\frac{\partial \ln \kappa'(T,\tilde{\tilde{V}})}{\partial \tilde{\tilde{V}}}\right]_{T,n} = k\left[\frac{\partial \ln \kappa'(T,\tilde{\tilde{V}})}{\partial \ln \tilde{\tilde{V}}}\right]_{T,n}. \qquad (21.5\text{–}14\text{a})$$

It is noted that

$$V = n\tilde{\tilde{V}}, \qquad (21.5\text{–}15)$$

and therefore that

$$\ln V = \ln n + \ln \tilde{\tilde{V}}. \qquad (21.5\text{–}15\text{a})$$

Thus, at constant V

$$\mathrm{d} \ln n = -\mathrm{d} \ln \tilde{\tilde{V}}, \qquad (21.5\text{–}16)$$

and therefore

$$kn\left[\frac{\partial \ln \kappa'(T,\tilde{\tilde{V}})}{\partial n}\right]_{T,V} = k\left[\frac{\partial \ln \kappa(T,\tilde{\tilde{V}})}{\partial \ln n}\right]_{T,V}$$

$$= -k\left[\frac{\partial \ln \kappa(T,\tilde{\tilde{V}})}{\partial \ln \tilde{\tilde{V}}}\right]_{T,n} = -\frac{P\tilde{\tilde{V}}}{T}. \qquad (21.5\text{–}17)$$

By substitution from equation (21.5–17), equation (21.5–13) can therefore be written

$$-\frac{\tilde{\mu}}{T} = k \ln \kappa' - \frac{P\tilde{\tilde{V}}}{T}, \qquad (21.5\text{–}18)$$

or

$$F = n\tilde{\mu} = -kT \ln (\kappa')^n + PV = A + PV, \qquad (21.5\text{–}19)$$

as is required if equation (21.5–9) defines the pressure.

An alternative expression for the Gibbs free energy is obtained by substitution for PV by use of equation (21.5–9):

$$F = kT\left\{\left[\frac{\partial \ln \mathrm{K}(T,V,n)}{\partial \ln V}\right]_{T,n} - \ln \mathrm{K}(T,V,n)\right\}. \qquad (21.5\text{–}20)$$

Since

$$S = \frac{E - A}{T}, \qquad (21.5\text{–}21)$$

the entropy is correctly given by

$$S = k\left\{\ln \mathrm{K}(T,V,n) + T\left[\frac{\partial \ln \mathrm{K}(T,V,n)}{\partial T}\right]_{V,n}\right\}$$

$$= k\left\{\ln \mathrm{K}(T,V,n) + \left[\frac{\partial \ln \mathrm{K}(T,V,n)}{\partial \ln T}\right]_{V,n}\right\}. \qquad (21.5\text{–}22)$$

Thus, by defining A as in equation (21.5–4), expressions for the thermodynamic quantities are obtained which differentiate as do the thermodynamic properties themselves, and the transcription is valid.

Problem 21.5-1. Prove that A as defined by 21.5–4 satisfies the relation

$$\left(\frac{\partial A}{\partial T}\right)_V = -S.$$

It is now possible to derive the expression for $\tilde{A}/T$ corresponding to the Debye approximation for a crystal, as already given by equation (21.4–26). By substituting the partition function as given by equation (21.4–10) into equation (21.5–4), the molar Helmholtz free energy is

$$\tilde{A} = \frac{9\mathrm{N}kT^4}{\theta_{\mathrm{D}}^{\,3}} \int_0^{\theta_{\mathrm{D}}/T} x^2 \ln(1 - e^{-x})\, dx + \tilde{E}_0. \qquad (21.5\text{–}23)$$

Integrating by parts,

$$\tilde{A} = 3\mathrm{N}kT \ln(1 - e^{-\theta_{\mathrm{D}}/T}) - \frac{3\mathrm{N}kT^4}{\theta_{\mathrm{D}}^{\,3}} \int_0^{\theta_{\mathrm{D}}/T} \frac{x^3}{e^x - 1}\, dx + \tilde{E}^\circ. \quad (21.5\text{–}24)$$

The second integral is $(\tilde{E}^\circ - \tilde{E})/3$, so that

$$(\tilde{A} - \tilde{E}^\circ) = 3RT \ln(1 - e^{-\theta/T}) - \tfrac{1}{3}(\tilde{E} - \tilde{E}^\circ), \qquad (21.5\text{–}25)$$

in agreement with equation (21.4–26).

21.6 Energy and Heat Capacity of a Crystal Composed of Molecules

In general, a molecule has six external degrees of freedom, three of angular oscillation or rotation and three of vibration. In the case of crystals composed of molecules, it is necessary therefore to replace 3N by 6N in equation (21.4–7) for calculating θ_{D}, and in the equations for $\tilde{C}_V$ and $\tilde{E}$ (equations 21.4–15 and 21.4–13a).[6] Suppose that the molecules have s degrees of freedom; in general, the internal thermal motion of the molecules will consist of $s - 6$ distinct modes of vibration, some of which may have the same frequency. The energy and heat capacity due to each of these is given by equations (20.3–7) and (20.3–8). Thus the expression for the total heat capacity at constant volume is

$$\tilde{C}_V = 18R\left[4\left(\frac{T}{\theta}\right)^3 \int_0^{\theta/T} \frac{x^3}{e^x - 1}\, dx - \left(\frac{\theta}{T}\right)\left(\frac{1}{e^{\theta/T} - 1}\right)\right] + \sum_{i=0}^{i=s-6} \frac{Rx_i^{\,2} e^{x_i}}{(e^{x_i} - 1)^2}. \qquad (21.6\text{–}1)$$

[6] R. C. Lord, J. E. Ahlberg, and D. H. Andrews, *J. Chem. Phys.*, **5**, 649 (1937).

The two sets of terms on the right side are known as the acoustical and internal contributions, and the sum in the last term is taken over all degrees of freedom $x_i = h\nu_i/kT$. $(\tilde{C}_P - \tilde{C}_V)$ may be taken as

$$\tilde{C}_P - \tilde{C}_V = 0.0214\left(\frac{T}{T_m}\right)\tilde{C}_V^2, \tag{21.6–2}$$

where T_m is the melting temperature, as derived by the method of Lord, Ahlberg, and Andrews from the relation

$$\tilde{C}_P - \tilde{C}_V = a^2\tilde{C}_V^2T, \tag{21.6–3}$$

where the constant a is to be determined empirically.

Table 21.6–1 gives results of the application of equation (21.6–1)

Table 21.6–1

Heat Capacity of Benzene (cal deg^{-1} mole^{-1})

Temperature (°K)	Acoustical $\tilde{C}_V$ (Debye)	Internal $\tilde{C}_V$ (Einstein)	$\tilde{C}_P - \tilde{C}_V$	Calculated $\tilde{C}_P$	Observed $\tilde{C}_P$
4	0.018	—	—	0.018	0.0195
10	0.270	—	—	0.270	0.346
20	1.932	—	—	1.932	1.84
30	4.41	—	0.04	4.45	4.24
40	6.45	—	0.11	6.56	6.47
50	7.90	—	0.20	8.10	8.14
60	8.90	0.02	0.31	9.23	9.32
80	10.07	0.17	0.54	10.78	10.85
100	10.70	0.51	0.81	12.02	11.99
150	11.32	2.31	1.80	15.43	15.49
200	11.58	4.95	3.53	20.06	20.02
270	11.74	9.46	7.83	29.03	29.70

to the calculation of the heat capacity of crystalline benzene. The value of θ was chosen as 150 to give the best agreement with experiment below 50°K. The vibrational frequencies used are those given in Fig. A6.4–1 (Appendix 6). To obtain the value of $\tilde{C}_P - \tilde{C}_V$, the constant a in equation (21.6–3) was obtained empirically from the difference between the experimental $\tilde{C}_P$ values and the calculated $\tilde{C}_V$ values for temperatures above 50°K.

For ionic crystals of the alkali halides, the calculation is made on the basis of 3θ rather than 6θ (three acoustical modes for each pair of ions), and three Einstein modes are assumed for each pair of ions. For such salts the frequency of these Einstein modes of vibration can be obtained from the infrared absorption spectrum of the crystal (*Reststrahlen*).

21.7 Thermodynamic Properties Due to Radiation

An interesting exercise in the use of the equations of the last section is the calculation of the pressure in an enclosure due to radiation. It is assumed that, because of oscillators in the walls which are in a steady state with respect to absorption and emission, standing waves are set up in the enclosure with their antinodes in the walls. These standing waves are harmonic in character and thus have energies given by equation (21.1–8).

There are two sets of standing waves at right angles to each other and to the direction of propagation, so that the number of modes with frequency between ν and $\nu + d\nu$ is twice that given by (21.3–7), that is,

$$dz = \frac{8\pi V\nu^2\,d\nu}{c^3}. \qquad (21.7\text{–}1)$$

Corresponding to the system partition function K of Section 21.4, for the modes with frequencies between ν and $\nu + d\nu$, the expression is

$$d \ln K = \frac{8\pi V\nu^2}{c^3} \ln\left[\frac{1}{(1 - e^{-h\nu/kT})}\right] d\nu, \qquad (21.7\text{–}2)$$

where $Q(\nu)$ has been again replaced by the value for a harmonic oscillator as given by equation (21.1–7).

For all the modes

$$\ln K = \frac{8\pi V}{c^3}\int_0^\infty \nu^2\left[\ln\frac{1}{(1 - e^{-h\nu/kT})}\right] d\nu. \qquad (21.7\text{–}3)$$

The energy zero is $h\nu/2$ for each mode. Since the modes do not interact, the frequencies and therefore also the zero point energy of each mode are independent of temperature; thus the reference point for the energy need not be changed. By substituting x for $h\nu/kT$, equation (21.7–3) can be rewritten

$$\ln K = -\frac{8\pi Vk^3T^3}{c^3h^3}\int_0^\infty x^2 \ln(1 - e^{-x})\,dx; \qquad (21.7\text{–}4)$$

by expansion of the logarithm into a power series, this becomes

$$\ln K = \frac{8\pi Vk^3T^3}{c^3h^3}\int_0^\infty \sum_{a=1}^{\infty} \frac{x^2}{a} e^{-ax}\,dx. \qquad (21.7\text{–}4a)$$

By substituting y for ax and taking the integral inside the sum, since the value of the integral is 2, the result is

$$\ln \mathrm{K} = \frac{8\pi V k^3 T^3}{c^3 h^3} \sum_{a=1}^{\infty} \frac{1}{a^4} \int_0^{\infty} y^2 e^{-y}\, \mathrm{d}y$$

$$= \frac{8\pi V k^3 T^3}{c^3 h^3} \sum_{a=1}^{\infty} \frac{2}{a^4}. \tag{21.7–4b}$$

The value of the sum is $\pi^4/45$, and thus

$$\ln \mathrm{K} = \frac{8\pi^5 V k^3 T^3}{45 c^3 h^3}. \tag{21.7–5}$$

The expression for the energy is obtained from equation (21.5–8):

$$E = kT^2 \left(\frac{\partial \ln K}{\partial T}\right)_{V,n} = \frac{8\pi^5 k^4 T^4 V}{15 c^3 h^3}. \tag{21.7–6}$$

The expression for the pressure is obtained from equation (21.5–9):

$$P = kT \left(\frac{\partial \ln \mathrm{K}}{\partial V}\right)_{T,n} = \frac{8\pi^5 k^4 T^4}{45 c^3 h^3}. \tag{21.7–7}$$

Thus

$$E = 3PV \tag{21.7–8}$$

or

$$P = \frac{1}{3} \frac{E}{V}. \tag{21.7–9}$$

An expression for the energy, dE, associated with frequencies between ν and $\nu + \mathrm{d}\nu$, is obtained by applying equation (21.5–8) to equation (21.7–2):

$$\mathrm{d}E = kT^2\, \mathrm{d}\left(\frac{\partial \ln \mathrm{K}}{\partial T}\right) = \frac{8\pi h}{c^3} V \frac{\nu^3\, \mathrm{d}\nu}{e^{h\nu/kT} - 1}. \tag{21.7–10}$$

This is Planck's law for the distribution of energy in a hohlraum.

Problem 21.2-1. Perform the detailed derivation of equation (21.7–10). (Note that the same result was derived in a less elegant fashion in Problem 17.5–1.)

Calculation of the Magnetic Contribution to Thermodynamic Properties

CHAPTER 22

22.1 Introduction

The statistical calculation of thermodynamic properties of molecules and simple solids has been discussed in previous chapters, where the various thermodynamic properties were related to the energy level spectrum of the substance. The energy levels of a paramagnetic material are affected by a magnetic field. In fact, it is just this dependence of energy on magnetic field that gives rise to the *magnetic susceptibility* of such materials. The energy levels used in a statistical calculation must thus be known as a function of magnetic field.

A simple but fundamental example of the effect of a magnetic field on energy levels is the Zeeman effect observed in atomic spectroscopy. The section to follow will discuss briefly the energy levels of paramagnetic substances and the effect of a magnetic field upon them. Succeeding sections will describe the statistical calculation of thermodynamic and magnetic properties of paramagnetic materials. The discussions will be limited to paramagnetism due to unpaired electrons. Nuclear paramagnetism is not different in principle, but it will be omitted for lack of data.

22.2 Energy Levels of a Paramagnetic Material

For an atom or an ion in the gaseous state, the effect of a magnetic field is determined by the quantum number J. In the absence of a magnetic field, there are states with a given set of values of L, S, and J that correspond to a single energy. Application of a magnetic field gives rise to $2J + 1$ states distinct in energy. The energies of those states are given by the equation

$$\epsilon = \epsilon_0 - g\frac{e}{2mc}\frac{h}{2\pi}m_J\mathscr{H}, \qquad (22.2\text{–}1)$$

where M_J takes values from $-J$ to $+J$. ϵ_J is the energy of the state in the absence of a magnetic field; the factor g is defined by the equation

$$g = 1 + \frac{J(J+1) + S(S+1) - L(L+1)}{2J(J+1)}. \qquad (22.2\text{–}2)$$

For molecules the effect of a magnetic field on the energy is determined not by the quantum number J, but by the quantum numbers Λ and S. The orbital quantum number Λ and the spin quantum number S may couple in a variety of ways, for each of which there is a particular expression for the energy. The magnetic susceptibility of free molecules is discussed by van Vleck.[1]

For material in the crystalline state, several complications arise. The individual ions and molecules interact strongly and can be considered independent only to a first approximation. For simplicity, however, most calculations are made on the basis that an otherwise independent ion has its properties "perturbed" by its surroundings. The common paramagnetic salts fall into two distinct classes, exemplified by the salts of the rare earth group and the iron (first transition) group, respectively.

The behavior of rare earth salts is like that of free atoms in that the magnetism is determined by the quantum number J. They differ from gaseous atoms in two essential respects. First, the $2J + 1$ energy levels do not all coincide in the absence of a magnetic field. Second, the effect of a magnetic field on the energy is generally more complicated than that given by equation (22.2–1). Praseodymium ion is considered below as an example.

In salts of the iron group, the coupling between L and S is weak, and the quantum number J has little significance. There are thus $2L + 1$ energy levels, some of which may coincide; each of these may be further split

[1] J. H. van Vleck, *The Theory of Electric and Magnetic Susceptibilities*, Oxford University Press, New York, 1932.

into $2S + 1$ sublevels. The separation of the $2L + 1$ orbital levels is ordinarily large enough that the paramagnetism is due primarily to the $2S + 1$ sublevels associated with the spin quantum number. For this reason, these salts are usually described as "spin-only" cases.

Many attempts have been made to calculate the energy levels of iron group salts. In most cases it is possible only to obtain approximate expressions for the partition function Q. The problem is further complicated by the fact that most iron group salts are magnetically anisotropic; that is, the effect of an applied field depends not only on its magnitude but also on its direction with respect to the crystal axes.

For some salts, principally those of the rare earths, the energy levels have been observed spectroscopically.[2] Outside of the microwave region, which observes only the "spin levels," this has not yet been done systematically for iron group salts.

22.3 Calculation of Thermodynamic and Magnetic Properties from the Partition Function

The partition function of a paramagnetic substance has a simple meaning only if (a) it is possible to treat the ions or molecules as individuals and if (b) the energy of the substance is a unique function of the variables of state (in this case P, T, and the magnetic field $\mathscr{H}$). In the discussion to follow it will be assumed that these conditions are fulfilled; the limitations so imposed will be discussed later.

The partition function will be defined as before:

$$Q = \Sigma p_k e^{-\epsilon_k/kT}. \tag{17.4–19}$$

The energy ϵ_k of a paramagnetic substance depends on the applied magnetic field. If the field is fixed, so are the energy levels, and the molar energy is given by

$$\tilde{E} = RT^2\left(\frac{\partial \ln Q}{\partial T}\right)_{\mathscr{H}}. \tag{22.3–1}$$

At first glance it might seem that, by analogy with the expression for translational energy (18.7–1), the differentiation in this case should be carried out with the intensive variable (intensity of magnetization) held constant. This is not so. The energy is in any case given by equation (18.2–2):

$$E = \frac{n\,\Sigma p_k \epsilon_k e^{-\epsilon_k/kT}}{\Sigma p_k e^{-\epsilon_k/kT}}. \tag{18.2–2}$$

[2] See, for example, F. Spedding and H. F. Hamlin, *J. Chem. Phys.*, **5**, 429 (1937).

The denominator of this expression is, by definition, the partition function Q. In order to express the numerator as a simple derivative of Q, it is necessary to hold constant all variables which affect the energy levels. In the case of translation, the energy levels are fixed by the dimensions of the container, and so the volume must be fixed. In the present case, the energy levels are determined by the magnetic field $\mathscr{H}$ (for example, in equation 22.2–1), and so the field must be held constant. This requirement is a matter of mathematics and has nothing to do with the fact that the property in terms of which the energy levels are given is intensive or extensive. The student may, if he chooses, follow the development of Section 18.2 to derive equation (22.3–1) for the case where ϵ_k depends on V and $\mathscr{H}$.

The entropy, is given (neglecting translation) by

$$\tilde{S} = \frac{\tilde{E}}{T} + R \ln Q. \tag{18.3–15}$$

The applicability of equation (18.3–15) to a system in a magnetic field may be proved by extension of the methods of Section 18.3. A simple method of proof is given below.

The *intensity of magnetization*, I, may also be related to the partition function. At constant temperature, the change in energy produced in a magnetic dipole of strength μ by application of a magnetic field $\mathscr{H}$ is given by

$$\epsilon - \epsilon_0 = -\mu \mathscr{H} \cos \theta, \tag{22.3–2}$$

where θ is the angle between the dipole and the field. The component of magnetic moment in the direction of the field ($\mu \cos \theta$) is thus

$$\mu \cos \theta = -\left(\frac{\partial \epsilon}{\partial \mathscr{H}}\right)_T. \tag{22.3–3}$$

The average of this component for a system of dipoles is

$$(\mu \cos \theta)_{\text{ave}} = -\frac{\Sigma p_k (\partial \epsilon_k / \partial \mathscr{H})_T e^{-\epsilon_k/kT}}{\Sigma p_k e^{-\epsilon_k/kT}} \tag{22.3–4}$$

$$= \frac{kT}{Q}\left(\frac{\partial Q}{\partial \mathscr{H}}\right)_T = kT\left(\frac{\partial \ln Q}{\partial \mathscr{H}}\right)_T. \tag{22.3–5}$$

Problem 22.3-1. Prove that the numerator of the right side of equation (22.3–4) is $kT(\partial Q/\partial \mathscr{H})_T$, and thus that (22.3–5) follows from (22.3–4).

The molal intensity of magnetization is just the magnetic moment, in the direction of the field, per mole of material. Thus

$$\tilde{I} = \mathbf{N}(\mu \cos \theta)_{\text{ave}} = RT\left(\frac{\partial \ln Q}{\partial \mathscr{H}}\right)_T. \tag{22.3–6}$$

The validity of (18.3–15) for the entropy (in a magnetic field) may now be demonstrated. According to equation (15.4–14), the effect of a magnetic field upon the entropy of a substance is given by

$$\left(\frac{\partial \tilde{S}}{\partial \mathscr{H}}\right)_T = \left(\frac{\partial \tilde{I}}{\partial T}\right)_{\mathscr{H}}, \tag{15.4–14}$$

so that the change in entropy produced by isothermal application of a magnetic field is, by equation (15.4–15),

$$\tilde{S}_{\mathscr{H}} - \tilde{S}_0 = \int_0^{\mathscr{H}} \left(\frac{\partial \tilde{I}}{\partial T}\right)_{\mathscr{H}} \mathrm{d}\mathscr{H}. \tag{22.3–7}$$

Upon use of (22.3–6), the derivative becomes

$$\left(\frac{\partial \tilde{I}}{\partial T}\right)_{\mathscr{H}} = R\left(\frac{\partial \ln Q}{\partial \mathscr{H}}\right)_T + RT\frac{\partial^2 \ln Q}{\partial \mathscr{H}\,\partial T}, \tag{22.3–8}$$

so that the change in entropy is

$$\tilde{S}_{\mathscr{H}} - \tilde{S}_0 = \int_0^{\mathscr{H}} R\left(\frac{\partial \ln Q}{\partial \mathscr{H}}\right)_T \mathrm{d}\mathscr{H} + \int_0^{\mathscr{H}} RT\left(\frac{\partial^2 \ln Q}{\partial \mathscr{H}\,\partial T}\right) \mathrm{d}\mathscr{H}. \tag{22.3–9}$$

Upon integration (at constant temperature),

$$\begin{aligned} \tilde{S}_{\mathscr{H}} - \tilde{S}_0 &= R\ln\frac{Q_{\mathscr{H}}}{Q_0} + RT\left[\left(\frac{\partial \ln Q}{\partial T}\right)_{\mathscr{H}}\right]_0^{\mathscr{H}} \\ &= R\ln\frac{Q_{\mathscr{H}}}{Q_0} + \frac{\tilde{E}_{\mathscr{H}} - \tilde{E}_0}{T}, \end{aligned} \tag{22.3–10}$$

where the subscripts $\mathscr{H}$ and 0 indicate the presence and absence of a magnetic field, respectively. In the absence of a magnetic field the entropy of the localized system is

$$\tilde{S}_0 = \frac{\tilde{E}_0}{T} + R\ln Q_0\,. \tag{22.3–11}$$

Upon addition of (22.3–10) and (22.3–11), one obtains

$$\tilde{S}_{\mathscr{H}} = \frac{\tilde{E}_{\mathscr{H}}}{T} + R\ln Q_{\mathscr{H}}\,. \tag{22.3–12}$$

Equation (22.3–12) is identical in form with (18.3–15) and (22.3–11). Thus the subscripts are unnecessary, and the same equation (18.3–15) may be used for the entropy whether or not a magnetic field is present.

Using equation (15.2–11) and, for simplicity, neglecting the $P\tilde{V}$ term, one obtains for the enthalpy

$$\tilde{H} = \tilde{E} - \mathscr{H}\tilde{I}. \qquad (22.3\text{–}13)$$

In terms of the partition function this becomes

$$\tilde{H} = RT^2\left(\frac{\partial \ln Q}{\partial T}\right)_{\mathscr{H}} - RT\mathscr{H}\left(\frac{\partial \ln Q}{\partial \mathscr{H}}\right)_T. \qquad (22.3\text{–}14)$$

The heat capacity at constant magnetic field is

$$\tilde{C}_{\mathscr{H}} = \left(\frac{\partial \tilde{H}}{\partial T}\right)_{\mathscr{H}} = \left(\frac{\partial}{\partial T}\right)_{\mathscr{H}}\left[RT^2\left(\frac{\partial \ln Q}{\partial T}\right)_{\mathscr{H}} - RT\mathscr{H}\left(\frac{\partial \ln Q}{\partial \mathscr{H}}\right)_T\right]. \qquad (22.3\text{–}15)$$

Finally the molal magnetic susceptibility measured at constant temperature is

$$\chi_m = \left(\frac{\partial \tilde{I}}{\partial \mathscr{H}}\right)_T = RT\left(\frac{\partial^2 \ln Q}{\partial \mathscr{H}^2}\right)_T. \qquad (22.3\text{–}16)$$

The equations above define the various thermodynamic properties of a paramagnetic substance in terms of the partition function. Examples of their use are given in succeeding sections.

22.4 Ideal Paramagnetic Material and Saturation Effects

An important special case of paramagnetic behavior is the substance, such as a gaseous ion, whose energy is a linear function of magnetic field. For convenience, equation (22.2–1) will be written

$$\epsilon = \epsilon_0 - gm_J\beta\mathscr{H}, \qquad (22.4\text{–}1)$$

where β has been written for the term $eh/4\pi mc$. The value of β is 0.917×10^{-20} ergs gauss^{-1}. The quantum number m_J takes values from $-J$ to $+J$. The partition function is

$$Q = \sum_{-J}^{+J} e^{-(\epsilon_0 - gm_J\beta\mathscr{H})/kT} = e^{-\epsilon_0/kT}\sum_{-J}^{+J} e^{gm_J\beta\mathscr{H}/kT}. \qquad (22.4\text{–}2)$$

At small magnetic fields and high temperatures, the term $gm_J\beta\mathscr{H}/kT$ is much less than unity, and the exponential may be expanded in series. In this case, the partition function becomes

$$Q = e^{-\epsilon_0/kT}\sum_{-J}^{+J}\left(1 + \frac{gm_J\beta\mathscr{H}}{kT} + \frac{g^2{m_J}^2\beta^2\mathscr{H}^2}{2k^2T^2} + \cdots\right). \qquad (22.4\text{–}3)^{**}$$

The various terms in the summation may now be evaluated. The first is, of course, $2J + 1$; the second is zero, since the terms coming from even and odd values of m_J cancel each other. The third term is of the form

$$\sum_{-n}^{+n} ax^2 = \frac{an(n+1)(2n+1)}{3}. \qquad (22.4\text{–}4)^{**}$$

The final result for the partition function is

$$Q = e^{-\epsilon_0/kT}\left[(2J+1) + \frac{g^2\beta^2\mathscr{H}^2}{6k^2T^2}J(J+1)(2J+1) + \cdots\right]. \qquad (22.4\text{–}5)^{**}$$

Upon differentiation of (22.4–5)** with respect to the magnetic field,

$$\left(\frac{\partial Q}{\partial \mathscr{H}}\right)_T = e^{-\epsilon_0/kT}\left[\frac{g^2\beta^2\mathscr{H}}{3k^2T^2}J(J+1)(2J+1) + \cdots\right]. \qquad (22.4\text{–}6)^{**}$$

The molal intensity of magnetization, I, is obtained by substitution of (22.4–5)** and (22.4–6)** into (22.3–6). To terms of order $(\mathscr{H}/T)^3$, it is

$$\tilde{I} = \frac{RT}{Q}\left(\frac{\partial Q}{\mathscr{H}}\right)_T \approx \frac{\mathbf{N}g^2\beta^2\mathscr{H}}{3kT}J(J+1). \qquad (22.4\text{–}7)^{**}$$

An approximate expression for the magnetic susceptibility is obtained by further differentiation. It is

$$\chi_m = \left(\frac{\partial \tilde{I}}{\partial \mathscr{H}}\right)_T \approx \frac{\mathbf{N}g^2\beta^2}{3kT}J(J+1) = \frac{\tilde{C}}{T}, \qquad (22.4\text{–}8)^{**}$$

to terms of order $(\mathscr{H}/T)^2$; it should be noted that higher-order terms in χ_m arise from differentiation of both Q and $(\partial Q/\partial \mathscr{H})_T$.

Equation (22.4–8)** is a statement of *Curie's law* for an "ideal paramagnetic substance." For a substance to follow Curie's law, it is necessary (a) that the energy be given by an equation like (22.4–1), and (b) that the ratio $\mathscr{H}/T$ be small enough that higher-order terms may be neglected. If only electron spin need be considered, the quantum number S replaces J, and the factor g becomes 2. In this case

$$\chi_m = \frac{4\mathbf{N}\beta^2}{3kT}S(S+1) = \frac{\tilde{C}'}{T}. \qquad (22.4\text{–}9)^{**}$$

Problem 22.4-1. Gadolinium sulfate octahydrate may be treated as an ideal paramagnetic substance at room temperature. The gadolinium ion is in an ^8S state. Calculate the Curie constant, C, for this salt.

The energy of a substance which obeys Curie's law is independent of magnetic field, as was shown from classical thermodynamics in Problem 15.4–7. The partition function (22.4–3)** gives this result to the same approximation involved in the deduction of Curie's law from it, that is, the energy is independent of magnetic field to terms of order $(\mathscr{H}/T)^2$.

On the other extreme, if the quantity $gm_J\beta\mathscr{H}/kT$ becomes very large, magnetic *saturation* occurs. In this case the only term of consequence in the partition function is that of lowest energy (i.e., the term with $m_J = +J$). The partition function is then

$$Q = e^{-\epsilon_0/kT} e^{gJ\beta\mathscr{H}/kT}, \tag{22.4–10)**}$$

and the molal intensity of magnetization is

$$\tilde{I} = \frac{RT}{Q}\left(\frac{\partial Q}{\partial \mathscr{H}}\right)_T = \mathbf{N}gJ\beta. \tag{22.4–11)**}$$

The quantity $\mathbf{N}gJ\beta$ is the maximum intensity of magnetization possible for the substance, hence the term *saturation.*

Problem 22.4-2. (a) Calculate the molal intensity of magnetization of gadolinium sulfate at 100 gauss, 300°K, using equation (22.4–7)**.
(b) Calculate the saturation value, and compare with the result of part (a).

Problem 22.4-3. (a) For an ion in an ^8S state, calculate the magnetic field for which $gS\beta\mathscr{H}/kT$ is (i) 10^{-4}, (ii) 0.1, and (iii) 10 at 300°K.
(b) Repeat the calculations for 1°K.

At *intermediate* fields, the partition function (22.4–2) may be expressed as a sum of hyperbolic functions or as a geometrical progression. The corresponding general solution for $\tilde{I}$ is given in terms of the Brillouin function B_J, as

$$\tilde{I} = \mathbf{N}g\beta J B_J\left(\frac{g\beta J\mathscr{H}}{kT}\right), \tag{22.4–12)}$$

with the function B_J defined, for $(g\beta J\mathscr{H}/kT) = y$, as

$$B_J(y) = \frac{2J+1}{2J}\coth\left(\frac{2Jy+y}{2J}\right) - \frac{1}{2J}\coth\frac{y}{2J}. \tag{22.4–13)}$$

A derivation of equation (22.4–13) is given in Appendix 8. Equation (22.4–12) reduces to (22.4–7)** for very low values of $g\beta\mathscr{H}/kT$, and to (22.4–11)** for very high values.

Problem 22.4-4. Show that equation (22.4–12) reduces to (22.4–11)** for very large values of the parameter y. Observe that $\coth x \to 1$ as $x \to \infty$.

The thermodynamic functions of a substance which obeys equation (22.4–1) may be calculated by use of the formulas of Section 22.3. The derivatives of the partition function can always be replaced by appropriate summations, such as that of equation (22.4–2); for example, $(\partial Q/\partial \mathscr{H})_T$ is given by

$$\left(\frac{\partial Q}{\partial \mathscr{H}}\right)_T = e^{-\epsilon_0/kT}\sum_{-J}^{+J}\frac{gm_J\beta}{kT}\,e^{gm_J\beta\mathscr{H}/kT}. \tag{22.4–14)}$$

The thermodynamic properties may then be calculated by direct summation.

Problem 22.4-5. Show that, for a substance whose energy follows equation (22.4–1,) the isothermal susceptibility is given by

$$\chi_m = \left(\frac{\partial \tilde{I}}{\partial \mathscr{H}}\right)_T = RT \frac{\Sigma e^{gm_J\beta\mathscr{H}/kT}\Sigma \dfrac{g^2 m_J{}^2\beta^2}{k^2T^2} e^{gm_J\beta\mathscr{H}/kT} - \left(\Sigma \dfrac{gm_J\beta}{kT} e^{gm_J\beta\mathscr{H}/kT}\right)^2}{(\Sigma e^{gm_J\beta\mathscr{H}/kT})^2}. \tag{22.4–15}$$

(Note the similarity to the equation for heat capacity in terms of summations.)

Problem 22.4-6. Ferric ammonium alum may be considered to follow equation (22.4–1) almost down to 1°K. The ferric ion is in a ^6S state.

(a) Calculate by direct summation the intensity of magnetization, $\tilde{I}$, and the isothermal magnetic susceptibility, $\partial\tilde{I}/\partial\mathscr{H}_T$, for ferric alum at 5000 gauss, 1°K.

(b) Calculate for comparison the magnetic susceptibility in zero field at 1°K, and the saturation magnetic moment.

Note that in each case the term $e^{-\epsilon_0/kT}$ cancels from the summations.

Problem 22.4-7. Calculate the entropy, enthalpy, and heat capacity of ferric alum at 1000 gauss, 1°K, with reference to their values in zero field.

22.5 Non-ideal Paramagnetic Materials

The effects of a magnetic field on the energy of a paramagnetic salt are usually more complex than those given by equation (22.4–1). The energy level pattern for isotropic praseodymium salts, as calculated by Penney and Schlapp,[3] is given in Table 22.5–1 in terms of a parameter a characteristic of the particular salt.

Table 22.5–1
Calculated Magnetic Energy Levels[3] of Pr^{3+}

W_1	$672a + 5G^2/252a$
W_2	$336a + G/2 + 7G^2/3840a$
W_3	$336a + 2G^2/105a$
W_4	$336a - G/2 + 7G^2/3840a$
W_5	$96a + G^2/180a$
W_6	$96a - G^2/180a$
W_7	$-624a + 5G/2 - 7G^2/3840a$
W_8	$-624a - G^2/180a$
W_9	$-624a - 5G/2 - 7G^2/3840a$

$G = g\beta\mathscr{H} = (4/5)\beta\mathscr{H}$

The pattern is characteristic of many rare earth salts. The spectroscopic state of Pr^{3+} is $^3H_4$, so that there are nine distinct states corresponding to the $2J + 1$ orientations of the magnetic moment. The total energy of a praseodymium salt

[3] W. G. Penney and R. Schlapp, *Phys. Rev.*, **41**, 194 (1932).

contains the contributions of lattice vibrations in addition to the magnetic terms of Table 22.5–1. The zero of the latter is arbitrarily chosen as the average energy of the nine states in the absence of a magnetic field.

For $Pr_2(SO_4)_3 \cdot 8H_2O$ the assignment of the constant a as -0.293 cm^{-1} gives the best fit with the susceptibility measurements of Gorter and de Haas.[4] On this basis, taking W_1 as zero, the energy levels become 0, 99, 169, and 380 cm^{-1} for this salt, in the absence of a magnetic field. Spedding, Howe, and Keller[5] studied the absorption spectrum of $Pr_2(SO_4)_3 \cdot 8H_2O$. They observed levels at 0, 110, 235, and 500 cm^{-1}. Thus the theoretical assignment is not completely satisfactory; we shall retain it for purposes of illustration.

It will be evident from inspection of Table 22.5–1 that in zero field the $2J + 1$ levels form four sets: a singlet, a doubly degenerate level, and two triplets. In no case is the increase in energy directly proportional to the magnetic field.

Problem 22.5-1. Taking the magnetic energy levels of $Pr_2(SO_4)_3 \cdot 8H_2O$ as given by Table 22.5–1, with the constant a taken as -0.29 cm^{-1}, calculate the contribution which these energy levels make to the entropy in zero magnetic field at 300°K. At very high temperatures, this set of levels contributes $R \ln 9$.

Problem 22.5-2. (a) Using Table 22.5–1 and the value of a given previously, calculate the intensity of magnetization per gram of $Pr_2(SO_4)_3 \cdot 8H_2O$ at 77°K and 100 gauss. Note that

$$\left(\frac{\partial Q}{\partial \mathscr{H}}\right)_T = \sum_i \frac{1}{kT}\left(\frac{\partial W_i}{\partial \mathscr{H}}\right)_T e^{-W_i/kT}.$$

(b) Under the conditions of part (a), the magnetic susceptibility may be taken as $\chi_m = \tilde{I}/\mathscr{H}$. Calculate χ_m from the results of part (a). The experimental value is 0.0139.

(c) Calculate for comparison a value of χ_m from equation (22.4–8)**.

Note. Use equation (22.2–2) for the factor g.

Salts of the iron group usually have a complex set of energy levels. At very low temperatures and zero magnetic field, usually only the lowest set of "spin" levels need be considered. The nature of these levels determines the contribution of paramagnetism to the heat capacity and entropy of the salt. Below 4°K, this is frequently the principal contribution to the thermodynamic properties.

Problem 22.5-3. Show that, if a paramagnetic ion in a salt has a singlet level (taken as the energy zero), and a doubly degenerate level above it by an amount δ, the heat capacity of the salt in zero field due to these levels is given by

$$\tilde{C} = \frac{2R(\delta/kT)^2 e^{-\delta/kT}}{(1 + 2e^{-\delta/kT})^2}. \tag{22.5–1}$$

(*Hint.* Apply equation 22.3–15.)

Problem 22.5-4. The lowest energy levels of vanadium alum in zero magnetic field may be considered as a singlet and a doublet, with the latter 5.0 cm^{-1} above the

[4] C. J. Gorter and W. J. de Haas, *Communs. Kamerlingh Onnes Lab. Univ. Leiden*, No. 218b (1931).

[5] F. H. Spedding, J. P. Howe, and W. H. Keller, *J. Chem. Phys.*, **5**, 416 (1937).

former. The heat capacity due to lattice vibrations may be taken as $7 \times 10^{-4}T^3$ cal $mole^{-1}$ deg^{-1}.

(a) Calculate the total heat capacity of vanadium ammonium alum in zero field at 1°, 2°, 4°, 6°, and 10°K. Graph the results against T.

(b) Calculate the magnetic contribution to the entropy of vanadium ammonium alum in zero field at 1° and 4°K.

(c) What is the maximum contribution these three states can make to the entropy of the salt?

The "magnetic" energy levels make substantial contributions to the entropy of the paramagnetic substance and must be considered in calculations of its entropy. The occupation of the upper levels is accompanied by a maximum in the magnetic heat capacity. For systems such as those considered above, where the ions can be considered to be substantially independent, the magnetic heat capacity describes a Schottky type of curve. The results for vanadium alum (Problem 22.5–4) are an example of this type of curve. As exemplified in Problem 22.5–4, the heat capacity and entropy due to the magnetic levels frequently are much greater, at low temperatures, than the contributions due to vibrations of the crystal lattice.

22.6 Magnetic Cooling

The thermodynamic basis of cooling by adiabatic demagnetization was discussed in Section 15.4. The statistical theory remains to be discussed. (This problem was first considered by Giauque.[6]) The isothermal magnetization of a paramagnetic salt reduces its total entropy by an amount which can be calculated from equation (22.3–10). The entropy after magnetization will then correspond to that which the salt has, in zero field, at a lower temperature. If the entropy due to lattice vibrations is negligible, the temperature attained upon isentropic demagnetization will be determined only by the nature of the "magnetic" energy levels. By suitable choice of materials, the spacing of these levels may be made very small, with the result that very low temperatures may be obtained. A simplified example is given in Problem 22.6–1.

Problem 22.6-1. By the procedure indicated below, estimate the final temperature obtained upon adiabatic demagnetization of potassium chromium alum from 5000 gauss, 1°K. For simplicity, assume that the alum behaves as if it were in a ^4S state; neglect the effect of lattice vibrations.

(a) Calculate the entropy of the salt at 5000 gauss, 1°K. Assume that under these conditions the energies of the four states are given by equation (22.4–1), with $g = 2$ and $m_J = -^3/_2, -^1/_2, ^1/_2$, and $^3/_2$. Take the entropy at 1°K, zero field, as $R \ln 4 = 2.76$ cal $mole^{-1}$ deg^{-1}.

(b) Calculate the entropy of the salt, in zero magnetic field, at 0.05°, 0.1°, and 0.2°K. Assume that in zero field the states form two doublets separated in energy by an amount

[6] W. F. Giauque, *J. Am. Chem. Soc.*, **49**, 1870 (1927).

$0.20k$. (The quantity $0.20k$ means $0.20 \times 1.38 \times 10^{-16}$ ergs per ion, the factor 0.20 having the dimensions of degrees; this separation is small compared to the differences in energy at 5000 gauss.)

(c) Estimate the final temperature obtained upon demagnetization by comparing the results of (a) and (b).

The temperatures obtained by adiabatic demagnetization are a measure of the separation of the energy levels of the material used. The results obtained are usually much more sensitive to the over-all spread between levels than to the detailed character of the separation. (The student may verify, if he chooses, that the results of Problem 22.6–1 would be altered only slightly if the four levels had been chosen to be equally spaced, with a separation of $0.067k$.) The heat capacity is more sensitive to the actual distribution. An example is given in Problem 22.6–2.

Problem 22.6-2. The heat capacity of a substance having three equally spaced energy levels is given by

$$\tilde{C} = \frac{R(\delta/kT)^2 e^{-\delta/kT} (1 + 4e^{-\delta/kT} + e^{-2\delta/kT})}{(1 + e^{-\delta/kT} + e^{-2\delta/kT})^2} . \tag{22.6–1}$$

(a) Calculate the heat capacity for a substance with three equally spaced energy levels for $\delta/kT = 1.8$, 2.0, and 2.5. Show that the heat capacity goes through a maximum of about 1.3 cal mole^{-1} deg^{-1}.

(b) Repeat the calculations for a substance with a singlet and a doublet level, whose heat capacity is given by equation (22.5–1), and show that in this case the maximum occurs at about 1.5 cal mole^{-1} deg^{-1}.

Problem 22.6-3. Calculate the magnetic heat capacity in zero field at 0.5°, 1.0°, 2.0°, and 4.0°K of a substance with four energy levels at 0, 2.0, 4.0, and 10.0 cm^{-1}, respectively. Plot the results against temperature.

The high temperature limit of the entropy due to the "magnetic" energy levels is $R \ln n$, where n is the number of levels. The number of low-lying levels and their separation may be deduced by analysis of experimental values of the "magnetic" entropy and heat.

22.7 Cooperative Effects

The discussions in Sections 22.3, 22.4, 22.5, and 22.6 have been based on the assumption that each of the paramagnetic ions of the crystalline salt can be treated as an individual. As evidenced by the examples given, this approach is often a good first approximation. Frequently the interactions between neighboring ions are so strong that this approach is not possible. Two important special cases lead to *ferromagnetism* and *antiferromagnetism.*

In *ferromagnetism*, adjacent atoms or ions of the crystal are aligned cooperatively in the direction of an applied magnetic field; that is, the alignment of one atom tends strongly to align those about it. As a result, large intensities of magnetization are produced by relatively small applied fields, so that the magnetic susceptibilities are very large at low fields. Moreover, *magnetic saturation* is approached in relatively small external magnetic fields. The alignment, once produced, is frequently destroyed only by application of a large field in the reverse direction. Thus ferromagnetic materials show *remanent magnetism*; that is, the *induction* within them does not return to zero on removal of an applied field. Whereas with paramagnetic materials the processes of magnetization and demagnetization are highly reversible, most ferromagnetic materials show pronounced hysteresis.

In *antiferromagnetism* there is also cooperation, but here alignment of a given ion with the field tends to align its neighbors against the field. Thus the magnetic susceptibility of an antiferromagnetic material (in low applied fields) will be considerably less than for an ideal paramagnetic material. Antiferromagnetic materials may also show remanence and hysteresis. At sufficiently high fields, or for particular field directions, the effect of cooperation may be eliminated, so that the substance displays ordinary paramagnetic behavior.

A detailed statistical treatment of ferromagnetism and antiferromagnetism is not available. Physical theories of ferromagnetism have been developed by Weiss[7] and by Heisenberg.[8] Physical theories of antiferromagnetism have been given by Néel,[9] Bitter,[10] and van Vleck.[11]

Ferromagnetism occurs with elements such as iron or nickel, and with many oxides and alloys. Antiferromagnetism has been found in anhydrous oxides and halides of iron, manganese, nickel, etc., and with some hydrated copper salts, such as $CuCl_2{\cdot}2H_2O$. In both cases the substances are paramagnetic at sufficiently high temperatures. With decreasing temperature the ferromagnetic or antiferromagnetic state is approached through a second-order transition. In the paramagnetic region the susceptibilities are given approximately by

$$\chi_m = \frac{\tilde{C}}{T \pm \theta}, \tag{22.7-1}$$

where θ is usually of the order of the "transition temperature"

[7] P. Weiss, *J. phys.*, [4] **6,** 661 (1907); [7] **1,** 163 (1930).

[8] W. Heisenberg, *Z. Physik*, **49,** 619 (1928).

[9] L. Néel, *Ann. phys.*, [10] **18,** 5 (1932); [11] **5,** 232 (1936).

[10] F. Bitter, *Phys. Rev.*, **54,** 79 (1938).

[11] J. H. van Vleck, *J. Chem. Phys.*, **9,** 85 (1941).

(approximately the peak of the second order transition). In equation (22.7–1), the minus sign refers to ferromagnetism; the transition temperature is then called the Curie point. The plus sign applies to antiferromagnetism, and the corresponding transition temperature is called the Néel point.

The General Principles of Statistical Mechanics (Methods of J. Willard Gibbs, Part II)

CHAPTER 23

23.1 Introduction

In Chapter 17 definitions have been given for some of the basic concepts needed for the discussion of the principles of statistical mechanics, and at this point the reader will do well to review Sections 17.1 to 17.3 inclusive.

The fundamental variables are the coordinates and momenta of the elements (atoms, molecules, etc.) which make up the system. If there are a atoms in a molecule, this element contributes $3a$ coordinates and $3a$ momenta to the variables of the system and it is associated with a μ-space of $6a$ dimensions.

The γ-space has two axes for each degree of freedom of the system, one for each of the coordinates and one for each of the momenta. Thus, if there are n molecules each with a atoms, the γ-space has $6an$ dimensions. A single point in the γ-space represents the coordinates and the momenta of all the atoms in the system.

In Section 17.2 *a microscopic state* of the system was defined. The assumption that individual quantum states have the same probability is equivalent to the assumption that all microscopic states have the same probability. This means that there will always be an equal number of systems in each microscopic state and that the points will be distributed with uniform density in the γ-space. In order to justify this statement it is necessary to show that a large number of systems chosen so that microscopic states are equally represented (i.e., the same number of systems in each) will retain a distribution of systems in which the number of them in each microscopic state is the same. This will be done in the next two sections. It is a special case of a more general theorem which is derived for systems distributed as a function solely of their energy.

23.2 The Liouville Theorem and the Ergodic Hypothesis

Consider a large and fixed number of systems, N, which are distributed arbitrarily.

Each of the systems is represented by a point in the γ-space. As time passes, each system undergoes a change in configuration; thus its representative point moves to another position in the γ-space, while the point representing some other system may take its place or a place very close to it. If at any time there is marked out a region in the γ-space of volume $\delta p_1 \cdots \delta p_f \, \delta q_1 \cdots \delta q_f$ containing N specified systems, after a time t this region will have changed its position and also its shape. It can be shown that by the laws of mechanics the volume of this region must remain constant.

Consider one of the δq that bounds the region. At the end of a time interval dt its value is $[\delta q + (d\,\delta q/dt)\,dt]$. However since $(d\,\delta q/dt)$ can be replaced by $\delta(dq/dt)$ or $\delta\dot{q}$, the value of δq is then $\delta q + \delta\dot{q}\,dt$. Similarly, the value of each δp becomes $\delta p + \delta\dot{p}\,dt$ at the end of the time dt. Thus after the time dt the volume element has become $(\delta q_1 + \delta\dot{q}_1\,dt) \cdots (\delta q_f + \delta\dot{q}_f\,dt)(\delta p_1 + \delta\dot{q}_1\,dt) \cdots (\delta p_f + \delta\dot{p}_f\,dt)$. If here we multiply out and neglect terms of higher order, this expression becomes

$$(\delta q_1 \cdots \delta q_f \, \delta p_1 \cdots \delta p_f) + \left(\sum_{i=1}^{i=f} \frac{\partial \dot{q}_i}{\partial q_i} + \frac{\partial \dot{p}_i}{\partial p_i}\right) \delta q_1 \cdots \delta q_f \, \delta t,$$

after we write $(\partial\dot{q}_i/\partial q_i)\,\delta q_i$ for $\delta\dot{q}_i$ and $(\partial\dot{p}_i/\partial p_i)\,\delta p_i$ for $\delta\dot{p}_i$, since only the time rate of change of q along the q axis is involved. Thus the total *fractional* change in the volume element is

$$\sum_{i=1}^{i=f} \left[\frac{\partial \dot{p}_i}{\partial p_i} + \frac{\partial \dot{q}_i}{\partial q_i}\right].$$

If cartesian coordinates are used for each particle, the momentum p_i is equal to $m\dot{q}_i$, and the total energy, H, is

$$\sum_i \frac{p_i^2}{2m_i} + V,$$

where the first term is the kinetic energy and the second term is the potential energy. Thus

$$\frac{\partial H}{\partial p_i} = \frac{p_i}{m_i} = \dot{q}_i, \tag{23.2–1}$$

$$\frac{\partial H}{\partial q_i} = \frac{\partial V}{\partial q_i} = -F_i = -\dot{p}_i, \tag{23.2–2}$$

when F_i is the force and consequently the rate of change of momentum. It is a consequence of the general definition of the momentum, p, for coordinates other than cartesian, that these two equations are always true.

As a consequence of the quantum mechanical definition of momentum they are also true for quantum mechanical systems. They are called the equations of motion in the canonical (simple) form (for a general derivation see Section A.5–8). As a consequence of these two equations,

$$\frac{\partial \dot{p}_i}{\partial p_i} + \frac{\partial \dot{q}_i}{\partial q_i} = -\frac{\partial^2 H}{\partial p_i \partial q_i} + \frac{\partial^2 H}{\partial p_i \partial q_i} = 0. \tag{23.2–3}$$

Thus there is no change in $\delta q_1 \cdots \delta q_f\, \delta p_1 \cdots \delta p_f$ as the volume element moves through the space during the course of time. This theorem is called the "principle of constancy of extension in phase."

The region in question contained a fixed number of systems, N. The constancy of volume as the region moves through the γ-space is thus equivalent to a constancy of density. The theorem that the density is constant as a region moves through the γ-space is called the "principle of constancy of density in phase" and is known as the Liouville theorem.

The Heisenberg principle of uncertainty states that

$$\delta p\, \delta q \sim h. \tag{16.5–11}$$

The result just obtained is in accord with this principle, since it states that the volume per system is always h^{3na}.

We shall eventually obtain the thermodynamic properties for a system with the most probable distribution of the energy. This is equivalent to considering the thermodynamic properties as averaged over systems with all possible distributions, since those with other than the most probable distribution are negligible. The most probable or average properties can be chosen by observing a system over a long time or by observing a great number of systems at one time. In any event, it is clear that the whole of the phase space must be available to all the systems.

If a system, as it moves through the γ-space, should, for a second time, reach the same value of all of the coordinates and momenta it must retrace its path; that is, *paths in the γ-space cannot cross.*

***Problem* 23.2-1.** Prove the last statement.

It is assumed that for those systems which travel in closed paths the paths are sufficiently long that states representative of all states are reached. This is called the *Ergodic Hypothesis.* Ortho and para states are exceptions (see Section 19.4).

23.3 Statistical Equilibrium

The theorem derived in the last section applies to a region in the γ-space as it moves through the γ-space with the progress of time. The proof of statistical equilibrium requires the proof that any given region fixed in space contains a number of systems independent of the time (i.e., that the volume assigned to a system in some particular region of the space is always the same and therefore that the probability of that configuration is time independent); that is $(\partial D/\partial t)_{\mathrm{p}_i\mathrm{q}_i}$ is equal to zero. The theorem derived in the last section can be written

$$\frac{\mathrm{d}D}{\mathrm{d}t} = 0, \tag{23.3–1}$$

which says that the total derivative of the density with respect to time is zero.

The density changes because at any specified position the density changes as the result of lapse of time and because, as time goes, on the coordinates describing the region change. Thus

$$\frac{\mathrm{d}D}{\mathrm{d}t} = \left(\frac{\partial D}{\partial t}\right)_{\mathrm{q}_i\mathrm{p}_i} + \sum_i \frac{\partial D}{\partial \mathrm{q}_i}\frac{\partial \mathrm{q}_i}{\partial t} + \sum_i \frac{\partial D}{\partial \mathrm{p}_i}\frac{\partial \mathrm{p}_i}{\partial t} = 0 \tag{23.3–2}$$

or

$$\left(\frac{\partial D}{\partial t}\right)_{\mathrm{q}_i\mathrm{p}_i} = -\left(\sum_i \frac{\partial D}{\partial \mathrm{q}_i}\frac{\partial \mathrm{q}_i}{\partial t} + \sum_i \frac{\partial D}{\partial \mathrm{p}_i}\frac{\partial \mathrm{p}_i}{\partial t}\right). \tag{23.3–3}$$

If the points are initially distributed with uniform density (microscopic states equally represented), the $\partial D/\partial \mathrm{q}_i$ and $\partial D/\partial \mathrm{p}_i$ are all zero and $(\partial D/\partial t)_{\mathrm{q}_i\mathrm{p}_i}$ is zero. This is a special case of a theorem about to be proved.

If the points are distributed initially as some function of their energy, the last two terms can be written

$$\left(\sum \frac{\partial D}{\partial E_i}\frac{\partial E_i}{\partial \mathrm{q}_i}\frac{\partial \mathrm{q}_i}{\partial t} + \sum \frac{\partial D}{\partial E_i}\frac{\partial E_i}{\partial \mathrm{p}_i}\frac{\partial \mathrm{p}_i}{\partial t}\right).$$

Because H is equal to the total energy of the system,

$$\frac{\partial E_i}{\partial \mathrm{q}_i} \equiv \frac{\partial \mathrm{H}}{\partial \mathrm{q}_i}, \tag{23.3–4}$$

$$\frac{\partial E_i}{\partial \mathrm{p}_i} \equiv \frac{\partial \mathrm{H}}{\partial \mathrm{p}_i}. \tag{23.3–5}$$

If here equations (23.2–1) and (23.2–2) are applied, equation (23.3–3) becomes

$$\left(\frac{\partial D}{\partial t}\right)_{\mathrm{q}_i\mathrm{p}_i} = \sum \frac{\partial D}{\partial E_i}\dot{\mathrm{p}}_i\dot{\mathrm{q}}_i - \sum \frac{\partial D}{\partial E_i}\dot{\mathrm{q}}_i\dot{\mathrm{p}}_i = 0. \qquad (23.3\text{–}6)$$

Thus any ensemble with a distribution in which the systems are distributed solely as a function of energy will conserve this distribution and is therefore in statistical equilibrium.

23.4 The Canonical Distribution

The purpose of this section is to lay a foundation for the discussion of the laws of thermodynamics in terms of the mechanics of molecules. In Section 17.4 an ensemble of systems was considered, all of which had the same energy or, more strictly, an ensemble of systems with energy lying between E and $E + \mathrm{d}E$. In any investigation of the laws of thermodynamics in terms of the mechanics of molecules the study of the conditions of transfer of energy between systems is a necessity. Thus an ensemble of systems with all possible values of the energy is desirable if not essential. It is equally desirable to have these systems distributed first as an arbitrary function of the energy and later to find the nature of the function that is consistent with the laws of thermodynamics. In the last section it was shown that any such distribution will not change with time.

Gibbs distributed the systems as an exponential function of their energy. There is a logical basis for such a distribution that has been given by Mayer and Mayer.[1] This, in a slightly modified form, we shall now outline.

Consider an ensemble consisting of a large number, N, of identical systems. If we are to consider the exchange of energy between these systems, it is simplest to exclude the gain or loss of energy by the ensemble and thus to keep its energy fixed at a value E_c. The subscript is used to distinguish the total energy of the ensemble from the variable value of each system.

Each system can be considered to be in a quantized energy state. Let the possible states be $E_1, E_2, \cdots, E_i, \cdots$. Each energy is determined by $3na$ degrees of freedom, where n is the number of elements in each system (each with a atoms) and each element has $3a$ degrees of freedom (a will be unity if the element is an elementary particle). With each degree of freedom there is associated a coordinate and a momentum.

In Section 17.4 it has been shown that in the classical limit there are $\mathbf{P}_D$ ways of making a particular distribution of energy E among the n

[1] J. E. Mayer and M. G. Mayer, *Statistical Mechanics*, Wiley, New York, 1940.

elements such that there are n_k elements with energy ϵ_k, where

$$\mathbf{P}_D = \prod_k \frac{p_k^{n_k}}{n_k!}, \tag{23.4–1}$$

subject to the conditions that Σn_k and $\Sigma n_k \epsilon_k$ are both constants (these two sums are, of course, respectively equal to the total number of molecules, n, and the energy, E, of each system). Since all the systems are identical, n is constant but E varies from system to system, having the values E_1, $E_2, \cdots, E_i, \cdots$. However there are many distributions of the energy each corresponding to different n_k. Thus the total number of distributions of the energy is

$$\mathbf{P} = \sum \mathbf{P}_D = \sum_{n_k} \prod_k \frac{p_k^{n_k}}{n_k!}. \tag{23.4–2}$$

The volume assigned to each of the quantum states, associated with each energy, in the $6na$ dimensional space, γ-space, is h^{6na}. Since there are $\mathbf{P}$ ways of assigning any value of the energy E, to each value of E_i must be assigned $\mathbf{P}_i$ quantum states with each $\mathbf{P}_i$ given by an expression like (23.4–2).

The problem is, then, to determine the number of systems, N_i, with energy E_i in an ensemble of N distinguishable systems and with constant total energy E_c.

The procedure is identical with that used in Section 17.4, except that here the number N_i is taken to be the number in the $\mathbf{P}_i$ states rather than that in any one of the states.

The number of ways in which the $N_1, N_2, \cdots, N_i$, etc., distinguishable systems can be assigned to groups of states with energies $E_1, E_2, \cdots, E_i$ etc., is

$$\mathbf{P} = \frac{N! \Pi \mathbf{P}_i^{N_i}}{\Pi N_i!}. \tag{23.4–3}$$

The factor $\Pi \mathbf{P}_i^{N_i}$ is due to the fact that there are $\mathbf{P}_i$ ways in which any system can be assigned to the $\mathbf{P}_i$ states of the group and that this choice can be made independently for each of the N_i systems.

The logarithm of the number $\mathbf{P}$ given by (23.4–3) is to be maximized subject to the conditions that

$$\Sigma N_i = N \tag{23.4–4}$$

and

$$\Sigma N_i E_i = E_c. \tag{23.4–5}$$

This leads to

$$\Sigma(\ln N_i - \ln \mathbf{P}_i + \beta E_i + \alpha)\, dN_i = 0, \tag{23.4–6}$$

as in Section 17.4. Thus, for each group of states of energy E_i,

$$\ln N_i - \ln \mathbf{P}_i + \beta E_i + \alpha = 0 \qquad (23.4\text{–}7a)$$

and

$$N_i = \mathbf{P}_i e^{-(\beta E_i + \alpha)}; \qquad (23.4\text{–}7b)$$

by equation (23.4–4),

$$\Sigma N_i = \Sigma \mathbf{P}_i e^{-(\beta E_i + \alpha)} = N \qquad (23.4\text{–}8)$$

and

$$e^{-\alpha} = \frac{N}{\Sigma \mathbf{P}_i e^{-\beta E_i}}. \qquad (23.4\text{–}9)$$

Thus

$$N_i = \frac{N\mathbf{P}_i e^{-\beta E_i}}{\Sigma \mathbf{P}_i e^{-\beta E_i}}. \qquad (23.4\text{–}10)$$

The quantity in the denominator of equation (23.4–10) will be denoted by Q, where Q is called the system partition function in keeping with the terminology of Section 21.4. Such a quantity for a crystal is given in (21.4–10).

It will be demonstrated presently that the value of N_i for *one particular value* of E_i ($E_{\max}$) is practically equal to N if the value of N is large. The average energy of the system is thus equal to the value of $E_{i\,\max}$ giving the maximum value of N_i. Since a detailed understanding of thermodynamics is sought, it is necessary to make logical definitions of temperature and pressure in terms of the mechanics of molecules. Thus, although the reader at once recognizes β as equal to $(kT)^{-1}$, this identification has yet to be made formally.

Equation (23.4–10) can be written

$$\frac{N_i}{N\mathbf{P}_i} = e^{(\psi - E_i)/\theta}. \qquad (23.4\text{–}11)$$

Gibbs[2] denotes the exponent of the right hand side by η. The quantity ψ is determined by the fact that ΣN_i is equal to N, that is,

$$\Sigma \mathbf{P}_i e^{(\psi - E_i)/\theta} = 1 \qquad (23.4\text{–}12a)$$

and

$$\Sigma \mathbf{P}_i e^{-E_i/\theta} = e^{-\psi/\theta}. \qquad (23.4\text{–}12b)$$

Thus, according to equation (23.4–9),

$$e^{-\psi/\theta} = Ne^{\alpha}, \qquad (23.4\text{–}13)$$

while θ is, of course, the same as β^{-1}.

[2] *The Collected Works of J. Willard Gibbs*, Vol. 1, Longmans, Green, New York, 1928, p. 33.

Gibbs identifies the average value of η, denoted by $\bar{\eta}$, with the negative of the entropy in initially unspecified units. Thus

$$S = -\bar{\eta} = -\Sigma \mathbf{P}_i \frac{\psi - E_i}{\theta} e^{(\psi - E_i)/\theta}. \qquad (23.4\text{–}14)$$

For large values of N, since E_i takes on a practically continuous series of values, the sum may be replaced by an integral. To do this we note that the *exact* positions and the *exact* momenta of the elements in a container are specified when a single point in the γ-space is fixed. However, even for a *single element* this specification is impossible and must be limited to values of $\delta q \, \delta \mathrm{q}$ equal to h for each degree of freedom (i.e., to $\delta \mathrm{q}_1 \, \delta \mathrm{p}_1 \cdots \delta \mathrm{q}_{3a} \, \delta \mathrm{q}_{\mathrm{p}a} = h^{3a}$). Moreover, it is not possible to distinguish exchanges of identical elements between the regions of the μ-space $\delta \mathrm{q}_1 \, \delta \mathrm{p}_1 \cdots \delta \mathrm{q}_{3a} \, \delta \mathrm{p}_{3a}$ of size h^{3a} to which they are thus limited. Thus, while the volume in the μ-space $\delta \mathrm{q}_1 \, \delta \mathrm{p}_1 \cdots \delta \mathrm{q}_{3a} \, \delta \mathrm{p}_{3a}$ for the jth element corresponds to a number of quantum states $p_j{}^*$ given by[3]

$$p_j{}^* = \frac{\delta \mathrm{q}_1 \, \delta \mathrm{p}_1 \cdots \delta \mathrm{q}_{3a} \, \delta \mathrm{p}_{3a}}{h^{3a}}, \qquad (23.4\text{–}15)$$

the corresponding volume in the γ-space for n elements (i.e., $\delta \mathrm{q}_1 \, \delta \mathrm{p}_1 \cdots \delta \mathrm{q}_{3na} \, \delta \mathrm{p}_{3na}$) corresponds to a number of quantum states equal to

$$\frac{1}{n!} \prod_{j=1}^{j=n} p_j{}^*$$

for a non-localized system, since the $n!$ possible interchanges of these elements do not produce new quantum states. If there are α physically distinguishable kinds of elements (say helium atoms, hydrogen molecules, etc.) with numbers ν of the νth kind respectively in each system, the number of quantum states is

$$\mathbf{P}_i = \frac{\delta \mathrm{q}_1 \, \delta \mathrm{p}_1 \cdots \delta \mathrm{q}_{3na} \, \delta \mathrm{p}_{3na}}{h^{3na} \prod_{\nu} \nu!}, \qquad (23.4\text{–}16a)$$

where ν may be a, b, c, etc., which are symbols denoting the kinds of molecules. Here to avoid extra subscripts the symbol denoting the kind of molecule (say a, b, c, etc.) is also used to denote the number of atoms of

[3] Note that p^* for the number of quantum states must not be confused with the p of Section 17.4.

that kind. For brevity, the volume element, equal to $dq_1\, dp_1 \cdots dq_{3na}\, dp_{3na}$, will be denoted by $\delta\tau$. Thus equation (23.4–14) can be replaced by

$$S = -\bar{\eta} = \sum_{\text{All}}^{\text{States}} \frac{\psi - E}{\theta}\, e^{(\psi - E)/\theta} \frac{\delta\tau}{h^{3na} \prod_{\nu} \nu!} \tag{23.4–17a}$$

In the sum

$$\sum_{\text{All}}^{\text{States}}$$

each of the quantities summed is multiplied by the quantity

$$\mathbf{P}_i = \frac{\delta\tau}{h^{3na} \prod_{\nu} \nu!}$$

which is the number of quantum states corresponding to energies between E and $E + \Delta E$. If the units of q and p are chosen so that the $\delta q\, \delta p$ are now equal to h, the quantity $\mathbf{P}_i$ can be written

$$\int_{q_i(E)}^{q_i(E+\Delta E)} \cdots \int_{p_i(E)}^{p_i(E+\Delta E)} \cdots d\tau = \mathbf{P}_i, \tag{23.4–16b}$$

where the integration extends over the volume of the γ-space which includes the $\mathbf{P}_i$ states (i.e., regions which merely correspond to exchange of identical particles are excluded); this is thus an alternative way of stating equation (23.4–16a).

Thus equation (23.4–17a) becomes replaced by

$$S = -\bar{\eta} = \int_{\text{All}}^{\text{Phases}} \left(\frac{\psi - E}{\theta}\right) e^{(\psi - E)/\theta}\, d\tau, \tag{23.4–17b}$$

where "All Phases" means that the variables $q_i p_i$ in the new units cover all possible values that do not include exchanges of identical particles. Gibbs does not exclude exchanges of identical particles at this point but only does so in his last chapter. We prefer to do it from the start. With this identification of entropy it is an easy matter to identify θ and ψ by considering the average energy, $\bar{E}$, of the systems of the ensemble and equating it to the energy of a thermodynamic system. Before doing this it is desirable to specify exactly how this average energy may be changed. In the type of ensemble (i.e., isolated) which we have considered, which has a fixed number of systems, this change implies a change in the total energy of the ensemble. This in turn involves a change in β (i.e., a change in θ) and therefore a change in ψ. Thus there is a change in N_i, the number of systems in each group of states of energy E_i. Thus an increase in the average energy of the ensemble is accompanied by an increase in the value of E_i for which N_i is a maximum.

This increase in the individual energies of the systems can be effected by the action with bodies external to the systems. Such bodies are connected to, but do not form part of, the system, and their energy is only affected by the work done on them (i.e., they have no kinetic energy). If the energy is increased in other ways, it must be so increased by exchange of energy with another system of the ensemble. In this case systems are said to exchange *heat*. Such systems are not isolated. It is only in this way the heat is definable in statistical mechanics. This definition will be elaborated below. The *exact* definition of the work done on a system remains to be considered. Fortunately the definition can be postponed by not specifying how energy changes are to be made in the individual systems of the ensemble other than that it is made by contact with other systems or by changing the coordinates of the external bodies (doing work on them but transmitting energy to them in no other way).

The quantity θ (or β) may now be identified by making use of the relation

$$\left(\frac{\partial S}{\partial E}\right)_V = \frac{1}{T}.$$

In terms of the dependent quantities of statistical mechanics, this equation is expressed as

$$-\left(\frac{\delta\bar{\eta}}{\delta\bar{E}}\right)_{\delta\bar{E}\to 0} = \left(\frac{\partial S}{\partial E}\right)_V = \frac{1}{T}. \tag{23.4–18}$$

The changes of $\bar{E}$ need not be restricted for constant volume, as each one of the systems of the ensemble has the same volume. The definition of $\bar{E}$ is, of course,

$$\bar{E} = \int_{\text{All}}^{\text{Phases}} Ee^{(\psi - E)/\theta}\,\mathrm{d}\tau; \tag{23.4–19}$$

in terms of $\bar{E}$, $\bar{\eta}$ becomes

$$\begin{aligned}\bar{\eta} &= \frac{\psi}{\theta}\int_{\text{All}}^{\text{Phases}} e^{(\psi - E)/\theta}\,\mathrm{d}\tau - \frac{1}{\theta}\int_{\text{All}}^{\text{Phases}} Ee^{(\psi - E)/\theta}\,\mathrm{d}\tau \\ &= \frac{\psi}{\theta} - \frac{\bar{E}}{\theta},\end{aligned} \tag{23.4–20}$$

since obviously

$$\int_{\text{All}}^{\text{Phases}} e^{(\psi - E)/\theta}\,\mathrm{d}\tau = 1.$$

The volume is constant; thus θ becomes the single independent variable, and

$$\mathrm{d}\bar{\eta} = \frac{\mathrm{d}\psi}{\theta} - \frac{\psi}{\theta^2}\,\mathrm{d}\theta + \frac{\bar{E}}{\theta^2}\,\mathrm{d}\theta - \frac{\mathrm{d}\bar{E}}{\theta}. \tag{23.4–21}$$

By transforming equation (23.4–12b) into the integral form we obtain,

$$e^{-\psi/\theta} = \int_{\text{All}}^{\text{Phases}} e^{-E/\theta}\,\mathrm{d}\tau \tag{23.4–22a}$$

$$\psi = -\theta \ln \int_{\text{All}}^{\text{Phases}} e^{-E/\theta}\,\mathrm{d}\tau. \tag{23.4–22b}$$

Since the limits are definite, it is possible to differentiate under the integral sign, and thus

$$\mathrm{d}\psi = -\ln \int_{\text{All}}^{\text{Phases}} e^{-E/\theta}\,\mathrm{d}\tau\,\mathrm{d}\theta - \frac{\displaystyle\int_{\text{All}}^{\text{Phases}} Ee^{-E/\theta}\,\mathrm{d}\tau}{\displaystyle\theta \int_{\text{All}}^{\text{Phases}} e^{-E/\theta}\,\mathrm{d}\tau}\,\mathrm{d}\theta. \tag{23.4–23}$$

By substituting from (23.4–22a), (23.4–22b), and (23.4–19) there results

$$\mathrm{d}\psi = \frac{\psi}{\theta}\,\mathrm{d}\theta - \frac{\bar{E}}{\theta}\,\mathrm{d}\theta. \tag{23.4–24}$$

Substituting this in equation (23.4–21),

$$\mathrm{d}\bar{\eta} = \frac{\psi}{\theta^2}\,\mathrm{d}\theta - \frac{\bar{E}}{\theta^2}\,\mathrm{d}\theta - \frac{\psi}{\theta^2}\,\mathrm{d}\theta + \frac{\bar{E}}{\theta^2}\,\mathrm{d}\theta - \frac{\mathrm{d}\bar{E}}{\theta} \tag{23.4–25a}$$

or

$$\mathrm{d}\bar{\eta} = -\frac{\mathrm{d}\bar{E}}{\theta}. \tag{23.4–25b}$$

Thus

$$-\left(\frac{\partial \eta}{\partial \bar{E}}\right) = \frac{1}{\theta} = \frac{1}{T}. \tag{23.4–26}$$

It is by equation (23.4–18) that we have equated θ to T (or strictly some multiple of it, since the units of entropy have not been defined; however, since only relative values of T are defined, this identifies θ with T).

Since nothing limits the above treatment to classical systems if the limits of integration are suitably chosen, this is a general identification of T with θ (or with β^{-1}).

It now remains to identify ψ. At the same time it is convenient to consider in a preliminary fashion what equilibrium means from the standpoint of statistical mechanics. The consequences of lack of equilibrium will be postponed to the next section. According to thermodynamics the heat withdrawn by a system from the surroundings under reversible conditions is given by

$$q = T\,\mathrm{d}S.$$

If the process is one at constant volume or at constant values of any of the other variables of Section 15.2 (see equation 15.2–1) and at constant temperature, there is no question of irreversibility unless mixing processes (i.e., changes of composition) are involved. As long as the system retains a fixed composition, the last complication is eliminated. The complications arising when the composition is variable will be discussed in Section 23.10.

In terms of statistical mechanics for a process at constant volume, in view of equation (23.4–25b) we may now write

$$q = T\,\mathrm{d}S = -\theta\,\mathrm{d}\bar{\eta} = \mathrm{d}\bar{E}, \tag{23.4–27}$$

and it is evident that when a system gains heat at constant volume this heat is used to increase the average energy of the molecules.

If the volume (or any of the variables x_i) is varied against opposing forces, it is most natural to consider that part of the heat withdrawn from the surroundings goes into increasing the potential energy of the mechanism supplying these forces and the remainder to increasing the average energy of the system. So the question arises: How does statistical mechanics interpret the mechanism by which the system converts this energy which is withdrawn from the surroundings into work (potential energy) and what is the maximum work which can be obtained?

The simplest way to regard the problem (see above) is to include with each system of the ensemble a set of bodies whose potential energy can be increased but which acquires no kinetic energy. In the usual case these bodies may be thought of as pistons with weights attached. In general, they exert forces X_i. Each system of the ensemble will have an identical set of bodies attached to it.

The equivalent of thermodynamic equilibrium will be that the total energy of each system obeys the canonical equation of motion, namely, equations (23.2–1) and (23.2–2).

If the system does not obey these equations, forces have been omitted and these are just those of friction, etc., which produce irreversibility. In other words, the kinetic energy of the bodies attached to the systems (pistons) cannot be neglected.

It is true that, if two systems at different temperatures exchange heat while each is kept at constant volume, the process is an irreversible one. In this case the process is in no sense one at constant temperature since one system increases its temperature and the other decreases its temperature. If the two uncombined systems are regarded as a single system from the standpoint of statistical mechanics, the *combined* system must be characterized by a single value of θ; this is impossible because the T's are different. When the uncombined systems are not in contact they do not, in general, as a pair, obey the canonical equations of motion. The same sort of proof given in Section 23.3 can be used to show that the combined systems will *not* then be in statistical equilibrium unless the canonical equations are obeyed accidentally. This will be true if two systems previously left in contact for a long time are separated momentarily and then reunited. In this case the systems have the same θ.

It will be shown later that the combination of two systems at constant volume and with different temperatures will lead to a decrease in the sum of the values of $(\psi - \bar{E})/\theta$. In terms of statistical mechanics, we now consider the case when there is change in the volume (or in the variables x_i of Section 15.2) under equilibrium conditions. The heat withdrawn from the surroundings by a system in undergoing any such process is seen to be identifiable by the equation

$$q = -\theta \, d\bar{\eta} = d\bar{E} - d\psi, \tag{23.4–28}$$

which is obtained by using equation (23.4–20) to obtain the *negative* of the entropy change. Comparing this with the equation

$$q = dE + w,$$

$-d\psi$ is seen to be identifiable with the work done in a reversible process. That is,

$$-d\psi = \sum X_i \, dx_i. \tag{23.4–29}$$

From the expression (23.4–22b) for ψ, if the temperature (i.e., θ) is held constant, $d\psi$ is given by

$$d\psi = \sum_i dx_i \frac{\displaystyle\int_{\text{All}}^{\text{Phases}} \frac{\partial E}{\partial x_i} e^{-E/\theta} \, d\tau}{\displaystyle\int_{\text{All}}^{\text{Phases}} e^{-E/\theta} \, d\tau}, \tag{23.4–30}$$

where x_i are the variables discussed in Chapter 15; or, by equation (23.4–22a), $d\psi$ is

$$d\psi = \sum_i dx_i \int_{\text{All}}^{\text{Phases}} \frac{\partial E}{\partial x_i} e^{(\psi - E)/\theta} \, d\tau. \tag{23.4–31}$$

Thus

$$\left(\frac{\partial \psi}{\partial x_i}\right) = \int_{\text{All}}^{\text{Phases}} \left(\frac{\partial E}{\partial x_i}\right) e^{(\psi - E)/\theta} \, d\tau. \tag{23.4–32}$$

According to equation (23.4–29) the thermodynamic force associated with the variable x_i is

$$X_i = -\left(\frac{\partial \psi}{\partial x_i}\right)_{T, x_j, \text{etc.}} . \tag{23.4–33}$$

Thus the forces (e.g., pressure) are given by the negative of the left side of equation (23.4–32) and as such they are values of $-\partial E/\partial x_i$ averaged over the systems of the ensemble.

The pressures are the usual manifestation of such forces, and the coordinates associated therewith are the volumes.

Finally, a comparison of equation (23.4–29) with the equation

$$\left(\frac{\partial A}{\partial V}\right)_T = -P, \tag{6.19–9}$$

derived in Problem 6.19–2 shows at once that ψ is identical with the Helmholtz free energy (or work function) A.

23.5 Some Maximum and Minimum Properties of the Canonical Distribution

In order to study further the relation of $\bar{\eta}$ and ψ to the thermodynamic properties, two mathematical theorems relating to $\bar{\eta}$ and ψ/θ must be derived.

Consider a distribution A in which the systems of an ensemble are distributed as a function, f, of their energy *only* (i.e., so that

$$f = e^{\eta} = e^{(\psi - E)/\theta}, \tag{23.5–1}$$

with ψ and θ constant).

Theorem A. The average value of the index η for the distribution in A *is less than that of any other distribution* B *in which the fraction n of the systems between E and $E + \Delta E$ is unaltered.*

The distribution in B would be one in which θ (temperature) differs arbitrarily from system to system. Thus ψ in equation (23.5–1) would be different, since $\int e^{(\psi - E)/\theta}\, d\tau$ over the part of the γ-space occupied by the ensemble must be unity.

Thus, although the number of systems in any energy range is the same for A and B, the number in the corresponding elements of volume in the γ-space ($dq_1\, dp_1 \cdots dq_{3na}\, dp_{3na}$) is not the same for A and B.[4]

In general, the indices η for the several systems will differ from those given by equation (23.5–1) by a quantity $\Delta\eta$. Thus distribution B can be written

$$f' = e^{\eta + \Delta\eta}. \tag{23.5–2}$$

The quantity $\Delta\eta$ is determined by the condition that the new distribution give the same fraction of the systems between E and $E + \Delta E$:

$$\int_{E=E'}^{E=E'+\Delta E} e^{\eta + \Delta\eta}\, d\tau = \int_{E=E'}^{E=E'+\Delta E} e^{\eta}\, d\tau. \tag{23.5–3}$$

[4] The reason is that $\prod_{j=1}^{j=n} p_j^*$ is not the same for A as for B, because the corresponding values of p_j^* as given by (23.4–15) are different, since the ψ/θ for the range, ΔE, are different.

That it is possible to keep the number of systems in each energy range the same in each distribution is due to the fact that the value of $\int_{E=E'}^{E=E'+\Delta E} d\tau$ for the distribution in A is not equal to $\int_{E=E'}^{E=E'+\Delta E} d\tau$ for the distribution in B, because the quantity $\prod_{j=1}^{j=n} p_j^*$ (or its equivalent) is not the same in each one. (In the case of canonical distribution A, the quantities $\prod_{j=1}^{j=n} p_j^*$ are those that correspond to a distribution such that all systems are in equilibrium with each other within the ensemble. This is not true of ensemble B.)

Since for both distributions the sum of all fractions equals unity,

$$\int_{\text{All}}^{\text{Phases}} e^{\eta+\Delta\eta}\, d\tau = \int_{\text{All}}^{\text{Phases}} e^{\eta}\, d\tau = 1, \tag{23.5–4a}$$

which is equivalent to

$$\int_{\text{All}}^{\text{Phases}} e^{\eta}\,(1 - e^{\Delta\eta})\, d\tau = 0. \tag{23.5–4b}$$

The average value of $\eta + \Delta\eta$ for the new distribution is to be compared with the average value of η for the old distribution. That is, we must ascertain

$$\int_{\text{All}}^{\text{Phases}} (\eta + \Delta\eta)e^{\eta+\Delta\eta}\, d\tau \gtreqless \int_{\text{All}}^{\text{Phases}} \eta e^{\eta}\, d\tau. \tag{23.5–5}$$

Now η in equation (23.5–3) depends only on the energy and is constant in the range ΔE, so that both sides of the equation may be multiplied by η under the integral if the integration is limited to the range ΔE. (*It is to be noted that $\eta + \Delta\eta$, the index of the new distribution, does not satisfy the requirements that allow such a multiplication.*) Thus

$$\int_{E=E'}^{E=E'+\Delta E} \eta e^{\eta+\Delta\eta}\, d\tau = \int_{E=E'}^{E=E'+\Delta E} \eta e^{\eta}\, d\tau. \tag{23.5–6}$$

Since this is true over all ranges of E, such an equation can be set up for each range from zero to ∞. Addition of all equations yields

$$\int_{\text{All}}^{\text{Phases}} \eta e^{\eta+\Delta\eta}\, d\tau = \int_{\text{All}}^{\text{Phases}} \eta e^{\eta}\, d\tau. \tag{23.5–7}$$

Thus the average index of the new distribution (i.e., the average corresponding to left side of equation 23.5–5) is greater than that corresponding to the old (i.e., right side of 23.5–5) by $\int_{\text{All}}^{\text{Phases}} \Delta\eta e^{\eta+\Delta\eta}\, d\tau$. Thus we must find whether

$$\int_{\text{All}}^{\text{Phases}} \Delta\eta e^{\eta+\Delta\eta}\, d\tau \gtreqless 0. \tag{23.5–8}$$

By addition of (23.5–4b) this is equivalent to finding whether

$$\int_{\text{All}}^{\text{Phases}} (\Delta\eta e^{\Delta\eta} + 1 - e^{\Delta\eta})e^{\eta}\, d\tau \gtreqless 0. \tag{23.5–9}$$

Since e^{η} is always positive, this amounts to finding whether the quantity in parentheses is equal to, greater than, or less than zero. For $\Delta\eta$ equal to zero it is obviously zero. Differentiation with respect to $\Delta\eta$ yields $\Delta\eta e^{\Delta\eta}$. For positive $\Delta\eta$ this quantity is always positive, and for negative $\Delta\eta$ it is always negative. Thus, as $\Delta\eta$ passes from large negative to large positive values, the function in parentheses in equation (23.5–9) *can only decrease* from positive values to zero at $\Delta\eta = 0$ and then *increases again* to positive values. Thus the left side of (23.5–9) is always positive or zero, and therefore the average index of the distribution given by (23.5–2) is greater than that given by (23.5–1), and the theorem is proved.

Theorem B. If θ is any positive constant, the average value of $\eta + (E/\theta)$ (where η and E have their usual significance) is less when the ensemble is distributed canonically with modulus θ than for any other distribution whatever.

The general canonical distribution with modulus θ' is, of course,

$$f' = e^{(\psi - E)/\theta'}. \tag{23.5–10}$$

The theorem says not only that the average value of $(\eta + E/\theta)$ is least when θ' of a canonical distribution is equal to θ, but also that it is less than for any distribution f other than canonical distribution with modulus θ. If the canonical distribution function with modulus θ is

$$f = e^{(\psi - E)/\theta}, \tag{23.5–11}$$

with *any* other distribution function including that of equation (23.5–10), let it be

$$f' = e^{(\psi - E)/\theta + \Delta\eta}. \tag{23.5–12}$$

For the canonical distribution, $\eta + E/\theta$ is equal to the constant ψ/θ, while for the other distribution it is $\psi/\theta + \Delta\eta$. Thus it is to be proved that

$$\int_{\text{All}}^{\text{Phases}} \frac{\psi}{\theta}\, e^{(\psi - E)/\theta}\, d\tau < \int_{\text{All}}^{\text{Phases}} \left(\frac{\psi}{\theta} + \Delta\eta\right) e^{(\psi - E)/\theta + \Delta\eta}\, d\tau. \tag{23.5–13}$$

But, as previously for both distributions,

$$\int_{\text{All}}^{\text{Phases}} e^{(\psi - E)/\theta}\, d\tau = \int_{\text{All}}^{\text{Phases}} e^{(\psi - E)/\theta + \Delta\eta}\, d\tau = 1. \tag{23.5–14}$$

Since ψ/θ is a constant, it may be taken outside the integral on the left side of equation (23.5–13). Thus in view of equation (23.5–14) the left-hand side of equation (23.5–13) is equal to ψ/θ and also can be written

$$\int_{\text{All}}^{\text{Phases}} \frac{\psi}{\theta}\, e^{(\psi-E)/\theta+\Delta\eta}\, d\tau.$$

Thus equation (23.5–13) can be written

$$0 < \int_{\text{All}}^{\text{Phases}} \Delta\eta e^{(\psi-E)/\theta+\Delta\eta}\, d\tau. \tag{23.5–15}$$

Since $(\psi - E)/\theta$ is equal to η, this equation is exactly the inequality (23.5–8) for which it is proved that the $\geqq$ signs apply. Thus the theorem is proved.

23.6 Effect of Certain Processes on a Canonical Ensemble. The Second Law of Thermodynamics

First let us consider two canonical ensembles [1] and [2] distributed with moduli θ_1 and θ_2. Let us think of each as containing the same number N of systems. To be specific, let [1] be thin-walled containers which are perfect heat insulators of volume V, each with n_1 molecules of hydrogen ($a_1 = 2$ atoms) in each, while [2] consists of thin-walled containers also of volume V, but with n_2 molecules of helium ($a_2 = 1$ atom). Thus for systems [1] and [2] there are respectively $3n_1a_1$ and $3n_2a_2$ degrees of freedom.

The containers of each of the two ensembles are paired off by the following process: The two containers are brought into contact in a convenient manner, but so that there is no interaction between them. A thermally insulated shutter in the [2] systems closes a wall in the [1] systems, which is permeable only to [1]. This has been previously closed by another shutter, opened after contact. This shutter in the [2] systems is opened and by means of a piston (external body), the n_1 molecules of [1] are all forced into the other container (of volume V) which contains n_2 molecules of [2]. Meanwhile a piston, in the second container, permeable to [2] only is moved back so as to keep the density of [1] always constant. Let η_{12}' refer to the combined systems and η_1' and η_2' respectively of the separate systems before the shutter is opened. There is no interaction between them; thus for each pair

$$e^{\eta_{12}'} = e^{\eta_1'}e^{\eta_2'} \tag{23.6–1a}$$

or

$$\eta_{12}' = \eta_1' + \eta_2', \tag{23.6–1b}$$

and, averaged over the ensemble,

$$\bar{\eta}_{12}' = \bar{\eta}_1' + \bar{\eta}_2'. \tag{23.6–2}$$

Similarly,

$$\bar{E}_1' + \bar{E}_2' = \bar{E}_{12}' \tag{23.6–3}$$

for the energies of the combined and uncombined systems.

After the shutter has been opened, while the system [1] is being forced into the container [2], there is a weak interaction between the systems (in this case collisions at least). (*Note.* If there were no interactions the systems would be separated by a reversal of the mixing process and would be the same as before.) The interaction causes exchange of energy between the two systems, and they will tend toward a canonical distribution with a common θ. Let the index of the distribution be η_{12}'' after a suitable time of interaction.

If one assumes that the interaction is small, there is no change in energy in allowing the systems to interact since the work done by the two pistons exactly cancels, because the force exerted by [1] on the external bodies is assumed to depend only on the density (kept constant) and not on the presence of the other system. If there is appreciable interaction, the force exerted on the pistons will be changed as a result of interaction and net work will be done on or by the systems.

Actually the thermal contact could have been made by pressing the containers together. In this case the pressure making the contact is assumed to be so small as to produce no distortion in the containers. Thus again no work is done. In very low temperature experiments where heat capacities are small, there is appreciable heating when such a contact is made.

Since the distribution with respect to the energy is thus unchanged, theorem A of the last section applies, since before interaction the distribution in the paired systems is *not* canonical. Thus

$$\bar{\eta}_{12}'' \leqq \bar{\eta}_{12}'. \tag{23.6–4}$$

After a sufficient time of interaction the two systems are separated by a reversal of the mixing process. If the interaction was weak, the final indices $\bar{\eta}_1''$ and $\bar{\eta}_2''$ will be related to that of the combined systems by

$$\bar{\eta}_1'' + \bar{\eta}_2'' = \bar{\eta}_{12}''. \tag{23.6–5a}$$

However, if the interaction is appreciable, the systems of the mixture are not independent. This causes the average index of the combined system to be greater than if they are separate.[5] Thus

$$\bar{\eta}_1'' + \bar{\eta}_2'' < \bar{\eta}_{12}'' \tag{23.6–5b}$$

and

$$\bar{\eta}_1'' + \bar{\eta}_2'' \leqq \bar{\eta}_1' + \bar{\eta}_2'. \tag{23.6–6}$$

[5] Equations (23.6–5a) and (23.6–5b) may seem to the reader obvious corollaries of theorems A and B. The proof of these equations follows the same lines as those of the previous theorems. It is given in detail by Gibbs (*op. cit.*, p. 133). An analogy to the situation is the fact that any interference with the laws of chance, as in cards or dice, will increase the probability of the win on the part of the one who causes the interference.

This corresponds to the second law in the form that states that in any process involving an isolated system

$$dS \geqq 0. \tag{23.6–7}$$

It is also possible to apply theorem B. Consider now that the contact is made by pressing the containers together. Consider that each of the ensembles of systems, before combining, was distributed canonically with moduli θ_1 and θ_2, respectively. However, if the systems are allowed to interact independently and are finally separated, they will no longer be canonically distributed with these moduli but each with a single modulus θ. Thus

$$\bar{\eta}_1' + \frac{\bar{E}_1'}{\theta_1} \leqq \bar{\eta}_1'' + \frac{\bar{E}_1''}{\theta_1} \tag{23.6–8}$$

and

$$\bar{\eta}_2' + \frac{\bar{E}_2'}{\theta_2} \leqq \bar{\eta}_2'' + \frac{\bar{E}_2''}{\theta_2}. \tag{23.6–9}$$

It is to be noted that the inequality arises from the fact that on the right side the averages are taken over distributions for which θ_1 and θ_2 are not the moduli (they are the respective moduli for the distributions on the left). Adding the two inequalities and rearranging, we obtain

$$\bar{\eta}_1' + \bar{\eta}_2' - (\bar{\eta}_1'' + \bar{\eta}_2'') \leqq \frac{\bar{E}_1'' - \bar{E}_1'}{\theta_1} + \frac{\bar{E}_2'' - \bar{E}_2'}{\theta_2}. \tag{23.6–10}$$

Noting the inequality (23.6–6),

$$\frac{\bar{E}_1'' - \bar{E}_1'}{\theta_1} + \frac{\bar{E}_2'' - \bar{E}_2'}{\theta_2} \geqq 0. \tag{23.6–11}$$

But, if work in amount w has been done on the systems by external bodies,

$$\bar{E}_1'' + \bar{E}_2'' = \bar{E}_1' + \bar{E}_2' + w. \tag{23.6–12}$$

Since w is assumed to be negligible, (23.6–11) may be written

$$(\bar{E}_1'' - \bar{E}_1')\left(\frac{1}{\theta_1} - \frac{1}{\theta_2}\right) \geqq 0. \tag{23.6–13}$$

If $\bar{E}_1'' - \bar{E}_1'$ is positive (system [1] has gained energy), $\theta_1 < \theta_2$ (i.e., the system gaining energy has the lower θ (temperature)); hence the thermodynamic principle that heat flows from the higher to the lower temperature. Let us now imagine that the distribution of systems [1] is not determined. Even so, after combining, the system will tend toward a canonical distribution with modulus θ. Thus, after separating, (23.6–6) applies.

Similarly, since the system [2] was initially canonically distributed with modulus θ_2, equation (23.6–9) applies. It is convenient to think of the systems [2] as forming a heat reservoir. By rewriting (23.6–9)

$$\bar{\eta}_2' - \bar{\eta}_2'' \lesseqgtr \frac{\bar{E}_2'' - \bar{E}_2'}{\theta_2}, \tag{23.6–14}$$

and using (23.6–6) in the form

$$\bar{\eta}_2' - \bar{\eta}_2'' \geqq \bar{\eta}_1'' - \bar{\eta}_1', \tag{23.6–15}$$

we obtain

$$\bar{\eta}_1'' - \bar{\eta}_1' \lesseqgtr \frac{\bar{E}_2'' - \bar{E}_2'}{\theta_2}. \tag{23.6–16}$$

We note that entropy is identified with $-\bar{\eta}$, so that this corresponds to the thermodynamic principle that the entropy decrease in a system when placed in contact with a bath must always be algebraically less than the heat gained by the bath divided by the temperature of the bath. Finally, it is instructive to consider the case when w is not only not negligible but an attempt is made to make it as large as possible. This time let each of the systems of the ensembles [1] and [2] be brought into contact only indirectly by contact with a third system. The third systems form an ensemble. By use of pistons the volumes of the systems of the third ensemble are changed so as to keep their distribution as close to canonical at all times during their contact with the systems [1] and [2] (heat reservoirs). Before the systems of the third ensemble are separated, their coordinates (volumes) and momenta are brought back to their initial values. An example of such a process is the Carnot cycle. The ensemble of third systems thus suffers no change.

Equation (23.6–11) must now be written

$$\frac{\bar{E}_1'' - \bar{E}_1'}{\theta_1} - \frac{\bar{E}_1'' - \bar{E}_1'}{\theta_2} \geqq -\frac{w}{\theta_2} \tag{23.6–17}$$

or

$$\frac{w}{\bar{E}_1' - \bar{E}_1''} \leqq \frac{\theta_1 - \theta_2}{\theta_1}. \tag{23.6–18}$$

The equality sign applies when the distribution is kept canonical at all times. This equation can be regarded as the expression for the efficiency of a heat engine in which a quantity of energy $(E' - E'')$ is transferred from the systems [1] to the systems [2]. It can also be regarded as a way of directly identifying θ with the thermodynamic temperature. This illustration shows the statistical mechanical meaning of work, perhaps more clearly than the qualitative discussion in Section 23.4.

23.7 The System Partition Function

In Section 23.4 we have seen that ψ is to be identified with the Helmholtz free energy A. The definition of ψ is

$$\psi = -\theta \ln \int_{\text{All}}^{\text{Phases}} e^{-E/\theta}\, d\tau. \tag{23.4–22b}$$

However, according to equation (23.4–12b) an alternative definition is

$$\psi = -\theta \ln \sum_{\text{All}}^{\text{Energies}} \mathbf{P}_i e^{-E_i/\theta}, \tag{23.7–1}$$

where the summation is made over groups of quantum states according to their energies. If the summation is made over individual quantum states, the definition is

$$\psi = -\theta \ln \sum_{\text{All}}^{\text{States}} e^{-E_j/\theta}. \tag{23.7–2}$$

A comparison of this equation with (21.5–4) makes it evident that the equivalent quantities

$$\int_{\text{All}}^{\text{Phases}} e^{-E/\theta}\, d\tau, \qquad \sum_{\text{All}}^{\text{Energies}} \mathbf{P}_i e^{-E_i/\theta}, \qquad \sum_{\text{All}}^{\text{States}} e^{-E_j/\theta}$$

are all generalizations of the system partition function of which $K(T,V,n)$ of Section 21.5 was an example for a crystal. In the case of a crystal there is no division by $n!$ in the expression for $\mathbf{P}_i$, as was done in equation (23.4–16), because, as pointed out in Section 21.1, a crystal is a localized system in which the elements are the modes of vibration. Each of these modes is distinguishable.

In the case of the system partition function for a gas, division by $n!$ is necessary since the individual molecules are not identifiable. If, and only if, there is no interaction can the system partition function be fashioned into the product of the partition functions for the individual molecules, as used in Section 18.7, which led to the expression for the Helmholtz free energy A,

$$A - E_0^\circ = -kT \ln \frac{Q^n}{n!}, \tag{18.7–21}$$

for the non-interacting molecules of a perfect gas. Reference to (23.7–2) for the system partition function makes it clear that, for n non-interacting like molecules with states of energy ϵ_j,

$$\sum_{\text{All}}^{\text{States}} e^{-E_j/\theta} = \frac{\left(\sum_{\text{All}}^{\text{States}} e^{-\epsilon_j/kT}\right)^n}{n!}, \tag{23.7–3}$$

where the sum on the right side is taken over all states of the molecule. The division by $n!$ eliminates states which would be created by interchanges of identical molecules.

It is equally clear that in the deduction of a theoretical equation of state for gases, when the molecules interact, the equivalent equations (23.4–22) for the Helmholtz free energy must be used.

Gibbs considers the probability of a system differing from its average energy. On this basis he shows that the thermodynamic properties are ordinarily unaffected by such differences.

23.8 The Microcanonical Ensemble

In Chapter 17 we considered an ensemble of systems all having the energy E (or, more strictly, with energy between E and $E + \Delta E$) and used the maximum properties of such an ensemble to derive expressions for the distribution of molecules among the energy levels in the most probable state. In Chapter 18 we used a relation between entropy and probability to derive expressions for the thermodynamic quantities in terms of the energies of the molecules. By probability we meant a quantity which was proportional to the number of quantum states that correspond to the thermodynamic state of the system.

In Section 23.4 we considered an ensemble in which systems with all possible energies were distributed according to a law, the *canonical distribution*. In deriving relations of the thermodynamic quantities to the energies of the systems we equated the entropy to the modulus of the distribution taken with the negative sign. It now remains to show that these methods are equivalent within the limitations of the former method.

In Section 23.4 the canonical distribution was shown to be the most probable distribution of the systems of the ensemble among the possible energies. The law was finally written in a form which (slightly rearranged) is

$$N_i = N\,\mathbf{P}_i e^{\psi/\theta} e^{-E_i/\theta}. \tag{23.8–1}$$

Since $e^{\psi/\theta}$ is a constant, N_i would be greatest when E_i had its lowest possible value and would decrease exponentially as E_i increased, were it not for the quantity $\mathbf{P}_i$. Actually there is a value of E_i for which N_i has a very strong maximum. This is due to the fact that $\mathbf{P}_i$ has its lowest value for the lowest value of E_i (there is only one way of giving the systems their lowest energy) and increases as E_i increases. [This can be seen qualitatively by reference to the approximate expression for $\mathbf{P}_i$,

$$\mathbf{P}_i = \Sigma \mathbf{P}_D = \sum_{n_k} \prod_k \frac{p_k^{\,n_k}}{n_k!}, \tag{23.8–2}$$

given as equation (23.4–2).] However, the lowest energy of a system can be obtained only when all elements are in the lowest group of quantum states (Einstein–Bose) or when one is in each of the lowest states (Fermi–Dirac). If, as is usually the case, the lowest quantum state for the Einstein–Bose and each of the lowest states for the Fermi–Dirac case have p_k equal to unity, equation (23.8–2) does not apply. Reference to equations (17.5–4) (Einstein–Bose) and (17.6–3) (Fermi–Dirac; here p_k for the group of states will be equal to n_k) shows that there is, in fact, only one way of giving the system its lowest energy if the lowest states are non-degenerate.] The maximum value of N_i, referred to above, which occurs where the value of the energy is equal to E is overwhelmingly greater than the value of N_i for which the energy has the values $E \pm \Delta E$. This is true for negligibly small values of ΔE. Let us denote this value of E by E_{max} and the value of $\mathbf{P}_i$ and N_i corresponding to E_{max} by $\mathbf{P}_{\text{max}}$ and N_{max} respectively.

The expression for the entropy in terms of the canonical ensemble is given by equation (23.4–14):

$$S = -\bar{\eta} = -\Sigma \mathbf{P}_i \frac{\psi - E_i}{\theta} e^{(\psi - E_i)/\theta}. \tag{23.4–14}$$

Because of the strong maximum for $\mathbf{P}_i e^{\psi - E_i/\theta}$ at E_{max}, terms in the sum except that for which E_i is equal to E_{max} may be neglected. Thus (23.4–14) becomes

$$S = -\bar{\eta} = -\mathbf{P}_{\text{max}} \frac{\psi - E_{\text{max}}}{\theta} e^{(\psi - E_{\text{max}})/\theta}, \tag{23.8–3}$$

but, according to equation (23.4–11) $e^{(\psi - E_{\text{max}})/\theta}$ can be replaced by $N_{\text{max}}/N\mathbf{P}_{\text{max}}$. However, the value of N_{max}, the number of systems with E_{max} is almost equal to the total number N. Thus

$$S = -\bar{\eta} = -\left(\frac{\psi - E_{\text{max}}}{\theta}\right). \tag{23.8–4}$$

This shows that the entropy can be expressed in terms of the most probable energy. But, according to equation (23.4–11),

$$\frac{\psi - E_{\text{max}}}{\theta} = \ln \frac{N_{\text{max}}}{N\mathbf{P}_{\text{max}}}. \tag{23.8–5}$$

Thus using equation (23.8–4),

$$S = -\ln \frac{N_{\text{max}}}{N\mathbf{P}_{\text{max}}}. \tag{23.8–6}$$

If, and only if, N_{max} is sufficiently nearly equal to the total number N,

$$S = \ln \mathbf{P}_{\text{max}}. \tag{23.8–7}$$

Except for the factor k, this is similar to the expression given in equation (18.1–9) from which the entropy for non-localized systems was later calculated (equation 18.4–3). Because θ is identified with the temperature, the energy is in units of temperature in all the equations of this chapter. In Chapter 18 kT is used where θ is used in this chapter. After converting to the proper units, (23.8–7) is still not exactly equivalent to (18.1–9). Previously we have seen that

$$\mathbf{P}_i = \sum_{n_k} \prod_k \frac{p_k^{n_k}}{n_k!}. \tag{23.4–2}$$

As a reminder, we note that the distribution laws derived in Chapter 17 all maximized expressions for $\mathbf{P}$ as the n_k were varied. In Section 18.4 it was shown that all these expressions reduced to the form

$$\mathbf{P}_D = \prod_k \frac{p_k^{n_k}}{n_k!} \tag{23.4–1}$$

after the value in the Boltzmann case had been divided by $n!$ to allow for the indistinguishability of the elements.

Thus all the terms, except one, in the sum (23.8–2) refer to distributions of the elements other than the most probable one. They are thus negligible compared to the value of $\mathbf{P}_D$ for the most probable distribution. Thus, after energy units are changed, equation (23.8–7) becomes

$$S = k \ln \prod_k \frac{p_k^{n_k}}{n_k!}, \tag{23.8–8}$$

where the n_k are for the most probable distribution. This is identical with equation (18.4–3).

Actually it matters little whether we take

$$S = k \ln \Sigma \mathbf{P}_D \tag{23.8–9}$$

or

$$S = k \ln \mathbf{P}_{D_{\max}}, \tag{23.8–10}$$

where $\mathbf{P}_{D_{\max}}$ is for the most probable distribution. If the former is taken, $\Sigma\mathbf{P}_D$ is equal to the total number of states which the system can occupy when it has the most probable value of the energy. If the latter is taken, $\mathbf{P}_{D_{\max}}$ refers to the number of states corresponding to the most probable distribution of the most probable energy among the molecules.

Finally, if we take

$$S = k \ln \int_0^E \Omega(E)\, \mathrm{d}E, \tag{23.8–11}$$

where Ω(E) represents the number of states between E and $E + \mathrm{d}E$, we are taking the entropy as k times the natural logarithm of the number of states below the energy E. We are including relatively few more states, and the definition is equally good. This is the definition of the entropy given by Mayer and Mayer.[6] It serves as the starting point of their elucidation of thermodynamic properties, a somewhat novel version of the Gibbs treatment which the reader will find interesting and instructive.

23.9 The Method of Fowler

This section may be read to advantage even by students with a paucity of mathematical background. However, it has been kept in mind that many students these days understand complex variable theory. The method makes use of certain theorems relating to the complex variable z. From what has been said in the foregoing section it is clear that the coefficient C of the term in z^E in the power series expansion of

$$[f(z)]^n = (p_0 z^{\epsilon_0} + p_1 z^{\epsilon_1} + p_2 z^{\epsilon_2} + \cdots)^n \tag{23.9–1}$$

is

$$C = n! \sum_{n_1, n_2, \text{etc}} \prod_k \frac{p_k^{n_k}}{n_k!}, \tag{23.9–2}$$

where

$$E = \sum_k n_k \epsilon_k \tag{23.9–3}$$

and

$$n = \Sigma n_k. \tag{23.9–4}$$

Problem 23.9-1. Obtain the value of the coefficient of z^E by direct multiplication, and compare your answer with C as given by equation (23.9–2).

By using the theory of a complex variable it can be shown that

$$C = \frac{1}{2\pi i} \oint \frac{f(z)^n}{z^E} \frac{dz}{z}. \tag{23.9–5}$$

We have thus a way of expressing $\Sigma \mathbf{P}_D$ of the last section. The value of the average energy $\bar{E}$ is given by

$$\sum_{n_1, n_2, \text{etc}} \frac{n!}{\Pi n_k!} \sum_k n_k \epsilon_k = (\Sigma \mathbf{P}_D)\bar{E} = C\bar{E}. \tag{23.9–6}$$

It is easy to show that the left side of equation (23.9–6) is given by the coefficient of z^E in the power series expansion of

$$z \frac{\partial}{\partial z} [f(z)]^n = nz[f(z)]^n \frac{\partial \ln f(z)}{\partial z}. \tag{23.9–7}$$

[6] Mayer and Mayer, *op. cit.*, p. 87.

Problem 23.9-2. (a) Verify the last statement by direct multiplication followed by differentiation on the left side of the identity.
(b) Prove the right side of the identity in (23.9–7).

Thus

$$\frac{1}{2\pi i}\oint \frac{[f(z)]^n}{(z)^E}\left\{nz\,\frac{\partial \ln f(z)}{\partial z}\right\}\frac{dz}{z} = C\bar{E}. \tag{23.9–8}$$

The integrand in equation (23.9–8) is equal to that in (23.9–5) multiplied by the extra factor $\{nz\,\partial \ln f(z)/\partial z\}$.

Each of the integrals is characterized by the fact that the quantity enclosed in [ ] which multiplies dz/z has a unique minimum along the positive axis of real z at $z = \theta$. The integrations can, of course, be performed around a contour which is a circle of radius θ with the origin as center; that is, $z = \theta e^{i\alpha}$. Along this contour the modulus of the factor [ ] has a maximum at $\alpha = 0$ (i.e., at $z = \theta$), and the differential coefficient of the integral vanishes at $\alpha = 0$. The maximum becomes very strong as n and E become very large (E/n being held constant). Thus the entire contribution to the integrals comes from values of α near zero and all complex terms vanish. For this reason the factor $\{nz\,\partial \ln f(z)/\partial z\}$ (or factors like it) contained in [ ] may be factored outside the integral sign as $n\theta\,\partial \ln f(\theta)/\partial\theta$ and the integrals cancelled.[7] Thus

$$\bar{E} = n\theta\,\frac{\partial \ln f(\theta)}{\partial\theta} \tag{23.9–9}$$

or

$$\bar{E} = \frac{\partial \ln [f(\theta)]^n}{\partial \ln \theta}. \tag{23.9–10}$$

If $\ln\theta$ is taken as $-(kT)^{-1}$ and $\bar{E}$ is interpreted as the energy of each of the N localized systems of a microcanonical ensemble, equation (23.9–10) is identical with equation (18.2–7).

Problem 23.9-3. Show that, with θ thus defined, (a)

$$f(\theta) \equiv \Sigma p_i e^{-\epsilon_i/kT} = Q\,; \tag{23.9–11}$$

(b) $f(\theta)^n$ is the system partition function for n non-interacting localized elements; (c) equation (23.9–10) leads directly to equation (18.2–7).

Moreover expressions for the average heat capacity, entropy, and Helmholtz free energy can be derived by making use of the usual thermodynamic relations. At no time is the Stirling approximation used; thus

[7] R. Fowler and E. A. Guggenheim, *Statistical Thermodynamics*, Cambridge University Press, 1949, p. 35. (See also R. Fowler, *Statistical Mechanics*, Cambridge University Press, 1936.

confusion is eliminated for cases where n_i is small in $n_i!$ The approximations involved in taking the contour integral are used instead. However, these relations become exact when $n(=\sum_k n_k)$ and $E\ (=\sum_k n_k\epsilon_k)$ are large. As shown in Problem 23.9–3 the function $f(\theta)$ is the partition function which we used in Chapter 17.

By using the same method values can be deduced for $\bar{n}_i$, the average number of molecules with the energy ϵ_i for localized systems, in which the value of $\bar{n}_i$ is the average over all distributions $\mathbf{P}_D$, not only the value for the most probable distribution.

Similarly values of $\bar{n}_i$ can be deduced for the non-localized ensembles for the Einstein–Bose and Fermi–Dirac cases by using similar methods and at the same time generalized expressions deduced for the thermodynamic properties of non-localized systems. These expressions are those deduced in Section 18.12.

23.10 The Grand Partition Function

Up to this point all systems of the ensembles under consideration, canonical or microcanonical, have contained the same number of elements. We have explained the thermodynamic properties of a system in terms of the average energies and in terms of the average forces exerted by the elements composing the systems. Energy could be lost from a system either by transfer of kinetic energy to another system or by the system doing work on an external body.

In Chapter 15 the partial molal free energy μ_i of a constituent of a system was defined as

$$\left(\frac{\partial E}{\partial n_i}\right)_{S,x_i} = \mu_i, \tag{23.10–1}$$

where x_i stands for the variables such as surface and volume.

With the use of the quantities μ_i, an expression was obtained for the electrical work performed in a galvanic cell. Thus one can think of an element (atom or molecule) as carrying energy with it. When it disappears from a system, this energy is *all* converted into electrical work provided there is *no change in entropy* and *no work done against external bodies* (the x_i are all constant).

In the previous sections the value of the canonical ensemble lay in the fact that it considered systems of variable energy and traced this variation of external energy to reversible transfer of kinetic energy (change in entropy of surroundings) and to work done against external bodies. To consider changes of energy in a galvanic cell, variation of energy due to loss of elements from the system must be considered; this requires a different type of ensemble.

Instead of arbitrarily picking an ensemble suited to the purpose and explaining the reason for the choice we shall attempt to pick the kind of ensemble we need by using logical considerations, as we did with the canonical ensemble. The procedure is essentially the same as that used in arriving at the canonical ensemble except that each system has a variable number of elements in it. Thus there are N systems in the ensemble, N_i of which have the energy E_i, and a number of elements of the νth kind, which we shall denote by ν_i. More specifically, there will be a_i elements of the kind a, b_i elements of the kind b, etc., in each system, so that ν can be a, b, etc. The label of the kind is thus used to symbolize its number also. The subscript i is required since the number of each kind differs from system to system. By this means an extra subscript is avoided (ν is used instead of n_ν). The total energy of the ensemble is constant, as in Section 23.4 with the value E_G, while the total number of elements of the νth kind in the ensemble has a constant value which will be denoted by ν_G.

As in Section 23.4, the number of ways in which the $N_1, N_2, \cdots, N_i$, etc., distinguishable systems can be assigned to groups of states with energies $E_1, E_2, \cdots, E_i$, etc., is

$$\mathscr{P} = \frac{N! \prod_i \mathbf{P}_i^{N_i}}{\prod_i N_i!}, \tag{23.10–2}$$

where there are $\mathbf{P}_i$ states in the group with energy E_i (see equation 23.4–3). The variation of $\ln \mathscr{P}$ around its maximum is subject to extra restrictions in addition to those of Section 23.4. There are equations

$$\sum_i N_i \nu_i = \nu_G \tag{23.10–3ν}$$

to be satisfied for each of the ν. There is an equation like (23.10–3ν) for each of the elements that constitute the ensemble. Thus, through use of the method employed in Section 17.4, the equation which expresses that $\ln \mathscr{P}$ is a maximum subject to the restrictions placed by equations (23.10–3ν) as well as those of equations (23.4–4) and (23.4–5) is

$$\sum_i (\ln N_i - \ln \mathbf{P}_i + \beta E_i + \alpha + \sum_\nu \gamma_\nu \nu_i)\, dN_i = 0, \tag{23.10–4}$$

where the sum $\sum_\nu$ *inside* the parentheses is taken over the ν kinds of elements. There is an undetermined multiplier γ_ν for each ν.

Problem 23.10-1. Derive equation (23.10–4) by methods analogous to those used in Sections 17.4 and 23.4, noting that equations (23.10–3ν) each require an undetermined multiplier γ_ν.

Thus

$$N_i = \mathbf{P}_i e^{-(\beta E_i + \alpha + \sum_\nu \gamma_\nu \nu_i)}. \tag{23.10–5}$$

Problem 23.10-2. Outline the argument that leads to equation (23.10–5).

By replacing Ne^α by $e^{-\Omega/\theta}$ as well as each γ_ν by $-\mu_\nu/\theta$, and identifying θ with β^{-1}, as was also done in Section 23.4, one obtains

$$\left(\frac{N_i}{N}\right) = \mathbf{P}_i e^{(\Omega - E_i + \sum_\nu \mu_\nu \nu_i)/\theta}. \tag{23.10–6}$$

$\mathbf{P}_i$ is now to be replaced, as in Section 23.4, by an expression of the type

$$\mathbf{P}_i = \prod_{j=1}^{j=3a\sum_\nu \nu_i} \frac{\mathrm{dq}_j\, \mathrm{dp}_j}{h^{3a\prod_\nu \nu_i}}. \tag{23.10–7}$$

It will be noted that $\mathbf{P}_i$ is not the same for each system, since the value of the ν_i is different in each system; that is, the number of molecules of each type is different in each system.

It is possible to collect all N_i systems with these values the same, say at ν_i, to form what Gibbs calls a *petit* ensemble of N_i systems, and to treat them as we did those for the canonical ensemble. Thus we have been able to write an expression for a value of the probability that one of the systems which has the number of elements of a species ν with the value ν_i will also have the energy E_i. This expression is that just given in equation (23.10–6) with $\mathbf{P}_i$ given by equation (23.10–7). The probability that a system will have particular values of ν_i for each of the species irrespective of the energy is given by

$$\frac{N_i}{N} = \int_{\text{All}}^{\text{Phases*}} \frac{1}{\prod_\nu \nu_i!} e^{(\Omega - E_i + \sum \mu_\nu \nu_i)/\theta}\, \mathrm{d}\tau; \tag{23.10–8}$$

here $\mathrm{d}\tau$ is in the same units as in Section 23.4, equal to

$$\prod_{i=1}^{i=3a\sum_\nu \nu_i} \mathrm{dq}_j\, \mathrm{dp}_j.$$

The asterisk on the limits denotes that the integration is now taken to extend over *the whole volume* corresponding to all positions and momenta of all ν_i, etc., elements. Since this *counts interchanges between identifiable elements*, the division by $\prod_\nu \nu_i!$ must be made. This factor was not included in Section 23.4 because the integration was taken only over regions of the space which did not include such interchanges. *If the elements are the modes of vibration of a crystal, this division must not be made.*

Phases which are considered different after interchange of like elements are called by Gibbs *specific* phases. Phases which are unchanged (considered the same) after an interchange of like elements between coordinates and momenta are called *generic* phases. It will be noted that in the case of gases such interchanges between elements do not give distinguishable new configurations even for classical elements (if there were such) which in themselves are identifiable. In this section the integration is over specific phases. In Section 23.4 the integration was over generic phases. Because Gibbs did not limit his integrations in this manner, there is a possibility of confusion which he clarifies in his last chapter. If the limits of integration are suitably chosen for the canonical ensemble, the P_i will correspond to Boltzmann, Einstein–Bose, or Fermi–Dirac systems.

In contradistinction to the *petit* canonical ensemble, where the collection of systems which have the number of elements of each kind with a particular value ν_i and with any of the possible values of the energy, the entire ensemble is called a *grand* (canonical) ensemble.

Now the extensive thermodynamic properties of the canonical ensembles which we have considered previously are obviously proportional to the constant number of elements contained in each system. Thus ψ_i, the value of ψ associated with a *petit* ensemble with ν_i, etc., of each of the elements of the different kinds, is proportional to the number of each. In view of this fact equation (23.10–8) becomes

$$\frac{N_i}{N} = \frac{1}{\prod_\nu \nu_i!} e^{(\Omega - \psi_i + \sum_\nu \mu_\nu \nu_i)/\theta}, \tag{23.10–9}$$

where ψ_i is defined by

$$e^{-\psi_i/\theta} = \int_{\text{All}}^{\text{Phases*}} e^{-E_i/\theta}\, d\tau, \tag{23.10–10}$$

the volume element being that appropriate to the number of elements in the *petit* ensemble chosen. It should be noted that exchanges of identical particles have not here been eliminated by the limits of integration. That is, ψ_i is obtained by integration over specific phases.

The value of Ω may now be determined by the relation

$$1 = \sum_i \frac{1}{\prod_\nu \nu_i!} e^{(\Omega - \psi_i + \sum_\nu \mu_\nu \nu_i)/\theta}; \tag{23.10–11}$$

or, returning to equation (23.10–8) which, if summed over all N_i, must yield unity, we may also write

$$e^{-\Omega/\theta} = \sum_i \frac{1}{\prod_\nu \nu_i!} \int_{\text{All}}^{\text{Phases}} e^{(\sum_\nu \mu_\nu \nu_i - E_i)/\theta}\, d\tau. \tag{23.10–12}$$

The sum is to be taken over all possible values of the quantities ν_i in the product $\prod_\nu \nu_i!$ Thus Ω is a function of θ and of the quantities μ_ν as well as of the external coordinates which appear implicitly in the E_i.

The average value $\bar{u}$ of any quantity u which is a function of the ν_i and the q's and p's is obtained from the equation

$$\bar{u} = \sum_i \frac{1}{\prod_\nu \nu_i!} \int_{\text{All}}^{\text{Phases*}} u e^{(\Omega + \sum_\nu \mu_\nu \nu_i - E_i)/\theta}\, d\tau. \tag{23.10–13}$$

Remembering the functional dependence of Ω, we can differentiate equation (23.10–12) on both sides to obtain an equation related to thermodynamics:

$$e^{-\Omega/\theta}\left(\frac{\Omega}{\theta^2}\, d\theta - \frac{d\Omega}{\theta}\right)$$

$$= -\frac{d\theta}{\theta^2}\sum_i \frac{1}{\prod_\nu \nu_i!}\int_{\text{All}}^{\text{Phases*}} \left(\sum_\nu \mu_\nu \nu_i - E_i\right) e^{(\sum_\nu \mu_\nu \nu_i - E_i)/\theta}\, d\tau$$

$$+ \sum_\nu \frac{d\mu_\nu}{\theta}\sum_i \frac{1}{\prod_\nu \nu_i!}\int_{\text{All}}^{\text{Phases*}} \nu_i e^{(\sum_\nu \mu_\nu \nu_i - E_i)/\theta}\, d\tau$$

$$-\sum_j \frac{dx_j}{\theta}\sum_i \frac{1}{\prod_\nu \nu_i!}\int_{\text{All}}^{\text{Phases*}} \frac{\partial E_i}{\partial x_j} e^{(\sum_\nu \mu_\nu \nu_i - E_i)/\theta}\, d\tau. \tag{23.10–14}$$

Noting equation (23.10–13) defining an average value and that $\partial \bar{E}_i/\partial x_j = -\bar{X}_j$, we write

$$\frac{\Omega}{\theta^2}\, d\theta - \frac{d\Omega}{\theta} = -\frac{d\theta}{\theta^2}\sum_\nu (\mu_\nu \bar{\nu} - \bar{E}) + \frac{1}{\theta}\sum_\nu \bar{\nu}\, d\mu_\nu + \frac{1}{\theta}\bar{X}_j\, dx_j. \tag{23.10–15}$$

Then we write η_i, the index of probability in a petit ensemble,

$$\eta_i = \frac{\Omega + \sum_\nu \mu_\nu \nu_i - E_i}{\theta}. \tag{23.10–16}$$

According to equation (23.10–13) the average value of η_i, which we shall denote by $\bar{\eta}_G$, is

$$\bar{\eta}_G = \Sigma \bar{\eta}_i = \sum_i \frac{1}{\prod \nu_i!}\int_{\text{All}}^{\text{Phases*}} \eta_i e^{(\Omega + \sum_\nu \mu_\nu \nu_i - E_i)/\theta}\, d\tau. \tag{23.10–17}$$

Thus

$$\bar{\eta}_G = \frac{\Omega + \sum_\nu \mu_\nu \bar{\nu} - \bar{E}}{\theta}. \tag{23.10–18}$$

Multiplying through by θ and differentiating, we obtain

$$\theta \, \mathrm{d}\bar{\eta}_G + \bar{\eta}_G \, \mathrm{d}\theta = \mathrm{d}\Omega + \sum_\nu \mu_\nu \, \mathrm{d}\bar{\nu} + \sum_\nu \bar{\nu} \, \mathrm{d}\mu_\nu - \mathrm{d}\bar{E}; \qquad (23.10\text{–}19)$$

also, rearranging equation (23.10–18),

$$\frac{\sum_\nu \mu_\nu \bar{\nu} - \bar{E}}{\theta} = \bar{\eta}_G - \frac{\Omega}{\theta}. \qquad (23.10\text{–}20)$$

Substituting this in equation (23.10–15),

$$\cdot \frac{\Omega}{\theta^2} \, \mathrm{d}\theta - \frac{\mathrm{d}\Omega}{\theta} = \left(\frac{\Omega}{\theta} - \bar{\eta}_G\right) \frac{\mathrm{d}\theta}{\theta} + \frac{1}{\theta} \sum_\nu \bar{\nu} \, \mathrm{d}\mu_\nu + \frac{1}{\theta} \bar{X}_j \, \mathrm{d}x_j. \qquad (23.10\text{–}21)$$

Thus

$$-\frac{\mathrm{d}\Omega}{\theta} = -\bar{\eta}_G \frac{\mathrm{d}\theta}{\theta} + \frac{1}{\theta} \sum_\nu \bar{\nu} \, \mathrm{d}\mu_\nu + \frac{1}{\theta} \sum_j \bar{X}_j \, \mathrm{d}x_j \qquad (23.10\text{–}22)$$

Elimination of $\mathrm{d}\Omega/\theta$ from equation (23.10–22) by using (23.10–19) yields

$$\mathrm{d}\bar{E} = -\theta \, \mathrm{d}\bar{\eta}_G + \sum_\nu \mu_\nu \, \mathrm{d}\nu - \Sigma \bar{X}_j \, \mathrm{d}x_j. \qquad (23.10\text{–}23)$$

Let us now identify θ with kT, $\bar{\eta}_G$ with $-S/k$, $\bar{E}$ with the thermodynamic energy E, $\bar{\nu}_i$ with the number of atoms or molecules of the ith kind, and ($\mathbf{N}\mu_\nu$) with the partial molal free energy μ (**N** is, of course, the Avogadro number). As in Section 23.4 (see equation 23.4–29), X_j and x_j are to be considered the usual thermodynamic variables X_j and x_j which are similar to the pressure and volume respectively. With this identification, equation (23.10–23) is identical with the thermodynamic equation

$$\mathrm{d}E = T \, \mathrm{d}S + \sum_\nu \mu_\nu \, \mathrm{d}\nu - \Sigma X_j x_j. \qquad (23.10\text{–}24)$$

This identification of θ with kT is perfectly general in the classical limit for localized and non-localized systems. For the identification of all the thermodynamic properties in the completely general case covering low temperatures and high densities (Einstein–Bose and Fermi–Dirac distributions) the integration must be carried out only over the allowed parts of the phase space. This means, among other things that regions involving interchange of identical elements are excluded; that is, integration must be made over generic phases, as was done with canonical ensembles. It is obvious that the factorial term must then be removed. This, however, would not change the argument. The integration was made over specific phases and the factorial was included here in order to have conformity with the original treatment of Gibbs.

With a little imagination the reader can now construct in his mind forces on electrical condensers analogous to those on mechanical pistons which make equation (23.10–6) identical with equation (23.4–11), remembering ψ was identified with the mechanical work and (below) Ω is identified with $-PV$. It should be noted that in the usual electromotive force cell the pressures of the components are held constant and are balanced against the atmosphere.

μ_ν having been identified with the partial molal free energy of the νth element,

$$F = \sum_\nu \nu \mu_\nu \tag{23.10–25}$$

is an expression for the Gibbs (Lewis) free energy. Then, according to equation (23.10–18), after $\bar{\eta}_G$ has been equated $-S/k$ and θ to kT,

$$\Omega = -TS - F + E. \tag{23.10–26}$$

Thus

$$\Omega = -\sum x_j X_j \tag{23.10–27}$$

or

$$kT \ln \left(\sum_i \frac{1}{\prod \nu_i!} \int_{\text{All}}^{\text{Phases}} e^{(\sum_\nu \mu_\nu \nu - E_i)/\theta} \, \mathrm{d}\tau \right) = \sum_j X_j x_j. \tag{23.10–28}$$

If pressure is the only force and volume the only variable, the right side is ΣPV. The quantity under the sum sign is often denoted by Ξ and called the "grand partition function." Thus we have another partition function which is often used in calculating theoretical equations of state:

$$PV = kT \ln \Xi. \tag{23.10–29}$$

23.11 Further Uses of Statistical Mechanics. Conclusion

The previous sections have dealt with a more generalized treatment than that by which the equations used for ideal gases and crystals were developed. This has been done partly to give an understanding of the underlying causes of the thermodynamic laws and partly to allow the reader to compare some of the equivalent developments of the subject and to understand more advanced treatises.[8]

In view of the availability of such advanced treatments, the calculation of values of λ, the absolute activity, for real gases and solutions has not been discussed in this book. The calculations of λ (fugacity) for real gases involves the same problem as evaluating the PV product. This in turn amounts to evaluating the grand partition function. The solution of the problem involves considering the energy of nearest-neighbor

[8] For example, R. Fowler and E. A. Guggenheim, *op. cit.*; T. Hill, *Statistical Mechanics*, Wiley, New York, 1956.

interaction. In liquids and solutions of non-electrolytes the problem is similar but even more complicated. Solutions of electrolytes can be treated by this method, but the reader is referred to more advanced treatises for discussion of them.

It has not seemed desirable to include detailed methods for calculating thermodynamic properties for Einstein–Bose and Fermi–Dirac gases other than in the classical limit. These calculations have a bearing on the theory of helium II and of metallic conductors as well as on the properties of gaseous helium at low temperatures, but they are quite complicated and perhaps belong more properly to physics.

The statistical mechanics adsorption of gases on solids has not been discussed. For these calculations the reader is again referred to more advanced textbooks.

Physical Constants and Useful Relationships[1]

APPENDIX 1

Velocity of light (c)	2.997902×10^{10} cm sec^{-1}
Planck constant (h)	6.62377×10^{-27} erg sec (molecule)$^{-1}$
Avogadro number (**N**)	6.02380×10^{23} molecules mole^{-1}
Faraday number ($\mathscr{F}$)	96,493.1 coulombs eq^{-1}
	23,062.4 cal (volt eq)$^{-1}$
Electronic charge (e)	1.601864×10^{-19} coulomb
	4.80223×10^{-10} esu
Rest mass of electron (m_0)	9.1085×10^{-28} g
Gas constant (R)	8.31439 joules mole^{-1} deg^{-1}
	1.98719 cal mole^{-1} deg^{-1}
	82.0567 cm^3 atm mole^{-1} deg^{-1}
	0.0820547 liter atm mole^{-1} deg^{-1}
Boltzmann constant (k)	1.380257×10^{-16} erg (molecule)$^{-1}$ deg^{-1}
Standard acceleration of gravity (g_0)	980.665 cm sec^{-2}
Standard atmosphere	1,013,250 dynes cm^{-2}
Calorie (defined)	4.1840 joules
	4.18331 international joules
	41.2929 cm^3 atm
	0.0412917 liter atm
1 volt (absolute)	0.999670 international volt = 10^8 cgsm
1 ampere (absolute)	1.000165 international amp = 10^{-1} cgsm
1 ohm (absolute)	0.999505 international ohm = 10^9 cgsm
1 joule (absolute)	0.999835 international joule

[1] All but a few of the entries in this appendix are from F. D. Rossini, F. T. Gucker, H. L. Johnston, L. Pauling, and G. W. Vinal, *J. Am. Chem. Soc.*, **74**, 2699 (1952).

Data of State

APPENDIX 2

Table A2–1
Critical and van der Waals Constants for Simple Gases

Gas	Critical Constants Temperature (°K)	Critical Constants Pressure (atm)	Critical Constants Density (g cm^{-3})	van der Waals Constants a (atm liter^2)	van der Waals Constants b (liters)
He	5.2	2.26	0.069	0.004	0.0236
Ne	44	25.9	0.484	0.242	0.0174
A	151	48	0.531	1.35	0.0323
H_2	33	12.8	0.031	0.242	0.0265
N_2	126	33.5	0.311	1.29	0.0377
O_2	154	49.7	0.430	1.30	0.0311
Cl_2	417	76	0.573	6.21	0.0550
CO	134	35	0.311	1.39	0.0384
CO_2	304	73	0.460	3.49	0.0418
H_2O	647	218	0.4	5.22	0.0298
NH_3	405	112	0.235	3.98	0.0363
SO_2	430	77.7	0.52	6.47	0.0555
CH_4	191	45.8	0.162	2.17	0.0418
C_2H_6	305	48.8	0.21	5.18	0.0627
C_3H_8	369	43		8.65	0.0863
n-C_4H_{10}	426	36		13.70	0.1187
C_2H_4	283	50.9		4.27	0.0558

The critical constants are from the *International Critical Tables*; the van der Waals constants have been calculated from T_c and P_c.

Table A2–2
Constants for the Beattie-Bridgeman Equation

Gas	A_0	a	B_0	b	c × 10^{-4}
He	0.0216	0.05984	0.01400	0.0	0.0040
Ne	0.2125	0.02196	0.02060	0.0	0.101
A	1.2907	0.02328	0.03931	0.0	5.99
H_2	0.1975	−0.00506	0.02096	−0.04359	0.0504
N_2	1.3445	0.02617	0.05046	0.00691	4.20
O_2	1.4911	0.02562	0.04624	0.00421	4.80
CO_2	5.0065	0.07132	0.10476	0.07235	66.00
NH_3	2.3930	0.17031	0.03415	0.19112	476.87
CH_4	2.2769	0.01855	0.05587	−0.01587	12.83

From J. A. Beattie and W. H. Stockmayer, in H. S. Taylor and S. Glasstone, *A Treatise on Physical Chemistry*, 3rd ed., Vol. 2, copyright 1951, D. Van Nostrand Company, Inc., Princeton, N.J.

Table A2–3
Constants for the Virial Equation

$$P\tilde{V}/RT = 1 + B/\tilde{V} + C/\tilde{V}^2 + D/\tilde{V}^4$$

Gas	Temperature (°C)	$B \times 10^3$	$C \times 10^6$	$D \times 10^8$
H_2	0	13.020	337	
	100	14.169	223	
Ne	0	9.267	580	
	20	10.78	388	
A	0	−16.89	2.5	7.79
	20.39	−12.55	310.	10.09

Values calculated from constants in Landolt-Börnstein, *Physikalisch-Chemische Tabellen*, Vol. 1, Springer, Berlin, 1923, p. 253.

Table A2–4
Constants for the Virial Equation

$$P\tilde{V}/RT = 1 + B'P + C'P^2 + W'P^3 + D'P^4$$

Gas	Temperature (°C)	$B' \times 10^3$	$C' \times 10^6$	$W' \times 10^9$	$D' \times 10^{12}$
H_2	25	0.5700	0.2561	0.2250	
N_2	0	−0.4600	3.003		−1.35
	25	−0.19148	2.1416		43.0
	50	−0.01077	1.7422		23.79
CH_4	20	−2.0236	3.723		43.59

Values calculated from constants in Landolt-Börnstein, *op. cit.*, Suppl. 3, pp. 96 ff.

Relationships for the Calculation of Partial Molal Properties for Binary Solutions

APPENDIX 3

In using the tables, one of the functions listed as y is plotted against one listed as x; the slope $\mathrm{d}y/\mathrm{d}x$ at any point is designated S; the partial molal property is then given by the expression tabulated for the particular combination of y and x used; for example, if the value of the property per mole of component 2,(G/n_2), is plotted against the mole fraction of component 2,$(\tilde{N}_2)$, $\bar{G}_1 = -\tilde{N}_2{}^2S$, from Table A.3–1, and $\bar{G}_2 = \tilde{N}_1\tilde{N}_2S + G/n_2$, from Table A3–2. The tables are taken directly from the work of Young and Vogel,[1] except for slight changes of nomenclature. The symbols used are defined below, as a matter of convenience. For further discussion of partial molal properties, the student is referred to Chapter 8.

G	value of property for solution containing n_1 moles of component 1 and n_2 moles of component 2
$\tilde{G}_1$	molal property of pure component 1
$\tilde{G}_2$	molal property of pure component 2
$\bar{G}_1$, $\bar{G}_2$	partial molal properties of components 1 and 2, respectively, in solution
G	specific property (per gram); $\mathrm{G} = G/(n_1\tilde{M}_1 + n_2\tilde{M}_2)$
n_1, n_2	moles of component 1 and component 2

[6] From T. F. Young and O. G. Vogel, *J. Am. Chem. Soc.*, **54**, 3025 (1932).

$\tilde{N}_1, \tilde{N}_2$	mole fractions of component 1 and component 2
$\tilde{M}_1, \tilde{M}_2$	molecular weights of components 1 and 2
m	molality
r_1	n_1/n_2; $r_2 = n_2/n_1$
ϕ	$(G - n_1\tilde{G}_1)/n_2$ (see Chapter 8)
Δ	$G - (n_1\tilde{G}_1 + n_2\tilde{G}_2)$ (see Chapter 8)
y	ordinate; x = abscissa; S = slope = $(\mathrm{d}y/\mathrm{d}x)$
C	any constant
k	any exponent

Table A3–I
Formulas for the calculation of $\bar{G}_1$

$y \downarrow \quad x \rightarrow$	$\bar{G}_1$: $\tilde{N}_1$	$\tilde{N}_2$	m	$m^{1/2}$
$\frac{G}{n_2} + C$	$\tilde{N}_2{}^2 S$	$-\tilde{N}_2{}^2 S$	$-\frac{mS}{r_1}$	$-\frac{m^{1/2}S}{2r_1}$
$\frac{G}{n_1 + n_2} + C$	$\tilde{N}_2 S + y - C$	$-\tilde{N}_2 S + y - C$	$-\frac{mS}{\tilde{N}_1} + y - C$	$-\frac{m^{1/2}S}{2\tilde{N}_1} + y - C$
$\frac{n_1 + n_2}{G} + C$	$-\frac{\tilde{N}_2 S}{(y - C)^2} + \frac{1}{y - C}$	$\frac{\tilde{N}_2 S}{(y - C)^2} + \frac{1}{y - C}$	$\frac{mS}{\tilde{N}_1(y - C)^2} + \frac{1}{y - C}$	$\frac{m^{1/2}S}{2\tilde{N}_1(y - C)^2} + \frac{1}{y - C}$
$\phi + C$	$\tilde{G}_1 + \tilde{N}_2{}^2 S$	$\tilde{G}_1 - \tilde{N}_2{}^2 S$	$\tilde{G}_1 - \frac{mS}{r_1}$	$\tilde{G}_1 - \frac{m^{1/2}S}{2r_1}$
Δ	$\tilde{G}_1 + y + \tilde{N}_2 S$	$\tilde{G}_1 + y - \tilde{N}_2 S$	$\tilde{G}_1 + y - \frac{mS}{\tilde{N}_1}$	$\tilde{G}_1 + y - \frac{m^{1/2}S}{2\tilde{N}_1}$
G	$\tilde{M}_1\left[y + \left(\tilde{N}_1\tilde{N}_2 + \frac{\tilde{N}_2{}^2\tilde{M}_2}{\tilde{M}_1}\right)S\right]$	$\tilde{M}_1\left[y - \left(\tilde{N}_1\tilde{N}_2 + \frac{\tilde{N}_2{}^2\tilde{M}_2}{\tilde{M}_1}\right)S\right]$	$\tilde{M}_1\left[y - \left(m + \frac{\tilde{M}_2 m^2}{1000}\right)S\right]$	$\tilde{M}_1\left[y - \left(\frac{m^{1/2}}{2} + \frac{m^{3/2}\tilde{M}_2}{2000}\right)S\right]$
	m^k	$\log m^k$	r_2	r_1
$\frac{G}{n_2} + C$	$-\frac{km^k S}{r_1}$	$-\frac{kS}{2.303 r_1}$	$-r_2{}^2 S$	S
$\frac{G}{n_1 + n_2} + C$	$-\frac{km^k S}{\tilde{N}_1} + y - C$	$-\frac{kS}{2.303\tilde{N}_1} + y - C$	$-\frac{r_2 S}{\tilde{N}_1} + y - C$	$\frac{S}{\tilde{N}_2} + y - C$
$\frac{n_1 + n_2}{G} + C$	$\frac{km^k S}{\tilde{N}_1(y - C)^2} + \frac{1}{y - C}$	$\frac{kS}{2.303\tilde{N}_1(y - C)^2} + \frac{1}{y - C}$	$\frac{r_2 S}{\tilde{N}_1(y - C)^2} + \frac{1}{y - C}$	$-\frac{S}{\tilde{N}_2(y - C)^2} + \frac{1}{y - C}$
$\phi + C$	$\tilde{G}_1 - \frac{km^k S}{r_1}$	$\tilde{G}_1 - \frac{kS}{2.303 r_1}$	$\tilde{G}_1 - r_2{}^2 S$	$\tilde{G}_1 + S$
Δ	$\tilde{G}_1 + y - \frac{km^k S}{\tilde{N}_1}$	$\tilde{G}_1 + y - \frac{kS}{2.303\tilde{N}_1}$	$\tilde{G}_1 + y - \frac{r_2 S}{\tilde{N}_1}$	$\tilde{G}_1 + y + \frac{S}{\tilde{N}_2}$
G	$\tilde{M}_1\left[y - \left(km^k + \frac{k\tilde{M}_2 m^{k+1}}{1000}\right)S\right]$	$\tilde{M}_1\left[y - \frac{k}{2.303}\left(1 - \frac{\tilde{M}_2 m}{1000}\right)S\right]$	$\tilde{M}_1\left[y - \left(r_2 + \frac{r_2{}^2\tilde{M}_2}{\tilde{M}_1}\right)S\right]$	$\tilde{M}_1\left[y + \left(r_1 + \frac{\tilde{M}_2}{\tilde{M}_1}\right)S\right]$

Table A3–2

Formulas for the calculation of $\bar{G}_2$

$y \downarrow \quad x \rightarrow$	$\bar{G}_2$: $\tilde{N}_1$	$\tilde{N}_2$	m	$m^{1/2}$
$\frac{G}{n_2} + C$	$-\tilde{N}_1\tilde{N}_2S + y - C$	$\tilde{N}_1\tilde{N}_2S + y - C$	$mS + y - C$	$\frac{m^{1/2}S}{2} + y - C$
$\frac{G}{n_1 + n_2} + C$	$-\tilde{N}_1S + y - C$	$\tilde{N}_1S + y - C$	$\frac{mS}{\tilde{N}_2} + y - C$	$\frac{m^{1/2}S}{2\tilde{N}_2} + y - C$
$\frac{n_1 + n_2}{G} + C$	$\frac{\tilde{N}_1S}{(y-C)^2} + \frac{1}{y-C}$	$-\frac{\tilde{N}_1S}{(y-C)^2} + \frac{1}{y-C}$	$-\frac{mS}{\tilde{N}_2(y-C)^2} + \frac{1}{y-C}$	$-\frac{m^{1/2}S}{2\tilde{N}_2(y-C)^2} + \frac{1}{y-C}$
$\phi + C$	$-\tilde{N}_1\tilde{N}_2S + y - C$	$\tilde{N}_1\tilde{N}_2S + y - C$	$mS + y - C$	$\frac{m^{1/2}S}{2} + y - C$
Δ	$\tilde{G}_2 + y - \tilde{N}_1S$	$\tilde{G}_2 + y + \tilde{N}_1S$	$\tilde{G}_2 + y + \frac{mS}{\tilde{N}_2}$	$\tilde{G}_2 + y + \frac{m^{1/2}S}{2\tilde{N}_2}$
G	$\tilde{M}_2\left[y - \left(\tilde{N}_1\tilde{N}_2 + \frac{\tilde{N}_1{}^2\tilde{M}_1}{\tilde{M}_2}\right)S\right]$	$\tilde{M}_2\left[y + \left(\tilde{N}_1\tilde{N}_2 + \frac{\tilde{N}_1{}^2\tilde{M}_1}{\tilde{M}_2}\right)S\right]$	$\tilde{M}_2\left[y + \left(m + \frac{1000}{\tilde{M}_2}\right)S\right]$	$\tilde{M}_2\left[y + \left(\frac{1000}{2m^{1/2}\tilde{M}_2} + \frac{m^{1/2}}{2}\right)S\right]$
	m^k	$\log m^k$	r_2	r_1
$\frac{G}{n_2} + C$	$km^kS + y - C$	$\frac{kS}{2.303} + y - C$	$r_2S + y - C$	$-r_1S + y - C$
$\frac{G}{n_1 + n_2} + C$	$\frac{km^kS}{\tilde{N}_2} + y - C$	$\frac{kS}{2.303\tilde{N}_2} + y - C$	$\frac{S}{\tilde{N}_1} + y - C$	$-\frac{r_1S}{\tilde{N}_2} + y - C$
$\frac{n_1 + n_2}{G} + C$	$-\frac{km^kS}{\tilde{N}_2(y-C)^2} + \frac{1}{y-C}$	$-\frac{kS}{2.303\tilde{N}_2(y-C)^2} + \frac{1}{y-C}$	$-\frac{S}{\tilde{N}_1(y-C^2)} + \frac{1}{y-C}$	$\frac{r_1S}{\tilde{N}_2(y-C)^2} + \frac{1}{y-C}$
$\phi + C$	$km^kS + y - C$	$\frac{kS}{2.303} + y - C$	$r_2S + y - C$	$r_1S + y - C$
Δ	$\tilde{G}_2 + y + \frac{km^kS}{\tilde{N}_2}$	$\tilde{G}_2 + y + \frac{kS}{2.303\tilde{N}_2}$	$\tilde{G}_2 + y + \frac{S}{\tilde{N}_1}$	$\tilde{G}_2 + y - \frac{r_1S}{\tilde{N}_2}$
G	$\tilde{M}_2\left[y + \left(\frac{1000km^{k-1}}{\tilde{M}_2} + km^k\right)S\right]$	$\tilde{M}_2\left[y + \frac{k}{2.303}\left(1 + \frac{1000}{m\tilde{M}_2}\right)S\right]$	$\tilde{M}_2\left[y + \left(\frac{\tilde{M}_1}{\tilde{M}_2} + r_2\right)S\right]$	$\tilde{M}_2\left[y - \left(\frac{r_1\tilde{M}_1}{\tilde{M}_2} + r_1\right)S\right]$

Debye, Einstein, and Hindered Rotor Functions

APPENDIX 4

Table A4–1
Heat Capacity, Energy, and Entropy from Debye Functions

θ/T	$\tilde{C}_V$	$\frac{\tilde{E} - \tilde{E}_0}{T}$	$\tilde{S}$	θ/T	$\tilde{C}_V$	$\frac{\tilde{E} - \tilde{E}_0}{T}$	$\tilde{S}$
0	5.957	5.957	∞	1.4	5.412	3.4002	6.220
0.1	5.954	5.7354	21.650	1.5	5.337	3.2590	5.850
0.2	5.945	5.5221	17.536	1.6	5.259	3.1229	5.508
0.3	5.930	5.3131	15.128	1.7	5.178	2.9920	5.191
0.4	5.909	5.1110	13.425	1.8	5.094	2.8660	4.898
0.5	5.883	4.9141	12.109	1.9	5.007	2.7446	4.624
0.6	5.851	4.7234	11.039	2.0	4.918	2.6280	4.3702
0.7	5.813	4.5381	10.139	2.2	4.737	2.4090	3.9115
0.8	5.770	4.3590	9.368	2.4	4.543	2.2054	3.5071
0.9	5.722	4.1854	8.690	2.6	4.345	2.0182	3.1507
1.0	5.669	4.0175	8.097	2.8	4.147	1.8468	2.8361
1.1	5.611	3.8551	7.551	3.0	3.947	1.6891	2.5564
1.2	5.549	3.6983	7.064	3.2	3.750	1.5450	2.3079
1.3	5.482	3.5465	6.624	3.4	3.556	1.4134	2.0867

From Landolt-Börnstein, *Physikalisch-Chemische Tabellen*, Suppl. IIb. Springer, Berlin, 1927, pp. 705 ff.

Table A4–I (*Continued*)

θ/T	$\tilde{C}_V$	$\frac{\tilde{E}-\tilde{E}_0}{T}$	$\tilde{S}$	θ/T	$\tilde{C}_V$	$\frac{\tilde{E}-\tilde{E}_0}{T}$	$\tilde{S}$
3.6	3.364	1.2903	1.8855	8.5	0.7042	0.1838	0.2463
3.8	3.178	1.1830	1.7121	9.0	0.6041	0.1560	0.2087
4.0	2.996	1.0824	1.5533	9.5	0.5213	0.1335	0.1784
4.2	2.822	0.9912	1.4116	10.0	0.4518	0.1149	0.1535
4.4	2.653	0.9077	1.2839	11.0	0.3446	0.08697	0.1161
4.6	2.497	0.8330	1.1709	12.0	0.2667	0.0672	0.0896
4.8	2.343	0.7635	1.0672	13.0	0.2109	0.0526	0.0701
5.0	2.197	0.7007	0.9746	14.0	0.1688	0.0420	0.0560
5.5	1.867	0.5676	0.7812	15.0	0.1373	0.0343	
6.0	1.582	0.4610	0.6295	16.0	0.1133		
6.5	1.341	0.3790	0.5143	18.0	0.0796		
7.0	1.137	0.3129	0.4226	20.0	0.0580		
7.5	0.9664	0.2601	0.3501	25.0	0.0298		
8.0	0.8233	0.2179	0.2925	30.0	0.0172		

Table A4–2
Thermodynamic Properties of a Harmonic Oscillator

$\tilde{\nu}/T$	$\tilde{C}$	$\frac{\tilde{E}-\tilde{E}_0^\circ}{T}$	$-\frac{(\tilde{F}-\tilde{E}_0^\circ)}{T}$	$\tilde{\nu}/T$	$\tilde{C}$	$\frac{\tilde{E}-\tilde{E}_0^\circ}{T}$	$-\frac{(\tilde{F}-\tilde{E}_0^\circ)}{T}$
0.10	1.9834	1.8473	3.9942	0.20	1.9731	1.7147	2.7542
0.11	1.9827	1.8338	3.8186	0.22	1.9703	1.6890	2.5920
0.12	1.9819	1.8203	3.6596	0.24	1.9671	1.6636	2.4662
0.13	1.9810	1.8068	3.5143	0.26	1.9638	1.6384	2.3140
0.14	1.9801	1.7935	3.3807	0.28	1.9601	1.6135	2.1935
0.15	1.9791	1.7801	3.2572	0.30	1.9563	1.5889	2.0831
0.16	1.9780	1.7670	3.1428	0.32	1.9521	1.5645	1.9813
0.17	1.9768	1.7538	3.0361	0.34	1.9478	1.5404	1.8872
0.18	1.9756	1.7407	2.9362	0.36	1.9430	1.5167	1.7998
0.19	1.9744	1.7276	2.8424	0.38	1.9381	1.4931	1.7185

The units of $\tilde{\nu}$ are wave numbers; the thermodynamic quantities are in cal mole^{-1} deg^{-1}.

Table condensed from "The Third Law of Thermodynamics," in H. S. Taylor and S. Glasstone, *A Treatise on Physical Chemistry*, 3rd ed., Vol. 1, Copyright 1942, D. Van Nostrand Company, Inc., Princeton, N.J., pp. 655 ff.

Table A4–2 (*Continued*)

$\tilde{\nu}/T$	$\tilde{C}$	$\frac{\tilde{E} - \tilde{E}_0^\circ}{T}$	$-\frac{(\tilde{F} - \tilde{E}_0^\circ)}{T}$	$\tilde{\nu}/T$	$\tilde{C}$	$\frac{\tilde{E} - \tilde{E}_0^\circ}{T}$	$-\frac{(\tilde{F} - \tilde{E}_0^\circ)}{T}$
0.40	1.9330	1.4698	1.6425	2.30	0.8570	0.2497	0.0740
0.42	1.9275	1.4468	1.5713	2.40	0.8000	0.2246	0.0640
0.44	1.9218	1.4240	1.5045	2.50	0.7453	0.2017	0.0553
0.46	1.9159	1.4016	1.4416	2.60	0.6928	0.1810	0.0478
0.48	1.9097	1.3793	1.3826	2.70	0.6429	0.1622	0.0413
0.50	1.9033	1.3573	1.3267	2.80	0.5953	0.1454	0.0357
0.55	1.8863	1.3034	1.2001	2.90	0.5502	0.1301	0.0309
0.60	1.8680	1.2513	1.0887	3.00	0.5080	0.1162	0.0267
0.65	1.8481	1.2007	0.9905	3.20	0.4305	0.0927	0.0200
0.70	1.8272	1.1517	0.9033	3.40	0.3627	0.0736	0.0150
0.75	1.8047	1.1041	0.8256	3.60	0.3038	0.0584	0.0112
0.80	1.7813	1.0582	0.7558	3.80	0.2532	0.0461	0.0084
0.85	1.7568	1.0138	0.6931	4.00	0.2099	0.0364	0.0063
0.90	1.7312	0.9708	0.6363	4.20	0.1732	0.0286	0.0047
0.95	1.7045	0.9295	0.5848	4.40	0.1424	0.0225	0.0035
1.00	1.6770	0.8893	0.5382	4.60	0.1166	0.0176	0.0027
1.10	1.6196	0.8133	0.4572	4.80	0.0952	0.0138	0.0020
1.20	1.5592	0.7427	0.3894	5.00	0.0775	0.0107	0.0015
1.30	1.4966	0.6771	0.3326	5.50	0.0454	0.0058	0.0007
1.40	1.4324	0.6164	0.2848	6.00	0.0265	0.0031	0.0004
1.50	1.3671	0.5604	0.2441	6.50	0.0151	0.0016	0.0002
1.60	1.3010	0.5088	0.2097	7.00	0.0085	0.0008	0.0001
1.70	1.2349	0.4613	0.1802	7.50	0.0047	0.0004	0.0000
1.80	1.1690	0.4177	0.1551	8.00	0.0027	0.0002	
1.90	1.1038	0.3777	0.1336	8.50	0.0015	0.0001	
2.00	1.0398	0.3412	0.1152	9.00	0.0008	0.0001	
2.10	0.9772	0.3077	0.0992	9.50	0.0004	0.0000	
2.20	0.9161	0.2773	0.0858	10.00	0.0002		

Table A4–3

Free Energy Function for a Hindered Rotor

Free energy $= -\tilde{F}/T$ (cal/deg mole)

	$1/r_m$											
$\tilde{V}/RT$	0.25	0.30	0.35	0.40	0.45	0.50	0.55	0.60	0.65	0.70	0.75	0.80
0.0	2.754	2.392	2.086	1.821	1.587	1.377	1.188					
0.2	2.710	2.359	2.061	1.803	1.574	1.368	1.182					
0.4	2.623	2.296	2.014	1.765	1.543	1.342	1.160					
0.6	2.518	2.208	1.944	1.708	1.498	1.309	1.134					
0.8	2.406	2.106	1.856	1.636	1.442	1.266	1.100					
1.0	2.296	2.004	1.764	1.559	1.379	1.214	1.059					
1.5	2.040	1.770	1.548	1.370	1.210	1.069	0.938					
2.0	1.819	1.563	1.360	1.193	1.052	0.927	0.817					
2.5	1.630	1.389	1.197	1.043	0.912	0.802	0.709					
3.0	1.473	1.240	1.059	0.914	0.793	0.695	0.612	0.53				
3.5	1.340	1.117	0.943	0.802	0.694	0.603	0.528	0.46				
4.0	1.225	1.013	0.847	0.713	0.613	0.527	0.456	0.40	0.34			
4.5	1.133	0.925	0.764	0.637	0.543	0.463	0.397	0.35	0.29			
5.0	1.053	0.849	0.696	0.577	0.483	0.408	0.347	0.30	0.25	0.22		
6.0	0.919	0.728	0.586	0.477	0.393	0.325	0.272	0.23	0.19	0.16	0.14	
7.0	0.819	0.636	0.503	0.402	0.325	0.267	0.218	0.183	0.15	0.12	0.10	0.08
8.0	0.735	0.564	0.440	0.346	0.275	0.221	0.178	0.146	0.119	0.10	0.08	0.06
9.0	0.667	0.504	0.388	0.300	0.235	0.186	0.149	0.119	0.096	0.079	0.06	0.05
10.0	0.610	0.456	0.345	0.264	0.203	0.159	0.125	0.099	0.079	0.064	0.051	0.04
12.0	0.521	0.380	0.280	0.209	0.157	0.120	0.092	0.071	0.055	0.043	0.033	0.027
14.0	0.452	0.321	0.232	0.169	0.124	0.092	0.069	0.052	0.038	0.030	0.022	0.018
16.0	0.396	0.276	0.195	0.139	0.100	0.072	0.053	0.039	0.028	0.021	0.016	0.012
18.0	0.351	0.240	0.166	0.117	0.082	0.058	0.042	0.030	0.022	0.016	0.012	0.009
20.0	0.315	0.211	0.144	0.098	0.068	0.047	0.033	0.024	0.017	0.012	0.009	0.006

From K. S. Pitzer, *Quantum Chemistry*, p. 495.

Table A4–4
Enthalpy Function for a Hindered Rotor

Enthalpy, $\tilde{E}/T$ (cal/deg mole)

$1/r_m$

$\tilde{V}/RT$	0.0	0.05	0.10	0.15	0.20	0.25	0.30	0.35	0.40	0.45	0.50	0.55	0.60	0.65	0.70	0.75	0.80
0.0	0.9934	0.993	0.993	0.993	0.993	0.993	0.993	0.993	0.993	0.993	0.993	0.993					
0.2	1.1822	1.142	1.106	1.074	1.050	1.032	1.022	1.015	1.008	1.004	1.000	0.997					
0.4	1.3513	1.300	1.249	1.200	1.151	1.106	1.073	1.051	1.036	1.025	1.015	1.009					
0.6	1.5011	1.437	1.374	1.311	1.251	1.190	1.138	1.099	1.072	1.049	1.030	1.019					
0.8	1.6324	1.556	1.482	1.411	1.340	1.272	1.211	1.157	1.114	1.077	1.048	1.028					
1.0	1.7460	1.660	1.576	1.495	1.418	1.344	1.275	1.211	1.155	1.106	1.065	1.037					
1.5	1.9607	1.856	1.753	1.654	1.561	1.472	1.385	1.306	1.230	1.164	1.103	1.054					
2.0	2.0934	1.971	1.854	1.742	1.636	1.536	1.440	1.350	1.265	1.190	1.120	1.056					
2.5	2.1657	2.031	1.900	1.779	1.662	1.550	1.448	1.351	1.260	1.179	1.104	1.032					
3.0	2.1971	2.049	1.909	1.777	1.651	1.535	1.426	1.321	1.224	1.140	1.060	0.988	0.92				
3.5	2.2030	2.043	1.893	1.753	1.621	1.497	1.382	1.275	1.176	1.088	1.006	0.931	0.88				
4.0	2.1944	2.024	1.864	1.715	1.577	1.448	1.329	1.221	1.121	1.030	0.947	0.870	0.82	0.77			
4.5	2.1788	1.998	1.829	1.673	1.529	1.394	1.273	1.162	1.061	0.968	0.884	0.807	0.75	0.71			
5.0	2.1607	1.971	1.794	1.631	1.481	1.344	1.218	1.104	1.002	0.909	0.824	0.748	0.67	0.63	0.59		
6.0	2.1261	1.918	1.727	1.552	1.392	1.247	1.115	0.999	0.893	0.799	0.714	0.641	0.56	0.51	0.47	0.42	
7.0	2.0984	1.875	1.670	1.484	1.315	1.164	1.029	0.908	0.802	0.708	0.624	0.553	0.482	0.42	0.38	0.34	0.31
8.0	2.0781	1.840	1.623	1.427	1.251	1.095	0.955	0.833	0.725	0.631	0.549	0.479	0.418	0.363	0.31	0.28	0.25
9.0	2.0634	1.811	1.583	1.379	1.196	1.035	0.892	0.768	0.661	0.569	0.488	0.420	0.363	0.315	0.269	0.23	0.20
10.0	2.0526	1.787	1.548	1.335	1.147	0.982	0.838	0.715	0.608	0.515	0.437	0.371	0.319	0.273	0.231	0.194	0.17
12.0	2.0382	1.749	1.492	1.264	1.067	0.896	0.745	0.624	0.519	0.431	0.356	0.296	0.244	0.203	0.169	0.140	0.116
14.0	2.0292	1.717	1.441	1.202	0.997	0.823	0.672	0.551	0.450	0.367	0.295	0.240	0.195	0.158	0.128	0.104	0.084
16.0	2.0229	1.690	1.401	1.150	0.937	0.760	0.613	0.493	0.394	0.314	0.249	0.198	0.157	0.127	0.099	0.078	0.063
18.0	2.0182	1.666	1.363	1.102	0.886	0.707	0.561	0.443	0.347	0.271	0.211	0.164	0.128	0.099	0.077	0.060	0.047
20.0	2.0147	1.646	1.329	1.061	0.841	0.660	0.515	0.399	0.307	0.236	0.181	0.138	0.105	0.080	0.061	0.047	0.036

From K. S. Pitzer, *Quantum Chemistry*, p. 499.

Mathematical and Geometrical Quantities

APPENDIX 5

A5.1 Relationships Involving Partial Derivatives

If the variables z and w may both be expressed as functions of x and y, the following relationships hold true.

$$dz = \left(\frac{\partial z}{\partial x}\right)_y dx + \left(\frac{\partial z}{\partial y}\right)_x dy.$$

$$\left(\frac{\partial z}{\partial x}\right)_y = \frac{1}{(\partial x/\partial z)_y}.$$

$$\left(\frac{\partial}{\partial y}\right)_x \left(\frac{\partial z}{\partial x}\right)_y \equiv \frac{\partial^2 z}{\partial x\, \partial y} \equiv \left(\frac{\partial}{\partial x}\right)_y \left(\frac{\partial z}{\partial y}\right)_x.$$

$$\left(\frac{\partial z}{\partial x}\right)_y \left(\frac{\partial x}{\partial y}\right)_z \left(\frac{\partial y}{\partial z}\right)_x = -1.$$

$$\left(\frac{\partial z}{\partial x}\right)_y = \frac{(\partial z/\partial w)_y}{(\partial x/\partial w)_y}.$$

$$\left(\frac{\partial z}{\partial x}\right)_y = -\frac{(\partial z/\partial y)_x}{(\partial x/\partial y)_z}.$$

$$\left(\frac{\partial z}{\partial x}\right)_w = \left(\frac{\partial z}{\partial x}\right)_y + \left(\frac{\partial z}{\partial y}\right)_x \left(\frac{\partial y}{\partial x}\right)_w.$$

A.5.2 Spherical Coordinates

$$x = r \sin \theta \cos \phi. \qquad \theta = \cos^{-1} \frac{z}{r}.$$

$$y = r \sin \theta \sin \phi. \qquad \phi = \cos^{-1} \frac{x}{(x^2 + y^2)^{1/2}}$$

$$z = r \cos. \qquad = \sin^{-1} \frac{y}{(x^2 + y^2)^{1/2}}.$$

$$r^2 = x^2 + y^2 + z^2.$$

Volume element $= d\tau = r^2 \sin \theta \, d\theta \, d\phi \, dr$.

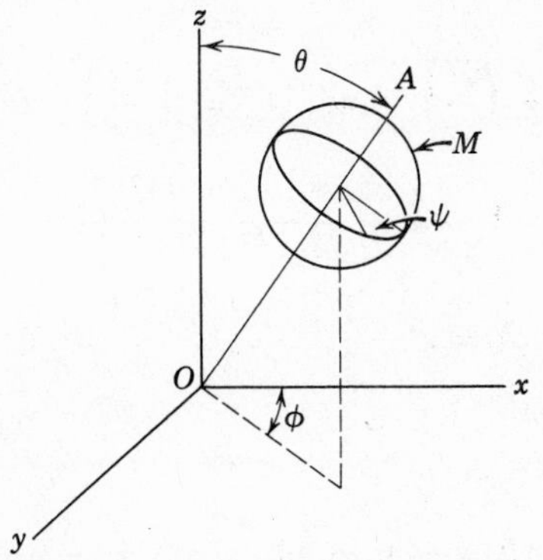

Fig. A5.4–1. The Eulerian angles.

A5.3 Laplacian Operator ∇^2

Cartesian coordinates:

$$\nabla^2 = \frac{\partial^2}{\partial x^2} + \frac{\partial^2}{\partial y^2} + \frac{\partial^2}{\partial z^2}.$$

Spherical coordinates:

$$\nabla^2 = \frac{1}{r^2}\frac{\partial}{\partial r}\left(r^2 \frac{\partial}{\partial r}\right) + \frac{1}{r^2 \sin \theta}\frac{\partial}{\partial \theta}\left(\sin \theta \frac{\partial}{\partial \theta}\right) + \frac{1}{r^2 \sin^2 \theta}\frac{\partial^2}{\partial \phi^2}.$$

A5.4 Eulerian Angles

The Eulerian angles θ, ϕ, and ψ (see Fig. A5.4–1), are defined as follows for a body M which is rotating about an axis OA within the body. θ is the angle between OA and the z axis of a fixed coordinate system x, y, z. ϕ is the angle in the x–y plane between the projection of OA and a line parallel to the x axis. ψ is the angle defining rotation of the body about OA. (For convenience the axis OA is drawn through the origin in the diagram; the descriptions given are independent of this limitation.)

A5.5 Series and Approximations

Taylor's series:

$$f(x+h) = f(x) + hf'(x) + \frac{h^2}{2!}f''(x) + \frac{h^3}{3!}f'''(x) + \cdots.$$

MacLaurin's series:

$$f(x) = f(0) + xf'(0) + \frac{x^2}{2!}f''(0) + \frac{x^3}{3!}f'''(0),$$

where

$$f' = \left(\frac{\mathrm{d}f}{\mathrm{d}x}\right) \quad \text{and} \quad f'' = \left(\frac{\mathrm{d}^2f}{\mathrm{d}x^2}\right), \text{ etc.}$$

$$e^x = 1 + x + \frac{x^2}{2!} + \frac{x^3}{3!} + \frac{x^4}{4!} + \cdots;$$

$$\ln(1+x) = x - \frac{1}{2}x^2 + \frac{1}{3}x^3 - \frac{1}{4}x^4 + \cdots;$$

$$-1 < x < 1.$$

Stirling's approximation:

$$\ln n! = n \ln n - n + \frac{1}{2}\ln(2\pi n) + \frac{1}{12n} + \cdots.$$

A5.6 Integrals

$$\int x^m e^{ax}\,\mathrm{d}x = \frac{x^m e^{ax}}{a} - \frac{m}{a}\int x^{m-1}e^{ax}\,\mathrm{d}x.$$

$$\int_0^\infty e^{-ax^2}\,\mathrm{d}x = \frac{1}{2}\left(\frac{\pi}{a}\right)^{1/2}.$$

$$\int_0^\infty x^{2n}e^{-ax^2}\,\mathrm{d}x = \frac{1\cdot 3\cdot 5\cdots(2n-1)}{2^{n+1}a^n}\left(\frac{\pi}{a}\right)^{1/2}.$$

$$\int_0^\infty\int_0^\infty\int_0^\infty e^{-a(x^2+y^2+z^2)}\,\mathrm{d}x\,\mathrm{d}y\,\mathrm{d}z$$

$$= \int_0^\infty e^{-ax^2}\,\mathrm{d}x \int_0^\infty e^{-ay^2}\,\mathrm{d}y \int_0^\infty e^{-az^2}\,\mathrm{d}z$$

$$= \left(\int_0^\infty e^{-ax^2}\,\mathrm{d}x\right)^3 = \frac{1}{8}\left(\frac{\pi}{a}\right)^{3/2}.$$

A5.7 Permutations

The number of ways of arranging N objects in i classes so as to give n_1 in one class, n_2 in another, etc., is

$$\mathrm{P} = \frac{N!}{n_1!n_2!n_3!\cdots n_i!}.$$

A5.8 Momentum and Equations of Motion

(a) *Equations of Motion in the Hamiltonian Form.* The Hamiltonian function (H) for a system is defined as

$$\mathrm{H} = T + V,$$

where T is the kinetic energy of the system, and V is the potential energy. For a Newtonian (conservative) system of N particles, the equations of motion are

$$\left(\frac{\partial \mathrm{H}}{\partial \mathrm{p}_i}\right) = \dot{\mathrm{q}}_i \quad \text{and} \quad \left(\frac{\partial \mathrm{H}}{\partial \mathrm{q}_i}\right) = -\dot{\mathrm{p}}_i \qquad i = 1, 2, \cdots, 3N,$$

where q_i are the $3N$ coordinates, and p_i are the momenta associated with these coordinates. (Note that the equations of motion are independent of the form of the coordinates, for example, cartesian coordinates, spherical coordinates, etc.)

(b) *Equations of Motion in the Lagrangian Form.* The Lagrangian function (L) is given by

$$\mathrm{L} = T - V.$$

The $3N$ equations of motion for a conservative (Newtonian) system of N particles are then

$$\frac{\mathrm{d}}{\mathrm{d}t}\frac{\partial \mathrm{L}}{\partial \dot{\mathrm{q}}_i} - \frac{\partial \mathrm{L}}{\partial \mathrm{q}_i} = 0 \qquad i = 1, 2, \cdots, 3N.$$

(c) *Potential and Kinetic Energy.* The potential energy V is given in general by an expression

$$2V = \sum_{ij} a_{ij}\mathrm{q}_i\mathrm{q}_j,$$

where the constants a_{ij} are the *force constants* of the system. Similarly, the kinetic energy T is given by the expression

$$2T = \sum_{ij} b_{ij}\dot{\mathrm{q}}_i\dot{\mathrm{q}}_j;$$

the coefficients b_{ij} are, in general, functions of the masses and coordinates of the components of the system considered.

(d) *Forces and Momenta.* The force in the direction of a coordinate q_i is given by

$$f_{q_i} = -\frac{\partial V}{\partial q_i}$$

and is expressed in general terms of all displacements q_i and the appropriate force constants a_{ij}.

The momentum associated with a coordinate q_i is given by

$$p_i = \frac{\partial T}{\partial q_i}.$$

(e) *Cartesian Coordinates.* In cartesian coordinates, the equations of motion (Newton's equations) are

$$m\ddot{x} = -\frac{\partial V}{\partial x}; \qquad m\ddot{y} = -\frac{\partial V}{\partial y}; \qquad m\ddot{z} = -\frac{\partial V}{\partial z}.$$

The kinetic energy T is

$$T = \frac{m}{2(\dot{x}^2 + \dot{y}^2 + \dot{z}^2)}.$$

For a conservative system, the Hamiltonian function is a constant; that is,

$$\frac{m}{2}(\dot{x}^2 + \dot{y}^2 + \dot{z}^2) + V(x,y,z) = C;$$

or

$$\frac{1}{2m}(p_x^2 + p_y^2 + p_z^2) + V(x,y,z) = C.$$

The momenta are

$$p_x = m\dot{x}; \qquad p_y = m\dot{y}; \qquad p_z = m\dot{z}.$$

(f) *Spherical Coordinates.*

$$p_r = mr, \qquad p_\theta = mr^2\dot{\theta}, \qquad \text{and} \qquad p_\phi = mr^2 \sin^2\theta\dot{\phi}.$$

$$\frac{1}{2m}\left(p_r^2 + \frac{p_\theta^2}{r^2} + \frac{p_\phi^2}{r^2 \sin^2\theta}\right) + V(r,\theta,\phi) = C.$$

In terms of the Eulerian angles θ, ϕ, ψ (see Section A5.4), the angular momenta of a particle are

$$p_\psi = mr^2\dot{\psi} \text{ about the axis } OA,$$

$$p_\theta = mr^2\dot{\theta} \text{ about an axis in the } xy \text{ plane,}$$

and

$$p_\phi = mr^2 \sin\theta\dot{\phi} \text{ about the } z \text{ axis.}$$

Wave Functions, Selection Rules, and Allowed Vibrational Modes

APPENDIX 6

A6.1 Hydrogen-like Wave Functions

The angular and radial portions of the wave function for a hydrogen-like atom are given in Tables A6.1–1 and A6.1–2. These wave functions and the choice of quantum numbers have been discussed in Section 16.7.

Table A6.1–1
Angular Factors for Two-Particle Wave Functions

$l = 0, m = 0$: $\quad A_{l,m} = \left(\frac{1}{4\pi}\right)^{1/2}$

$l = 1, m = 0$: $\quad A_{l,m} = \left(\frac{3}{4\pi}\right)^{1/2} \cos\theta$

$l = 1, m = \pm 1$: $\quad A_{l,m} = \left(\frac{3}{8\pi}\right)^{1/2} \sin\theta e^{\pm i\phi}$ or $\left(\frac{3}{4\pi}\right)^{1/2} \sin\theta\cos\phi$

and $\left(\frac{3}{4\pi}\right)^{1/2} \sin\theta\sin\phi$

$l = 2, m = 0$: $\quad A_{l,m} = \left(\frac{5}{16\pi}\right)^{1/2} (3\cos^2\theta - 1)$

$l = 2, m = \pm 1$: $\quad A_{l,m} = \left(\frac{15}{8\pi}\right)^{1/2} \sin\theta\cos\theta e^{\pm i\phi}$

Table A6.1–1 (*Continued*)

$$\text{or} \quad \left(\frac{15}{4\pi}\right)^{1/2} \sin\theta \cos\theta \cos\phi$$

$$\text{and} \quad \left(\frac{15}{4\pi}\right)^{1/2} \sin\theta \cos\theta \sin\phi$$

$$l = 2, m = \pm 2: \qquad A_{l,m} = \left(\frac{15}{32\pi}\right)^{1/2} \sin^2\theta e^{\pm 2i\phi}$$

$$\text{or} \quad \left(\frac{15}{16\pi}\right)^{1/2} \sin^2\theta \cos 2\phi$$

$$\text{and} \quad \left(\frac{15}{16\pi}\right)^{1/2} \sin^2\theta \sin 2\phi.$$

Table A6.1–2

Radial Factors for Hydrogen-like Wave Functions

$$n = 1, l = 0: \qquad R_{1s} = 2\left(\frac{Z}{a_0}\right)^{3/2} e^{-\sigma}$$

$$n = 2, l = 0: \qquad R_{2s} = \left(\frac{Z}{2a_0}\right)^{3/2} (2 - \sigma)e^{-\sigma/2}$$

$$n = 2, l = 1: \qquad R_{2p} = 3^{-1/2}\left(\frac{Z}{2a_0}\right)^{3/2} \sigma e^{-\sigma/2}$$

$$n = 3, l = 0: \qquad R_{3s} = \frac{2}{27}\left(\frac{Z}{3a_0}\right)^{3/2} (27 - 18\sigma + 2\sigma^2)e^{-\sigma/3}$$

$$n = 3, l = 1: \qquad R_{3p} = \frac{1}{81\sqrt{3}}\left(\frac{2Z}{a_0}\right)^{3/2} (6 - \sigma)\sigma e^{-\sigma/3}$$

$$n = 3, l = 2: \qquad R_{3d} = \frac{1}{81\sqrt{15}}\left(\frac{2Z}{a_0}\right)^{3/2} \sigma^2 e^{-\sigma/3}$$

Note: $\sigma = Zr/a_0 = \dfrac{4\pi^2\mu e^2 Zr}{k^2}$.

A6.2 Rules for Coupling of Angular Momenta in Diatomic Molecules

The brief discussion below is adapted from that of Herzberg.[1] For a more thorough treatment the reader is referred to the original. The two

[1] G. Herzberg, *Spectra of Diatomic Molecules*, Van Nostrand, Princeton, N.J., 1950, p. 218.

types of coupling most frequently encountered are known as Hund's case (a) and Hund's case (b).

In Hund's case (a), the orbital and spin momenta are strongly coupled. The orbital momentum is in any case directed along the "figure axis" (line joining the nuclei) of the molecule; its value is $\Lambda h/2\pi$. The component of the spin momentum along the figure axis will be described by a quantum number Σ, which may take values of $0, \pm 1, +2, \cdots, \pm S$; the momentum is thus $\Sigma h/2\pi$. The orbital momentum and the spin momentum couple to give a resultant angular momentum Ω about the figure axis; the quantum number Ω can take values

$$\Omega = \Lambda, \Lambda \pm 1, \Lambda \pm 2, \Lambda \pm 3, \cdots, \Lambda \pm S. \qquad \text{(A6.2–1)}$$

The angular momentum about the figure axis is then coupled with that for the nuclear rotation, $Nh/2\pi$, to give the total momentum $Jh/2\pi$. The quantum number J can take values of Ω, $\Omega + 1$, $\Omega + 2$, etc.

For Hund's case (a), there is a complete set of J values for each value of Ω with the exception that J can never be less than Ω. The effect of Λ and J on the energy is given by equation (16.12–11). However, the states with different values of Ω differ in electronic energy by an appreciable amount. Nitric oxide (NO), whose ground state is a $^2\Pi$, is an example of Hund's case (a). The state for which Ω is $^1/_2$ is described as $^2\Pi_{1/2}$; it has J values of $^1/_2$, $^3/_2$, $^5/_2$, etc. The $^2\Pi_{3/2}$ state has an electronic energy 121 cm^{-1} above the $^2\Pi_{1/2}$ state; it takes on J values of $^3/_2$, $^5/_2$, $^7/_2$, etc.

If Λ is zero, or if the coupling between orbit and spin is weak, Hund's case (b) applies. Then the orbital momentum ($\Lambda h/2\pi$) couples with the nuclear angular momentum ($Nh/2\pi$) to give a resultant $Kh/2\pi$, with $K = \Lambda, \Lambda + 1, \Lambda + 2$, etc. This resultant then couples with the *total* spin momentum $Sh/2\pi$ (not $\Sigma h/2\pi$) to give the resultant $Jh/2\pi$. Thus, for each value of K, the quantum number J takes on the $2S + 1$ values $K + S - 1, \cdots, K - S$. The energy is determined primarily by the value of K; it is given by (16.12–11) for levels where $J = K$. The other levels for each K value usually lie closely spaced near this level. The $^3\Sigma_g{}^-$ ground state of oxygen is an example of Hund's case (b). Its energies are discussed in detail in Section 16.15.

A6.3 Vibrational Modes of Carbon Dioxide. General Theory of Vibration of a Polyatomic Molecule

The coordinates necessary for description of the modes of vibration may be seen from Fig. 16.18–3. For generality, the atoms will be labeled in order from the left, 1, 2, and 3; the masses are then denoted by m_1, m_2, and m_3. The displacements from the equilibrium position along the line joining the atoms are taken as x_1, x_2, and x_3 respectively; the corresponding displacements at right angles are y_1, y_2, y_3. In the case of carbon dioxide m_2 is the mass of the carbon atom; m_1 and m_3 are the masses of oxygen atoms and are equal. Furthermore, since there is no interaction between the x and y displacements, only the displacements x_1, x_2, and x_3 will be considered in detail. It will be assumed that the restoring force acting on an atom is proportional to each of the changes in length or of angle of the bonds to it.

In the carbon dioxide molecule, the force on atom 1 is due to the shortening of the distance between the atoms 1 and 2. This force (which is in the opposite direction to the displacement) can be equated to $-f(x_1 - x_2)$, where f is called the *force constant*. Thus the acceleration of atom 1 is given by

$$m_1 \frac{d^2x_1}{dt^2} = -fx_1 + fx_2. \qquad \text{(A6.3–1a)}$$

The force acting on atom 2 is due to the decrease in the distance between atoms 2 and 3 and the increase in that between atoms 1 and 2. The force on atom 2 is thus given by $-f(x_2 - x_3) - f(x_2 - x_1)$, and

$$m_2 \frac{d^2x_2}{dt^2} = fx_1 - 2fx_2 + fx_3. \qquad \text{(A6.3–1b)}$$

The acceleration of atom 3 is similarly given by

$$m_3 \frac{d^2x_3}{dt^2} = fx_2 - fx_3. \qquad \text{(A6.3–1c)}$$

Equations (A6.3–1a,b,c) may be rewritten in more general terms:

$$m_1 \frac{d^2x_1}{dt^2} = -k_{xx}^{11}x_1 - k_{xx}^{12}x_2 - k_{xx}^{13}x_3, \qquad \text{(A6.3–2a)}$$

$$m_2 \frac{d^2x_2}{dt^2} = -k_{xx}^{21}x_1 - k_{xx}^{22}x_2 - k_{xx}^{23}x_3, \qquad \text{(A6.3–2b)}$$

and

$$m_3 \frac{d^2x_3}{dt^2} = -k_{xx}^{31}x_1 - k_{xx}^{32}x_2 - k_{xx}^{33}x_3, \qquad \text{(A6.3–2c)}$$

where $k_{xx}^{11} = f$, $k_{xx}^{12} = -f$, $k_{xx}^{13} = 0$, $k_{xx}^{21} = -f$, $k_{xx}^{22} = 2f$, $k_{xx}^{23} = -f$, $k_{xx}^{31} = 0$, $k_{xx}^{32} = -f$, $k_{xx}^{33} = f$.

Any coefficient k_{xx}^{ij} gives the force in the x direction exerted on the ith atom by a displacement in the x direction of the jth atom. This nomenclature will be generalized to three dimensions below.

In a vibrational mode, each of the atoms moves harmonically with the frequency ν, characteristic of that mode. The equation giving the values of the x's as a function of time is thus

$$x_i = x_i^0 \sin 2\pi\nu t, \tag{A6.3–3}$$

where x_i^0 is the maximum amplitude of vibration of the ith atom in the x direction. Thus,

$$\frac{d^2x_i}{dt^2} = -4\pi^2\nu^2 x_1^0 \sin 2\pi\nu t \tag{A6.3–4}$$

The results of substituting such a relation for each of the x's and dividing each equation by $\sin 2\pi\nu t$ are

$$4\pi^2\nu^2 \mathrm{m}_1 x_1^0 = k_{xx}^{11}x_1^0 + k_{xx}^{12}x_2^0 + k_{xx}^{13}x_3^0, \tag{A6.3–5a}$$

$$4\pi^2\nu^2 \mathrm{m}_2 x_2^0 = k_{xx}^{21}x_1^0 + k_{xx}^{22}x_2^0 + k_{xx}^{23}x_3^0, \tag{A6.3–5b}$$

and

$$4\pi^2\nu^2 \mathrm{m}_3 x_3^0 = k_{xx}^{31}x_1^0 + k_{xx}^{32}x_2^0 + k_{xx}^{33}x_3^0, \tag{A6.3–5c}$$

which, on rearrangement and substitution of the symbol λ for $4\pi^2\nu^2$, become

$$(k_{xx}^{11} - \mathrm{m}_1\lambda)x_1^0 + k_{xx}^{12}x_2^0 + k_{xx}^{13}x_3^0 = 0, \tag{A6.3–6a}$$

$$k_{xx}^{21}x_1^0 + (k_{xx}^{22} - \mathrm{m}_2\lambda)x_2^0 + k_{xx}^{23}x_3^0 = 0, \tag{A6.3–6b}$$

$$k_{xx}^{31}x_1^0 + k_{xx}^{32}x_2^0 + (k_{xx}^{33} - \mathrm{m}_3\lambda)x_3^0 = 0. \tag{A6.3–6c}$$

These three equations can be solved only for the ratios x_2^0/x_1^0 and x_3^0/x_1^0; even this is possible only if two of the equations are identical. Two equations will be identical if and only if the determinant of the coefficients of equations (A6.3–6a,b,c) vanishes. Thus

$$\begin{vmatrix} k_{xx}^{11} - \mathrm{m}_1\lambda & k_{xx}^{12} & k_{xx}^{13} \\ k_{xx}^{21} & k_{xx}^{22} - \mathrm{m}_2\lambda & k_{xx}^{23} \\ k_{xx}^{31} & k_{xx}^{32} & k_{xx}^{33} - \mathrm{m}_3\lambda \end{vmatrix} = 0. \tag{A6.3–7}$$

Replacing the coefficients $k_{xx}^{11}, \cdots$ by their values and noting that $\mathrm{m}_1 = \mathrm{m}_3$, the result for carbon dioxide is

$$\begin{vmatrix} (f - \mathrm{m}_1\lambda) & -f & 0 \\ -f & (2f - \mathrm{m}_2\lambda) & -f \\ 0 & -f & (f - \mathrm{m}_1\lambda) \end{vmatrix} = 0. \tag{A6.3–8}$$

Upon simplification, the determinant becomes

$$\gamma(f - \mathrm{m}_1\lambda)[-(\mathrm{m}_2 + 2\mathrm{m}_1)f + \mathrm{m}_1\mathrm{m}_2\lambda] = 0. \tag{A6.3–9}$$

The three roots of this equation are

$$\lambda_1 = \frac{f}{m_1}; \qquad \lambda_2 = f\left(\frac{1}{m_1} + \frac{2}{m_2}\right); \qquad \lambda_3 = 0. \tag{A6.3–10}$$

Each of these values of λ corresponds to a vibrational mode, or other degree of freedom, whose frequency may be calculated from the value of λ. The displacements associated with a particular mode are obtained by substituting the value of λ into (A6.3–6a,b,c) and then solving for the ratios of the x_i's. For the values of λ given above, the results are: from λ_1,

$$x_1^{10} = -x_3^{10}; \qquad x_2^{10} = 0; \tag{A6.3–11a}$$

from λ_2,

$$x_1^{20} = x_3^{20} = -x_2^{20}\frac{m_2}{2m_1}; \tag{A6.3–11b}$$

from λ_3,

$$x_1^{30} = x_2^{30} = x_3^{30}. \tag{A6.3–11c}$$

The superscripts 1, 2, and 3 indicate the value of λ to which each displacement corresponds.

The vibration of the molecule characterized by each value of λ is called a *normal vibration*. In this case, comparison with Fig. 16.18–3 clearly shows the motion associated with λ_1 to be that labeled ν_1 in the diagram; the motion for λ_2 is the same as that labeled ν_3. The motion associated with λ_3 is clearly a translation of the molecule as a whole; it has zero frequency, as do all translations and rotations.

It is evident from equation (A6.3–3) that, for each value of λ (λ_i), the ratios x_2^i/x_1^i, x_3^i/x_1^i are the same as the ratios of the corresponding x_i^0's; the ratios do not change with time, since each of the x's change with time in the same manner. That is,

$$\frac{x_2^i}{x_1^i} = \frac{x_2^{i0}}{x_1^{i0}}; \qquad \frac{x_3^i}{x_1^i} = \frac{x_3^{i0}}{x_1^{i0}}; \qquad \text{etc.} \tag{A6.3–11d}$$

The *normal coordinate* for the molecule, ξ, gives the simultaneous changes in each of the coordinates for a particular value of λ_i. In this case a displacement in the normal coordinate corresponds to equal and opposite displacements of atoms 1 and 3 in the x direction, with no motion of atom 2.

Problem A6.3-1. Draw to scale the displacements corresponding to ξ_1 and ξ_2 in the example above, taking x_1 as 1 cm in each case. Compare with ν_1 and ν_3 in Fig. 16.18–3.

The normal coordinate for each vibration changes with time as $\xi_i = \xi_i^0 \sin 2\pi\nu t$ just as the individual coordinates do.

In order to obtain the vibrations labeled ν_{2a} and ν_{2b} in Fig. 16.18–3, it is necessary to consider the motions in the y and z directions. The procedure is similar to that given above. Although the forces may be obtained in the same manner as above, it is more convenient to do so by a more general procedure. According to Newton's laws, the force on the ith atom in a given coordinate direction is the derivative of the potential energy with respect to the chosen coordinate; for example, $f_x^1 = -\partial V/\partial x_1$. The required force constants are the coefficients of various coordinates in the force expressions, as illustrated below. For the triatomic molecule, the potential energy may be expressed in terms of the changes in bond length (Q_1 and Q_2) and bond angle (δ). It is

$$2V = k(Q_1^2 + Q_2^2) + k_\delta \delta^2. \qquad \text{(A6.3–12)}$$

In order to obtain the required derivatives, these changes must be expressed in terms of the cartesian coordinates. In this case,

$$Q_1 = x_2 - x_1; \qquad Q_2 = x_3 - x_2;$$
$$\delta = -\frac{1}{l}(y_1 + y_3 - 2y_2) \quad \text{or} \quad -\frac{1}{l}(z_1 + z_3 - 2z_2). \qquad \text{(A6.3–13)}$$

(Note that, in this linear molecule, the y and z directions do not interact and must be kept separate; in general, the expression for δ contains both coordinates simultaneously.)

The expression for the potential energy then becomes

$$2V = k(x_1^2 + 2x_2^2 + x_3^2 - 2x_1x_2 - 2x_2x_3)$$
$$+ \frac{k_\delta}{l^2}(y_1^2 + y_3^2 + 4y_2^2 - 4y_1y_2 + 2y_1y_3 + \cdots). \qquad \text{(A6.3–14)}$$

Two of the forces required are

$$f_x^1 = -\frac{\partial V}{\partial x_1} = -kx_1 + kx_2, \qquad \text{(A6.3–15a)}$$

and

$$f_y^1 = -(k_\delta/l^2)y_1 + 2(k_\delta/l^2)y_2 - (k_\delta/l^2)y_3. \qquad \text{(A6.3–15b)}$$

Equation (A6.3–15a) is identical with (A6.3–1a), except for the labeling of the force constant. From equation (A6.3–15b), one obtains the force constants

$$k_{yy}^{11} = \frac{k_\delta}{l^2}; \qquad k_{yy}^{12} = -\frac{2k_\delta}{l^2}; \qquad k_{yy}^{13} = \frac{k_\delta}{l^2}. \qquad \text{(A6.3–16a)}$$

Continuation of this procedure yields the complete set of force constants for the y direction:

$$k_{yy}^{11} = k_{yy}^{33} = k_{yy}^{13} = k_{yy}^{31} = \frac{k_\delta}{l^2}; \qquad k_{yy}^{12} = k_{yy}^{21} = -\frac{2k_\delta}{l^2};$$

$$k_{yy}^{22} = \frac{4k_\delta}{l^2}; \qquad k_{yy}^{23} = k_{yy}^{32} = -\frac{2k_\delta}{l^2}. \tag{A6.3–16b}$$

For simplicity, the ratio k_δ/l^2 will be denoted by k'. The secular determinant for the y direction then becomes

$$\begin{vmatrix} (k' - m_1\lambda) & -2k' & k' \\ -2k' & (4k' - m_2\lambda) & -2k' \\ k' & -2k' & (k' - m_1\lambda) \end{vmatrix} = 0. \tag{A6.3–17}$$

Its solutions are

$$\lambda_4 = \lambda_5 = 0$$

and

$$\lambda_6 = \frac{2k'}{m_1}\left(1 + \frac{2m_1}{m_2}\right) = \frac{2k_\delta}{m_1 l^2}\left(1 + \frac{2m_1}{m_2}\right). \tag{A6.3–18}$$

The motions corresponding to each value of λ are obtained by substituting each in turn into a set of equations like (A6.3–6). The results are: from λ_4, λ_5,

$$y_1 = y_2 = y_3 \quad \text{(translation)}; \tag{A6.3–19a}$$

$$y_1 = -y_3, \qquad y_2 = 0 \quad \text{(rotation about } z \text{ axis)}; \tag{A6.3–19b}$$

and, from λ_6,

$$y_1 = y_3, \qquad y_2 = -\frac{2m_1}{m_2} y_1. \tag{A6.3–19c}$$

The motion associated with λ_6 is that shown as ν_{2a} in Fig. 16.18–3.

The solutions for motion in the z direction are identical with those for the y direction except for the replacement of y by z throughout. They give rise to another mode of vibration ν_{2b}, with frequency identical to that of ν_{2a}.

Problem A6.3-2. Taking the values of f and k_δ/l^2 for carbon dioxide as 1.5×10^5 and 0.57×10^5 dynes cm^{-1} respectively, calculate ν_1, $\nu_{2a,b}$, and ν_3 in wave numbers. Compare with the measured values given previously.

The geometry of the CO_2 molecule simplified the calculations above in two respects. First, a displacement in the direction of any coordinate axis caused a restoring force only along that axis; second, the symmetry of the molecule made motions in the y and z directions equivalent.

For most molecules the motions in several coordinate directions cannot be separated as above. The determinantal equation which results in the most general case of N atoms is

$$\begin{vmatrix} k_{xx}^{11}-m_1\lambda & k_{xy}^{11} & k_{xz}^{11} & k_{xx}^{12} & \cdots & k_{xz}^{1N} \\ k_{yx}^{11} & k_{yy}^{11}-m_1\lambda & k_{yz}^{11} & k_{yx}^{12} & \cdots & k_{yz}^{1N} \\ k_{zx}^{11} & k_{zy}^{11} & k_{zz}^{11}-m_1\lambda & k_{zx}^{12} & \cdots & k_{zz}^{1N} \\ k_{xx}^{21} & k_{xy}^{21} & k_{xz}^{21} & k_{xx}^{22}-m_2\lambda & \cdots & k_{xz}^{2N} \\ \cdots & \cdots & \cdots & \cdots & \cdots & \cdots \\ k_{zx}^{N1} & k_{zy}^{N1} & k_{zz}^{N1} & k_{zx}^{N2} & \cdots & k_{zz}^{NN}-m_N\lambda \end{vmatrix} = 0. \tag{A6.3–20}$$

Such an equation is known as a *secular* equation. The equation results from a treatment analogous to that above with the acceleration on the x direction of the ith molecule of mass m_i given by

$$m_i \frac{d^2x_i}{dt^2} = -k_{xx}^{i1}x_1 - k_{xy}^{i1}y_1 - k_{xz}^{i1}z_1 - k_{xx}^{i2}x_2 - \cdots - k_{xz}^{iN}x_N \tag{A6.3–21}$$

with similar expressions for the y and z directions in which y and z replace x in the first term and in the first subscript of the k's. Thus a coefficient k_{xy}^{ij} gives the force exerted in the x direction on atom i by a unit displacement in the y direction of atom j. These coefficients may be obtained by the same general mechanical considerations as used above for carbon dioxide, the geometry and force constants appropriate to the molecule considered being used. A general theorem of mechanics states that $k_{pq}^{ij} = k_{qp}^{ji}$, where p and q represent particular cartesian coordinates, for all subscripts and superscripts.

Problem A6.3-3. Set up the determinantal equation in the form of equation A6.3–20 for the water molecule, using force constants k and k_δ of the same form as those discussed above for carbon dioxide. Simplify the determinant so as to factor out the six zero roots due to translation and rotation.

The solution for normal vibrations may be considerably simplified by use of *symmetry coordinates* which, like the normal coordinates themselves, involve simultaneous displacements of all atoms of the molecule. The secular equation in terms of symmetry coordinates is similar to that given above, but it has no roots for translation or rotation; moreover, it can generally be factored readily. The proper choice of symmetry coordinates requires knowledge of the symmetry of vibrations, discussed in Section 16.20. The use of these coordinates in determination of normal vibrations will not be discussed further here. A detailed discussion is given by

Herzberg.[2] In Section 16.18 we referred to the *fundamental* frequencies, ν_i, of carbon dioxide. The term was used in the sense defined in Section 16.12. The values of λ (given by equation (A6.3–10)) which are the roots of equation (16.3–7) are related to the corresponding v's by

$$\lambda_i = 4\pi^2\nu_i^2. \tag{A6.3–22a}$$

Thus

$$\nu_1 = \frac{1}{2\pi}\left(\frac{f}{m_1}\right)^{1/2}. \tag{A6.3–22b}$$

Thus the ν_i are analogous to the fundamental frequency, $c\omega_e$, for a diatomic molecule, whose significance has been discussed in Section 16.12.

For the mode of fundamental frequency ν_i, the formula for the energy levels, as deduced by quantum mechanics for purely harmonic vibrations, is

$$E_i = (v + \tfrac{1}{2})h\nu_i, \tag{16.19–1}$$

where v has the values 0, 1, 2 etc. Problem A6.3–3 considers the vibrations of the water molecule. It is clear from this problem that, in general, the modes of vibration of a polyatomic molecule are highly complicated. The case of benzene is considered in the next section.

A6.4 Normal Modes of Benzene. Degenerate Vibrations

The normal modes of vibration of benzene will be considered as an example of the behavior of a complex molecule. Figure A6.4–1[3] shows the thirty normal moles of vibration and fundamental vibration frequencies of benzene. The relative displacements at right angles to the plane of the paper are indicated by numbers. There are only twenty distinct frequencies, since there are ten pairs of equal frequencies, namely, 6*AB*, 7*AB*, 8*AB*, 9*AB*, 10*AB*, 16*AB*, 17*AB*, 18*AB*, 19*AB*, and 20*AB*.

This same situation was encountered for the out-of-plane frequencies ν_{2a} and ν_{2b} of carbon dioxide shown in Fig. 16.18–3. These correspond to the two equal roots obtained when the appropriate secular equation (A6.3–20) is solved. The corresponding modes are said to be *doubly degenerate*. Since the frequencies, ν_{2a} or ν_{2b}, for carbon dioxide (in

[2] G. Herzberg, *Infra-Red and Raman Spectra*, Van Nostrand, Princeton, N.J., 1945, pp. 145 ff.

[3] Data from E. A. Braude and F. C. Nachod, eds., *Determination of Organic Structures by Physical Methods*, Academic Press, N.Y., 1955; K. S. Pitzer and D. W. Scott, *J. Am. Chem. Soc.*, **65**, 803 (1943).

Fig. 16.18–3) or of 6*AB*, etc., for benzene (Fig. A6.4–1) are the same, any linear combination of the degenerate vibrations (e.g., the sum of 6*A* and 6*B*) gives another vibration of the same frequency. Thus there are an

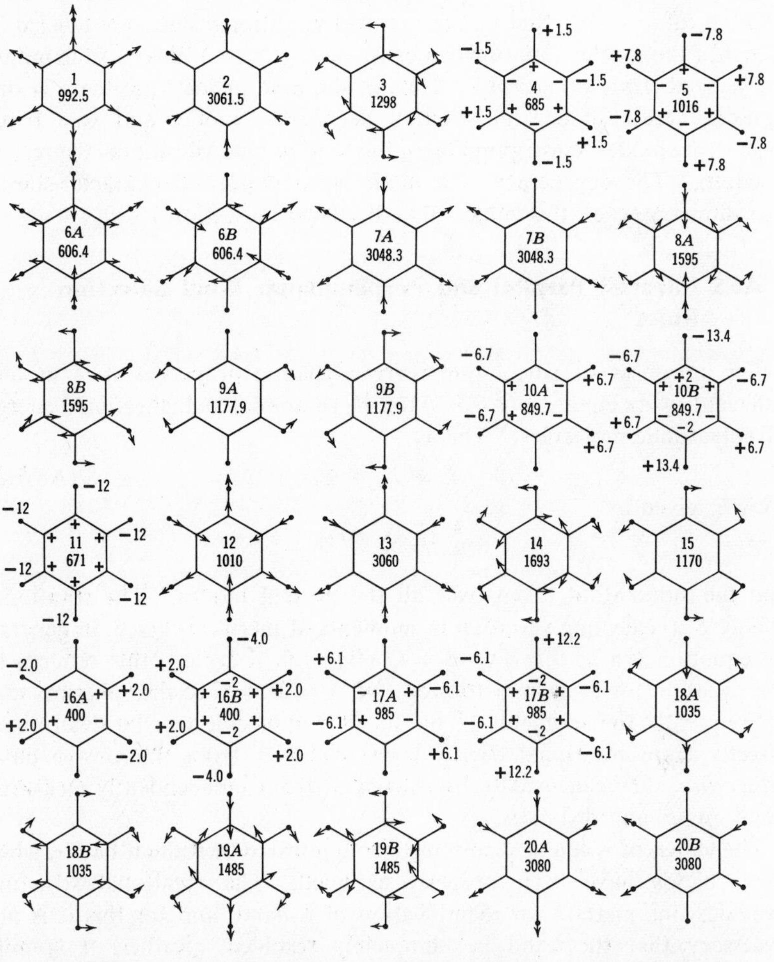

Fig. A6.4–1. The thirty normal modes of vibration and fundamental frequencies of benzene.[3]

(From *Determination of Organic Structures by Physical Methods*, edited by E. A. Braude and F. C. Nachod, Academic Press, Inc., 1955.)

infinite number of modes of a doubly degenerate frequency. Only two of these (but any two) are independent. In general, degenerate modes are neither symmetric nor antisymmetric in the nuclei, whereas non-degenerate modes are always symmetric or antisymmetric.

For carbon dioxide the addition of ν_{2a} to ν_{2b}, with ν_{2b} 90° out of phase, produces rotation of all atoms around the symmetric axis. Thus the excited vibrational states of the modes ν_{2a} and ν_{2b} are analogous to Π, Δ, etc., electronic states, and their type is labeled Π, Δ, etc. Since there is no such rotation in ν_1 and ν_3, their excited vibrational states are labeled Σ. Roots of the secular equation can be equal in groups of three; such modes are termed *triply degenerate*. Thus in the case of methane there is one non-degenerate mode, one doubly degenerate mode, and two triply degenerate modes, corresponding to the total of nine vibrational degrees of freedom. The degeneracy of a mode is an important characteristic of its symmetry type; this subject was discussed in Section 16.20.

A6.5 Infrared Parallel and Perpendicular Band Selection Rules

For purposes of calculating thermodynamic properties it is usually sufficient to use equation (A6.5–1) for the rotational and vibrational energy of polyatomic molecules. This is

$$E = E_v + E_r \tag{A6.5–1}$$

with E_v given by

$$\sum_i (v_i + \tfrac{1}{2})h\nu_i$$

and the summation taken over all the normal modes. The rotational energy E_r (neglecting variation in moments of inertia) is given, in general, by equation (16.22–9). For B = C ($W_\tau = 0, 1, 2$, etc.), this reduces to the equation for the symmetric top, for A = B = C to the spherical top.

Frequently the moments of inertia of a molecule can be determined directly from rotational energy levels deduced from microwave data. Otherwise, they can usually be calculated from independently measured bond angles and distances.

The values of ν_i can be determined from infrared or Raman bands, when these bands have been properly assigned. The rotational structure provides one method for identification of a band, and for this it is not necessary that the band be completely resolved. Rather, it is only necessary that the general distribution of intensities (band contour) be known. This contour differs greatly, depending on whether the vibration is accompanied by a change of electric moment along the figure axis or at right angles to it.

If there is to be any band at all in the infrared, there must be a change of electric moment during the process responsible for it, either in the direction of the figure axis or at right angles to it. Thus the absence in the infrared of a band that is present in the Raman spectrum is an important clue to the nature of the band. Similarly, the failure of an infrared band to appear in the Raman spectrum is an equally important clue.

Quantum mechanics requires for infrared absorption that at least one of the quantities be other than zero (i.e., that its integrand be symmetric). In these expressions M_x, etc., are defined as $\Sigma e_i x_i$, etc. (i.e., as the sum over all atoms of the molecule of the charge, e_i, of the atom times its corresponding coordinate x_i, etc.). ψ' and ψ'' are the vibrational wave functions in the upper and lower states.

$$[M_x]^{v'v''} = \int \psi_v'' M_x \psi_v' \, d\tau, \qquad [M_y]^{v'v''} = \int \psi_v'' M_y \psi_v' \, d\tau, \qquad (A6.5\text{–}2)$$

$$[M_z]^{v'v''} = \int \psi_v'' M_z \psi_v' \, d\tau$$

It is evident that the quantities M_x, etc., must have the same symmetry as $\psi_v''\psi_v'$. If ψ_v' refers to the ground state, the symmetry is that of ψ_v''. Thus the selection rules are readily worked out from the tables of Section A6.8 which give the symmetry of M_x, M_y, and M_z.

Actually, for any given line to occur in the absorption band, the above condition must apply to the total wave function $\psi_r\psi_v$ (product of rotational and vibrational wave function). The symmetry of the rotational levels is either the same as that of the vibrational level in both the lower or upper states or different from it in both for any nuclear spin species. Thus the symmetry of $\int \psi_r''\psi_v'' M \psi_r'\psi_v' \, d\tau$ is always the same as that of $\int \psi_v'' M \psi_v' \, d\tau$, and the above condition is sufficient. However, for molecules of certain symmetry certain rotational levels are excluded entirely, and the excluded ones depend on the symmetry of the vibrational wave functions. Thus the rotational structure of an infrared band depends on the symmetry of the vibrational mode. The bands of ammonia, of point group C_{3v}, will serve to illustrate.

There are two totally symmetric fundamental modes. These are of species A_1 and are shown in Fig. 16.20–1. Table A6.8–10 shows that for the point group C_{3v} only M_z has the symmetry A_1 for the vibrational level with $v = 1$; hence these modes will produce absorption in the infrared for the transition $v = 0$ to $v = 1$. However, the level $v = 0$ must be of species A_1 in all modes. Thus the levels $v = 0$ and $v = 1$ both require rotational levels of species A_1. This means that only the levels $K = 0$, 3, 6, 9, etc., are allowed for any value of J in each vibrational level. The selection rules allow only the transitions $\Delta K = 0, \pm 1$; thus only transitions in which $\Delta K = 0$ are allowed.

There are two modes of vibration belonging to species E. For point group C_{3v}, M_x and M_y have the symmetry E. The level $v = 0$, of course, belongs to the species A_1, while the level $v = 1$ belongs to the species E.

For this level K can have the value 1, 2, 4, 5, 7, 8, etc. In the lower level K can have the values of only 0, 3, 6, etc. Thus transitions of $\Delta K = \pm 1$ are possible, while $\Delta K = 0$ is not possible.

Obviously the absorption bands for the modes of species A_1 must be simpler. Figure A6.5–1a shows the groups of infrared lines produced in this type of band for transitions $\Delta J = \pm 1$ for various values of K. In all

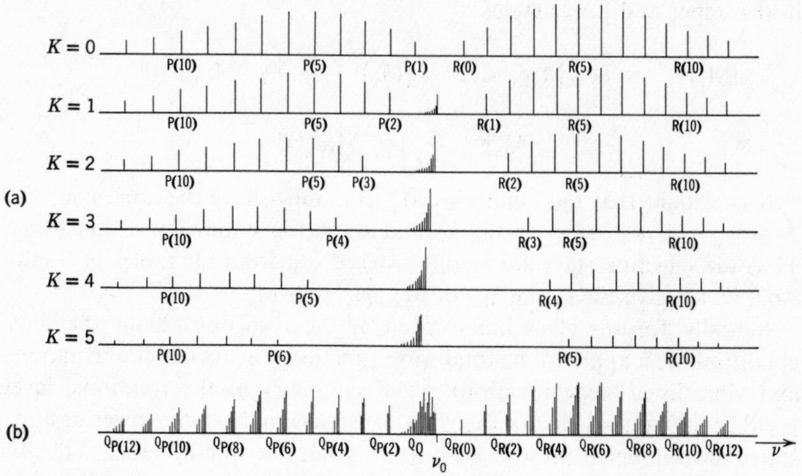

Fig. A6.5–1. Sub-bands of a parallel band and a complete parallel band of a symmetric top.

The sub-bands in (a) are directly superimposed in (b). In both (a) and (b) only a slight difference between $A'-B'$ and $A''-B''$ is assumed. The heights of the lines indicate the intensities calculated on the basis of the assumption that $A'' = 5.25$, $B'' = 1.70\ \text{cm}^{-1}$, and $T = 144°\text{K}$. The intensities indicated for the sub-band $K = 0$ should be divided by 2.

(From G. Herzberg, "*Molecular Spectra and Molecular Structure*, Vol. II, "Infrared and Raman Spectra of Polyatomic Molecules," 2nd ed. Copyright 1950, D. Van Nostrand Company, Inc.)

cases except that for $K = 0$ there is a Q branch (for $K = 0$ the transition $\Delta J = 0$ is not allowed). If the moments of inertia did not change with rotation and vibration, the Q branch would be a line and for all values of K the lines of the P and R branches would coincide. Actually this is not the case. Thus the observed band which contains all these lines appears as shown in Fig. A6.5–1b, which is simply a superposition of all the systems of lines of Fig. A6.5–1a. Such a band is called a parallel band. For the mode of species E, transitions of $\Delta K = \pm 1$ are allowed. Figure A6.5–2 shows all the possible groups of infrared lines for the transition $\Delta J = 0$, ± 1, and $\Delta K = \pm 1$, for several initial values of K. The bottom part of

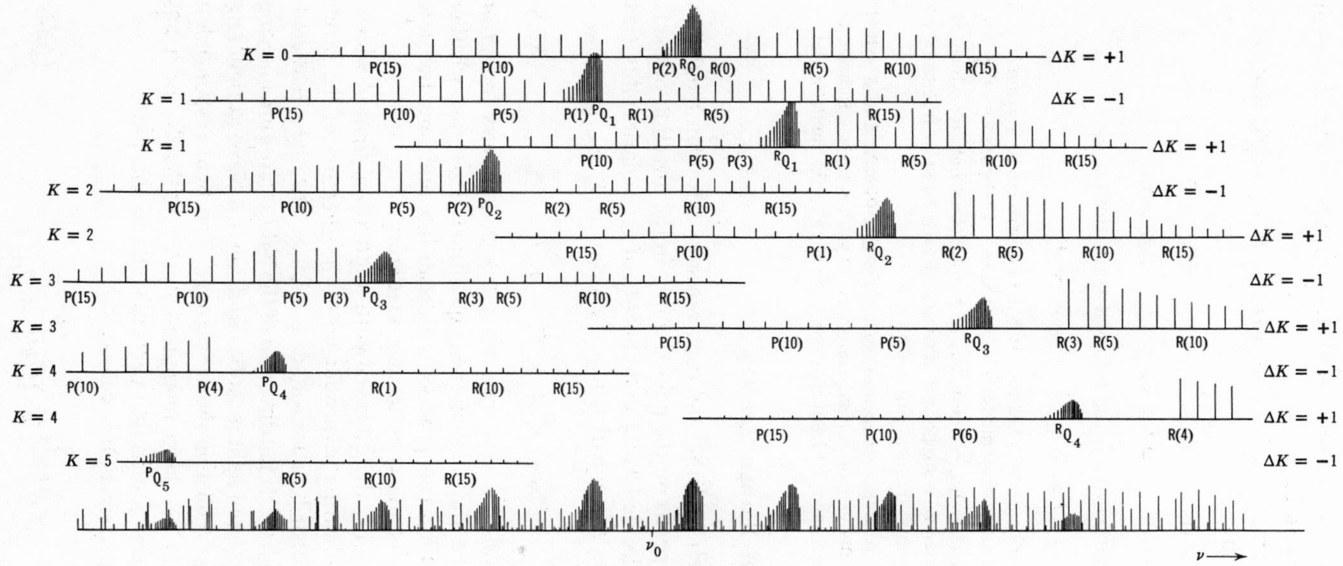

Fig. A6.5–2. Sub-bands of a ⊥ band and complete ⊥ band of a symmetric top.

The complete band is shown in the bottom strip. The spectrum is drawn under the assumption that $A' = 5.18$, $A'' = 5.25$, $B' = 0.84$, $B'' = 0.85$ cm^{-1}, and $\mathscr{T}_i = 0$. The intensities were calculated for a temperature of 144°K. It should be realized that, if the lines of an individual Q branch are not resolved, the resulting "line" would stand out much more prominently than might appear from the spectra given.

(From G. Herzberg, *Molecular Spectra and Molecular Structure*, Vol. II, "Infrared and Raman Spectra of Polyatomic Molecules," 2nd ed. Copyright 1950, D. Van Nostrand Company, Inc.)

the figure gives the superposition of all these groups of lines to produce the observed absorption band.

The selection rules may now be summarized. If M_z only is symmetrical, the allowed transitions are

$$K = 0; \qquad \Delta J = \pm 1; \qquad \Delta K = 0.$$
$$K = 0; \qquad \Delta J = 0, \pm 1; \qquad \Delta K = 0.$$

If M_x and M_y are symmetrical, the allowed transitions are

$$\Delta J = 0, \pm 1; \qquad \Delta K = \pm 1.$$

Problem A6.5-1. By reference to Section A6.8 assign benzene to a symmetry class and ascertain the number of normal modes in each species. Compare with Fig. A6.4–1.

Problem A6.5-2. By reference to the tables of Section A6.8 indicate which of the normal modes of vibration of benzene will have an infrared band of frequency corresponding to the fundamental frequency ($v = 0$ to $v = 1$).

Problem A6.5-3. By reference to Section A6.8 assign cyclopropane to a symmetry class and ascertain the number of normal vibrations in each species. Indicate which of these will give infrared bands of frequency corresponding to the fundamental.

A6.6 Vibrational Raman Spectra

It has already been seen that the occurrence of a Raman band (sometimes called line) depends on the polarizability in the direction of the field intensity. Any molecule has six components of the polarizability (really nine, but three pairs are equal) which are denoted by α_{xx}, α_{yy}, α_{zz}, α_{xy}, α_{yz}, α_{xz} such that

$$P_x = \alpha_{xx}F_x + \alpha_{xy}F_y + \alpha_{xz}F_z. \qquad \text{(A6.6–1)}$$

By an argument similar to that used for the selection rules for infrared absorption, it can be shown that these quantities determine whether a given mode of vibration can produce a Raman line and how the polarization of the light is changed on Raman scattering.

Raman spectra are usually observed with unpolarized light in which all electric vectors are vibrating perpendicular to the direction of the incident beam and evenly distributed around a circle. The light scattered is observed at right angles. If the direction of the light vectors are unchanged by scattering, the scattered light must be vibrating in a plane at right angles to the incident beam (call this the xy plane). The light responsible for the Raman spectrum has been re-emitted by the molecule, so it has a component polarized in a direction perpendicular to this plane.

The degree of depolarization is defined as

$$\rho_m = \frac{I_\perp}{I_\parallel} = \frac{6\beta^2}{45(\alpha^I)^2 + 7\beta^2}. \qquad \text{(A6.6–2)}$$

Quantum mechanically,

$$\beta^2 = \tfrac{1}{2}\{([\alpha_{xx}]^{v'v''}[\alpha_{yy}]^{v'v''})^2 + ([\alpha_{yy}]^{v'v''}[\alpha_{zz}]^{v'v''})^2 + ([\alpha_{zz}]^{v'v''}[\alpha_{xx}]^{v'v''})^2$$
$$+ 6([\alpha_{xy}]^{v'v''})^2 + ([\alpha_{yz}]^{v'v''})^2 + ([\alpha_{zx}]^{v'v''})^2\}. \qquad \text{(A6.6–3a)}$$

and

$$\alpha^I = \tfrac{1}{3}([\alpha_{xx}]^{v'v''} + [\alpha_{yy}]^{v'v''} + [\alpha_{zz}]^{v'v''}). \qquad \text{(A6.6–3b)}$$

The quantities $[\alpha_{xx}]^{v'v''}$ are related to the six components of polarizability in the same way that $[M_x]^{v'v''}$, etc., are related to the corresponding electrical moments; that is,

$$[\alpha_{xx}]^{v'v''} = \int \psi_v{}'' \, \alpha_{xx} \psi_v{}' \, d\tau.$$

The quantities will be non-zero only when the integrand is totally symmetric. This in turn will be true only when one of the α_{xx} has the same symmetry as $\psi_v{}''\psi_v{}'$. Since the ground state is totally symmetric, for transition from $v = 0$ to $v = 1$, this requirement is satisfied as for the quantities $[M_x]^{v'v''}$, when the α_{xx} have the same symmetry as $\psi_v{}''$. This latter condition means that α_{xx} must have the same symmetry as the normal coordinate. In the tables of Section A6.8 the symmetry species of α_{xx}, etc., is given.

In none of the three quantities α_{xx}, α_{yy}, α_{zz} has the same symmetry as the mode of vibration but any one of the three quantities α_{xy}, α_{yz}, α_{zx} does, $\rho = {}^6/_7$. If one of the quantities α_{xx} and one of the quantities α_{xy} has the same symmetry as the normal mode, $\rho < {}^6/_7$. If, and only if, α_{xx}, α_{yy}, α_{zz} have the symmetry of the normal mode and none of the α_{xy} has the same symmetry as the normal mode, will ρ_n be zero (under these circumstances $\alpha_{xx} = \alpha_{yy} = \alpha_{zz}$). The mode is then said to be polarized; this is denoted by the symbol *p* in the tables of Section A6.8. If ρ is other than zero, the mode is said to be depolarized and indicated by *dp* in the tables of Section A6.8.

If none of the three quantities α_{xx} and none of the three quantities α_{xy} have the same symmetry as the normal mode, the mode is Raman inactive and there is no Raman line. This is indicated by the symbol *ia* in the tables of Section A6.8. Since the Raman line (or band) is seldom resolved into fine structure, nothing about the rotational levels need be said.

As an example of the above we shall consider carbon dioxide of the point group $D_{\infty h}$. The mode ν_1 is of species $\Sigma_g{}^+$. α_{xx}, α_{yy}, α_{zz} are all of species $\Sigma_g{}^+$, and α_{xy}, α_{yz}, and α_{zx} have a different symmetry. Thus the fundamental of ν_1 is completely polarized. The mode ν_2 is degenerate. α_{xy}, α_{yz}, and α_{zx} are all degenerate, so there is a depolarized Raman line corresponding to the fundamental frequency. The mode ν_3 is of the species

Σ_u^+. None of the α's has this symmetry, so this mode cannot appear as a fundamental frequency.

As a second example we shall consider ammonia, which belongs to the point group C_{3v}. The modes ν_{3a}, ν_{3b} and ν_{4a} and ν_{4b} both belong to the class E. For C_{3v}, α_{xy}, α_{yz}, and α_{xz} all have the symmetry E, so the Raman lines corresponding to both fundamental frequencies are depolarized. The frequencies ν_1 and ν_2 belong to class A_1, for which α_{xy}, α_{yz}, and α_{xz} have a symmetry different from A_1, while α_{xx}, α_{yy}, and α_{zz} all have the symmetry A_1. Thus both of these fundamental frequencies are completely polarized.

An important rule can be applied if a molecule has a center of symmetry. This is the case if there is a point O, such that when a line is drawn through it from any atom at a point P_i in the molecule and continued to a point P_i', with OP_i' equal to OP, there is an atom at P_i' identical with that P. The point O is called the center of symmetry of the molecule. When a molecule has a center of symmetry, modes of vibration for which there is an infrared band corresponding to the fundamental have no Raman line corresponding to the fundamental; those modes for which there is a Raman line corresponding to the fundamental have no corresponding infrared band.

Problem A6.6-1. Check the statement immediately above for methane and benzene by reference to the tables of Section A6.8.

Problem A6.6-2. Indicate the Raman activity and polarization for the transition corresponding to the fundamental ($v = 0$ to $v = 1$) frequencies of benzene. Compare with Fig. A6.7-1.

Problem A6.6-3. For cyclopropane (see Problem A6.5-3) indicate the Raman activity and polarization of the transitions corresponding to the fundamental frequencies of cyclopropane.

Problem A6.6-4. Ascertain the number of vibrational modes in each species for cyclopropyl iodide. Indicate the infrared activity, Raman activity, and polarization of the transitions corresponding to the fundamental frequencies.

A6.7 Characterization of Normal Vibrations.[4] The Point Groups

The symmetry of a molecule or of a vibration may be described in terms of the results of a set of *symmetry operations*, which are the rotations, reflections, and related operations whose only result is to exchange identical

[4] The material of this section is almost a literal translation of the material in K. W. F. Kohlrausch, *Der Smekal-Raman-Effekt*, Supplementary Volume, Springer, Berlin, 1938.

particles. The possible symmetry operations are

C_p = rotation by $2\pi/p$ about a designated axis.
σ = reflection in a plane.
S_p = rotation by $2\pi/p$ about an axis, followed by reflection in plane perpendicular to that axis (rotary reflection, or "improper rotation").
i = inversion; each point is moved along a line through a designated central point and placed as far on the opposite side of the center as it was originally on the side where it occurred.

The symmetry of the molecule is designated by assigning it to a *point group*, as described below.

Symmetry operations have group character; that is, a sequence of two symmetry operations gives another symmetry operation. Accordingly, the simultaneous presence of several (independent) symmetry elements conditions the existence of further (dependent) symmetry elements, so that it is arbitrary which ones are considered primary or generating. Simple practical examples are: $C_2 \cdot i = \sigma$ (in words: 180° rotation and subsequent inversion about a point i is identical with reflection on a plane of symmetry σ; whereby $\sigma \perp C_2$); $S_2 \equiv C_2 \cdot \sigma_h \equiv i$ (180° rotation around C_2 and reflection on a plane vertical to C_2 is identical with inversion; i.e., reflection from the inversion center i); $i \cdot C_s \equiv C_2 \cdot S_{2p} \cdot S_{2p} \equiv C_p$ (double rotary reflection on axis S_{2p} is identical with rotation of $2\pi/p$ around axis C_p). $(S_{2p})^p \equiv i$ (for uneven p), as for the symmetry elements themselves; $S_2 \equiv i$.

By point group is understood, in each case, the entirety of the symmetry operations (for finite point systems) which are such that they leave unchanged the point common to all symmetry elements (excluding translation). According to the designation of Schoenfleis the point groups are denoted by their distinct rotational axes C_p, S_p lying vertically; if there are symmetry planes in addition, the indices are h (horizontal), v (vertical) or d (diagonal), all according to whether they refer to horizontal (σ_h) or vertical (σ_v) planes. The symbols are

C_{p} = systems with a p-fold axis of symmetry.
$C_{\mathrm{p}v}$ = systems with a p-fold axis of symmetry and p (vertical) symmetry planes σ_v through this axis.
D_{p} = systems with C_{p} and p twofold axes of rotation C_2 perpendicular to C_{p}, which make an angle π/p with one another.
$C_{\mathrm{p}h}$ = systems with C_{p} and one plane of symmetry σ_h perpendicular to C_{p}.
$D_{\mathrm{p}h}$ = systems with C_{p}, with p planes of symmetry σ_v through it and with one plane of symmetry σ_h perpendicular to C_{p}, which contains p twofold axes of symmetry C_2 perpendicular to C_{p}.

S_p = systems with p-fold rotation-reflection axes for even values of p only; for odd ones $S_p = C_{ph}$.

S_{pu} = systems with S_p, with p/2 planes of symmetry σ_v through these axes and p/2 twofold axes of symmetry perpendicular to C_p, which bisect the angle between the planes of symmetry (for even values of p only).

O, T = octahedral and tetrahedral systems, whose symmetry is described separately.

The designations of special cases are:

C_1 = identity; the system is considered asymmetrical.

$C_{1h} = C_s$; systems with one plane of symmetry.

$D_2 = V$; D stems from the term *Diedergruppe* V from *Vierergruppe*, in which none of the three now mutually perpendicular axes is designated.

$D_{2n} = V_n$; axes and planes are mutually perpendicular, as in the cartesian coordinate system.

$S_2 = C_i$; systems with inversion centers.

$S_6 = C_{3i}$; systems with C_3 and inversion center i.

$S_{4u} = V_d = D_{2d}$; systems with three mutually perpendicular axes of rotation C_2 and two planes of symmetry σ_v bisecting the angle between them.

$S_{6u} = D_{3d}$; systems with C_z, three axes C, perpendicular to it, making an angle of $2\pi/3$ with one another; and in addition three vertical planes of symmetry σ_v, which bisect the angles between the axes.

For the crystallographic point groups, only axes with $p = 2, 3, 4, 6$ need be considered, as follows:

C_1, C_i = triclinic point group.
C_s, C_2, C_{2h} = monoclinic point group.
C_{2v}, D_2, D_{2d} = orthorhombic point group.
$S_4, V_d, C_4, C_{4h}, C_{4v}, D_4, D_{4h}$ = tetragonal point group.
$C_3, C_{3i}, C_{3v}, D_3, D_{3d}, C_{3h}, D_{3h}, C_6, C_{6v}, C_{6h}, D_6, D_{6h}$ = hexagonal point group.
T, T_d, O, T_h = cubic point group.

The cubic groups are derived from the tetrahedral group T (systems with three mutually perpendicular twofold axes C_2 and four threefold axes C_3, which make equal angles with the former) by addition of symmetry elements.

The more frequently occurring linear systems of the non-crystallographic point groups are dealt with later. Since all their system points lie on a straight line, they have an "infinite-fold" symmetry axis C_∞ with an infinite number of symmetry planes σ_v going through it; if the points are symmetrically arranged with respect to a centrally located point, there is another symmetry plane σ_h perpendicular to C_∞ and accordingly also an inversion center i. The groups can be characterized by analogy to those above, by the symbols $C_{\infty v}$ or $D_{\infty h}$.

A6.8 Enumeration of the Modes of Vibration of a Given Symmetry †

The normal vibrations of a molecule are affected in three distinct ways by application of a symmetry operation. First, the vibration may be unaffected by the operation, in which case it is said to be *symmetrical* (*s*) to the operation. Second, each of the displacements may change sign, in which case the vibration is *antisymmetrical* (*as*) to the operation. Third, the displacements may change by more than sign; in this case the vibration is said to be *degenerate* (*e*) to the operation.

The normal vibrations of a given molecule are divided into types or *species* in terms of their behavior with respect to the essential symmetry operations of the point group to which the molecule belongs.

To obtain the number of vibrations belonging to a specific type for a given system with N mass points, first subtract as many degrees of freedom from the total number ($s = 3N$) as are defined by the symmetry requirements for this type; then subtract from the remaining degrees of freedom the number of "null vibrations" (translations and rotations) belonging to the same type.

Example. $Cl_2C = CCl_2$ is in the point group $D_{2h} = V_h$ (see Table A6.8–2) and has three mutually perpendicular planes of symmetry; σ_z is chosen as the molecular plane, σ_y as the bisector of the Cl—C—Cl angle. For example, one may seek the number of vibrations which are symmetrical (*s*) to σ_y and σ_z, but antisymmetrical (*as*) to σ_x. (These are of types B_{3u} in Table 2.) If the components of the amplitudes of chlorine atoms are designated x_i, y_i, z_i ($i = 1, 2, 3, 4$ numbered clockwise, 1 and 4 symmetrical to $\sigma(x)$), and those of the carbon atom x_i', y_i', z_i' ($i = 1, 2$), then for fulfillment of the symmetry requirements the following relationships must hold true.

If the vibration is to be symmetrical to σ_z:

$$z_1 = z_2 = z_3 = z_4 = 0; \qquad z_1' = z_2' = 0.$$

If the vibrations in the plane are to be symmetrical to σ_y,

$$x_1 = x_2; \qquad y_1 = -y_2; \qquad x_3 = x_4; \qquad y_3 = -y_4; \qquad y_1' = y_2' = 0.$$

If the vibrations in the xy plane and symmetrical to σ_y are to be antisymmetrical to σ_x,

$$x_1 = x_4; \qquad y_1 = -y_4; \qquad x_1' = x_2'.$$

† The text of this section and Tables A6.8–1 through A6.8–29 are almost a literal translation of material in Kohlrausch, *op. cit.*

As many degrees of freedom are used up in these specifications as there are signs of equality (i.e., 15). Of the total number of degrees of freedom ($3 \cdot 6 = 18$) only 3 are still "available." Of these another one is used up for the "null vibration" of the same symmetry (i.e., for translation in the x direction), so that only 2 remain for the performance of 2 normal vibrations.

It is also possible to start at the other end and count the number of degrees of freedom which the single "point types" make available to the vibration concerned. (The mass points are divided into "point types" according to their "characteristic symmetry," that is, according to the symmetry element on which they lie.) From the sum of these degrees of freedom the number of the null vibrations of like symmetry must again be subtracted.

Example. Consider again the vibration $as(\sigma_x)$, $s(\sigma_y)$, $s(\sigma_z)$ of $Cl_2C = CCl_2$. The points corresponding to the chlorine atoms lie on the σ_z plane; one Cl atom suffices for a base point from which all others may be produced by symmetry operation. The chlorine atoms are thus defined by a single mass point, which has 3 degrees of freedom. If this mass point (and along with it all other Cl points) should vibrate in the σ_z plane, because $s(\sigma_z z)$, then only the x and y directions are available; that is, it supplies 2 degrees of freedom. The C atoms, on the other hand, lie on the intersection of the σ_z and σ_y planes; again only one point of its type counts, since the other can be produced by reflection. If this point should move in the intersection (become symmetric to σ_x and σ_y), it can do so only in the x direction; thus it supplies 1 degree of freedom. There are thus $2 + 1 = 3$ degrees of freedom; subtraction of the translation in the x direction leaves again 2 degrees of freedom, which can describe 2 normal vibrations.

Every problem can be treated in one or the other of the ways described above. The counting of degenerate forms is somewhat harder; regarding this the reader may refer to the original literature.[5,6] Only "δ" points (see below) in degenerate vibrations take part in the motion of the system; they revolve in a closed orbit with the frequency belonging to the normal vibration.

The ability of a particular normal vibration to produce infrared and Raman spectra is determined by the symmetry requirements of the species to which it belongs. The *selection rules* for the vibration may then be stated immediately upon assignment of the vibration to the appropriate species. The behavior of a large number of molecular forms with central atoms has been described by Wilson.[7]

Tables A6.8–1 to A6.8–29 give the information required for specification of the number of vibrations of each species for the various point

[5] C. J. Brester, Dissertation, Utrecht, 1923.
[6] J. Cabannes, *J. chim. phys.*, **29**, 436 (1932).
[7] E. B. Wilson, Jr., *J. Chem. Phys.*, **2**, 432 (1934).

groups. They contain in addition the selection rules for each species. The procedure to be used for a particular molecule is as follows:

First, determine by inspection the symmetry elements present in the system under consideration and then assign it to the proper point group by use of the descriptions in the Section A.6–7. If an obvious axis is present in the molecule, place it in the z direction. Then determine that portion (unit cell) of the system by reflection or rotation of which it is possible (with the aid of the permissible symmetry operations) to build up the entire remaining system. Next, count the number of points of the unit cell which belong to each of the following particular "point types."

1. m, number of "general" points which lie on no symmetry element.
2. δ, number of points in the origin of the coordinates (one, or none); they count as δ points in all systems, except in those of the point groups C_s, C_p, C_{pv}, where coordinate origin is not defined by the symmetry.
3. c_x, c_y, c_z, c, number of points which lie on the x, y, z axes, on C_x, C_y, C_z, or on any other of the C_2 axes of the cell; δ points are not counted among these.
4. s_x, s_y, s_z, s, number of points which lie on one of the planes σ_x, σ_y, σ_z perpendicular to the x, y, z axes or on one of the symmetry planes σ_v going through the cell; δ and c points are to be excluded.

At the head of each table is given, in addition to the designation of the point group, a list of the applicable symmetry elements. The **necessary** symmetry elements (i.e., those required to generate the entire set) are in **boldface type**. Each row of the table describes the properties of the particular species designated on the left of that row. The section of the table headed "numbers" (of vibrations) gives an equation for the number of normal vibrations of that species in terms of the values of m, δ, c, etc., for the chosen system. The number of vibrations of each species is obtained by insertion of the appropriate values of m, δ, c, etc., throughout the appropriate table. At the foot of each table is a similar equation for the total number of mass points of the system.

The correctness of the assignment of vibrations to the particular species may be checked in two ways. First, determine whether or not the correct number of mass points of the system (N) is obtained by insertion of the determined numbers m, δ, c, s in the summation formula below the table for the point groups chosen. Second, determine whether or not the total number of vibrations is equal to $3N - 6$; for a planar molecule, $2N - 3$ vibrations must be in the plane of the molecule.

The contents of the tables are as follows: The first column contains the designation[8] of the species of vibrations. In most cases these are as given by Placzek,[9] except where modified to conform with the notation of Herzberg.[10] The second column or group of columns lists the symmetry properties of the vibration. Frequently more symmetry elements than necessary are given, for convenience in making comparisons. The meanings of the symbols are (as above): *s*, symmetrical: *as*, antisymmetrical; *e*, degenerate. The third section contains the selection rules: v means forbidden; *p*, polarized; and *dp*, polarized in the Raman effect. The symbol *ia* indicates that the mode is inactive in infrared absorption; M_x, M_y, M_z indicate active modes with electric moments in the x, y, z directions; $M_\perp$ indicates a mode in which the electric moment vibrates perpendicular to z. The fourth section gives number of vibrations per mass point of types m, s_x, etc.; the unlabeled negative numbers correspond to the null vibrations. Beneath each table is given the symmetry of the electric moments M_x, etc., and the polarizability components α_{xx}, etc. The use of these entries in determination of selection rules is discussed in Sections A6.5 and A6.6.

Example. $Cl_2C = CCl_2$; the point group is D_{2h}; the chlorine atoms lie on σ_z, the C atoms on C_x; accordingly $m = 0$, $s_x = s_y = 0$, $s_z = 1$, $c_x = 1$, $c_y = c_z = \delta = 0$. And $N = 4s_z + 2c_x = 6$; there must be $3N - 6\,(=12)$ vibrations of which $2N - 3$ (9) must be in the plane and $N - 3$ (3) perpendicular to the plane σ_z. The number of vibrations of each symmetry class is equal to the sum of the numbers listed under s_z and c_x for that class, multiplied by one in each case, since $s_z = c_x = 1$. For each set of the B type a null vibration must be subtracted as indicated. Thus the number of type A_g is $2\,(1) + 1\,(1) = 3$; that of $B_{2g} = 1\,(1) + 1\,(1) - 1 = 1$. (If s_z had been 2, each number undeı s_z would have to be doubled, and so on.) Furthermore, the vibrations of type A_g are polarized in the Raman spectra (*p*) and inactive (*ia*) in the infrared; that of type B_{2g} is depolarized (*dp*) in Raman spectra and inactive (*ia*) in the infrared. The results are: 3 vibrations of type A_g (p,ia), 1 vibration A_u (v,ia), 2 vibrations $B_{1g}\,(dp,ia)$; 1 vibration $B_{1u}\,(v,M_z)$, 1 vibration $B_{2g}\,(dp,ia)$, 2 vibrations B_{2u} (v,M_y), no vibrations B_{3g}, 2 vibrations B_{3u} (v,M_x); total 12, of which 3 (namely A_{1u}, B_{1u}, B_{2g}) are perpendicular to σ_z.

The selection rules for overtones and combination frequencies of non-degenerate vibrations can also be obtained from the tables. To determine the types of the states where combination frequencies will be observed, multiply the rows giving the symmetry data of the two states, using only

[8] In general, A, B, E, F mean: symmetrical, asymmetrical, two- or threefold degenerate with respect to an axis C_p. The indices mean: g (even), u (odd), with reference to the center of symmetry i; prime (′) and double prime (″), symmetrical or asymmetrical to a plane of symmetry σ; E^* means "separable" degenerate.

[9] G. Placzek, *Rayleigh-Streuung und Raman Effekt*, Akademische Verlagsgesellschaft, Leipzig, 1934.

[10] G. Herzberg, *op. cit.*, Van Nostrand, Princeton, N.J., 1945, Vol. II, Chapter II.

the **necessary** symmetry elements. In doing so, the multiplication rules are $s \cdot s = as \cdot as = s$; and $s \cdot as = as$. The line corresponding to the set of products will give the class of the combination frequency and thus the selection rule.

Example. The selection rules for the combination of a vibration belonging to B_{1g} with a vibration belonging to B_{2g} or B_{1u} of $Cl_2C = CCl_2$ are obtained from Table A6.8–2 as follows:

	C_2^z	σ_z	C_x		C_2^z	σ_z	C_x
B_{1g}	s	s	as	B_{1g}	s	s	as
B_{2g}	as	as	as	B_{1u}	s	as	as
Product I	as	as	s	Product II	s	as	s

Product I contains the symmetry properties of the B_{3g} group; the combination frequency is thus depolarized in Raman and inactive in infrared. Product II corresponds to A_u, the combination frequency is *v*, *ia*.

Further information is necessary for determination of the selection rules of combinations or overtones involving degenerate frequencies. These may be obtained from tables of *characters* of the various point groups such as those given by Herzberg.[10] Tables A6.8–30 and A6.8–31 contain the species of overtone and combination frequencies involving degenerate modes, as given by Herzberg.[10] Combinations of degenerate frequencies result in more than one final state; these states are usually of almost the same energy. Combinations involving more than two modes, or a fundamental and a harmonic, may be obtained in the same fashion, whether degenerate or non-degenerate modes are involved.

Only Tables A6.8–2, A6.8–8, A6.8–13, A6.8–20, and A6.8–28 are independent, and all the others can be derived from them. As an example, Table A6.8–3 (point group D_2) will be derived from Table A6.8–2 (D_{2h}). D_2 differs from D_{2h} by its lack of the symmetry elements σ_x, σ_y, σ_z,i, with several consequences. First, the multiplicity of certain types of points is changed; for D_{2h}, $N = 8m + 4s_x + 4s_y + 4s_z + 2c_x + 2c_y + 2c_z + \delta$ holds; for D_2, $N = 4m + 2c_x + 2c_y + 2c_z + \delta$. On the one hand, the points s_x, s_y, and s_z became "general" points (m); on the other hand, the multiplicity of the point m is decreased from 8 to 4 (because of lack of reflection on σ_z). Second, the distinction of classes because of behavior with respect to σ_x, σ_y, σ_z, and i disappears. This A_g and A_u become a single class A, in which C_2^z, C_y, and C_x have symmetry s, s, s, respectively; $B_{1g} = B_{1u} = B$ (s, as, as); $B_{2g} = B_{2u} = B_2$ (as, s, as); $B_{3g} = B_{3u} = B_3$ (as, as, s). The selection rules are then obtained by (1) choosing from the original classes any common selection rules, and (2) in case of disagreement choosing the one more favorable to transitions. Thus, for class A, the selection rules for A_g, A_u are polarized in Raman, inactive in infrared; for B_{1g}, B_{1u}, $\cdots$, dp, M_z; for B_{2g}, B_{2u}, $\cdots$, dp, M_y; for B_{3g}, B_{3u}, $\cdots$, dp, M_x. The rules for number of vibrations per mass point are obtained by adding the data for the classes which have been combined and then correcting the result in ratio to the reduced multiplicity of single point types. For example, the sum of the first and second lines of Table A6.8–2 (with the omission of s_x, s_y, s_z) is $6m + c_x + c_y + c_z$; because the multiplicity of the points m has been halved (see above), the specification for Table A6.8–2 is $3m + c_x + c_y + c_z$.

Figure A6.8–1 contains stereographic properties for systems with two-, three-, four-, sixfold axes of symmetry, as an aid in classification of transitions. They show projections of the symmetry elements of each point group on the xy plane.

The symbols used are as follows:

Full (or dotted) circle.	The system has one (or no) symmetry plane σ_z.
Solid straight lines.	Intersections of vertical symmetry planes σ_v with the plane of the paper.
Dotted straight lines.	Twofold symmetry axes C in the plane of the paper.
● ▲ ■ ⬢	End points of two-, three-, four-, sixfold axes; such symbols in the middle of the figures belong to C_p axes in the z direction; this is, perpendicular to the paper. The first symbol, when at ends of a solid straight line in the plane of the paper, shows that the intersection of σ_v with σ_z is also a C_2 axis.
⬭ □ ⬡	End points of two-, four-, or sixfold rotation-reflection axes, S_p; ◙ means that the direction of S_4^z coincides with that of C_2^z.
+ ○	Position of a "general" point above (+) or below (○) the plane of the paper; from these symbols the multiplicity of the point types m may be determined.

The symmetry characteristics of each of the point groups and the classes within them are listed in Tables A6.8–1 to A6.8–29. The meanings of the symbols have been given above.

Behavior of Systems with a Single-Fold Axis C

1. $C_{1h} = C_s$, monoclinic point group; symmetry element σ (Table A6.8–1).

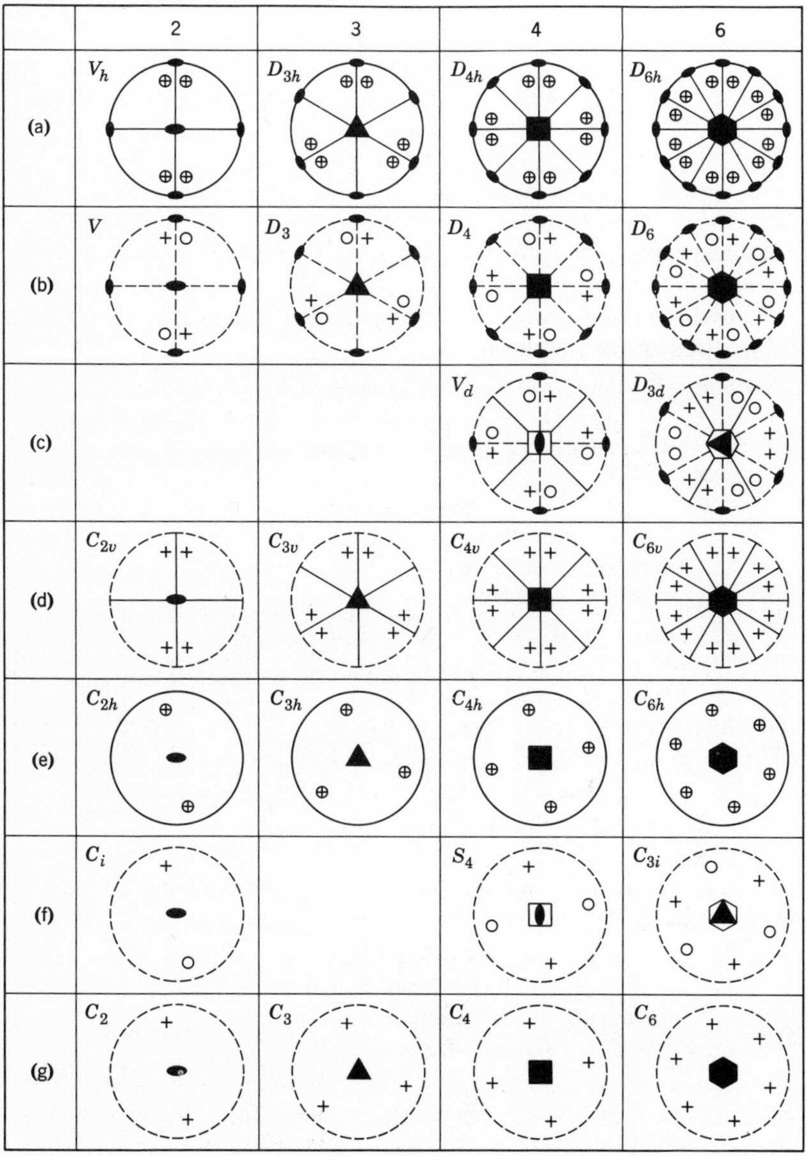

Fig. A6.8–1. Stereographic projections of crystalline point groups.

(a) Holohedral; (b) enantiomorphic; (c) hemihedral (II); (d) hemimorphic; (e) paramorphic; (f) tetartohedral (II); (g) tetartohedral (I).[4] (From *Der Smekal-Raman-Effekt*, by K. W. Kohlrausch, Erganzungsband (1931–37). Springer-Verlag, 1938.)

Table A6.8–1

Point Group $C_{1h} = C_s$

Type	σ_z	Selection Rules		Numbers
A'	s	p	$M_\perp$	$3m + 2s_z - 3$
A''	as	dp	M_z	$3m + s_z - 3$

$$N = 2m + s_z$$

M_x	M_y	M_z	α_{xx}	α_{yy}	α_{zz}	α_{xy}	α_{xz}	α_{yz}
A'	A'	A''	A'	A'	A'	A'	A''	A''

If the symmetry is destroyed, the distinction between m and s vanishes, and one obtains

C_1, triclinic point group; no symmetry elements; $3N - 6$ polarized and infrared active vibrations.

Behaviour of Systems with Twofold Symmetry Axis C_2 or S_2

2. $D_{2h} = V_h$, rhombic point group; symmetry elements C_2^z, C_x, C_y, σ_x, σ_y, $\boldsymbol{\sigma}_z = \boldsymbol{\sigma}_h$; i (Table A6.8–2).

Table A6.8–2

Point Group $D_{2h} = V_h$

Type	Symmetry C_2^z	σ_x	σ_z	C_x	i	Selection Rules		Numbers
A_g	s	s	s	s	s	p	ia	$3m + 2s_x + 2s_y + 2s_z + c_x + c_y + c_z$
A_u	s	as	as	s	as	v	ia	$3m + s_x + s_y + s_z$
B_{1g}	s	as	s	as	s	dp	ia	$3m + s_x + s_y + 2s_z + c_x + c_y - 1$
B_{1u}	s	s	as	as	as	v	M_z	$3m + 2s_x + 2s_y + s_z + c_x + c_y + c_z + \delta - 1$
B_{2g}	as	as	as	as	s	dp	ia	$3m + s_x + 2s_y + s_z + c_x + c_z - 1$
B_{2u}	as	s	s	as	as	v	M_y	$3m + 2s_x + s_y + 2s_z + c_x + c_y + c_z + \delta - 1$
B_{3g}	as	s	as	s	s	dp	ia	$3m + 2s_x + s_y + s_z + c_y + c_z - 1$
B_{3u}	as	as	s	s	as	v	M_x	$3m + s_x + 2s_y + 2s_z + c_x + c_y + c_z + \delta - 1$

$$N = 8m + 4s_x + 4s_y + 4s_z + 2c_x + 2c_y + 2c_z + \delta$$

M_x	M_y	M_z	α_{xx}	α_{yy}	α_{zz}	α_{xy}	α_{xz}	α_{yz}
B_{3u}	B_{2u}	B_{1u}	A_g	A_g	A_g	B_{1g}	B_{2g}	B_{3g}

3. $D_2 = V$, rhombic point group; symmetry elements C_2^z, C_x, C_y (Table A6.8–3).

Table A6.8–3

Point Group $D_2 = V$

Type	Symmetry C_2^z	C_x	C_y	Selection Rules		Numbers
A	s	s	s	p	ia	$3m + c_x + c_z + c_y$
B_1	s	as	as	dp	M_z	$3m + 2c_x + 2c_y + c_z + \delta - 2$
B_2	as	as	s	dp	M_y	$3m + 2c_x + c_y + 2c_z + \delta - 2$
B_3	as	s	as	dp	M_x	$3m + c_x + 2c_y + 2c_z + \delta - 2$

$$N = 4m + 2c_x + 2c_y + 2c_z + \delta$$

M_x	M_y	M_z	α_{xx}	α_{yy}	α_{zz}	α_{xy}	α_{xz}	α_{yz}
B_3	B_2	B_1	A	A	A	B_1	B_2	B_3

4. C_{2h}, rhombic point group; symmetry elements C_{2x}, $\boldsymbol{\sigma}_x$, σ_y (Table A6.8–4).

Table A6.8–4
Point Group C_{2v}

Type	Symmetry C_2^z	σ_x	σ_y	Selection Rules		Numbers
A_1	s	s	s	p	M_z	$3m + 2s_x + 2s_y + c_z - 1$
A_2	s	as	as	dp	ia	$3m + s_x + s_y - 1$
B_1	as	as	s	dp	M_x	$3m + s_x + 2s_y + c_z - 2$
B_2	as	s	as	dp	M_y	$3m + 2s + s_y + c_z - 2$

$$N = 4m + 2s_x + 2s_y + c_z$$

M_x	M_y	M_z	α_{xx}	α_{yy}	α_{zz}	α_{xy}	α_{xz}	α_{yz}
B_1	B_2	A_1	A_1	A_1	A_1	A_2	B_1	B_2

5. C_{2h}, monoclinic point group; symmetry elements C_2^z, $\boldsymbol{\sigma}_z = \boldsymbol{\sigma}_h$; i (Table A6.8–5).

Table A6.8–5
Point Group C_{2h}

Type	Symmetry C_2^z	σ_z	i	Selection Rules		Numbers
A_g	s	s	s	p	ia	$3m + 2s_z + c_z - 1$
A_u	s	as	as	v	M_z	$3m + s_z + c_z + \delta - 1$
B_g	as	as	s	dp	ia	$3m + s_z + 2c_z - 2$
B_u	as	s	as	v	$M_\perp$	$3m + 2s_z + 2c_z + 2\delta - 2$

$$N = 4m + 2s_z + 2c_z + \delta$$

M_x	M_y	M_z	α_{xx}	α_{yy}	α_{zz}	α_{xy}	α_{xz}	α_{yz}
B_u	B_u	A_u	A_g	A_g	A_g	A_g	B_g	B_g

6. $S_2 = C_i$, triclinic point group; symmetry element $\boldsymbol{i}$ (Table A6.8–6).

Table A6.8–6
Point Group $S_2 = C_i$

Type	Symmetry i	Selection Rules		Numbers
g	s	p	ia	$3m - 3$
u	as	dp	a	$3m + 3\delta - 3$

$$N = 2m + \delta$$

M_x	M_y	M_z	α_{xx}	α_{yy}	α_{zz}	α_{xy}	α_{xz}	α_{yz}
u	u	u	g	g	g	g	g	g

7. C_2, monoclinic point group; symmetry element C_2 (Table A6.8–7).

Table A6.8–7
Point Group C_2

Type	Symmetry C_2	Selection Rules		Numbers
A	s	p	M_z	$3m + c_z - 2$
B	as	dp	$M_\perp$	$3m + 2c_z - 4$

$$N = 2m + c_z$$

M_x	M_y	M_z	α_{xx}	α_{yy}	α_{zz}	α_{xy}	α_{xz}	α_{yz}
B	B	A	A	A	A	A	B	B

Behavior of Systems with Threefold Axis C_3

As in all systems with symmetry axis of odd multiplicity, there are no vibrations asymmetric to the axis C_p.

8. D_{3h}, hexagonal point group; symmetry elements $C_3{}^z$, C_y, $2C$, σ_x, $2\sigma_v$, $\boldsymbol{\sigma}_z = \boldsymbol{\sigma}_h$ (Table A6.8–8).

Table A6.8–8
Point Group D_{3h}

Type	Symmetry $C_3{}^z$	σ_x	σ_z	C_y	Selection Rules		Numbers
A_1'	s	s	s	s	p	ia	$3m + 2s_x + 2s + 2s_z + c_y + c + c_z$
A_1''	s	as	as	s	v	ia	$3m + s_x + s + s_z$
A_2'	s	as	s	as	v	ia	$3m + s_x + s + 2s_z + c_y + c - 1$
A_2''	s	s	as	as	v	M_z	$3m + 2s_x + 2s + s_z + c_y + c + c_z + \delta - 1$
E'	e	e	s	e	dp	$M_\perp$	$6m + 3s_x + 3s + 4s_z + 2c_y + 2c + c_z + \delta - 1$
E''	e	e	as	e	dp	ia	$6m + 3s_x + 3s + 2s_z + c_y + c + c_z - 1$

$$N = 12m + 6s_x + 6s + 6s_z + 3c_y + 3c + 2c_z + \delta$$

M_x	M_y	M_z	α_{xx}	α_{yy}	α_{zz}	α_{xy}	α_{xz}	α_{yz}
E'	E'	A_2''	A_1', E'	A_1', E'	A_1'	E'	E''	E''

9. D_3, rhombohedral point group; symmetry elements $C_3{}^z$, C_y, $2C$ (Table A6.8–9).

Table A6.8–9
Point Group D_3

Type	Symmetry $C_3{}^z$	C_y	Selection Rules		Numbers
A_1	s	s	p	ia	$3m + c_y + c + c_z$
A_2	s	as	v	M_z	$3m + 2c_y + 2c + c_z + \delta - 2$
E	e	e	dp	$M_\perp$	$6m + 3c_y + 3c + 2c_z + \delta - 2$

$$N = 6m + 3c_y + 3c + 2c_z + \delta$$

M_x	M_y	M_z	α_{xx}	α_{yy}	α_{zz}	α_{xy}	α_{xz}	α_{yz}
E	E	A_2	A_1, E	A_1, E	A_1	E	E	E

10. C_{3v}, rhombohedral point group; symmetry elements C_3^z, $\boldsymbol{\sigma}_x$, $2\boldsymbol{\sigma}_v$ (Table A6.8–10).

Table A6.8–10
Point Group C_{3v}

Type	Symmetry C_3^z	σ_x	Selection Rules		Numbers
A_1	s	s	p	M_z	$3m + 2s_x + 2s + c_z - 1$
A_2	s	as	v	ia	$3m + s_x + s - 1$
E	e	e	dp	$M_\perp$	$6m + 3s_x + 3s + c_z - 2$

$$N = 6m + 3s_x + 3s + c_z$$

M_x	M_y	M_z	α_{xx}	α_{yy}	α_{zz}	α_{xy}	α_{xz}	α_{yz}
E	E	A_1	A_1, E	A_1, E	A_1	E	E	E

11. C_{3h}, hexagonal point group; symmetry elements C_3^z, $\boldsymbol{\sigma}_z = \boldsymbol{\sigma}_h$ (Table A6.8–11).

Table A6.8–11
Point Group C_{3h}

Type	Symmetry C_3^z	z	Selection Rules		Numbers
A'	s	s	p	ia	$3m + 2s_z + c_z - 1$
A''	s	as	v	M_z	$3m + s_z + c_z + \delta - 1$
E'*	e	s	dp	$M_\perp$	$3m + 2s_z + c_z + \delta - 1$
E''*	e	as	dp	ia	$3m + s_z + c_z - 1$

$$N = 6m + 3s_z + 2c_z + \delta$$

M_x	M_y	M_z	α_{xx}	α_{yy}	α_{zz}	α_{xy}	α_{xz}	α_{yz}
E'	E'	A''	A', E'	A', E'	A'	E'*	E''*	E''*

12. C_3, rhombohedral point group; symmetry element C_3^z (Table A6.8–12).

Table A6.8–12
Point Group C_3

Type	Symmetry C_3	Selection Rules		Numbers
A	s	p	M_z	$3m + c_z - 2$
E*	e	dp	$M_\perp$	$3m + c_z - 2$

$$N = 3m + c_z$$

M_x	M_y	M_z	α_{xx}	α_{yy}	α_{zz}	α_{xy}	α_{xz}	α_{yz}
E	E	A	A, E	A, E	A	E	E	E

Behavior of Systems with Fourfold Axis C_4, S_4 (Tetragonal Point Groups)

13. D_{4h}; symmetry elements S_4^z, C_4^z, C_2^z, C_x, C_y, $2C$, σ_x, σ_y, $2\sigma_v$, $\boldsymbol{\sigma}_z = \boldsymbol{\sigma}_h$, i (Table A6.8–13).

Table A6.8–13

Point Group D_{4h}

Type	Symmetry S_4	C_4^z	C_y	σ_x	σ_z	Selection Rules		Numbers
A_{1g}	s	s	s	s	s	p	ia	$3m + 2s_x + 2s + 2s_z + c_y + c_z + c$
A_{1u}	as	s	s	as	as	v	ia	$3m + s_x + s + s_z$
A_{2g}	s	s	as	as	s	v	ia	$3m + s_x + s + 2s_z + c_y + c_z - 1$
A_{2u}	as	s	as	s	as	v	M_z	$3m + 2s_x + 2s + s_z + c_y + c_z + c + \delta - 1$
B_{1g}	as	as	s	s	s	dp	ia	$3m + 2s_x + s + 2s_z + c_y + c$
B_{1u}	s	as	s	as	as	v	ia	$3m + s_x + 2s + s_z + c$
B_{2g}	as	as	as	as	s	dp	ia	$3m + s_x + 2s + 2s_z + c_y + c$
B_{2u}	s	as	as	s	as	v	ia	$3m + 2s_x + s + s_z + c_y$
E_g	e	e	e	e	as	dp	ia	$6m + 3s_x + 3s + 2s_z + c_y + c_z + c - 1$
E_u	e	e	e	e	s	v	$M_\perp$	$6m + 3s_x + 3s + 4s_z + 2c_y + 2c_z + c + \delta - 1$

$$N = 16m + 8s_x + 8s + 8s_z + 4c_y + 4c_z + 2c + \delta$$

M_x	M_y	M_z	α_{xx}	α_{yy}	α_{zz}	α_{xy}	α_{xz}	α_{yz}
E_u	E_u	A_{2u}	A_{1g}, B_{1g}	A_{1g}, B_{1g}	A_{1g}	B_{2g}	E_g	E_g

14. D_4; symmetry elements C_4^z, C_2^z, C_x, C_y, $2C_2$ (Table A6.8–14).

Table A6.8–14

Point Group D_4

Type	Symmetry C_4^z	C_y	C	Selection Rules		Numbers
A_1	s	s	s	p	ia	$3m + c_y + c + c_z$
A_2	s	as	as	v	M_z	$3m + 2c_y + 2c + c_z + \delta - 2$
B_1	as	s	as	dp	ia	$3m + c_y + 2c$
B_2	as	as	s	dp	ia	$3m + 2c_y + c$
E	e	e	e	dp	$M_\perp$	$6m + 3c_y + 3c + 2c_z + \delta - 2$

$$N = 8m + 4c_y + 4c + 2c_z + \delta$$

M_x	M_y	M_z	α_{xx}	α_{yy}	α_{zz}	α_{yx}	α_{xz}	α_{yz}
E	E	A_2	A_1, B_1	A_1, B_1	A_1	B_2	E	E

15. $V_d = D_{2d} = S_{4u}$; symmetry elements S_4^z, C_2^z, C_y, C_x, $2\sigma_v$ (Table A6.8–15).

Table A6.8–15

Point Group $V_d = D_{2d} = S_{4u}$

Type	Symmetry S_4	C_2^z	C_y	σ_v	Selection Rules		Numbers
A_1	s	s	s	s	p	ia	$3m + 2s + c_y + c_z$
A_2	s	s	as	as	v	ia	$3m + s + 2c_y$
B_1	as	s	s	as	dp	ia	$3m + s + c_y$
B_2	as	s	as	s	dp	M_z	$3m + 2s + 2c_y + c_z + \delta - 1$
E	e	as	e	e	dp	$M_\perp$	$6m + 3s + 3c_y + 2c_z + \delta - 2$

$$N = 8m + 4s + 4c_y + 2c_z + \delta$$

M_x	M_y	M_z	α_{xx}	α_{yy}	α_{zz}	α_{xy}	α_{xz}	α_{yz}
E	E	B_2	A_1, B_1	A_1, B_1	A_1	B_2	E	E

16. C_{4v}; symmetry elements C_4^z, C_2^z, $\boldsymbol{\sigma}_x$, σ_y, $2\sigma_v$ (Table A6.8–16).

Table A6.8–16
Point Group C_{4v}

Type	Symmetry C_4^z	σ_x	σ_v	Selection Rules		Numbers
A_1	s	s	s	p	M_z	$3m + 2s_x + 2s + c_z - 1$
A_2	s	as	as	v	ia	$3m + s_x + s - 1$
B_1	as	as	s	dp	ia	$3m + s_x + 2s$
B_2	as	s	as	dp	ia	$3m + 2s_x + s$
E	e	e	e	dp	$M_\perp$	$6m + 3s_x + 3s + c_z - 2$

$$N = 8m + 4s_x + 4s + c_z$$

M_x	M_y	M_z	α_{xx}	α_{yy}	α_{zz}	α_{xy}	α_{xz}	α_{yx}
E	E	A_1	A_1,B_1	A_1,B_1	A_1	B_2	E	E

17. C_{4h}; symmetry elements S_4^z, C_4^z, $\boldsymbol{\sigma}_z = \boldsymbol{\sigma}_h$, i (Table A6.8–17).

Table A6.8–17
Point Group C_{4h}

Type	Symmetry C_4^z	σ_z	i	Selection Rules		Numbers
A_g	s	s	s	p	ia	$3m + 2s_z + c_z - 1$
A_u	s	as	as	v	M_z	$3m + s_z + c_z + \delta - 1$
B_g	as	s	s	dp	ia	$3m + 2s_z$
B_u	as	as	as	v	ia	$3m + s_z$
E_g*	e	as	s	dp	ia	$3m + s_z + c_z - 1$
E_u*	e	s	as	v	$M_\perp$	$3m + 2s_z + c_z + \delta - 1$

$$N = 8m + 4s_z + 2c_z + \delta$$

M_x	M_y	M_z	α_{xx}	α_{yy}	α_{zz}	α_{xy}	α_{xz}	α_{yz}
E_u	E_u	A_u	A_g, B_g	A_g, B_g	A_g	B_g	E_g	E_g

18. S_4; symmetry elements S_4^z, C_2^z (Table A6.8–18).

Table A6.8–18
Point Group S_4

Type	Symmetry S_4^z	C_2^z	Selection Rules		Numbers
A	s	s	p	ia	$3m + c_z - 1$
B	as	s	dp	M_z	$3m + c_z + \delta - 1$
E*	e	as	dp	$M_\perp$	$3m + 2c_z + \delta - 2$

$$N = 4m + 2c_z + \delta$$

M_x	M_y	M_z	α_{xx}	α_{yy}	α_{zz}	α_{xy}	α_{xz}	α_{yz}
E	E	A	A,B	A,B	A	B	E	E

19. C_4; symmetry elements C_4^z, C_2^z (Table A6.8–19).

Table A6.8–19

Point Group C_4

Type	Symmetry C_4^z	C_2^z	Selection Rules		Numbers
A	s	s	p	M_z	$3m + c_z - 2$
B	as	s	dp	ia	$3m$
E^*	e	as	dp	$M_\perp$	$3m + c_z - 2$

$$N = 4m + c_z$$

M_x	M_y	M_z	α_{xx}	α_{yy}	α_{zz}	α_{xy}	α_{xz}	α_{yz}
E	E	A	A, B	A, B	A	B	E	E

Behavior of Systems with Sixfold Axis C_6, S_6 (Hexagonal Point Groups)

20. D_{6h}; symmetry elements C_6^z, C_3^z, C_2^z, C_x, C_y, $4C$, σ_x, σ_y, $4\sigma_v$, $\sigma_z = \sigma_h$, i (Table A6.8–20).

Table A6.8–20

Point Group D_{6h}

Type	Symmetry C_6^z	C_3^z	C_2^z	C_y	σ_y	σ_z	Selection Rules		Numbers
A_{1g}	s	s	s	s	s	s	p	ia	$3m+2s_x+2s+2s_z+c_y+c+c_z$
A_{1u}	s	s	s	s	as	as	v	ia	$3m+s_x+s+s_z$
A_{2g}	s	s	s	as	as	s	v	ia	$3m+s_x+s+2s_z+c_y+c-1$
A_{2u}	s	s	s	as	s	as	v	M_z	$3m+2s_x+2s+s_z+c_y+c+c_z+\delta-1$
B_{1g}	as	s	as	s	s	as	v	ia	$3m+s_x+2s+s_z$
B_{1u}	as	s	as	s	as	s	v	ia	$3m+2s_x+s+2s_z+c_y+c$
B_{2g}	as	s	as	as	as	as	v	ia	$3m+2s_x+s+s_z+c_y$
B_{2u}	as	s	as	as	s	s	v	ia	$3m+s_x+2s+2s_z+c_y+c$
E_{2g}	e	e	s	e	e	s	dp	ia	$6m+3s_x+3s+4s_z+2c_y+2c$
E_{2u}	e	e	s	e	e	as	v	ia	$6m+3s_x+3s+2s_z+c_y+c$
E_{1g}	e	e	as	e	e	as	dp	ia	$6m+3s_x+3s+2s_z+c_y+c+c_z-1$
E_{1u}	e	e	as	e	e	s	v	$M_\perp$	$6m+3s_x+3s+4s_z+2c_y+2c+c_z+\delta-1$

$$N = 24m + 12s_x + 12s + 12s_z + 6c_y + 6c + 2c_z + \delta$$

M_x	M_y	M_z	α_{xx}	α_{yy}	α_{zz}	α_{xy}	α_{xz}	α_{yz}
E_{1u}	E_{1u}	A_{2u}	A_{1g}, E_{2g}	A_{1g}, E_{2g}	A_{1g}	E_{2g}	E_{1g}	E_{1g}

21. D_6; symmetry elements C_6^z, C_3^z, C_2^z, C_x, C_y, $4C$ (Table A6.8–21).

Table A6.8–21

Point Group D_6

Type	Symmetry C_6^z	C_2^z	C_y	C	Selection Rules		Numbers
A_1	s	s	s	s	p	ia	$3m + c_y + c + c_z$
A_2	s	s	as	as	v	M_z	$3m + 2c_y + 2c + c_z + \delta - 2$
B_1	as	as	s	as	v	ia	$3m + c_y + 2c$
B_2	as	as	as	s	v	ia	$3m + 2c_y + c$
E_2	e	s	e	e	dp	ia	$6m + 3c_y + 3c$
E_1	e	as	e	e	dp	$M_\perp$	$6m + 3c_y + 3c + 2c_z + \delta - 2$

$$N = 12m + 6c_y + 6c + 2c_z + \delta$$

M_x	M_y	M_z	α_{xx}	α_{yy}	α_{zz}	α_{xy}	α_{xz}	α_{yz}
E_1	E_1	A_2	A_1, E_2	A_1, E_2	A_1	E_2	E_1	E_1

22. $D_{3d} = S_{6u}$; symmetry elements S_6^z, C_3^z, C_y, $2C$, σ_y, $2\sigma_v$, i (Table A6.8–22).

Table A6.8–22
Point Group $D_{3d} = S_{6u}$

Type	Symmetry C_3	C_y	σ_v	i	Selection Rules		Numbers
A_{1g}	s	s	s	s	p	ia	$3m + 2s + c_y + c_z$
A_{1u}	s	s	as	as	v	ia	$3m + s + c_y$
A_{2g}	s	as	as	s	v	ia	$3m + s + 2c_y - 1$
A_{2u}	s	as	s	as	v	M_z	$3m + 2s + 2c_y + c_z + \delta - 1$
E_g	e	e	e	s	dp	ia	$6m + 3s + 3c_y + c_z - 1$
E_u	e	e	e	as	v	$M_\perp$	$6m + 3s + 3c_y + c_z + \delta - 1$

$$N = 12m + 6s + 6c_y + 2c_z + \delta$$

M_x	M_y	M_z	α_{xx}	α_{yy}	α_{zz}	α_{xy}	α_{xz}	α_{yz}
E_u	E_u	A_{2u}	A_{1g}, E_g	A_{1g}, E_g	A_{1g}	E_g	E_g	E_g

23. C_{6v}; symmetry elements C_6^z, C_3^z, C_2^z, σ_x, $\boldsymbol{\sigma}_y$, $4\sigma_v$ (Table A6.8–23).

Table A6.8–23
Point Group C_{6v}

Type	Symmetry C_6	σ_y	σ_v	Selection Rules		Numbers
A_1	s	s	s	p	M_z	$3m + 2s_y + 2s + c_z - 1$
A_2	s	as	as	v	ia	$3m + s_y + s - 1$
B_1	as	as	s	v	ia	$3m + s_y + 2s$
B_2	as	s	as	v	ia	$3m + 2s_y + s$
E_2	e	e	e	dp	ia	$6m + 3s_y + 3s$
E_1	e	e	e	dp	$M_\perp$	$6m + 3s_y + 3s + c_z - 2$

$$N = 12m + 6s_y + 6s + c_z$$

M_x	M_y	M_z	α_{xx}	α_{yy}	α_{zz}	α_{xy}	α_{xz}	α_{yz}
E_1	E_1	A_1	A_1, E_2	A_1, E_2	A_1	E_2	E_1	E_1

24. C_{6h}; symmetry elements C_6^z, C_3^z, C_2, $\boldsymbol{\sigma}_z = \sigma_h$, i (Table A6.8–24).

Table A6.8–24
Point Group C_{6h}

Type	Symmetry C_6^z	Symmetry σ_z	Selection Rules		Numbers
A_g	s	s	p	ia	$3m + 2s_z + c_z - 1$
A_u	s	as	v	M_z	$3m + s_z + c_z + \delta - 1$
B_g	as	as	v	ia	$3m + s_z$
B_u	as	s	v	ia	$3m + 2s_z$
E_{2g}	e	s	dp	ia	$3m + 2s_z$
E_{2u}	e	as	v	ia	$3m + s_z$
E_{1g}	e	as	dp	ia	$3m + s_z + c_z - 1$
E_{1u}	e	s	v	$M_\perp$	$3m + 2s_z + c_z + \delta - 1$

$$N = 12m + 6s_z + 2c_z + \delta$$

M_x	M_y	M_z	α_{xx}	α_{yy}	α_{zz}	α_{xy}	α_{xz}	α_{yz}
E_{1u}	E_{1u}	A_u	A_g, E_{2g}	A_g, E_{2g}	A_g	E_{2g}	E_{1g}	E_{1g}

25. $C_{3i} = S_6$; symmetry elements S_6^z, C_3^z, $\boldsymbol{i}$ (Table A6.8–25).

Table A6.8–25
Point Group $C_{3i} = S_6$

Type	Symmetry C_3^z	Symmetry i	Selection Rules		Numbers
A_g	s	s	p	ia	$3m + c_z - 1$
B_u	s	as	v	M_z	$3m + c_z + \delta - 1$
E_g	e	s	dp	ia	$3m + c_z - 1$
E_u	e	as	v	$M_\perp$	$3m + c_z + \delta - 1$

$$N = 6m + 2c_z + \delta$$

M_x	M_y	M_z	α_{xx}	α_{yy}	α_{zz}	α_{xy}	α_{xz}	α_{yz}
E_{1u}	E_{1u}	B_u	A_g, E_{2g}	A_g, E_{2g}	A_g	E_{2g}	E_{2g}	E_{2g}

26. C_6; symmetry elements C_6^z, C_3^z, C_2^z (Table A6.8–26).

Table A6.8–26
Point Group C_6

Type	Symmetry C_6^z	Symmetry C_2^z	Selection Rules		Numbers
A	s	s	p	M_z	$3m + c_z - 2$
B	as	as	v	ia	$3m$
E_2	e	s	dp	ia	$3m$
E_1	e	as	dp	$M_\perp$	$3m + c_z - 2$

$$N = 6m + c_z$$

M_x	M_y	M_z	α_{xx}	α_{yy}	α_{zz}	α_{yx}	α_{xz}	α_{yz}
E_1	E_1	A	A, E_2	A, E_2	A	E_2	E_1	E_1

Behavior of Linear Systems with Symmetry Axis C_∞

These systems fall into point groups $D_{\infty h}$ and $C_{\infty v}$.

27. $D_{\infty h}$; symmetry elements C_∞, i. $C_{\infty v}$, symmetry element C_∞ (Table A6.8–27).

Table A6.8–27
Point Groups $D_{\infty h}$ and $C_{\infty v}$

Type	Symmetry $D\infty$	Symmetry i	Selection Rules		Numbers
Σ_g^+	s	s	p	ia	c_z
Σ_u^+	s	as	v	M_z	$c_z + \delta - 1$
Π_g	e	s	dp	ia	$c_z \quad - 1$
Π_u	e	as	v	$M_\perp$	$c_z + \delta - 1$

$$N = 2c_z + \delta$$

Type	Symmetry $C\infty$	Selection Rules		Numbers
Σ^+	e	p	M_z	$c_z - 1$
Π	e	dp	$M_\perp$	$c_z - 2$

$$N = c_z$$

	M_x	M_y	M_z	α_{xx}	α_{yy}	α_{zz}	α_{xy}	α_{xz}	α_{yz}
For $D_{\infty h}$	Π_u	Π_u	Σ_u^+	Σ_g^+, Δ_g	Σ_g^+, Δ_g	Σ_g^+	Δ_g	Π_g	Π_g
For $C_{\infty v}$	Π	Π	Σ^+	Σ^+, Δ	Σ^+, Δ	Σ^+	Δ	Π	Π

The Cubic Point Groups

28. O_h. The symmetry elements contain (a) those of the "regular" (tetrahedral) system, that is, three mutually perpendicular twofold axes, chosen as the coordinate axes, and four threefold axes which make equal axes with the others. These *regular* elements are common to all cubic systems. The point group O_h has in addition (b) six C_2 axes which bisect the angles between the coordinate axes; (c) six σ through the four threefold axes C_3; (d) planes of symmetry σ_x, σ_y, σ_z, and i. The designation of types of points is as before, except that the number of points, C_3, which lie

on a threefold axis, C_3, is increased. Types E and F of Table 28 are doubly or triply degenerate. (See Table A6.8–28.) The selection and counting rules for cubic systems of lower symmetry are readily derived from the table in the manner described previously.

Table A6.8–28
Point Group O_h

Type	Symmetry C_2^z	C_y	C_3	S_4	C_4	i	Selection Rules		Numbers
A_{1g}	s	s	s	s	s	s	$\rho=0$	ia	$3m + c_3 + c_y + c + 2s_z + 2s$
A_{1u}	s	s	s	as	s	as	v	ia	$3m + s_z + s$
A_{2g}	s	s	s	as	as	s	v	ia	$3m + c + 2s_z + s$
A_{2u}	s	s	s	s	as	as	v	ia	$3m + c_3 + c + s_z + 2s$
E_g	s	s	e	e	e	s	dp	ia	$6m + c_3 + c_y + 2c + 4s_z + 3s$
E_u	s	s	e	e	e	as	v	ia	$6m + c_3 + c + 2s_z + 3s$
F_{1g}	e	e	e	e	e	s	v	ia	$9m + c_3 + c_y + 2c + 4s_z + 4s - 1$
F_{1u}	e	e	e	e	e	as	v	M	$9m + 2c_3 + 2c_y + 3c + 5s_z + 5s + \delta - 1$
F_{2g}	e	e	e	e	e	s	dp	ia	$9m + 2c_3 + c_y + 2c + 4s_z + 5s_z$
F_{2u}	e	e	e	e	e	as	v	ia	$9m + c_3 + c_y + 2c + 5s_z + 4s$

$$N = 48m + 8c_z + 6c_y + 12c + 24s_z + 24s + \delta$$

M_x	M_y	M_z	α_{xx}	α_{yy}	α_{zz}	α_{xy}	α_{xz}	α_{yz}
F_{1u}	F_{1u}	F_{1u}	A_{1g}, E_g	A_{1g}, E_g	A_{1g}, E_g	F_{2g}	F_{2g}	F_{2g}

29. T_d (tetrahedral group); symmetry elements as given in (a) and (c) of number 28 (see Table A6.8–29).

Table A6.8–29
Tetrahedral Group T_d

Type	Symmetry C_2^z	C_y	C_3	S_4	Selection Rules		Numbers
A_1	s	s	s	s	$\rho = 0$	ia	$3m + 2s + c_3 + c_y$
A_2	s	s	s	as	v	ia	$3m + s$
E	s	s	e	e	dp	ia	$6m + 3s + c_3 + c_y$
F_1	e	e	e	e	v	ia	$9m + 4s + c_3 + 2c_y - 1$
F_2	e	e	e	e	dp	M	$9m + 5s + 2c_3 + 3c_y + \delta - 1$

$$N = 24m + 12s + 4c_3 + 6c_y + \delta$$

M_x	M_y	M_z	α_{xx}	α_{yy}	α_{zz}	α_{xy}	α_{xz}	α_{yz}
F_2	F_2	F_2	A_1,E	A_1,E	A_1,E	F_2	F_2	F_2

30. T_h; symmetry elements as given in (a) and (d) of number 28. The table for this group is obtained from Table A6.8–28 by setting $A_{1g} = A_{2g} = A_g$; $A_{1u} = A_{2u} = A_u$; $F_{1g} = F_{2g} = F_g$; and $F_{1u} = F_{2u} = F_u$. The number of vibrations is $N = 24m + 8c_3 + 6c_y + 12s_z + \delta$.

31. O; symmetry elements as given in (a) and (b) of number 28. The table for this group is obtained from Table A6.8–28 by setting $A_{1g} = A_{1u} = A_1$; $A_{2g} = A_{2u} = A_2$; $E_g = E_u = E$; $F_{1g} = F_{1u} = F_1$; $F_{2g} = F_{2u} = F_2$. $N = 24m + 8c_3 + 6c_y + 12c + \delta$.

32. T; symmetry elements as given in (a) of number 28. The table is obtained from Table A6.8–28 by setting $A_{1g} = A_{1u} = A_{2g} = A_{2u} = A$; $E_g = E_u = E$; $F_{1g} = F_{1u} = F_{2g} = F_{2u} = F$. $N = 12m + 4c_3 + 6c_y + \delta$.

The symmetry species for combination frequencies and higher vibrational levels are given in Tables A6.8–30 and A6.8–31, taken from the work of Herzberg.[10]

Table A6.8–30

Symmetry Species for Combination Frequencies Involving Degenerate Modes†

Point Group	Vibrations Excited	Resulting States	Vibrations Excited	Resulting States	Vibrations Excited	Resulting States
D_{3h}	$A_1' \cdot E'$	E'	$A_2' \cdot E'$	E'	$E' \cdot E'$	$A_1' + A_2' + E'$
	$A_1' \cdot E''$	E''	$A_2' \cdot E''$	E''	$E' \cdot E''$	$A_1'' + A_2'' + E''$
	$A_1'' \cdot E'$	E''	$A_2'' \cdot E'$	E''	$E'' \cdot E''$	$A_1' + A_2' + E'$
	$A_1'' \cdot E''$	E'	$A_2'' \cdot E''$	E'		
C_{4v}	$A_1 \cdot E$	E	$B_1 \cdot E$	E	$E \cdot E$	$A_1 + A_2 + B_1 + B_2$
	$A_2 \cdot E$	E	$B_2 \cdot E$	E		
C_{6v}	$A_1 \cdot E_1$	E_1	$B_1 \cdot E_1$	E_2	$E_1 \cdot E_1$	$A_1 + A_2 + E_2$
	$A_1 \cdot E_2$	E_2	$B_1 \cdot E_2$	E_1	$E_2 \cdot E_2$	$A_1 + A_2 + E_2$
	$A_2 \cdot E_1$	E_1	$B_2 \cdot E_1$	E_2	$E_1 \cdot E_2$	$B_1 + B_2 + E_1$
	$A_2 \cdot E_2$	E_2	$B_2 \cdot E_2$	E_1		
D_{4d}	$A_1 \cdot E_1$	E_1	$B_1 \cdot E_1$	E_3	$E_1 \cdot E_1$	$A_1 + A_2 + E_2$
	$A_1 \cdot E_2$	E_2	$B_1 \cdot E_2$	E_2	$E_1 \cdot E_2$	$E_1 + E_3$
	$A_1 \cdot E_3$	E_3	$B_1 \cdot E_3$	E_1	$E_1 \cdot E_3$	$B_1 + B_2 + E_2$
	$A_2 \cdot E_1$	E_1	$B_2 \cdot E_1$	E_3	$E_2 \cdot E_2$	$A_1 + A_2 + B_1 + B_2$
	$A_2 \cdot E_2$	E_2	$B_2 \cdot E_2$	E_2	$E_2 \cdot E_3$	$E_1 + E_3$
	$A_2 \cdot E_3$	E_3	$B_2 \cdot E_3$	E_1	$E_3 \cdot E_3$	$A_1 + A_2 + E_2$
$C_{\infty v}$	$\Sigma^+ \cdot \Pi$	Π	$\Pi \cdot \Pi$	$\Sigma^+ + \Sigma^- + \Delta$	$\Pi \cdot \Phi$	$\Delta + \Gamma$
	$\Sigma^+ \cdot \Delta$	Δ	$\Pi \cdot \Delta$	$\Pi + \Phi$		
T_d, O	$A_1 \cdot E$	E	$A_2 \cdot F_1$	F_2	$E \cdot F_2$	$F_1 + F_2$
	$A_1 \cdot F_1$	F_1	$A_2 \cdot F_2$	F_1	$F_1 \cdot F_1$	$A_1 + E + F_1 + F_2$
	$A_1 \cdot F_2$	F_2	$E \cdot E$	$A_1 + A_2 + E$	$F_1 \cdot F_2$	$A_2 + E + F_1 + F_2$
	$A_2 \cdot E$	E	$E \cdot F_1$	$F_1 + F_2$	$F_2 \cdot F_2$	$A_1 + E + F_1 + F_2$

† From G. Herzberg, *Molecular Spectra and Molecular Structure*, Vol. II, "Infrared and Raman Spectra of Polyatomic Molecules," 2nd ed. Copyright 1950. D. Van Nostrand Company, Inc., Princeton, N. J.

Note 1. For point groups such as D_{4h} and D_{6h} which have g and u states, the symmetry of the final state is g if the initial states were both g or both u, and it is u if they were different.

Note 2. The species for point groups not listed are obtained as follows:

(a) From D_{3h}: C_{3v} and D_3 are obtained by dropping the $'$ and $''$; C_{3h} by dropping the subscripts; and C_3 by dropping both subscripts and superscripts.

(b) From C_{4v}: D_{4h}, D_4, and D_{2d} are identical with C_{4v}; C_{4h}, C_4, and S_4 are obtained by dropping the subscripts.

(c) From C_{6v}: D_{6h} and D are identical with C_{6v}; C_{6h}, C_6, and S_6 are obtained by dropping subscripts of A and B; for D_{3d}, A and B are set equal, and the subscripts 1 and 2 of E are dropped.

(d) $D_{\infty h}$ is identical with $C_{\infty v}$.

(e) T is obtained from T_d by dropping subscripts 1 and 2.

Table A6.8–31
Symmetry Species of Higher Vibrational Levels of Degenerate Modes†

Point Group	Vibrational Level	Resulting States	Vibrational Level	Resulting States
D_{3h}	$(E')^2$	$A_1' + E'$	$(E'')^2$	$A_1' + E'$
	$(E')^3$	$A_1' + A_2' + E'$	$(E'')^3$	$A_1'' + A_2'' + E''$
	$(E')^4$	$A_1' + 2E'$	$(E'')^4$	$A_1' + 2E'$
C_{4v}	$(E)^2$	$A_1 + B_1 + B_2$		
	$(E)^3$	$2E$		
	$(E)^4$	$2A_1 + A_2 + B_1 + B_2$		
C_{6v}	$(E_1)^2$	$A_1 + E_2$	$(E_2)^2$	$A_1 + E_2$
	$(E_1)^3$	$B_1 + B_2 + E_1$	$(E_2)^3$	$A_1 + A_2 + E_3$
	$(E_1)^4$	$A_1 + 2E_2$	$(E_2)^4$	$A_1 + 2E_2$
D_{4d}	$(E_1)^2$	$A_1 + E_2$	$(E_2)^4$	$2A_1 + A_2 + B_1 + B_2$
	$(E_1)^3$	$E_1 + E_3$	$(E_3)^2$	$A_1 + E_2$
	$(E_1)^4$	$A_1 + B_1 + B_2 + E_2$	$(E_3)^3$	$E_1 + E_3$
	$(E_2)^2$	$A_1 + B_1 + B_2$	$(E_3)^4$	$A_1 + B_1 + B_2 + E_2$
	$(E_2)^3$	$2E_2$		
$C_{\infty v}$	$(\Pi)^2$	$\Sigma^+ + \Delta$		
	$(\Pi)^3$	$\Pi + \Phi$		
	$(\Pi)^4$	$\Sigma^+ + \Delta + \Gamma$		
T_d, O	$(E)^2$	$A_1 + E$	$(F_2)^2$	$A_1 + E + F_2$
	$(E)^3$	$A_1 + A_2 + E$	$(F_2)^3$	$A_1 + F_1 + 2F_2$
	$(E)^4$	$A_1 + 2E_1$	$(F_2)^4$	$2A_1 + 2E + F_1 + 2F_2$
	$(F_1)^2$	$A_1 + E + F_2$		
	$(F_1)^3$	$A_2 + 2F_1 + F_2$		
	$(F_1)^4$	$2A_1 + 2E = F_1 + 2F_2$		

† From G. Herzberg, *Molecular Spectra and Molecular Structure*, Vol II, "Infrared and Raman Spectra of Polyatomic Molecules," 2nd ed. Copyright 1950. D. Van Nostrand Company, Inc., Princeton, N. J.

Note 1. The species for point groups not listed are obtained in the same fashion as for Table A6.8–30.

Note 2. The numbers in front of some of the resulting species indicate the number of states of that species which occur.

Note 3. The species for the fifth, sixth, etc., vibrational levels are given by Herzberg.[10] They may be obtained by continuing the indicated multiplication process with the aid of Table A6.8–30.

Thermodynamic Properties of Simple Molecules in the Ideal Gas State from Statistical Calculations

APPENDIX 7

Table A7–1
Thermodynamic Functions for Normal Hydrogen
(Neglecting Nuclear Spin and Entropy of Mixing Ortho and Para Varieties)

T(°K)	$\tilde{C}_P{}^\circ/R$	$(\tilde{H}^\circ - \tilde{E}_0{}^\circ)/RT$	$\tilde{S}^\circ/R$	$-(\tilde{F}^\circ - \tilde{E}_0{}^\circ)/RT$
100	2.714	3.819	12.272	8.453
150	3.053	3.509	13.439	9.930
200	3.280	3.426	14.352	10.926
250	3.407	3.411	15.099	11.688
300	3.469	3.416	15.726	12.310
350	3.498	3.426	16.264	12.838
400	3.510	3.436	16.732	13.296
450	3.516	3.445	17.145	13.701
500	3.519	3.452	17.516	14.064
600	3.527	3.464	18.158	14.694

Table A7–1 (*Continued*)

$T(°K)$	$\tilde{C}_P°/R$	$(\tilde{H}° - \tilde{E}_0°)/RT$	$\tilde{S}°/R$	$-(\tilde{F}° - \tilde{E}_0°)/RT$
700	3.541	3.473	18.703	15.230
800	3.563	3.483	19.177	15.694
900	3.594	3.494	19.598	16.104
1000	3.637	3.506	19.978	16.472
1200	3.727	3.534	20.649	17.115
1400	3.833	3.569	21.232	17.663
1600	3.936	3.609	21.750	18.141
1800	4.033	3.651	22.219	18.568
2000	4.124	3.694	22.649	18.955
2500	4.310	3.799	23.590	19.791
3000	4.458	3.897	24.389	20.492
3500	4.591	3.987	25.087	21.100
4000	4.701	4.069	25.707	21.638
4500	4.807	4.145	26.267	22.122
5000	4.906	4.217	26.779	22.562

From "Tables of Thermal Properties of Gases," *Natl. Bur. Standards* (*U.S.*) *Circ.*, No. **564,** 1955.

Table A7–2

Thermodynamic Functions for Nitrogen

$T(°K)$	$\tilde{C}_P°/R$	$(\tilde{H}° - \tilde{E}_0°)/RT$	$\tilde{S}°/R$	$-(\tilde{F}° - \tilde{E}_0°)/RT$
100	3.5004	3.490	19.2043	15.714
150	3.5006	3.494	20.6237	17.130
200	3.5008	3.496	21.6308	18.135
250	3.5013	3.497	22.4120	18.915
300	3.5030	3.498	23.0505	19.553
350	3.5078	3.499	23.5908	20.092
400	3.5179	3.500	24.0598	20.560
450	3.5344	3.503	24.4750	20.972
500	3.5578	3.508	24.8486	21.341
600	3.6214	3.521	25.5025	21.982
700	3.6990	3.540	26.0665	22.526
800	3.7806	3.566	26.5658	23.000
900	3.8596	3.574	27.0156	23.422
1000	3.9326	3.624	27.4261	23.802
1200	4.0562	3.686	28.1544	24.468

Table A7–2 (*Continued*)

$T(°K)$	$\tilde{C}_P°/R$	$(\tilde{H}° - \tilde{E}_0°)/RT$	$\tilde{S}°/R$	$-(\tilde{F}° - \tilde{E}_0°)/RT$
1400	4.1518	3.743	28.7872	25.041
1600	4.2252	3.802	29.3467	25.545
1800	4.2821	3.848	29.8477	25.996
2000	4.3268	3.897	30.3013	26.404
2500	4.4047	3.992	31.2759	27.284
3000	4.4545	4.065	32.0836	28.019
3500	4.4900	4.123	32.7731	28.650
4000	4.5173	4.151	33.3745	29.204
4500	4.5398	4.211	33.9079	29.697
5000	4.5598	4.244	34.3873	30.143

From *Natl. Bur. Standards* (*U.S.*) *Circ.*, No. **564**, 1955.

Table A7–3
Thermodynamic Functions for Oxygen

$T(°K)$	$\tilde{C}_P°/R$	$(\tilde{H}° - \tilde{E}_0°)/RT$	$\tilde{S}°/R$	$-(\tilde{F}° - \tilde{E}_0°)/RT$
100	3.5014	3.489	20.8348	17.346
150	3.5013	3.494	22.2545	18.761
200	3.5032	3.496	23.2619	19.766
250	3.5122	3.497	24.0444	20.547
300	3.5344	3.502	24.6865	21.185
350	3.5717	3.509	25.2340	21.725
400	3.6212	3.520	25.7140	22.194
450	3.6787	3.534	26.1438	22.610
500	3.7396	3.552	26.5345	22.983
600	3.8599	3.593	27.2271	23.634
700	3.9672	3.639	27.8303	24.191
800	4.0577	3.686	28.3662	24.680
900	4.1327	3.732	28.8486	25.117
1000	4.1948	3.774	29.2874	25.513
1200	4.2912	3.853	30.0611	26.208
1400	4.3651	3.921	30.7284	26.807
1600	4.4282	3.981	31.3155	27.335
1800	4.4868	4.033	31.8404	27.807
2000	4.5436	4.082	32.3161	28.234
2500	4.6808	4.188	33.3449	29.157

Table A7–3 (*Continued*)

$T(°K)$	$\tilde{C}_P°/R$	$(\tilde{H}° - \tilde{E}_0°)/RT$	$\tilde{S}°/R$	$-(\tilde{F}° - \tilde{E}_0°)/RT$
3000	4.8062	4.280	34.2096	29.929
3500	4.9125	4.364	34.9587	30.595
4000	4.9979	4.437	35.6204	31.183
4500	5.0638	4.514	36.2132	31.709
5000	5.1109	4.562	36.7493	32.187

From *Natl. Bur. Standards* (*U.S.*) *Circ.*, No. **564,** 1955.

Table A7–4

Thermodynamic Functions for Chlorine

(All units cal mole^{-1} deg^{-1})

$T(°K)$	$\tilde{C}_P°$	$(\tilde{H}° - \tilde{E}_0°)/T$	$\tilde{S}°$	$-(\tilde{F}° - \tilde{E}_0°)/T$
298.16	8.11	7.268	53.296	45.928
400	8.44	7.606	55.730	48.124
600	8.74	7.945	59.217	51.272
800	8.88	8.166	61.754	53.588
1000	8.96	8.319	63.745	55.426
1200	9.02	8.435	65.385	56.950
1400	9.06	8.520	66.777	58.257
1600	9.09	8.576	67.976	59.40
1800	9.11	8.63	69.646	60.42
2000	9.13	8.67	70.00	61.33
2200	9.14	8.72	70.89	62.17
2400	9.14	8.75	71.68	62.93
2600	9.14	8.77	72.40	63.63
2800	9.15	8.79	73.08	64.29
3000	9.15	8.80	73.73	64.92

From M. G. Ribaud, "Constantes Thermodynamiques des Gas aux Températures Elevées ," *Publs. sci. et tech. ministère d'air* (*France*), No. **266** (1952).

Table A7–5

Thermodynamic Functions for Hydrogen Chloride

(All units cal mole^{-1} deg^{-1})

$T(°K)$	$\tilde{C}_P°$	$(\tilde{H}° - \tilde{E}_0°)/T$	$\tilde{S}°$	$-(\tilde{F}° - \tilde{E}_0°)/T$
200	6.961	6.909	41.895	34.986
300	6.964	6.926	44.717	37.791
400	6.973	6.937	46.722	39.785
500	7.004	6.946	48.280	41.334
600	7.068	6.961	49.563	42.602

Table A7–5 (*Continued*)

$T(°K)$	$\tilde{C}_P°$	$(\tilde{H}° - \tilde{E}_0°)/T$	$\tilde{S}°$	$-(\tilde{F}° - \tilde{E}_0°)/T$
800	7.289	7.013	51.623	44.610
1000	7.560	7.095	53.279	46.184
1200	7.819	7.195	54.681	47.486
1400	8.043	7.300	55.903	48.603
1600	8.230	7.405	56.990	49.585
1800	8.382	7.506	57.969	50.463
2000	8.509	7.600	58.858	51.258

From C. W. Arnold and K. A. Kobe, *Chem. Eng. Progr.*, **48,** 293 (1952).

Table A7–6
Thermodynamic Functions for Carbon Monoxide

$T(°K)$	$\tilde{C}_P°/R$	$(\tilde{H}° - \tilde{E}_0°)/RT$	$\tilde{S}°/R$	$-(\tilde{F}° - \tilde{E}_0°)/RT$
100	3.500	3.491	19.935	16.444
150	3.501	3.494	21.354	17.860
200	3.501	3.496	22.362	18.866
250	3.502	3.497	23.143	19.646
300	3.505	3.498	23.782	20.284
350	3.513	3.499	24.322	20.823
400	3.529	3.502	24.792	21.290
450	3.552	3.506	25.209	21.703
500	3.583	3.512	25.585	22.073
600	3.661	3.530	26.245	22.715
700	3.749	3.555	26.816	23.261
800	3.837	3.586	27.323	23.737
900	3.918	3.617	27.779	24.162
1000	3.991	3.652	28.196	24.544
1200	4.110	3.718	28.934	25.216
1400	4.199	3.781	29.575	25.794
1600	4.267	3.837	30.140	26.303
1800	4.319	3.888	30.646	26.758
2000	4.359	3.933	31.103	27.170
2500	4.429	4.026	32.084	28.058
3000	4.476	4.098	32.896	28.798
3500	4.510	4.155	33.589	29.434
4000	4.536	4.200	34.192	29.992
4500	4.559	4.239	34.728	30.489
5000	4.579	4.272	35.209	30.937

From *Natl. Bur. Standards* (*U.S.*) *Circ.*, No. **564,** 1955.

Table A7–7

Thermodynamic Functions for Nitric Oxide

(All units cal mole^{-1} deg^{-1})

T(°K)	$\tilde{C}_P°$	$(\tilde{H}° - \tilde{E}_0°)/T$	$\tilde{S}°$	$-(\tilde{F}° - \tilde{E}_0°)/T$
100	7.714	7.427	42.271	34.844
150	7.451	7.481	45.345	37.864
200	7.278	7.453	47.465	40.012
250	7.183	7.411	49.078	41.667
300	7.134	7.356	50.384	43.028
400	7.162	7.302	52.436	45.134
500	7.289	7.288	54.048	46.760
600	7.468	7.302	55.392	48.090
700	7.657	7.338	56.557	49.219
800	7.833	7.387	57.589	50.202
900	7.990	7.445	58.520	51.075
1000	8.126	7.506	59.370	51.864
1200	8.342	7.627	60.872	53.245
1400	8.498	7.742	62.170	54.428
1500	8.560	7.796	62.760	54.964
1750	8.682	7.914	64.088	56.174
2000	8.771	8.015	65.252	57.237
2500	8.895	8.180	67.225	59.045
3000	8.981	8.308	68.857	60.549
3500	9.049	8.408	70.247	61.839
4000	9.107	8.493	71.459	62.966
4500	9.158	8.567	72.535	63.968
5000	9.208	8.636	73.504	64.868

From "Selected Values of Physical and Thermodynamic Properties of Hydrocarbons and Related Substances," *Am. Petrol. Inst. Bull.*, **44**, 1953.

Table A7–8

Thermodynamic Functions for Water

T(°K)	$\tilde{C}_P°/R$	$(\tilde{H}° - \tilde{E}_0°)/RT$	$\tilde{S}°/R$	$-(\tilde{F}° - \tilde{E}_0°)/RT$
100	4.0058	3.9559	14.3588	18.3147
150	4.0072	3.9728	15.9664	19.9392
200	4.0102	3.9816	17.1107	21.0923
250	4.0191	3.9882	17.9998	21.9880
300	4.0394	3.9948	18.7275	22.7223

Table A7–8 (*Continued*)

$T(°K)$	$\tilde{C}_P°/R$	$(\tilde{H}° - \tilde{E}_0°)/RT$	$\tilde{S}°/R$	$-(\tilde{F}° - \tilde{E}_0°)/RT$
350	4.0733	4.0034	19.3440	23.3474
400	4.1192	4.0149	19.8793	23.8942
450	4.1739	4.0294	20.3530	24.3824
500	4.2345	4.0469	20.7784	24.8253
600	4.3659	4.0890	21.5198	25.6088
700	4.5059	4.1384	22.1538	26.2922
800	4.6525	4.1935	22.7099	26.9034
900	4.8038	4.2539	23.2072	27.4601
1000	4.9569	4.3157	23.6585	27.9742
1200	5.2555	4.4579	24.4569	28.9046
1400	5.5286	4.5829	25.1527	29.7356
1600	5.7678	4.7165	25.7734	30.4899
1800	5.9725	4.8450	26.3364	31.1814
2000	6.1460	4.9667	26.8532	31.8199
2500	6.4727	5.2373	27.9915	33.2288
3000	6.6945	5.4629	28.9669	34.4298
3600	6.8782	5.6844	29.9832	35.6676
4000	6.9694	5.8085	30.5887	36.3972
4600	7.0758	5.9672	31.4117	37.3789
5000	7.1325	6.0582	31.9131	37.9713

From *Natl. Bur. Standards (U.S.) Circ.*, No. **564,** 1955.

Table A7–9

Thermodynamic Functions for Carbon Dioxide

$T(°K)$	$\tilde{C}_P°/R$	$(\tilde{H}° - \tilde{E}_0°)/RT$	$\tilde{S}°/R$	$-(\tilde{F}° - \tilde{E}_0°)/RT$
100	3.5128	3.4995	21.5160	18.0165
150	3.6372	3.5202	22.9585	19.4383
200	3.8916	3.5795	24.0377	20.4582
250	4.1892	3.6716	24.9379	21.2663
300	4.4763	3.7821	25.7274	21.9453
350	4.7371	3.9002	26.4373	22.5371
400	4.9704	4.0197	27.0854	23.0657
450	5.1792	4.1371	27.6831	23.5460
500	5.3671	4.2509	28.2387	23.9878
600	5.6915	4.4648	29.2468	24.7820

Table A7–9 (*Continued*)

$T(^\circ K)$	$\tilde{C}_P{}^\circ/R$	$(\tilde{H}^\circ - \tilde{E}_0{}^\circ)/RT$	$\tilde{S}^\circ/R$	$-(\tilde{F}^\circ - \tilde{E}_0{}^\circ)/RT$
700	5.9611	4.6799	30.1451	25.4852
800	6.1860	4.8370	30.9562	26.1192
900	6.3742	4.9977	31.6960	26.6983
1000	6.5318	5.1434	32.3759	27.2325
1200	6.776	5.396	33.589	28.193
1400	6.952	5.607	34.649	29.042
1600	7.082	5.783	35.585	29.802
1800	7.180	5.933	36.425	30.492
2000	7.258	6.062	37.186	31.124
2500	7.393	6.316	38.822	32.506
3000	7.484	6.503	40.178	33.675
3500	7.551	6.649	41.337	34.688
4000	7.608	6.765	42.349	35.584
4500	7.657	6.861	43.248	36.387
5000	7.702	6.943	44.057	37.114

From *Natl. Bur. Standards* (*U.S.*) *Circ.*, No. **564,** 1955.

Table A7–10

Thermodynamic Functions for Sulfur Dioxide

(All units cal $mole^{-1}$ deg^{-1})

$T(^\circ K)$	$\tilde{C}_P{}^\circ$	$(\tilde{H}^\circ - \tilde{E}_0{}^\circ)/T$	$\tilde{S}^\circ$	$-(\tilde{F}^\circ - \tilde{E}_0{}^\circ)/T$
298.16	9.51	8.45	59.40	50.95
300	9.53	8.30	59.45	51.00
400	10.35	8.83	62.32	53.49
500	11.08	9.22	64.72	55.50
600	11.67	9.58	66.79	57.21
800	12.44	10.21	70.26	60.05
1000	12.90	10.70	73.09	62.39
1200	13.17	11.10	75.47	64.37
1400	13.35	11.41	77.52	66.11
1600	13.47	11.64	79.30	67.66
1800	13.56	11.86	80.90	69.04

From M. G. Ribaud, *op. cit.*

Table A7–11
Thermodynamic Functions for Ammonia
(All units cal mole^{-1} deg^{-1})

T(°K)	$\tilde{C}_P{}^\circ$	$(\tilde{H}^\circ - \tilde{E}_0{}^\circ)/T$	$\tilde{S}^\circ$	$-(\tilde{F}^\circ - \tilde{E}_0{}^\circ)/T$
298.16	8.52	8.02	46.01	37.99
300	8.54	7.97	46.06	38.09
400	9.21	8.18	48.56	40.38
500	9.95	8.35	50.63	42.28
600	10.69	8.72	52.55	43.83
800	12.14	9.43	55.88	46.45
1000	13.43	10.12	58.75	48.63
1200	14.52	10.77	61.30	50.53
1400	15.43	11.36	63.60	52.24
1600	16.17	11.91	65.70	53.79
1800	16.75	12.43	67.66	55.23
2000	17.21	12.89	69.45	56.56

From M. G. Ribaud, *op. cit.*

Table A7–12
Thermodynamic Functions for Methane
(All units cal mole^{-1} deg^{-1})

T(°K)	$\tilde{C}_P{}^\circ$	$(\tilde{H}^\circ - \tilde{E}_0{}^\circ)/T$	$\tilde{S}^\circ$	$-(\tilde{F}^\circ - \tilde{E}_0{}^\circ)/T$
100	7.949	7.949	35.72	27.77
150	7.953	7.949	38.94	30.99
200	8.002	7.954	41.23	33.28
250	8.185	7.979	43.03	35.05
300	8.552	8.042	44.55	36.51
350	9.082	8.151	45.91	37.76
400	9.721	8.307	47.17	38.86
450	10.42	8.502	48.35	39.85
500	11.13	8.730	49.48	40.75
600	12.55	9.249	51.64	42.39
700	13.88	9.816	53.68	43.86
800	15.10	10.401	55.61	45.21
900	16.21	10.985	57.45	46.47
1000	17.21	11.56	59.21	47.65
1200	18.88	12.65	62.50	49.86
1400	20.18	13.63	65.51	51.88
1500	20.71	14.09	66.93	52.84

From *Am. Petrol. Inst. Bull.*, **44,** 1953.

Derivations of Equations

APPENDIX 8

A8.1 Derivation of Equation (22.4–13).

From equation (22.3–6),

$$\bar{I} = RT\left(\frac{\partial \ln Q}{\partial \mathscr{H}}\right)_T = \frac{RT}{Q}\left(\frac{\partial Q}{\partial \mathscr{H}}\right)_T, \tag{22.3–6}$$

with the partition function defined by equation (22.4–2),

$$Q = e^{-\epsilon_0/kT} \sum_{-J}^{+J} e^{gm_J\beta\mathscr{H}/kT}, \tag{22.4–2}$$

$$Q = e^{-\epsilon_0/kT} e^{-gJ\beta\mathscr{H}/kT} \sum_{m=0}^{m=2J} e^{gm\beta\mathscr{H}/kT}. \tag{A8.1–1}$$

The summation in (A8.1–1) is a geometrical progression in the function $e^{g\beta\mathscr{H}/kT}$. Inserting the value of this sum,

$$\sum_0^n x^n = \frac{1 - x^{n+1}}{1 - x}$$

into equation (A8.1–1) yields

$$Q = e^{-\epsilon_0/kT} e^{-gJ\beta\mathscr{H}/kT} \frac{1 - e^{g(2J+1)\beta\mathscr{H}/kT}}{1 - e^{g\beta\mathscr{H}/kT}}. \tag{A8.1–2}$$

Equation (A8.1–2) is transformed into hyperbolic form by multiplying out the exponentials and then multiplying numerator and denominator by $e^{-g\beta\mathscr{H}/2kT}$. The result is

$$Q = e^{-\epsilon_0/kT} \frac{e^{-g(2J+1)\beta\mathscr{H}/2kT} - e^{g(2J+1)\beta\mathscr{H}/2kT}}{e^{-g\beta\mathscr{H}/2kT} - e^{g\beta\mathscr{H}/2kT}}, \qquad \text{(A8.1–3)}$$

$$Q = e^{-\epsilon_0/kT} \frac{\sinh \dfrac{g(2J+1)\beta\mathscr{H}}{2kT}}{\sinh \dfrac{g\beta\mathscr{H}}{2kT}}. \qquad \text{(A8.1–4)}$$

The derivative $(\partial Q/\partial \mathscr{H})_T$ is then

$$\left(\frac{\partial Q}{\partial \mathscr{H}}\right)_T = e^{-\epsilon_0/kT} \left[\frac{g\beta\left(\dfrac{2J+1}{2kT}\right) \cosh \dfrac{g(2J+1)\beta\mathscr{H}}{2kT}}{\sinh \dfrac{g\beta\mathscr{H}}{2kT}} - \frac{\dfrac{g\beta}{2kT} \cosh \dfrac{g\beta\mathscr{H}}{2kT} \sinh \dfrac{(2J+1)\beta\mathscr{H}}{2kT}}{\sinh^2 \dfrac{g\beta\mathscr{H}}{2kT}} \right]. \qquad \text{(A8.1–5)}$$

The molal intensity of magnetization is obtained by substituting (A8.1–4) and (A8.1–5) into equation (22.3–6). After cancellation of terms and use of the relationship $\coth x = \cosh x/\sinh x$, the result is

$$\tilde{I} = RT\left[\left(\frac{2J+1}{2kT}\right) g\beta \coth \frac{g(2J+1)\beta\mathscr{H}}{2kT} - \frac{g\beta}{2kT} \coth \frac{g\beta\mathscr{H}}{kT}\right], \qquad \text{(A8.1–6)}$$

$$\tilde{I} = \tilde{N} g\beta \left[\left(\frac{2J+1}{2}\right) \coth \frac{g(2J+1)\beta\mathscr{H}}{2kT} - \frac{1}{2} \coth \frac{g\beta\mathscr{H}}{2kT}\right]. \qquad \text{(A8.1–7)}$$

When the Brillouin function has been defined as in equation (22.4–13),

$$B_J(y) = \frac{2J+1}{2J} \coth \left(\frac{2Jy+y}{2J}\right) - \frac{1}{2J} \coth \frac{y}{2J}, \qquad \text{(22.4–13)}$$

equation (A8.1–7) reduces to equation (22.4–12),

$$\tilde{I} = \tilde{N} g\beta J B_J\left(\frac{g\beta J\mathscr{H}}{kT}\right). \qquad \text{(22.4–12)}$$

A8.2 Derivation of the Equation $PV = 2E/3$ for a Perfect Gas[1]

The perfect gas is considered an isotropic system of N point masses whose velocities are given by a distribution function $N(v_x, v_y, v_z)$ such that the number of molecules dn with velocities between v_x and $v_x + dv_x$, v_y and $v_y + dv_y$, v_z and $v_z + dv_z$ is

$$dn = N(v_x, v_y, v_z)\, dv_x\, dv_y\, dv_z, \tag{A8.2–1}$$

where v_x, v_y, and v_z are the velocities in the x, y, and z directions, respectively. The total number of molecules is obviously obtained by integrating dn over all values of v_x, v_y, and v_z. The number of molecules $N'(v_x)$ having velocities between v_x and $v_x + dv_x$ is obtained by integration of equation (A8.2–1) over all values of v_y and v_z. It is

$$N'(v_x) = \int_{-\infty}^{+\infty}\int_{-\infty}^{+\infty} N(v_x, v_y, v_z)\, dv_y\, dv_z, \tag{A8.2–2}$$

with similar equations for distribution with respect to velocities in the y and z directions. The assumption of isotropy requires that

$$N(v_x, v_y, v_z) = N(-v_x, v_y, v_z);$$
$$N'(v_x) = N'(-v_x); \tag{A8.2–3}$$

and that the average value of any property must be the same along each coordinate direction.

The pressure on any wall bounding the gas is equal to the change in momentum per second of the particles hitting unit area of the wall. In particular, we shall consider the pressure on a 1-cm^2 area perpendicular to the x axis. If each molecule were perfectly reflected, its change in momentum on collision with this wall would be $2mv_x$, where m is the mass of the particle. For imperfect reflection the change in momentum will be different from this. However, to keep the velocity distribution isotropic, as many molecules must leave the wall with velocities $-v_x$, v_y, v_z as hit it with velocities v_x, v_y, v_z. Thus the over-all change in momentum for the assembly must be the same *as if* there were perfect reflection.

Of the molecules with a given set of velocity components v_x, v_y, v_z, those which will hit a unit area of the chosen wall are contained in a parallelepiped of base 1 cm^2 and height v_x, whose volume is v_x. This volume is a fraction v_x/V of the total volume of the gas. It thus contains a total number of molecules v_xN/V, of which the number with velocity v_x, v_y, v_z is $v_xN(v_x, v_y, v_z)/V$. The total number of molecules hitting unit area of

[1] This treatment is taken, with slight modifications, from J. E. Mayer and M. G. Mayer, *Statistical Mechanics*, Wiley, New York, 1940, p. 8.

the wall per second is obtained by integration of this number over all values of v_y and v_z and is $v_x N'(v_x)/V$. The pressure produced by these molecules, dP, is then

$$\mathrm{d}P = \frac{(\mathrm{m}v_x)v_x N'(v_x)}{V}. \tag{A8.2–4}$$

The total pressure on the wall is obtained by integration of (A8.2–4) over all values of v_x. It is

$$P = \frac{2\mathrm{m}}{V}\int_0^\infty v_x^2 N'(v_x)\,\mathrm{d}v_x. \tag{A8.2–5}$$

The sum of all v_x^2, which is N times the average of this quantity and is denoted by $N\bar{v}_x^2$, is obtained by integration of $\bar{v}_x^2(N')v_x$ over all values of v_x from $-\infty$ to $+\infty$. Since $N'(v_x) = N'(-v_x)$, the integral required for (A8.2–5) is just half of this; that is, ${}^1/_2 N\bar{v}_x^2$. Thus

$$PV = 2N(\tfrac{1}{2}\mathrm{m}v_x^2), \tag{A8.2–6}$$

where the quantity in parentheses is the average *kinetic energy* in the x direction. Since isotropy has been assumed, $\bar{v}_x^2 = \bar{v}_y^2 = \bar{v}_z^2 = {}^1/_3\bar{v}^2$, where $\bar{v}^2$ is the average of the square of the total velocity. Therefore

$$PV = \tfrac{2}{3}N(\tfrac{1}{2}\mathrm{m}\bar{v}^2) = \tfrac{2}{3}E. \tag{A8.2–7}$$

If the number of molecules is taken as Avogadro's number, **N**, the volume $\tilde{V}$ is the molar volume and $\tilde{E}$ is the total kinetic energy per mole.

List of Symbols

APPENDIX 9

This list gives the symbols for thermodynamic and other quantities which are used commonly throughout this book. The ordinary symbols of mathematics have not been included, nor have symbols which are used only in connection with specific equations. These are defined where used. The specific forms of the various symbols for extensive quantities have the following meanings:

(1) Amount in general, *italic*; e.g., V, etc.
(2) Amount per mole (molal), italic with tilde; e.g., $\tilde{V}$, etc.
(3) Amount per molecule (molecular), italic with double tilde; e.g., $\tilde{\tilde{V}}$, etc.
(4) Amount per gram (specific), small capitals; e.g., v, etc.
(5) Partial molal, italic with bar; e.g., $\bar{V}$, etc.
(6) Partial specific quantity, small capitals with bar; e.g., $\bar{\text{v}}$, etc.

Intensive quantities, universal constants, and other variables are visually symbolized in italics; where necessary ordinary or script letters have been introduced to avoid confusion. In some few cases, convention has given the same symbol to two or more widely different things (e.g., γ for surface tension, for activity coefficient, and for C_P/C_V); we have retained these usages and made special notes in the text concerning the duplication.

A, $\tilde{A}$, A, $\bar{A}$	Helmholtz free energy
A	area
a	activity
a	van der Waals constant
B	induction
b	van der Waals constant

$C, \tilde{C}, \textsc{c}, \bar{C}$	heat capacity
c	concentration, velocity of light
d	density
$E, \tilde{E}, \textsc{e}, \bar{E}$	energy
$\mathscr{E}$	potential difference
$\boldsymbol{\mathscr{E}}$	electric field
$F, \tilde{F}, \textsc{f}, \bar{F}$	Gibbs free energy
F	force
f	fugacity
$\mathscr{F}$	Faraday number
$G, \tilde{G}, \textsc{g}, \bar{G}$	generalized property
g	gravitational acceleration
$H, \tilde{H}, \textsc{h}, \bar{H}$	enthalpy (heat content)
$\mathscr{H}$	magnetic field
h	height
h	Planck's constant
I	moment of inertia
$I, \tilde{I}$	intensity of magnetization
K	equilibrium constant
k	Boltzmann constant
$\bar{L}$	relative partial molal enthalpy
l	length
$\tilde{M}$	molar weight
m	mass
m	molality
N	number of systems
$\mathbf{N}$	Avogadro's number
$\tilde{N}$	mole fraction
$\mathscr{N}$	number of equivalents
n	number of moles, number of elements
P	pressure
p	vapor pressure
p	momentum
$\mathscr{P}$	polarization
$\mathbf{P}$	probability (number of states)
p_k	statistical weight
$\mathscr{Q}$	charge
q	heat absorbed
q	a generalized coordinate
Q	partition function
R	gas constant
$\mathbf{R}$	Rydberg constant

r	mole ratio ($r_1 = n_1/n_2$)
$S, \tilde{S}, \mathrm{s}, \bar{S}$	entropy
T	absolute temperature
$\mathbf{T}$	term value
$\mathcal{T}$	tension
t	centigrade temperature
$V, \tilde{V}, \mathrm{v}, \bar{V}$	volume
W	chance of occurrence
w	work
Z	compressibility ($=PV/nRT$)
z	charge on ion
β	conventional temperature parameter ($=1/kT$)
γ	activity coefficient
γ	ratio of C_P to C_V
γ	surface tension
ϵ	energy of a molecule
η	Gibbs probability index ($S = -\eta$)
λ	wave length
μ	chemical potential (partial molal free energy)
$\tilde{\mu}$	partial molecular free energy
μ	Joule-Thomson coefficient
ν	frequency (sec^{-1}); also general letter for number of elements of the νth kind
$\tilde{\nu}$	wave number (cm^{-1})
Π	osmotic pressure
ρ	density
σ	surface area
σ	symmetry number
ϕ	apparent molal property
χ	magnetic susceptibility
Ψ	wave function (time included)
ψ	amplitude wave function
ω	fundamental frequency (cm^{-1})
θ	Gibbs temperature parameter ($=1/T$)

Answers to Numerical Problems

APPENDIX 10

The answers to most of the numerical problems are given below. These are intended as a guide to the student and not as a check on numerical accuracy. In general, they have been obtained by use of a slide rule and have the accuracy corresponding to this. In problems where many answers are required, only a few examples of the results are recorded below.

2.2–1	763.60 mm Hg; 763.32 mm Hg.
2.2–2	(a) 12,660 dynes cm^{-1}; (b) 12,664 dynes cm^{-1}.
2.6–1	(a) 5×10^6 ergs, 0.5 joule, 0.1192 cal; (b) 510 g.
3.3–1	1590 cal.
3.3–2	(a) 1700 ft; (b) 1000 ft.
3.3–3	(a) 20,000 cal; (b) 23,000 cal, 20,000 cal: (c) 20,000 cal.
3.6–1	1.3×10^{11} cal.
3.7–1	280 cal.
3.7–2	(a) 35 cal; (b) 336 cal.
3.7–3	(a) 33,500 cal, $0.041 per 1000 Btu.
4.4–1	(c) 60 atm at −70°C, 75 atm at 25°C, 250 atm at 200°C.
4.4–3	(b) 528 atm, 203 atm, 22 atm; (c) up to 22 atm.
4.5–1	(a) 112 atm, (b) 86 atm.
4.5–3	3.58 atm $liter^2$; 0.0427 liter.
4.5–6	-1.00×10^{-3}.
5.2–1	(a) $\Delta H = 6070$; $q = 6070$; $\Delta E = 5701$; $w = 369$ cal; (b) $\Delta H = 6084$; $q = 5710$; $\Delta E = 5710$; $w = 0$.
5.2–2	(a) $\Delta H = 8.3$; (b) $w = 2880$; $q = 2886$.
5.2–3	$q = 5.9$; $w = 0$; $\Delta E = 5.9$; $\Delta H = 8.3$.
5.3–2	227.6 cal $mole^{-1}$.
5.3–3	6.52, 9.26, 11.66 cal $mole^{-1}$ deg^{-1}.
5.7–1	153.4 cal. $mole^{-1}$.
5.7–3	(a) 0.16; (b) 0.30.

5.7–4 (a) 0.10; (b) 0.22; (c) 0.38.
5.7–6 7.3×10^{-3} cal mole^{-1} deg^{-1} atm^{-1}.
5.7–7 0.160 deg atm^{-1}.
5.7–8 To avoid local cooling due to work done against the orifice by the gas stream from the valve.
5.8–2 3920 cal mole^{-1}.
5.8–5 0.464.
5.8–6 (a) -903 cal; (b) -1161 cal.
5.8–7 90°K.
6.7–8 (a) -24.1; (b) 26.51; (c) 2.41.
6.7–9 (a) 0; (b) 1.38.
6.7–10 (a) -26.24; (b) 94.90; (c) 68.66.
6.7–12 (a) 6.71; (b) 33.55; (c) 40.26.
6.7–13 ΔS_{total}: (a) 0.50; (b) 0.93; (c) 0.16.
6.10–1 (b) -321 cal; (c) 0.116.
6.10–2 2.55 cal atm^{-1}.
6.12–5 0.38 cal mole^{-1} deg^{-1}.
6.15–2 (a) 1250 cal, 175°K; (b) -2.66, 2.66, 0.
6.15–3 (a) 480 cal, 252°K; (b) -0.86, 5.20; (c) 4.34.
6.15–4 (a) 900 cal, 120°K; (b) 150 cal, 195°K; (c) 1.26.
6.15–5 (a) 236°K; (b) 1600 cal; (c) 0.
6.19–7 0.0028 atm.
6.19–8 7.88, 0.0079 atm.
6.19–9 (a) 3.22; (b) -8290; (c) -8640.
6.19–10 (a) -0.52; (b) 7.55; (c) -2320; (d) -2318.
6.22–1 224.4.
6.23–3 1.41×10^{-7}.
6.23–4 5×10^{-8} atm.
7.3–1 29 mm Hg deg^{-1}.
7.3–2 -1.3 liter mole^{-1}.
7.3–3 -0.0075 deg atm^{-1}.
7.3–4 0.0309 deg atm^{-1}.
7.4–2 3.7×10^{-3} mm Hg atm^{-1}.
8.2–1 (a) 497.1 cm^3, 0.812; (b) 106.8 cm^3, 0.937.
8.3–1 (a) H_2SO_4, 38.90 at 2.0 molal.
8.3–2 $\bar{C}_{P_2}$, -5.0, 13.0, 21.4; $\bar{C}_{P_1}$, 19.92, 17.29, 16.69.
8.3–8 $\bar{V}_1$, 17.97, 17.94, 17.94; $\bar{V}_2$, 13.6, 16.6, 14.1.
8.3–10 $\bar{V}_1$, 48.81, 48.30, 47.96; $\bar{V}_2$, 69.68, 70.66, 71.16.
8.3–11 $\bar{V}_2$, 69.50, 70.74, 71.00.
8.3–13 $\bar{V}_1$, 18.02, 17.82, 17.19, 16.42, 16.22; $\bar{V}_2$, 53.5, 54.9, 56.8, 57.7, 57.8.
8.4–1 (c) $\bar{L}_1$, 0.020, 0.00356, 0.00114; $\bar{L}_2$, 47.8, 24.1, 15.2.
8.4–2 1565 cal.
8.5–1 308.46, 308.69.
8.5–2 -0.37 cm^3.
8.5–3 (b) -2.52 cm^3.
8.6–1 (a) 989.85; (b) 859.0.
10.2–3 1.043.
10.3–5 4.87, 23.88, 46.59, 90.82; 4.89, 24.21, 47.84, 93.76 atm.
10.3–6 57.5, 81.8, 163.9, 289.3 atm.
10.3–7 1.0065, 1.0205, 1.0580, 1.15.

10.4–2 (b) f/P 0.986, 0.979, 0.972, 0.965, 0.958; (c) f/P 0.975, 0.963, 0.951, 0.939, 0.927.
10.4–3 (b) −0.0051.
10.8–1 41°K.
10.8–2 (a) 0.35; (b) −6 cal mole^{-1} deg^{-1}; (c) 10, 4.0 cal mole^{-1} deg^{-1}.
10.8–3 (a) 43°K; (b) 1.15 cal mole^{-1} deg^{-1} in heat exchanger; (c) 3.25 cal mole^{-1} deg^{-1} at valve.
10.8–4 0.189.
10.8–5 (a) 6.5 cal mole^{-1} deg^{-1}; (b) 6.8 cal mole^{-1} deg^{-1}.
10.8–6 (a) 18.2°K.
10.8–7 (a) 50%; (b) gas, 8 cm^3 g^{-1}; liquid, 4 cm^3 g^{-1}.
10.8–8 (a) 1.25 cal g^{-1}; (b) 1.8 cal g^{-1}.
11.1–3 275.06, 249.4, 213.0 mm Hg.
11.2–4 61.10, 61.24, 61.07, 60.50.
11.2–6 $\tilde{N}_2 = 0.817$.
11.2–7 225°K, $\tilde{N}_1 = 0.348$.
11.3–6 0.22 mole per cent.
11.3–7 320°C.
11.3–8 2.44, 7.32, 12.20 atm.
11.5–2 $\tilde{N}_2 = 0.10$, $a_2 = 0.123$; $\tilde{N}_2 = 0.50$, $a_2 = 0.520$.
11.5–3 $\tilde{N}_2 = 0.682$, $a_2 = 0.708$; $\tilde{N}_2 = 0.509$, $a_2 = 0.319$; $\tilde{N}_2 = 0.259$, $a_2 = 0.0224$.
11.6–4 $m = 0.6389$, $\gamma = 1.0095$; $m = 1.143$, $\gamma = 1.0278$, $m = 1.852$, $\gamma = 1.060$.
11.6–5 $\gamma_2 = 0.9166$, 0.727, 0.464, 0.597.
12.2–2 (a) −84,300 cal; (e) −166,340 cal, (j) −39,490 cal.
12.2–3 (a) −80,046 cal, (c) −9710 cal.
12.3–1 −32,741, −21,981, 78,356 cal.
12.3–2 11.27 cal mole^{-1}.
12.3–3 (a) 5414.4, (b) 4929.3, (c) 2819.7, (d) 15.401.
12.3–4 17,769 cal.
12.4–1 (a) 14,780, (b) 9708, (c) 18,142.
12.4–2 4.78 cal g^{-1} atm^{-1}.
12.4–3 1358.8 cal g^{-1} atm^{-1}.
12.4–4 $\tilde{C}_P - \tilde{C}_V = 0.31$; $\tilde{C}_P = 6.12$ cal mole^{-1} deg^{-1}.
12.5–1 (a) 2.22×10^{-4}; (b) 5110 cal; (c) −10,000 cal; (d) −15,110.
12.6–1 −1278 cal, 0.0277 v.
12.6–2 6082 cal, −0.131 v.
12.6–3 (a) 56,600; (b) 1.764 v.
12.6–4 (a) −5136 cal, 0.2223 v; (b) 0.186 v.
12.7–1 (a) 0.00297; (b) 5070.
12.7–2 5×10^{-42}.
12.7–3 1100.
12.8–1 $K_{700} = 10^{-7}$.
12.8–2 (a) 10^{-5}; (b) 0.81.
12.8–3 0.70.
12.8–4 (a) 0.20437 v; (b) −9440, 36.5, 1420.
12.10–1 35.43.
12.10–2 10.139.
12.10–3 10.15.
12.10–6 −21,820; 10^{16}.
12.10–7 29.0.
12.10–8 (a) 23.37; (b) −73,010.

13.4–6 0.618, 0.570.
13.4–7 (a) at 1.0 molal, −359, 108, 438, 775; (c) 20 cal, 1.3 cal $mole^{-1}$ deg^{-1}.
14.2–2 (a) 3740; (b) 3500, 3080, 2300; (c) −0.1515, −0.1339.
14.2–3 0.2374 v.
14.2–4 −0.2106 v.
14.2–5 4×10^{-5}, 4×10^{-3}, 1×10^{-2} mm Hg.
14.2–6 (b) at 25°C, −10,300, −19,200, −29.8, −90.5; (c) 23.7, −29.7.
14.3–1 (a) 0.2318; (b) 0.2315; (c) at 1 molal, $\gamma_{\pm} = 0.840$.
14.3–2 (a) at 10 molal, $\gamma_{\pm} = 12.7$; (b) $\gamma_{\pm} = 13.3$.
15.4–4 0.86, 0.215, 0.053.
15.4–5 (b) 0.43.
15.4–6 0, 9×10^{-5}, 9.5×10^{-4}.
15.5–2 0.1062, 0.473.
15.7–3 1, 107.
15.7–6 12,100, 12,500.
15.7–7 920, 890, 720.
16.4–1 (a) 3, 4, 5; (b) $\epsilon_1 = -2.17 \times 10^{-13}$ erg; $\epsilon_2 = -5.43 \times 10^{-12}$ erg.
16.4–2 (a) $B_e = 10.18$; $\tilde{\nu}_0 = 2885.90$; (b) $v = 1$, $k = 7/2$, 3007.4 cm^{-1}.
16.12–1 (a) $\Omega = 1$; $J = 1, 2$, etc.; $\Omega = 2$, $J = 2, 3$, etc.; $\Omega = 3$, $J = 3, 4$, etc.;
(b) for $K = 1$, $J = 0, 1, 2$; for $K = 3$, $J = 2, 3, 4$, etc.
16.13–1 ω_e', 1102.05; $\omega_e' x_e'$, −7.25; ω_e'' 1336.36; $\omega_e'' x_e''$, −6.98.
16.13–2 39685.6.
16.15–2 8453.7.
16.15–3 21.
16.15–4 (b) −5.70 cm^{-1};
16.15–5 R(2) = 13126.39; $R_Q(2) = 13128.27$; $P_Q(2) = 13114.10$.
16.17–1 $E_{12} = 4402.7$; $\tilde{\nu} = 2925.8$.
16.17–2 R branch, 6495.84, 6499.69, 6503.53, etc.
16.17–3 $E_{30} = 15{,}470$; $E_{34} = 16{,}720$.
16.22–1 $I_{xx} = 1.25 \times 10^{-40}$; $I_{yy} = 3.17 \times 10^{-40}$; $I_{zz} = 1.92 \times 10^{-40}$.
16.22–2 (b) 1.17, 4.4, 2.9×10^{-40}; 22°30′.
16.22–3 A = 2.816×10^{-40}, C = 4.437×10^{-40} g cm^2.
16.22–4 5.12×10^{-40}.
16.22–6 1.9×10^{-115}.
17.4–1 10.
17.4–2 0.027.
17.4–3 (a) 0.246, 0.00097, 0.410.
17.4–5 $P = 11{,}340$; $P_{max} = 2520$.
17.4–11 (a) $n = 1, p = 2$; $n = 3, p = 18$.
17.4–12 (a) 2, 4; (c) 1:2.
17.4–13 (b) 1, 3, 5.
17.4–14 11, 13.
17.4–15 33, 13.
17.4–16 (a) 4, 5, 6; (b) −33.
17.4–18 25, 117, 273.
17.4–19 (c) 10^{17}.
17.4–20 (a) 0.032; (b) 0.12.
17.4–21 (i) 2.08; (ii) 0.93.
17.4–22 6.97.
17.4–23 3400°K.

17.4–24 (c) 380°K.
18.4–3 19.747.
18.4–4 19.946.
18.4–5 7.874.
18.4–6 7.906.
18.5–2 $Q = 8 \times 10^{26}$.
18.5–3 1.14×10^{-11}, 2.28×10^{-11}, 3.42×10^{-11}.
18.6–3 (a) 36.70; (b) 36.30.
18.6–4 44.6.
18.7–6 1421, 2014, 6.90, 4.91, 44.6, −11,606, −12,200.
18.11–1 44.62.
19.2–4 3107.2, 3105.1, 3105.3 cm^{-1}.
19.2–5 (b) 36.30, (c) 49.00.
19.2–6 (a) 2147.0; (b) 2.45; (c) 0.04.
19.2–8 1:0.0733:0.009.
19.2–9 $K = 10$.
19.3–1 (a) 373.5; (b) 13.46, 3.68; (c) 55.44, 6.66.
19.3–2 (a) 0.187; (b) 5.32, 43.87.
19.4–3 (a) 323; (b) 569.
19.4–4 (a) 262 cal; (b) 48 cal.
19.4–5 $1.337 + {}^3/_2R$: (b) $0.367 + {}^3/_2R$.
19.4–6 (a) $1.85 + {}^5/_2R$; (b) 208.
19.4–7 28.22.
19.4–8 31.05.
19.4–9 (b) 0.5; (c) 2.0.
19.4–10 31.25.
19.4–11 5.18.
19.5–1 (a) 46.05.
19.5–2 (a) 41.76; (b) 46.15.
20.1–4 1.987, 396, 396, 11.52, −9.53.
20.1–5 −12.92.
20.2–3 6240, −17.5, 20.52.
20.3–1 9.56.
20.3–2 (a) −34.43, 30.87; (b) −41.93, 48.00.
20.4–1 1206.
20.5–1 (a) 2.88; (b) $S_t = 36.22$; $S_r = 20.58$; (c) 61.08; (d) 1525 cm^{-1}.
20.5–4 (b) 1.3%; (c) 1%.
20.5–8 $S = 60.85$.
20.5–9 54.88.
22.4–2 (a) 2.55; (b) 3.9×10^4.
22.4–3 (b) (i) 0.22; (ii) 217; (iii) 2.2×10^4.
22.4–6 (a) 1.82×10^4.
22.4–7 −0.62, −0.870, 0.0322.
22.5–1 4.042.
22.5–2 (a) 11.7; (b) 0.0195; (c) 0.020.
22.5–4 (b) 0.022; 1.43.
22.6–1 (a) 2.304; (c) 0.15°K.
22.6–3 0.223, 1.04, 1.15, 0.81.

Author Index

Subject Index

The **boldface** numbers in the index denote either pages largely devoted to the subject or important definitions. Since every effort has been made to make the index selective, few of the entries are trivial.